Quantitative Methods and Finance

Volume One: Readings for Autumn Term BE300

Quantitative Methods and Finance

Volume One: Readings for Autumn Term BE300

Compiled from:

Mathematics for Economics and Business
Eighth Edition
Ian Jacques

Statistics for Economics, Accounting and Business Studies
Fifth Edition
Michael Barrow

Harlow, England • London • New York • Boston • San Francisco • Toronto • Sydney • Auckland • Singapore • Hong Kong
Tokyo • Seoul • Taipei • New Delhi • Cape Town • Sao Paulo • Mexico City • Madrid • Amsterdam • Munich • Paris • Milan

Pearson Education Limited
Edinburgh Gate
Harlow
Essex CM20 2JE

And associated companies throughout the world

Visit us on the World Wide Web at:
www.pearson.com/uk

Compiled from:

Mathematics for Economics and Business Eighth Edition
Ian Jacques
ISBN 978-1-292-07423-8
© Addision-Wesley Publishers Ltd 1991, 1994 (print)
© Pearson Education Limited 1999, 2009 (print)
© Pearson Education Limited 2013, 2015 (print and electronic)

Statistics for Economics, Accounting and Business Studies Fifth Edition
Michael Barrow
ISBN 978-0-273-71794-2
© Pearson Education Limited 1988, 2009

ISBN 978-1-78448-321-0

Printed and bound in Great Britain by Ashford Colour Press, Gosport, Hampshire.

Contents

CHAPTER 1
Linear Equations

The main aim of this chapter is to introduce the mathematics of linear equations. This is an obvious first choice in an introductory text, since it is an easy topic which has many applications. There are seven sections, which are intended to be read in the order that they appear.

Sections 1.1, 1.2, 1.3, 1.4 and 1.6 are devoted to mathematical methods. They serve to revise the rules of arithmetic and algebra, which you probably met at school but may have forgotten. In particular, the properties of negative numbers and fractions are considered. A reminder is given on how to multiply out brackets and how to manipulate mathematical expressions. You are also shown how to solve simultaneous linear equations. Systems of two equations in two unknowns can be solved using graphs, which are described in Section 1.3. However, the preferred method uses elimination, which is considered in Section 1.4. This algebraic approach has the advantage that it always gives an exact solution and it extends readily to larger systems of equations.

The remaining two sections are reserved for applications in microeconomics and macroeconomics. You may be pleasantly surprised by how much economic theory you can analyse using just the basic mathematical tools considered here. Section 1.5 introduces the fundamental concept of an economic function and describes how to calculate equilibrium prices and quantities in supply and demand theory. Section 1.7 deals with national income determination in simple macroeconomic models.

The first six sections underpin the rest of the book and are essential reading. The final section is not quite as important and can be omitted at this stage.

SECTION 1.1
Introduction to algebra

Objectives

At the end of this section you should be able to:

* Add, subtract, multiply and divide negative numbers.
* Understand what is meant by an algebraic expression.
* Evaluate algebraic expressions numerically.
* Simplify algebraic expressions by collecting like terms.
* Multiply out brackets.
* Factorise algebraic expressions.

ALGEBRA IS BORING

There is no getting away from the fact that algebra *is* boring. Doubtless there are a few enthusiasts who get a kick out of algebraic manipulation, but economics and business students are rarely to be found in this category. Indeed, the mere mention of the word 'algebra' is enough to strike fear into the heart of many a first-year student. Unfortunately, you cannot get very far with mathematics unless you have completely mastered this topic. An apposite analogy is the game of chess. Before you can begin to play a game of chess it is necessary to go through the tedium of learning the moves of individual pieces. In the same way it is essential that you learn the rules of algebra before you can enjoy the 'game' of mathematics. Of course, just because you know the rules does not mean that you are going to excel at the game and no one is expecting you to become a grandmaster of mathematics. However, you should at least be able to follow the mathematics presented in economics books and journals, as well as being able to solve simple problems for yourself.

Advice

If you have studied mathematics recently then you will find the material in the first few sections of the book fairly straightforward. You may prefer just to try the questions in the starred exercise at the end of each section to get yourself back up to speed. However, if it has been some time since you have studied this subject our advice is very different. Please work through the material thoroughly even if it is vaguely familiar. Make sure that you do the problems as they arise, checking your answers with those provided at the back of this book. The material has been broken down into three subsections:

* negative numbers
* expressions
* brackets.

You might like to work through these subsections on separate occasions to enable the ideas to sink in. To rush this topic now is likely to give you only a half-baked understanding, which will result in hours of frustration when you study the later chapters of this book.

1.1.1 Negative numbers

In mathematics numbers are classified into one of three types: positive, negative or zero. At school you were probably introduced to the idea of a negative number via the temperature on a thermometer scale measured in degrees centigrade. A number such as -5 would then be interpreted as a temperature of 5 degrees below freezing. In personal finance a negative bank balance would indicate that an account is 'in the red' or 'in debit'. Similarly, a firm's profit of $-500\,000$ signifies a loss of half a million.

The rules for the multiplication of negative numbers are

$$\text{negative} \times \text{negative} = \text{positive}$$

$$\text{negative} \times \text{positive} = \text{negative}$$

It does not matter in which order two numbers are multiplied, so

$$\text{positive} \times \text{negative} = \text{negative}$$

These rules produce, respectively,

$$(-2) \times (-3) = 6$$
$$(-4) \times 5 = -20$$
$$7 \times (-5) = -35$$

Also, because division is the same sort of operation as multiplication (it just undoes the result of multiplication and takes you back to where you started), exactly the same rules apply when one number is divided by another. For example,

$$(-15) \div (-3) = 5$$
$$(-16) \div 2 = -8$$
$$2 \div (-4) = -1/2$$

In general, to multiply or divide lots of numbers it is probably simplest to ignore the signs to begin with and just to work the answer out. The final result is negative if the total number of minus signs is odd and positive if the total number is even.

Example

Evaluate

(a) $(-2) \times (-4) \times (-1) \times 2 \times (-1) \times (-3)$ (b) $\dfrac{5 \times (-4) \times (-1) \times (-3)}{(-6) \times 2}$

Solution

(a) Ignoring the signs gives

$$2 \times 4 \times 1 \times 2 \times 1 \times 3 = 48$$

There are an odd number of minus signs (in fact, five) so the answer is -48.

(b) Ignoring the signs gives

$$\frac{5 \times 4 \times 1 \times 3}{6 \times 2} = \frac{60}{12} = 5$$

There are an even number of minus signs (in fact, four) so the answer is 5.

Advice

Attempt the following problem yourself both with and without a calculator. On most machines a negative number such as -6 is entered by pressing the button labelled $(-)$ followed by 6.

Practice Problem

1. **(1)** Without using a calculator evaluate

(a) $5 \times (-6)$ (b) $(-1) \times (-2)$ (c) $(-50) \div 10$

(d) $(-5) \div (-1)$ (e) $2 \times (-1) \times (-3) \times 6$ (f) $\dfrac{2 \times (-1) \times (-3) \times 6}{(-2) \times 3 \times 6}$

(2) Confirm your answer to part (1) using a calculator.

To add or subtract negative numbers it helps to think in terms of a number line:

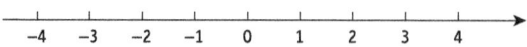

If b is a positive number then

$a - b$

can be thought of as an instruction to start at a and to move b units to the left. For example,

$1 - 3 = -2$

because if you start at 1 and move 3 units to the left, you end up at -2:

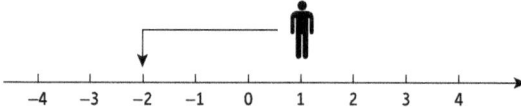

Similarly,

$-2 - 1 = -3$

because 1 unit to the left of -2 is -3.

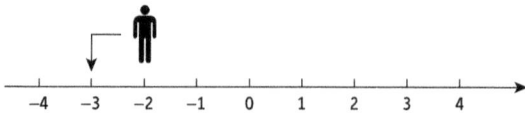

On the other hand,

$a - (-b)$

is taken to be $a + b$. This follows from the rule for multiplying two negative numbers, since

$-(-b) = (-1) \times (-b) = b$

Consequently, to evaluate

$a - (-b)$

you start at a and move b units to the right (that is, in the positive direction). For example,

$$-2 - (-5) = -2 + 5 = 3$$

because if you start at -2 and move 5 units to the right you end up at 3.

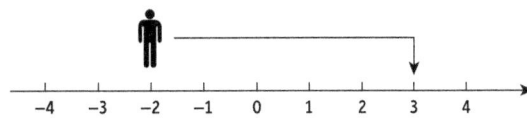

Practice Problem

2. (1) Without using a calculator evaluate

    (a) $1 - 2$ **(b)** $-3 - 4$ **(c)** $1 - (-4)$

    (d) $-1 - (-1)$ **(e)** $-72 - 19$ **(f)** $-53 - (-48)$

(2) Confirm your answer to part (1) using a calculator.

1.1.2 Expressions

In algebra letters are used to represent numbers. In pure mathematics the most common letters used are x and y. However, in applications it is helpful to choose letters that are more meaningful, so we might use Q for quantity and I for investment. An algebraic expression is then simply a combination of these letters, brackets and other mathematical symbols such as $+$ or $-$. For example, the expression

$$P\left(1 + \frac{r}{100}\right)^n$$

can be used to work out how money in a savings account grows over a period of time. The letters P, r and n represent the original sum invested (called the principal – hence the use of the letter P), the rate of interest and the number of years, respectively. To work it all out, you not only need to replace these letters by actual numbers, but you also need to understand the various conventions that go with algebraic expressions such as this.

In algebra when we multiply two numbers represented by letters we usually suppress the multiplication sign between them. The product of a and b would simply be written as ab without bothering to put the multiplication sign between the symbols. Likewise when a number represented by the letter Y is doubled we write $2Y$. In this case we not only suppress the multiplication sign but adopt the convention of writing the number in front of the letter. Here are some further examples:

$P \times Q$ is written as PQ

$d \times 8$ is written as $8d$

$n \times 6 \times t$ is written as $6nt$

$z \times z$ is written as z^2 (using the index 2 to indicate squaring a number)

$1 \times t$ is written as t (since multiplying by 1 does not change a number)

In order to evaluate these expressions it is necessary to be given the numerical value of each letter. Once this has been done you can work out the final value by performing the operations in the following order:

Brackets first	(B)
Indices second	(I)
Division and Multiplication third	(DM)
Addition and Subtraction fourth	(AS)

This is sometimes remembered using the acronym BIDMAS and it is essential that this ordering is used for working out all mathematical calculations. For example, suppose you wish to evaluate each of the following expressions when $n = 3$:

$2n^2$ and $(2n)^2$

Substituting $n = 3$ into the first expression gives

$2n^2 = 2 \times 3^2$ (the multiplication sign is revealed when we switch from algebra to numbers)

$= 2 \times 9$ (according to BIDMAS indices are worked out before multiplication)

$= 18$

whereas in the second expression we get

$(2n)^2 = (2 \times 3)^2$ (again the multiplication sign is revealed)

$= 6^2$ (according to BIDMAS we evaluate the inside of the brackets first)

$= 36$

The two answers are not the same so the order indicated by BIDMAS really does matter. Looking at the previous list, notice that there is a tie between multiplication and division for third place, and another tie between addition and subtraction for fourth place. These pairs of operations have equal priority and under these circumstances you work from left to right when evaluating expressions. For example, substituting $x = 5$ and $y = 4$ in the expression, $x - y + 2$, gives

$x - y + 2 = 5 - 4 + 2$

$= 1 + 2$ (reading from left to right, subtraction comes first)

$= 3$

Example

(a) Find the value of $2x - 3y$ when $x = 9$ and $y = 4$.

(b) Find the value of $2Q^2 + 4Q + 150$ when $Q = 10$.

(c) Find the value of $5a - 2b + c$ when $a = 4$, $b = 6$ and $c = 1$.

(d) Find the value of $(12 - t) - (t - 1)$ when $t = 4$.

Solution

(a) $2x - 3y = 2 \times 9 - 3 \times 4$ (substituting numbers)

$= 18 - 12$ (multiplication has priority over subtraction)

$= 6$

(b) $2Q^2 + 4Q + 150 = 2 \times 10^2 + 4 \times 10 + 150$ (substituting numbers)

$\qquad\qquad\qquad = 2 \times 100 + 4 \times 10 + 150$ (indices have priority over multiplication and addition)

$\qquad\qquad\qquad = 200 + 40 + 150$ (multiplication has priority over addition)

$\qquad\qquad\qquad = 390$

(c) $5a - 2b + c = 5 \times 4 - 2 \times 6 + 1$ (substituting numbers)

$\qquad\qquad\qquad = 20 - 12 + 1$ (multiplication has priority over addition and subtraction)

$\qquad\qquad\qquad = 8 + 1$ (addition and subtraction have equal priority, so work from left to right)

$\qquad\qquad\qquad = 9$

(d) $(12 - t) - (t - 1) = (12 - 4) - (4 - 1)$ (substituting numbers)

$\qquad\qquad\qquad = 8 - 3$ (brackets first)

$\qquad\qquad\qquad = 5$

Practice Problem

3. Evaluate each of the following by replacing the letters by the given numbers:

   (a) $2Q + 5$ when $Q = 7$.

   (b) $5x^2 y$ when $x = 10$ and $y = 3$.

   (c) $4d - 3f + 2g$ when $d = 7, f = 2$ and $g = 5$.

   (d) $a(b + 2c)$ when $a = 5, b = 1$ and $c = 3$.

Like terms are multiples of the same letter (or letters). For example, $2P$, $-34P$ and $0.3P$ are all multiples of P and so are like terms. In the same way, xy, $4xy$ and $69xy$ are all multiples of xy and so are like terms. If an algebraic expression contains like terms which are added or subtracted together then it can be simplified to produce an equivalent shorter expression.

Example

Simplify each of the following expressions (where possible):

(a) $2a + 5a - 3a$

(b) $4P - 2Q$

(c) $3w + 9w^2 + 2w$

(d) $3xy + 2y^2 + 9x + 4xy - 8x$

Solution

(a) All three are like terms since they are all multiples of a so the expression can be simplified:

$\qquad 2a + 5a - 3a = 4a$

(b) The terms $4P$ and $2Q$ are unlike because one is a multiple of P and the other is a multiple of Q so the expression cannot be simplified.

(c) The first and last are like terms since they are both multiples of w so we can collect these together and write

$$3w + 9w^2 + 2w = 5w + 9w^2$$

This cannot be simpified any further because $5w$ and $9w^2$ are unlike terms.

(d) The terms $3xy$ and $4xy$ are like terms, and $9x$ and $8x$ are also like terms. These pairs can therefore be collected together to give

$$3xy + 2y^2 + 9x + 4xy - 8x = 7xy + 2y^2 + x$$

Notice that we write just x instead of $1x$ and also that no further simplication is possible since the final answer involves three unlike terms.

Practice Problem

4. Simplify each of the following expressions, where possible:

(a) $2x + 6y - x + 3y$ **(b)** $5x + 2y - 5x + 4z$ **(c)** $4Y^2 + 3Y - 43$

(d) $8r^2 + 4s - 6rs - 3s - 3s^2 + 7rs$ **(e)** $2e^2 + 5f - 2e^2 - 9f$ **(f)** $3w + 6W$

(g) $ab - ba$

1.1.3 Brackets

It is useful to be able to take an expression containing brackets and rewrite it as an equivalent expression without brackets and vice versa. The process of removing brackets is called 'expanding brackets' or 'multiplying out brackets'. This is based on the **distributive law**, which states that for any three numbers a, b and c

$$a(b + c) = ab + ac$$

It is easy to verify this law in simple cases. For example, if $a = 2$, $b = 3$ and $c = 4$ then the left-hand side is

$$2(3 + 4) = 2 \times 7 = 14$$

However,

$$ab = 2 \times 3 = 6 \quad \text{and} \quad ac = 2 \times 4 = 8$$

and so the right-hand side is $6 + 8$, which is also 14.

This law can be used when there are any number of terms inside the brackets. We have

$$a(b + c + d) = ab + ac + ad$$
$$a(b + c + d + e) = ab + ac + ad + ae$$

and so on.

It does not matter in which order two numbers are multiplied, so we also have

$$(b + c)a = ba + ca$$
$$(b + c + d)a = ba + ca + da$$
$$(b + c + d + e)a = ba + ca + da + ea$$

Example

Multiply out the brackets in

(a) $x(x - 2)$

(b) $2(x + y - z) + 3(z + y)$

(c) $x + 3y - (2y + x)$

Solution

(a) The use of the distributive law to multiply out $x(x - 2)$ is straightforward. The x outside the bracket multiplies the x inside to give x^2. The x outside the bracket also multiplies the -2 inside to give $-2x$. Hence

$$x(x - 2) = x^2 - 2x$$

(b) To expand

$$2(x + y - z) + 3(z + y)$$

we need to apply the distributive law twice. We have

$$2(x + y - z) = 2x + 2y - 2z$$
$$3(z + y) = 3z + 3y$$

Adding together gives

$$2(x + y - z) + 3(z + y) = 2x + 2y - 2z + 3z + 3y$$
$$= 2x + 5y + z \quad \text{(collecting like terms)}$$

(c) It may not be immediately apparent how to expand

$$x + 3y - (2y + x)$$

However, note that

$$-(2y + x)$$

is the same as

$$(-1)(2y + x)$$

which expands to give

$$(-1)(2y) + (-1)x = -2y - x$$

Hence

$$x + 3y - (2y + x) = x + 3y - 2y - x = y$$

after collecting like terms.

Advice

In this example the solutions are written out in painstaking detail. This is done to show you precisely how the distributive law is applied. The solutions to all three parts could have been written down in only one or two steps of working. You are, of course, at liberty to compress the working in your own solutions, but please do not be tempted to overdo this. You might want to check your answers at a later date and may find it difficult if you have tried to be too clever.

Practice Problem

5. Multiply out the brackets, simplifying your answer as far as possible.

   (a) $(5 - 2z)z$ **(b)** $6(x - y) + 3(y - 2x)$ **(c)** $x - y + z - (x^2 + x - y)$

Mathematical formulae provide a precise way of representing calculations that need to be worked out in many business models. However, it is important to realise that these formulae may only be valid for a restricted range of values. Most large companies have a policy to reimburse employees for use of their cars for travel: for the first 50 miles they may be able to claim 90 cents a mile but this could fall to 60 cents a mile thereafter. If the distance, x miles, is no more than 50 miles then travel expenses, E, (in dollars) could be worked out using formula, $E = 0.9x$. If x exceeds 50 miles the employee can claim \$0.90 a mile for the first 50 miles but only \$0.60 a mile for the last $(x - 50)$ miles. The total amount is then

$$E = 0.9 \times 50 + 0.6(x - 50)$$
$$= 45 + 0.6x - 30$$
$$= 15 + 0.6x$$

Travel expenses can therefore be worked out using two separate formulae:

- $E = 0.9x$ when x is no more than 50 miles
- $E = 15 + 0.6x$ when x exceeds 50 miles.

Before we leave this topic a word of warning is in order. Be careful when removing brackets from very simple expressions such as those considered in part (c) in the previous worked example and practice problem. A common mistake is to write

$$(a + b) - (c + d) = a + b - c + d \qquad \text{This is NOT true}$$

The distributive law tells us that the -1 multiplying the second bracket applies to the d as well as the c so the correct answer has to be

$$(a + b) - (c + d) = a + b - c - d$$

In algebra, it is sometimes useful to reverse the procedure and put the brackets back in. This is called **factorisation**. Consider the expression $12a + 8b$. There are many numbers which divide into both 8 and 12. However, we always choose the biggest number, which is 4 in this case, so we attempt to take the factor of 4 outside the brackets:

$$12a + 8b = 4(? + ?)$$

where the ? indicate some mystery terms inside the brackets. We would like 4 multiplied by the first term in the brackets to be $12a$ so we are missing $3a$. Likewise if we are to generate an $8b$ the second term in the brackets will have to be $2b$.

Hence

$$12a + 8b = 4(3a + 2b)$$

As a check, notice that when you expand the brackets on the right-hand side you really do get the expression on the left-hand side.

Example

Factorise

(a) $6L - 3L^2$

(b) $5a - 10b + 20c$

Solution

(a) Both terms have a common factor of 3. Also, because $L^2 = L \times L$, both $6L$ and $-3L^2$ have a factor of L. Hence we can take out a common factor of $3L$ altogether.

$$6L - 3L^2 = 3L(2) - 3L(L) = 3L(2 - L)$$

(b) All three terms have a common factor of 5 so we write

$$5a - 10b + 20c = 5(a) - 5(2b) + 5(4c) = 5(a - 2b + 4c)$$

Practice Problem

6. Factorise

(a) $7d + 21$ (b) $16w - 20q$ (c) $6x - 3y + 9z$ (d) $5Q - 10Q^2$

We conclude our discussion of brackets by describing how to multiply two brackets together. In the expression $(a + b)(c + d)$ the two terms a and b must each multiply the single bracket $(c + d)$ so

$$(a + b)(c + d) = a(c + d) + b(c + d)$$

The first term $a(c + d)$ can itself be expanded as $ac + ad$. Likewise, $b(c + d) = bc + bd$. Hence

$$(a + b)(c + d) = ac + ad + bc + bd$$

This procedure then extends to brackets with more than two terms:

$$(a + b)(c + d + e) = a(c + d + e) + b(c + d + e) = ac + ad + ae + bc + bd + be$$

Example

Multiply out the brackets

(a) $(x + 1)(x + 2)$ (b) $(x + 5)(x - 5)$ (c) $(2x - y)(x + y - 6)$

simplifying your answer as far as possible.

Solution

(a) $(x + 1)(x + 2) = x(x + 2) + (1)(x + 2)$
$$= x^2 + 2x + x + 2$$
$$= x^2 + 3x + 2$$

(b) $(x + 5)(x - 5) = x(x - 5) + 5(x - 5)$
$$= x^2 - 5x + 5x - 25$$
$$= x^2 - 25 \qquad \text{(the xs cancel)}$$

(c) $(2x - y)(x + y - 6) = 2x(x + y - 6) - y(x + y - 6)$
$$= 2x^2 + 2xy - 12x - yx - y^2 + 6y$$
$$= 2x^2 + xy - 12x - y^2 + 6y$$

Practice Problem

7. Multiply out the brackets.

(a) $(x + 3)(x - 2)$

(b) $(x + y)(x - y)$

(c) $(x + y)(x + y)$

(d) $(5x + 2y)(x - y + 1)$

Looking back at part (b) of the previous worked example, notice that

$$(x + 5)(x - 5) = x^2 - 25 = x^2 - 5^2$$

Quite generally

$$(a + b)(a - b) = a(a - b) + b(a - b)$$
$$= a^2 - ab + ba - b^2$$
$$= a^2 - b^2$$

The result

$$a^2 - b^2 = (a + b)(a - b)$$

is called the **difference of two squares** formula. It provides a quick way of factorising certain expressions.

Example

Factorise the following expressions:

(a) $x^2 - 16$ (b) $9x^2 - 100$

Solution

(a) Noting that

$$x^2 - 16 = x^2 - 4^2$$

we can use the difference of two squares formula to deduce that

$$x^2 - 16 = (x + 4)(x - 4)$$

(b) Noting that

$$9x^2 - 100 = (3x)^2 - (10)^2$$

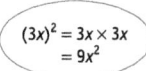

$(3x)^2 = 3x \times 3x$
$\qquad = 9x^2$

we can use the difference of two squares formula to deduce that

$$9x^2 - 100 = (3x + 10)(3x - 10)$$

Practice Problem

8. Factorise the following expressions:

   (a) $x^2 - 64$ (b) $4x^2 - 81$

Advice

This completes your first piece of mathematics. We hope that you have not found it quite as bad as you first thought. There now follow a few extra problems to give you more practice. Not only will they help to strengthen your mathematical skills, but also they should improve your overall confidence. There are two alternative exercises available. Exercise 1.1 is suitable for students whose mathematics may be rusty and who need to consolidate their understanding. Exercise 1.1* contains more challenging problems and so is more suitable for those students who have found this section very easy.

Key Terms

Difference of two squares   The algebraic result which states that $a^2 - b^2 = (a + b)(a - b)$.

Distributive law   The law of arithmetic which states that $a(b + c) = ab + ac$ for any numbers, a, b, c.

Factorisation   The process of writing an expression as a product of simpler expressions using brackets.

Like terms   Multiples of the same combination of algebraic symbols.

Exercise 1.1

1. Without using a calculator evaluate

   (a) $10 \times (-2)$

   (b) $(-1) \times (-3)$

   (c) $(-8) \div 2$

   (d) $(-5) \div (-5)$

   (e) $24 \div (-2)$

   (f) $(-10) \times (-5)$

   (g) $\dfrac{20}{-4}$

   (h) $\dfrac{-27}{-9}$

   (i) $(-6) \times 5 \times (-1)$

   (j) $\dfrac{2 \times (-6) \times 3}{(-9)}$

2. Without using a calculator evaluate

   (a) $5 - 6$

   (b) $-1 - 2$

   (c) $6 - 17$

   (d) $-7 + 23$

   (e) $-7 - (-6)$

   (f) $-4 - 9$

   (g) $7 - (-4)$

   (h) $-9 - (-9)$

   (i) $12 - 43$

   (j) $2 + 6 - 10$

3. Without using a calculator evaluate

   (a) $5 \times 2 - 13$

   (b) $\dfrac{-30 - 6}{-18}$

   (c) $\dfrac{(-3) \times (-6) \times (-1)}{2 - 3}$

   (d) $5 \times (1 - 4)$

   (e) $1 - 6 \times 7$

   (f) $-5 + 6 \div 3$

   (g) $2 \times (-3)^2$

   (h) $-10 + 2^2$

   (i) $(-2)^2 - 5 \times 6 + 1$

   (j) $\dfrac{(-4)^2 \times (-3) \times (-1)}{(-2)^3}$

4. Simplify each of the following algebraic expressions:

   (a) $2 \times P \times Q$

   (b) $I \times 8$

   (c) $3 \times x \times y$

   (d) $4 \times q \times w \times z$

   (e) $b \times b$

   (f) $k \times 3 \times k$

5. Simplify the following algebraic expressions by collecting like terms:

   (a) $6w - 3w + 12w + 4w$

   (b) $6x + 5y - 2x - 12y$

   (c) $3a - 2b + 6a - c + 4b - c$

   (d) $2x^2 + 4x - x^2 - 2x$

   (e) $2cd + 4c - 5dc$

   (f) $5st + s^2 - 3ts + t^2 + 9$

6. Without using a calculator find the value of the following:

   (a) $2x - y$ when $x = 7$ and $y = 4$.

   (b) $x^2 - 5x + 12$ when $x = 6$.

   (c) $2m^3$ when $m = 10$.

   (d) $5fg^2 + 2g$ when $f = 2$ and $g = 3$.

   (e) $2v + 4w - (4v - 7w)$ when $v = 20$ and $w = 10$.

7. If $x = 2$ and $y = -3$ evaluate

   (a) $2x + y$

   (b) $x - y$

   (c) $3x + 4y$

   (d) xy

   (e) $5xy$

   (f) $4x - 6xy$

8. (a) Without using a calculator, work out the value of $(-4)^2$.

(b) Press the following key sequence on your calculator:

$(-)$ 4 x^2

Explain carefully why this does not give the same result as part **(a)** and give an alternative key sequence that *does* give the correct answer.

9. Without using a calculator work out

(a) $(5 - 2)^2$ **(b)** $5^2 - 2^2$

Is it true in general that $(a - b)^2 = a^2 - b^2$?

10. Use your calculator to work out the following. Round your answer, if necessary, to 2 decimal places.

(a) $5.31 \times 8.47 - 1.01^2$ **(b)** $(8.34 + 2.27)/9.41$

(c) $9.53 - 3.21 + 4.02$ **(d)** $2.41 \times 0.09 - 1.67 \times 0.03$

(e) $45.76 - (2.55 + 15.83)$ **(f)** $(3.45 - 5.38)^2$

(g) $4.56(9.02 + 4.73)$ **(h)** $6.85/(2.59 + 0.28)$

11. Multiply out the brackets:

(a) $7(x - y)$ **(b)** $3(5x - 2y)$ **(c)** $4(x + 3)$ **(d)** $7(3x - 1)$

(e) $3(x + y + z)$ **(f)** $x(3x - 4)$ **(g)** $y + 2z - 2(x + 3y - z)$

12. Factorise

(a) $25c + 30$ **(b)** $9x - 18$ **(c)** $x^2 + 2x$

(d) $16x - 12y$ **(e)** $4x^2 - 6xy$ **(f)** $10d - 15e + 50$

13. Multiply out the brackets:

(a) $(x + 2)(x + 5)$ **(b)** $(a + 4)(a - 1)$ **(c)** $(d + 3)(d - 8)$ **(d)** $(2s + 3)(3s + 7)$

(e) $(2y + 3)(y + 1)$ **(f)** $(5t + 2)(2t - 7)$ **(g)** $(3n + 2)(3n - 2)$ **(h)** $(a - b)(a - b)$

14. Simplify the following expressions by collecting together like terms:

(a) $2x + 3y + 4x - y$ **(b)** $2x^2 - 5x + 9x^2 + 2x - 3$

(c) $5xy + 2x + 9yx$ **(d)** $7xyz + 3yx - 2zyx + yzx - xy$

(e) $2(5a + b) - 4b$ **(f)** $5(x - 4y) + 6(2x + 7y)$

(g) $5 - 3(p - 2)$ **(h)** $x(x - y + 7) + xy + 3x$

15. Use the formula for the difference of two squares to factorise

(a) $x^2 - 4$ **(b)** $Q^2 - 49$ **(c)** $x^2 - y^2$ **(d)** $9x^2 - 100y^2$

16. Simplify the following algebraic expressions:

(a) $3x - 4x^2 - 2 + 5x + 8x^2$ **(b)** $x(3x + 2) - 3x(x + 5)$

17. A law firm seeks to recruit top quality experienced lawyers. The total package offered is the sum of three separate components: a basic salary which is 1.2 times the candidate's current salary together with an additional $3000 for each year worked as a qualified lawyer and an extra $1000 for every year that they are over the age of 21.

Work out a formula that could be used to calculate the total salary, S, offered to someone who is A years of age, has E years of relevant experience and who currently earns $N. Hence work out the salary offered to someone who is 30 years old with 5 years' experience and who currently earns $150,000.

18. Write down a formula for each situation:

(a) A plumber has a fixed call-out charge of $80 and has an hourly rate of $60. Work out the total charge, C, for a job that takes L hours in which the cost of materials and parts is $K.

(b) An airport currency exchange booth charges a fixed fee of $10 on all transactions and offers an exchange rate of 1 dollar to 0.8 euros. Work out the total charge, C, (in $) for buying x euros.

(c) A firm provides 5 hours of in-house training for each of its semi-skilled workers and 10 hours of training for each of its skilled workers. Work out the total number of hours, H, if the firm employs a semi-skilled and b skilled workers.

(d) A car hire company charges C a day together with an additional c per mile. Work out the total charge, X, for hiring a car for d days and travelling m miles during that time.

Exercise 1.1*

1. Without using a calculator evaluate

(a) $(12 - 8) - (6 - 5)$ (b) $12 - (8 - 6) - 5$ (c) $12 - 8 - 6 - 5$

2. Put a pair of brackets in the left-hand side of each of the following to give correct statements:

(a) $2 - 7 - 9 + 3 = -17$ (b) $8 - 2 + 3 - 4 = -1$ (c) $7 - 2 - 6 + 10 = 1$

3. Without using a calculator work out the value of each of the following expressions in the case when $a = 3$, $b = -4$ and $c = -2$:

(a) $a(b - c)$ (b) $3c(a + b)$ (c) $a^2 + 2b + 3c$ (d) $2abc^2$

(e) $\dfrac{c + b}{2a}$ (f) $\sqrt{2(b^2 - c)}$ (g) $\dfrac{b}{2c} - \dfrac{a}{3b}$ (h) $5a - b^3 - 4c^2$

4. Without using a calculator evaluate each of the following expressions in the case when $x = -1$, $y = -2$ and $z = 3$:

(a) $x^3 + y^2 + z$ (b) $\sqrt{\left(\dfrac{x^2 + y^2 + z}{x^2 + 2xy - z}\right)}$ (c) $\dfrac{xyz(x + z)(z - y)}{(x + y)(x - z)}$

5. Multiply out the brackets and simplify

$(x - y)(x + y) - (x + 2)(x - y + 3)$

6. Simplify

    (a) $x - y - (y - x)$ **(b)** $(x - ((y - x) - y))$ **(c)** $x + y - (x - y) - (x - (y - x))$

7. Multiply out the brackets:

    (a) $(x + 4)(x - 6)$ **(b)** $(2x - 5)(3x - 7)$ **(c)** $2x(3x + y - 2)$

    (d) $(3 + g)(4 - 2g + h)$ **(e)** $(2x + y)(1 - x - y)$ **(f)** $(a + b + c)(a - b - c)$

8. Factorise

    (a) $9x - 12y$ **(b)** $x^2 - 6x$ **(c)** $10xy + 15x^2$

    (d) $3xy^2 - 6x^2y + 12xy$ **(e)** $x^3 - 2x^2$ **(f)** $60x^4y^6 - 15x^2y^4 + 20xy^3$

9. Use the formula for the difference of two squares to factorise

    (a) $p^2 - 25$ **(b)** $9c^2 - 64$ **(c)** $32v^2 - 50d^2$ **(d)** $16x^4 - y^4$

10. Evaluate the following without using a calculator:

    (a) $50\,563^2 - 49\,437^2$ **(b)** $90^2 - 89.99^2$

    (c) $759^2 - 541^2$ **(d)** $123\,456\,789^2 - 123\,456\,788^2$

11. A specialist paint manufacturer receives \$12 for each pot sold. The initial set-up cost for the production run is \$800 and the cost of making each tin of paint is \$3.

    (a) Write down a formula for the total profit, π, if the firm manufactures x pots of paint and sells y pots.

    (b) Use your formula to calculate the profit when $x = 1000$ and $y = 800$.

    (c) State any restrictions on the variables in the mathematical formula in part (a).

    (d) Simplify the formula in the case when the firm sells all that it manufactures.

12. Factorise

    (a) $2KL^2 + 4KL$ **(b)** $L^2 - 0.04K^2$ **(c)** $K^2 + 2LK + L^2$

SECTION 1.2
Further algebra

> ## Objectives
>
> At the end of this section you should be able to:
>
> - Simplify fractions by cancelling common factors.
> - Add, subtract, multiply and divide fractions.
> - Solve equations by doing the same thing to both sides.
> - Recognise the symbols $<$, $>$, $\leq$ and $\geq$.
> - Solve linear inequalities.

This section is broken down into three manageable subsections:

- fractions
- equations
- inequalities.

The advice offered in Section 1.1 applies equally well here. Please try to study these topics on separate occasions and be prepared to put the book down and work through the practice problems as they arise in the text.

1.2.1 Fractions

For a numerical fraction such as

$$\frac{7}{8}$$

the number 7, on the top, is called the **numerator** and the number 8, on the bottom, is called the **denominator**. In this book we are also interested in the case when the numerator and denominator involve letters as well as numbers. These are referred to as **algebraic fractions**. For example,

$$\frac{1}{x^2 - 2} \quad \text{and} \quad \frac{2x^2 - 1}{y + z}$$

are both algebraic fractions. The letters x, y and z are used to represent numbers, so the rules for the manipulation of algebraic fractions are the same as those for ordinary numerical fractions. It is therefore essential that you are happy manipulating numerical fractions without a calculator so that you can extend this skill to fractions with letters.

Two fractions are said to be **equivalent** if they represent the same numerical value. We know that 3/4 is equivalent to 6/8 since they are both equal to the decimal number 0.75. It is also intuitively obvious. Imagine breaking a bar of chocolate into four equal pieces and eating three of them. You eat the same amount of chocolate as someone who breaks the bar into eight equal pieces and eats six of them. Each piece is only half the size so you need to compensate by eating twice as many. Formally we say that when the numerator and denominator are both multiplied by the same number the value of the fraction remains unchanged. In this example we have

$$\frac{3}{4} = \frac{3 \times 2}{4 \times 2} = \frac{6}{8}$$

This process can be reversed so equivalent fractions are produced when the numerator and denominator are both divided by the same number. For example,

$$\frac{16}{24} = \frac{16/8}{24/8} = \frac{2}{3}$$

so the fractions 16/24 and 2/3 are equivalent. A fraction is said to be in its simplest form or reduced to its lowest terms when there are no factors common to both the numerator and denominator. To express any given fraction in its simplest form you need to find the highest common factor of the numerator and denominator and then divide the top and bottom of the fraction by this.

Example

Reduce each of the following fractions to its lowest terms:

(a) $\dfrac{14}{21}$ (b) $\dfrac{48}{60}$ (c) $\dfrac{2x}{3xy}$ (d) $\dfrac{3a}{6a + 3b}$ (e) $\dfrac{x-2}{(x-2)(x+1)}$

Solution

(a) The largest number which divides into both 14 and 21 is 7 so we choose to divide top and bottom by 7:

$$\frac{14}{21} = \frac{14/7}{21/7} = \frac{2}{3}$$

An alternative way of writing this (which will be helpful when we tackle algebraic fractions) is:

$$\frac{14}{21} = \frac{2 \times \cancel{7}}{3 \times \cancel{7}} = \frac{2}{3}$$

(b) The highest common factor of 48 and 60 is 12 so we write:

$$\frac{48}{60} = \frac{4 \times \cancel{12}}{5 \times \cancel{12}} = \frac{4}{5}$$

(c) The factor x is common to both $2x$ and $3xy$ so we need to divide top and bottom by x, that is, we cancel the xs:

$$\frac{2x}{3xy} = \frac{2 \times \cancel{x}}{3 \times \cancel{x} \times y} = \frac{2}{3y}$$

(d) Factorising the denominator gives

$$6a + 3b = 3(2a + b)$$

which shows that there is a common factor of 3 in the top and bottom which can be cancelled:

$$\frac{3a}{6a+3b} = \frac{\cancel{3}a}{\cancel{3}(2a+b)} = \frac{a}{2a+b}$$

(e) We see immediately that there is a common factor of $(x-2)$ in the top and bottom so this can be cancelled:

$$\frac{\cancel{x-2}}{\cancel{(x-2)}(x+1)} = \frac{1}{x+1}$$

Before we leave this topic a word of warning is in order. Notice that you can only cancel by dividing by a **factor** of the numerator or denominator. In part (d) of the above example you must not get carried away and attempt to cancel the as, and write something daft like:

$$\frac{a}{2a+b} = \frac{1}{2+b} \qquad \text{This is NOT true}$$

To see that this is totally wrong let us try substituting numbers, $a = 3$, $b = 4$, say, into both sides. The left-hand side gives $\dfrac{a}{2a+b} = \dfrac{3}{2 \times 3 + 4} = \dfrac{3}{10}$ whereas the right-hand side gives $\dfrac{1}{2+b} = \dfrac{1}{2+4} = \dfrac{1}{6}$, which is not the same value.

Practice Problem

1. Reduce each of the following fractions to its lowest terms:

(a) $\dfrac{9}{15}$ (b) $\dfrac{24}{30}$ (c) $\dfrac{x}{2xy}$ (d) $\dfrac{3x}{6x+9x^2}$ (e) $\dfrac{x(x+1)}{x(x-4)(x+1)}$

The rules for multiplication and division are as follows:

to multiply fractions you multiply their corresponding numerators and denominators

In symbols,

$$\frac{a}{b} \times \frac{c}{d} = \frac{a \times c}{b \times d} = \frac{ac}{bd}$$

to divide by a fraction you turn it upside down and multiply

In symbols,

$$\frac{a}{b} \div \frac{c}{d} = \frac{a}{b} \times \frac{d}{c} \qquad \text{turn the divisor upside down}$$

$$= \frac{ad}{bc} \qquad \text{rule for multiplying fractions}$$

Example

Calculate

(a) $\dfrac{2}{3} \times \dfrac{5}{4}$ (b) $2 \times \dfrac{6}{13}$ (c) $\dfrac{6}{7} \div \dfrac{4}{21}$ (d) $\dfrac{1}{2} \div 3$

Solution

(a) The multiplication rule gives

$$\frac{2}{3} \times \frac{5}{4} = \frac{2 \times 5}{3 \times 4} = \frac{10}{12}$$

We could leave the answer like this, although it can be simplified by dividing top and bottom by 2 to get $^5/_6$. It is also valid to 'cancel' by 2 at the very beginning: that is,

$$\frac{{}^1\cancel{2}}{3} \times \frac{5}{\cancel{4}_2} = \frac{1 \times 5}{3 \times 2} = \frac{5}{6}$$

(b) The whole number 2 is equivalent to the fraction $^2/_1$, so

$$2 \times \frac{6}{13} = \frac{2}{1} \times \frac{6}{13} = \frac{2 \times 6}{1 \times 13} = \frac{12}{13}$$

(c) To calculate

$$\frac{6}{7} \div \frac{4}{21}$$

the divisor is turned upside down to get $^{21}/_4$ and then multiplied to get

$$\frac{6}{7} \div \frac{4}{21} = \frac{{}^3\cancel{6}}{\cancel{7}_1} \times \frac{\cancel{21}^3}{\cancel{4}_2} = \frac{3 \times 3}{1 \times 2} = \frac{9}{2}$$

(d) We write 3 as $^3/_1$, so

$$\frac{1}{2} \div 3 = \frac{1}{2} \div \frac{3}{1} = \frac{1}{2} \times \frac{1}{3} = \frac{1}{6}$$

Practice Problem

2. **(1)** Without using a calculator evaluate

   (a) $\dfrac{1}{2} \times \dfrac{3}{4}$ (b) $7 \times \dfrac{1}{4}$ (c) $\dfrac{2}{3} \div \dfrac{8}{9}$ (d) $\dfrac{8}{9} \div 16$

(2) Confirm your answer to part (1) using a calculator.

The rules for addition and subtraction are as follows:

**to add (or subtract) two fractions you write them as equivalent fractions
with a common denominator and add (or subtract) their numerators**

Example

Calculate

(a) $\dfrac{1}{5}+\dfrac{2}{5}$ (b) $\dfrac{1}{4}+\dfrac{2}{3}$ (c) $\dfrac{7}{12}-\dfrac{5}{8}$

Solution

(a) The fractions $^1/_5$ and $^2/_5$ already have the same denominator, so to add them we just add their numerators to get

$$\frac{1}{5}+\frac{2}{5}=\frac{1+2}{5}=\frac{3}{5}$$

(b) The fractions $^1/_4$ and $^2/_3$ have denominators 4 and 3. One number that is divisible by both 3 and 4 is 12, so we choose this as the common denominator. Now 4 goes into 12 exactly 3 times, so

$$\frac{1}{4}=\frac{1\times3}{4\times3}=\frac{3}{12}$$ multiply top and bottom by 3

and 3 goes into 12 exactly 4 times, so

$$\frac{2}{3}=\frac{2\times4}{3\times4}=\frac{8}{12}$$ multiply top and bottom by 4

Hence

$$\frac{1}{4}+\frac{2}{3}=\frac{3}{12}+\frac{8}{12}=\frac{3+8}{12}=\frac{11}{12}$$

(c) The fractions $^7/_{12}$ and $^5/_8$ have denominators 12 and 8. One number that is divisible by both 12 and 8 is 24, so we choose this as the common denominator. Now 12 goes into 24 exactly twice, so

$$\frac{7}{12}=\frac{7\times2}{24}=\frac{14}{24}$$

and 8 goes into 24 exactly 3 times, so

$$\frac{5}{8}=\frac{5\times3}{24}=\frac{15}{24}$$

Hence

$$\frac{7}{12}-\frac{5}{8}=\frac{14}{24}-\frac{15}{24}=\frac{-1}{24}$$

It is not essential that the lowest common denominator is used. Any number will do provided that it is divisible by the two original denominators. If you are stuck then you could always multiply the original two denominators together. In part (c) the denominators multiply to give 96, so this can be used instead. Now

$$\frac{7}{12}=\frac{7\times8}{96}=\frac{56}{96}$$

and

$$\frac{5}{8} = \frac{5 \times 12}{96} = \frac{60}{96}$$

so

$$\frac{7}{12} - \frac{5}{8} = \frac{56}{96} - \frac{60}{96} = \frac{56-60}{96} = \frac{-4}{96} = -\frac{1}{24}$$

as before.

Notice how the final answer to part (c) of this example has been written. We have simply used the fact that when a negative number is divided by a positive number the answer is negative. It is standard practice to write negative fractions like this so we would write $-\frac{3}{4}$ in preference to either $\frac{3}{-4}$ or $\frac{-3}{4}$ and, of course, $\frac{-3}{-4}$ is written as $\frac{3}{4}$.

Before we leave this topic a word of warning is in order. Notice that you can only add or subtract fractions after you have gone to the trouble of finding a common denominator. In particular, the following short-cut does not give the correct answer:

$$\frac{a}{b} + \frac{c}{d} = \frac{a+c}{b+d} \qquad \text{This is NOT true}$$

As usual you can check for yourself that it is complete rubbish by using actual numbers of your own choosing.

Practice Problem

3. **(1)** Without using a calculator evaluate

(a) $\frac{3}{7} - \frac{1}{7}$ (b) $\frac{1}{3} + \frac{2}{5}$ (c) $\frac{7}{18} - \frac{1}{4}$

(2) Confirm your answer to part (1) using a calculator.

Provided that you can manipulate ordinary fractions, there is no reason why you should not be able to manipulate algebraic fractions just as easily, since the rules are the same.

Example

Find expressions for each of the following:

(a) $\dfrac{x}{x-1} \times \dfrac{2}{x(x+4)}$ (b) $\dfrac{2}{x-1} \div \dfrac{x}{x-1}$ (c) $\dfrac{x+1}{x^2+2} + \dfrac{x-6}{x^2+2}$ (d) $\dfrac{x}{x+2} - \dfrac{1}{x+1}$

Solution

(a) To multiply two fractions we multiply their corresponding numerators and denominators, so

$$\frac{x}{x-1} \times \frac{2}{x(x+4)} = \frac{2x}{(x-1)x(x+4)} = \frac{2}{(x-1)(x+4)}$$

the x' cancel top and bottom

(b) To divide by

$$\frac{x}{x-1}$$

we turn it upside down and multiply, so

$$\frac{2}{x-1} \div \frac{x}{x-1} = \frac{2}{x-1} \times \frac{x-1}{x} = \frac{2}{x}$$

the $(x-1)$s cancel top and bottom

(c) The fractions

$$\frac{x+1}{x^2+2} \quad \text{and} \quad \frac{x-6}{x^2+2}$$

already have the same denominator, so to add them we just add their numerators to get

$$\frac{x+1}{x^2+2} + \frac{x-6}{x^2+2} = \frac{x+1+x-6}{x^2+2} = \frac{2x-5}{x^2+2}$$

(d) The fractions

$$\frac{x}{x+2} \quad \text{and} \quad \frac{1}{x+1}$$

have denominators $x+2$ and $x+1$. An obvious common denominator is given by their product, $(x+2)(x+1)$. Now $x+2$ goes into $(x+2)(x+1)$ exactly $x+1$ times, so

$$\frac{x}{x+2} = \frac{x(x+1)}{(x+2)(x+1)}$$

multiply top and bottom by $(x+1)$

Also $x+1$ goes into $(x+2)(x+1)$ exactly $x+2$ times, so

$$\frac{1}{x+1} = \frac{(x+2)}{(x+2)(x+1)}$$

multiply top and bottom by $(x+2)$

Hence

$$\frac{x}{x+2} - \frac{1}{x+1} = \frac{x(x+1)}{(x+2)(x+1)} - \frac{(x+2)}{(x+2)(x+1)} = \frac{x(x+1)-(x+2)}{(x+2)(x+1)}$$

It is worth multiplying out the brackets on the top to simplify: that is,

$$\frac{x^2+x-x-2}{(x+2)(x+1)} = \frac{x^2-2}{(x+2)(x+1)}$$

Practice Problem

4. Find expressions for the following algebraic fractions, simplifying your answers as far as possible.

(a) $\dfrac{5}{x-1} \times \dfrac{x-1}{x+2}$ (b) $\dfrac{x^2}{x+10} \div \dfrac{x}{x+1}$ (c) $\dfrac{4}{x+1} + \dfrac{1}{x+1}$ (d) $\dfrac{2}{x+1} - \dfrac{1}{x+2}$

1.2.2 Equations

In Section 1.1.2 and again in Section 1.2.1 we have seen how to rewrite an algebraic expression in a simpler but equivalent form. For example, when we write things like

$$x^2 + 3x + 3x^2 - 10x = 4x^2 - 7x \qquad \text{(collecting like terms)}$$

or

$$\frac{x}{x+2} - \frac{1}{x+1} = \frac{x^2-2}{(x+2)(x+1)} \qquad \text{(part (d) of the previous worked example)}$$

we have at the back of our minds the knowledge that the left- and right-hand sides are identical so that each statement is true for all possible values of x. For this reason the above relations are called **identities**. Compare these with statements such as:

$$7x - 1 = 13$$

or

$$x^2 - 5x = 1$$

These relations are called **equations** and are only true for particular values of x which need to be found. It turns out that the first equation above has just one solution, whereas the second has two solutions. The latter is called a quadratic equation and will be considered in the next chapter.

One naïve approach to the solution of equations such as $7x - 1 = 13$ might be to use trial and error: that is, we could just keep guessing values of x until we find the one that works. Can you see what x is in this case? However, a more reliable and systematic approach is to actually solve this equation using the rules of mathematics. In fact, the only rule that we need is:

> you can apply whatever mathematical operation you like to an equation,
> *provided that you do the same thing to both sides*

There is only one exception to this rule: you must never divide both sides by zero. This should be obvious because a number such as 11/0 does not exist. (If you do not believe this, try dividing 11 by 0 on your calculator.)

The first obstacle that prevents us from writing down the value of x immediately from the equation $7x - 1 = 13$ is the presence of the -1 on the left-hand side. This can be removed by adding 1. For this to be legal we must also add 1 to the right-hand side to get

$$7x - 1 + 1 = 13 + 1$$
$$7x = 14$$

The second obstacle is the number 7 which is multiplying the x. This can be removed by dividing the left-hand side by 7. Of course, we must also do the same thing to the right-hand side to get

$$\frac{7x}{7} = \frac{14}{7}$$

$$x = 2$$

This is no doubt the solution that you spotted earlier by simple trial and error and you may be wondering why you need to bother with the formal method. The reason is simple: guesswork will not help to solve more complicated equations in which the solution is non-obvious or even simple equations in which the solution is a fraction. In these circumstances we need to follow the approach of 'balancing the equation' described above.

Example

Solve

(a) $6x + 1 = 10x - 9$ (b) $3(x - 1) + 2(2x + 1) = 4$

(c) $\dfrac{20}{3x - 1} = 7$ (d) $\dfrac{9}{x + 2} = \dfrac{7}{2x + 1}$ (e) $\sqrt{\dfrac{2x}{x - 6}} = 2$

Solution

(a) To solve

$$6x + 1 = 10x - 9$$

the strategy is to collect terms involving x on one side of the equation, and to collect all of the number terms on to the other side. It does not matter which way round this is done. In this particular case, there are more xs on the right-hand side than there are on the left-hand side. Consequently, to avoid negative numbers, you may prefer to stack the x terms on the right-hand side. The details are as follows:

$$1 = 4x - 9 \qquad \text{(subtract } 6x \text{ from both sides)}$$
$$10 = 4x \qquad \text{(add 9 to both sides)}$$
$$\frac{10}{4} = x \qquad \text{(divide both sides by 4)}$$

Hence $x = {}^5/_2 = 2^1/_2$.

(b) The novel feature of the equation

$$3(x - 1) + 2(2x + 1) = 4$$

is the presence of brackets. To solve it, we first remove the brackets by multiplying out, and then collect like terms:

$$3x - 3 + 4x + 2 = 4 \qquad \text{(multiply out the brackets)}$$
$$7x - 1 = 4 \qquad \text{(collect like terms)}$$

Note that this equation is now of the form that we know how to solve:

$$7x = 5 \qquad \text{(add 1 to both sides)}$$
$$x = \frac{5}{7} \qquad \text{(divide both sides by 7)}$$

(c) The novel feature of the equation

$$\frac{20}{3x-1} = 7$$

is the fact that it involves an algebraic fraction. This can easily be removed by multiplying both sides by the bottom of the fraction:

$$\frac{20}{3x-1} \times (3x-1) = 7(3x-1)$$

which cancels down to give

$$20 = 7(3x-1)$$

The remaining steps are similar to those in part (b):

$20 = 21x - 7$	(multiply out the brackets)
$27 = 21x$	(add 7 to both sides)
$\dfrac{27}{21} = x$	(divide both sides by 21)

Hence $x = {}^9\!/_7 = 1{}^2\!/_7$.

(d) The next equation,

$$\frac{9}{x+2} = \frac{7}{2x+1}$$

looks particularly daunting since there are fractions on both sides. However, these are easily removed by multiplying both sides by the denominators, in turn:

$9 = \dfrac{7(x+2)}{2x+1}$	(multiply both sides by $x + 2$)
$9(2x + 1) = 7(x + 2)$	(multiply both sides by $2x + 1$)

With practice you can do these two steps simultaneously and write this as the first line of working. The procedure of going straight from

$$\frac{9}{x+2} = \frac{7}{2x+1}$$

to

$$9(2x + 1) = 7(x + 2)$$

is called 'cross-multiplication'. In general, if

$$\frac{a}{b} = \frac{c}{d}$$

then

$$ad = bc$$

The remaining steps are similar to those used in the earlier parts of this example:

$18x + 9 = 7x + 14$	(multiply out the brackets)
$11x + 9 = 14$	(subtract $7x$ from both sides)

$$11x = 5 \qquad \text{(subtract 9 from both sides)}$$

$$x = \frac{5}{11} \qquad \text{(divide both sides by 11)}$$

(e) The left-hand side of the final equation

$$\sqrt{\frac{2x}{x-6}} = 2$$

is surrounded by a square root, which can easily be removed by squaring both sides to get

$$\frac{2x}{x-6} = 4$$

The remaining steps are 'standard':

$$2x = 4(x - 6) \qquad \text{(multiply both sides by } x - 6)$$
$$2x = 4x - 24 \qquad \text{(multiply out the brackets)}$$
$$-2x = -24 \qquad \text{(subtract } 4x \text{ from both sides)}$$
$$x = 12 \qquad \text{(divide both sides by } -2)$$

Looking back over each part of the previous example, notice that there is a common strategy. In each case, the aim is to convert the given equation into one of the form

$$ax + b = c$$

which is the sort of equation that we can easily solve. If the original equation contains brackets then remove them by multiplying out. If the equation involves fractions then remove them by cross-multiplying.

Advice

If you have the time, it is always worth checking your answer by substituting your solution back into the original equation. For the last part of the above example, putting $x = 12$ into

$$\sqrt{\frac{2x}{x-6}} \text{ gives } \sqrt{\frac{2 \times 12}{12-6}} = \sqrt{\frac{24}{6}} = \sqrt{4} = 2 \qquad \checkmark$$

Practice Problem

5. Solve each of the following equations. Leave your answer as a fraction, if necessary.

(a) $4x + 1 = 25$ (b) $4x + 5 = 5x - 7$ (c) $3(3 - 2x) + 2(x - 1) = 10$

(d) $\dfrac{4}{x-1} = 5$ (e) $\dfrac{3}{x} = \dfrac{5}{x-1}$

1.2.3 Inequalities

In Section 1.1.1 we made use of a **number line**:

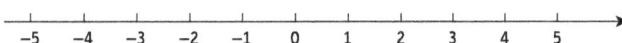

Now although only whole numbers are marked on this diagram it is implicitly assumed that it can also be used to indicate fractions and decimal numbers as well. To each point on the line there corresponds a particular number. Conversely, every number can be represented by a particular point on the line. For example, $-2\frac{1}{2}$ lies exactly halfway between -3 and -2. Similarly, $4\frac{7}{8}$ lies $\frac{7}{8}$ ths of the way between 4 and 5. In theory, we can even find a point on the line corresponding to a number such as $\sqrt{2}$, although it may be difficult to sketch such a point accurately in practice. My calculator gives the value of $\sqrt{2}$ to be 1.414 213 56 to eight decimal places. This number therefore lies just less than halfway between 1 and 2.

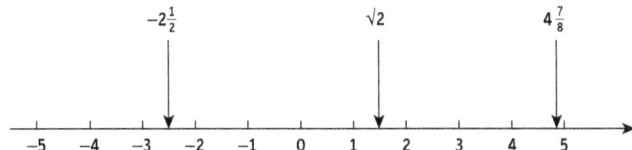

A number line can be used to decide whether or not one number is greater or less than another number. We say that a number a is greater than a number b if a lies to the right of b on the line and write this as

$a > b$

Likewise, we say that a is less than b if a lies to the left of b and write this as

$a < b$

From the diagram we see that

$-2 > -4$

because -2 lies to the right of -4. This is equivalent to the statement

$-4 < -2$

Similarly,

$0 > -1$ (or equivalently $-1 < 0$)

$2 > -2\frac{1}{2}$ (or equivalently $-2\frac{1}{2} < 2$)

$4\frac{7}{8} > \sqrt{2}$ (or equivalently $\sqrt{2} < 4\frac{7}{8}$)

There are occasions when we would like the letters a and b to stand for mathematical expressions rather than actual numbers. In this situation we sometimes use the symbols $\geq$ and $\leq$ to mean 'greater than or equal to' and 'less than or equal to', respectively.

We have already seen that we can manipulate equations in any way we like, provided that we do the same thing to both sides. An obvious question to ask is whether this rule extends to inequalities.

Consider the true statement

$1 < 3$ (*)

- Adding 4 to both sides gives $5 < 7$, which is true
- Adding -5 to both sides gives $-4 < -2$, which is true
- Multiplying both sides by 2 gives $2 < 6$, which is true

However,

- Multiplying both sides by -6 gives $-6 < -18$, which is false. In fact quite the reverse is true; -6 is actually greater than -18. This indicates that the rule needs modifying before we can extend it to inequalities and that we must be careful when manipulating inequalities.

Practice Problem

6. Starting with the true statement

$6 > 3$

decide which of the following are valid operations when performed on both sides:

(a) add 6	**(b)** multiply by 2	**(c)** subtract 3
(d) add -3	**(e)** divide by 3	**(f)** multiply by -4
(g) multiply by -1	**(h)** divide by -3	**(i)** add -10

These examples show that the usual rule does apply to inequalities with the important proviso that

if both sides are multiplied or divided by a negative number then the sense of the inequality is reversed

By this we mean that '>' changes to '<', '≤' changes to '≥' and so on.

To see how this works out in practice, consider the inequality

$2x + 3 < 4x + 7$

If we try and solve this like we did for equations, the first step would be to subtract $4x$ from both sides to get

$-2x + 3 < 7$

and then take 3 away from both sides to get

$-2x < 4$

Finally we divide both sides by -2 to get

$x > -2$

Notice that the sense has been reversed at this stage because we have divided by a negative number.

Advice

You should check your answer using a couple of test values. Substituting $x = 1$ (which lies to the right of -2, so should work) into both sides of the original inequality $2x + 3 < 4x + 7$ gives $5 < 11$, which is true. On the other hand, substituting $x = -3$ (which lies to the left of -2, so should fail) gives $-3 < -5$, which is false. Of course, just checking a couple of numbers like this does not prove that the final inequality is correct, but it should protect you against gross blunders.

Practice Problem

7. Simplify the inequalities

   (a) $2x < 3x + 7$ (b) $21x - 19 \geq 4x + 15$

Inequalities arise in business when there is a budgetary restriction on resource allocation. The following example shows how to set up and solve the relevant inequality.

Example

A firm's Human Resources department has a budget of $25 000 to spend on training and laptops. Training courses cost $700 and new laptops are $1200.

(a) If the department trains E employees and buys L laptops, write down an inequality for E and L.

(b) If 12 employees attend courses, how many laptops could be bought?

Solution

(a) The cost of training E employees is $700E$ and the cost of buying L laptops is $1200L$. The total amount spent must not exceed $25 000 so $700E + 1200L \leq 25\ 000$.

(b) Substituting $E = 12$ into the inequality gives $8400 + 1200L \leq 25\ 000$.

$$1200L \leq 16\ 600 \qquad \text{(subtract 8400 from both sides)}$$

$$L \leq 13\frac{5}{6} \qquad \text{(divide both sides by 1200)}$$

so a maximum of 13 laptops could be bought.

Key Terms

Algebraic fraction   Ratio of two expressions; $p(x)/q(x)$ where $p(x)$ and $q(x)$ are algebraic expressions such as $ax^2 + bx + c$ or $dx + e$.

Denominator   The number (or expression) on the bottom of a fraction.

Equation   Equality of two algebraic expressions which is only true for certain values of the variable.

Equivalent fractions   Fractions which may appear different but which have the same numerical value.

Factor   Part of an expression which, when multiplied by all the other factors, gives the complete expression.

Identity   Equality of two algebraic expressions which is true for all values of the variable.

Number line   An infinite line on which the points represent real numbers by their (signed) distance from the origin.

Numerator   The number (or expression) on the top of a fraction.

Exercise 1.2

1. Reduce each of the following numerical fractions to their lowest terms:

    (a) $\dfrac{13}{26}$ (b) $\dfrac{9}{12}$ (c) $\dfrac{18}{30}$ (d) $\dfrac{24}{72}$ (e) $\dfrac{36}{27}$

2. In 2011 in the USA, 35 out of every 100 adults owned a smartphone. By 2013 this figure increased to 56 out of every 100.

    (a) Express both of these figures as fractions reduced to their lowest terms.

    (b) By what factor did smartphone ownership increase during this period? Give your answer as a mixed fraction in its lowest terms.

3. Reduce each of the following algebraic fractions to their lowest terms:

    (a) $\dfrac{6x}{9}$ (b) $\dfrac{x}{2x^2}$ (c) $\dfrac{b}{abc}$ (d) $\dfrac{4x}{6x^2y}$ (e) $\dfrac{15a^2b}{20ab^2}$

4. By factorising the numerators and/or denominators of each of the following fractions reduce each to its lowest terms:

    (a) $\dfrac{2p}{4q+6r}$ (b) $\dfrac{x}{x^2-4x}$ (c) $\dfrac{3ab}{6a^2+3a}$ (d) $\dfrac{14d}{21d-7de}$ (e) $\dfrac{x+2}{x^2-4}$

5. Which one of the following algebraic fractions can be simplified? Explain why the other two fractions cannot be simplified.

    $$\dfrac{x-1}{2x-2}, \quad \dfrac{x-2}{x+2}, \quad \dfrac{5t}{10t-s}$$

6. **(1)** Without using a calculator work out the following giving your answer in its lowest terms:

(a) $\dfrac{1}{7}+\dfrac{2}{7}$ (b) $\dfrac{2}{9}-\dfrac{5}{9}$ (c) $\dfrac{1}{2}+\dfrac{1}{3}$ (d) $\dfrac{3}{4}-\dfrac{2}{5}$ (e) $\dfrac{1}{6}+\dfrac{2}{9}$ (f) $\dfrac{1}{6}+\dfrac{2}{3}$

(g) $\dfrac{5}{6}\times\dfrac{3}{4}$ (h) $\dfrac{4}{15}\div\dfrac{2}{3}$ (i) $\dfrac{7}{8}\times\dfrac{2}{3}$ (j) $\dfrac{2}{75}\div\dfrac{4}{5}$ (k) $\dfrac{2}{9}\div3$ (l) $3\div\dfrac{2}{7}$

(2) Use your calculator to check your answers to part (1).

7. It takes $1\frac{1}{4}$ hours to complete an annual service of a car. If a garage has $47\frac{1}{2}$ hours available, how many cars can it service?

8. Work out each of the following, simplifying your answer as far as possible:

(a) $\dfrac{2}{3x}+\dfrac{1}{3x}$ (b) $\dfrac{2}{x}\times\dfrac{x}{5}$ (c) $\dfrac{3}{x}-\dfrac{2}{x^2}$ (d) $\dfrac{7}{x}+\dfrac{2}{y}$ (e) $\dfrac{a}{2}\div\dfrac{a}{6}$

(f) $\dfrac{5c}{12}+\dfrac{5d}{18}$ (g) $\dfrac{x+2}{y-5}\times\dfrac{y-5}{x+3}$ (h) $\dfrac{4gh}{7}\div\dfrac{2g}{9h}$ (i) $\dfrac{t}{4}\div5$ (j) $\dfrac{P}{Q}\times\dfrac{Q}{P}$

9. Solve each of the following equations. If necessary give your answer as a mixed fraction reduced to its lowest terms.

(a) $x+2=7$ (b) $3x=18$ (c) $\dfrac{x}{9}=2$ (d) $x-4=-2$

(e) $2x-3=17$ (f) $3x+4=1$ (g) $\dfrac{x}{6}-7=3$ (h) $3(x-1)=2$

(i) $4-x=9$ (j) $6x+2=5x-1$ (k) $5(3x+8)=10$ (l) $2(x-3)=5(x+1)$

(m) $\dfrac{4x-7}{3}=2$ (n) $\dfrac{4}{x+1}=1$ (o) $5-\dfrac{1}{x}=1$

10. Which of the following inequalities are true?

(a) $-2<1$ (b) $-6>-4$ (c) $3<3$

(d) $3\le3$ (e) $-21\ge-22$ (f) $4<25$

11. Simplify the following inequalities:

(a) $2x>x+1$ (b) $7x+3\le9+5x$ (c) $x-5>4x+4$ (d) $x-1<2x-3$

12. Simplify the following algebraic expression:

$$\dfrac{4}{x^2y}\div\dfrac{2x}{y}$$

13. **(a)** Solve the equation

$$6(2+x)=5(1-4x)$$

(b) Solve the inequality

$$3x+6\ge5x-14$$

Exercise 1.2*

1. Simplify each of the following algebraic fractions:

   (a) $\dfrac{2x-6}{4}$ (b) $\dfrac{9x}{6x^2-3x}$ (c) $\dfrac{4x+16}{x+4}$ (d) $\dfrac{x-1}{1-x}$

   (e) $\dfrac{x+6}{x^2-36}$ (f) $\dfrac{(x+3)(2x-5)}{(2x-5)(x+4)}$ (g) $\dfrac{3x}{6x^3-15x^2+9x}$ (h) $\dfrac{4x^2-25y^2}{6x-15y}$

2. **(1)** Without using your calculator evaluate

   (a) $\dfrac{4}{5}\times\dfrac{25}{28}$ (b) $\dfrac{2}{7}\times\dfrac{14}{25}\times\dfrac{5}{8}$ (c) $\dfrac{9}{16}\div\dfrac{3}{8}$ (d) $\dfrac{2}{5}\times\dfrac{1}{12}\div\dfrac{8}{25}$

   (e) $\dfrac{10}{13}-\dfrac{12}{13}$ (f) $\dfrac{5}{9}+\dfrac{2}{3}$ (g) $2\dfrac{3}{5}+1\dfrac{3}{7}$ (h) $5\dfrac{9}{10}-\dfrac{1}{2}+1\dfrac{2}{5}$

   (i) $3\dfrac{3}{4}\times1\dfrac{3}{5}$ (j) $\dfrac{3}{5}\times\left(2\dfrac{1}{3}+\dfrac{1}{2}\right)$ (k) $\dfrac{5}{6}\times\left(2\dfrac{1}{3}-1\dfrac{2}{5}\right)$ (l) $\left(3\dfrac{1}{3}\div2\dfrac{1}{6}\right)\div\dfrac{5}{13}$

   (2) Confirm your answer to part (1) using a calculator.

3. Find expressions for the following fractions:

   (a) $\dfrac{x^2+6x}{x-2}\times\dfrac{x-2}{x}$ (b) $\dfrac{1}{2}\div\dfrac{1}{x+1}$ (c) $\dfrac{2}{xy}+\dfrac{3}{xy}$ (d) $\dfrac{x}{2}+\dfrac{x+1}{3}$

   (e) $\dfrac{3}{x}+\dfrac{4}{x+1}$ (f) $\dfrac{3}{x}+\dfrac{5}{x^2}$ (g) $x-\dfrac{2}{x+1}$ (h) $\dfrac{5}{x(x+1)}-\dfrac{2}{x}+\dfrac{3}{x+1}$

4. Solve the following equations:

   (a) $5(2x+1)=3(x-2)$ (b) $5(x+2)+4(2x-3)=11$

   (c) $5(1-x)=4(10+x)$ (d) $3(3-2x)-7(1-x)=10$

   (e) $9-5(2x-1)=6$ (f) $\dfrac{3}{2x+1}=2$

   (g) $\dfrac{2}{x-1}=\dfrac{3}{5x+4}$ (h) $\dfrac{x}{2}+3=7$

   (i) $5-\dfrac{x}{3}=2$ (j) $\dfrac{5(x-3)}{2}=\dfrac{2(x-1)}{5}$

   (k) $\sqrt{(2x-5)}=3$ (l) $(x+3)(x-1)=(x+4)(x-3)$

   (m) $(x+2)^2+(2x-1)^2=5x(x+1)$ (n) $\dfrac{2x+7}{3}=\dfrac{x-4}{6}+\dfrac{1}{2}$

   (o) $\sqrt{\dfrac{45}{2x-1}}=3$ (p) $\dfrac{4}{x}-\dfrac{3}{4}=\dfrac{1}{4x}$

5. Two-thirds of Ariadne's money together with five-sevenths of Brian's money is equal to three-fifths of Catriona's money. If Ariadne has \$2.40 and Catriona has \$11.25, write down an equation that you could use to work out how much Brian has. Solve this equation.

6. An amount $P is placed in a savings account. The interest rate is $r\%$ compounded annually so that after n years the savings, S, will be

$$S = P\left(1 + \frac{r}{100}\right)^n$$

   (a) Find S when $P = 2000$, $n = 5$ and $r = 10$.

   (b) Find P when $S = 65\,563.62$, $n = 3$ and $r = 3$.

   (c) Find r when $S = 7320.50$, $P = 5000$ and $n = 4$.

7. Solve the following inequalities:

   (a) $2x - 19 > 7x + 24$ (b) $2(x - 1) < 5(3x + 2)$ (c) $\dfrac{2x-1}{5} \geq \dfrac{x-3}{2}$

   (d) $3 + \dfrac{x}{3} < 2(x+4)$ (e) $x < 2x + 1 \leq 7$

8. The design costs of an advertisement in a glossy magazine are $9000 and the cost per cm^2 of print is $50.

   (a) Write down an expression for the total cost of publishing an advert which covers x cm^2.

   (b) The advertising budget is between $10\,800 and $12\,500. Write down and solve an inequality to work out the minimum and maximum area that could be used.

9. List all the whole numbers that satisfy both of the following inequalities simultaneously:

   $-7 \leq 2x < 6$ and $4x + 1 \leq x + 2$

10. (a) Simplify

$$\frac{31x - 8}{(2x-1)(x+2)} - \frac{14}{x+2}$$

   (b) Solve the equation

$$\frac{x+1}{8} = \frac{x+3}{4} - \frac{1}{2}$$

   (c) Simplify the inequality

$$(2x + 1)(x - 5) \leq 2(x + 2)(x - 4)$$

11. Simplify

$$\frac{x^2}{x+1} \div \frac{2x}{x^2 - 1}$$

SECTION 1.3
Graphs of linear equations

Objectives

At the end of this section you should be able to:

- Plot points on graph paper given their coordinates.
- Sketch a line by finding the coordinates of two points on the line.
- Solve simultaneous linear equations graphically.
- Sketch a line by using its slope and intercept.

Consider the two straight lines shown in Figure 1.1. The horizontal line is referred to as the *x* axis and the vertical line is referred to as the *y* axis. The point where these lines intersect is known as the **origin** and is denoted by the letter O. These lines enable us to identify uniquely any point, P, in terms of its **coordinates** (x, y). The first number, x, denotes the horizontal distance along the x axis and the second number, y, denotes the vertical distance along the y axis. The arrows on the axes indicate the positive direction in each case.

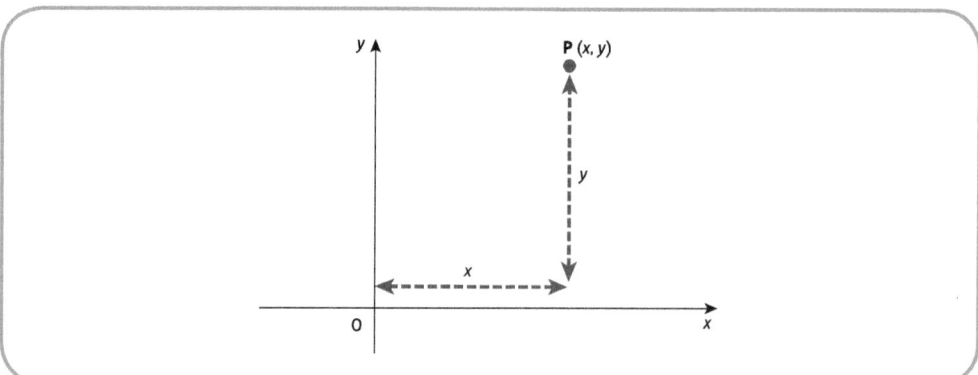

Figure 1.1

Figure 1.2 shows the five points A(2, 3), B(−1, 4), C(−3, −1), D(3, −2) and E(5, 0) plotted on coordinate axes. The point A with coordinates (2, 3) is obtained by starting at the origin, moving 2 units to the right and then moving 3 units vertically upwards. Similarly, the point B with coordinates (−1, 4) is located 1 unit to the left of O (because the x coordinate is negative) and 4 units up.

Note that the point C lies in the bottom left-hand quadrant since its x and y coordinates are both negative. It is also worth noticing that E actually lies on the x axis since its y coordinate is zero. Likewise, a point with coordinates of the form $(0, y)$ for some number y would lie somewhere on the y axis. Of course, the point with coordinates (0, 0) is the origin, O.

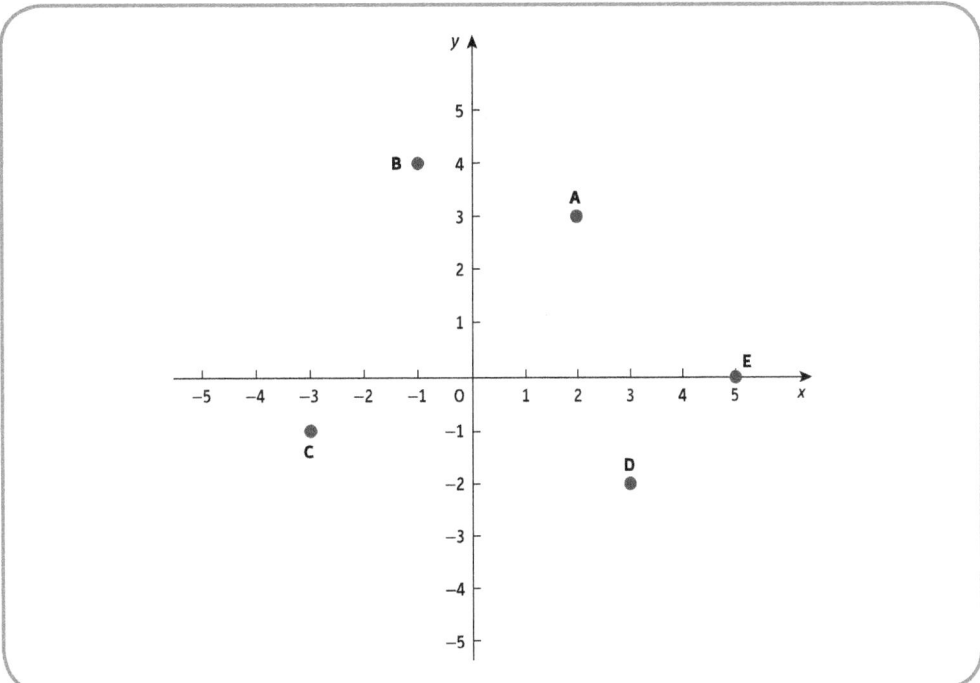

Figure 1.2

Practice Problem

1. Plot the following points on graph paper. What do you observe?

(2, 5), (1, 3), (0, 1), (−2, −3), (−3, −5)

In economics we need to do rather more than just plot individual points on graph paper. We would like to be able to sketch curves represented by equations and to deduce information from such a picture. We restrict our attention in this section to those equations whose graphs are straight lines, deferring consideration of more general curve sketching until Chapter 2.

In Practice Problem 1 you will have noticed that the five points (2, 5), (1, 3), (0, 1), (−2, −3) and (−3, −5) all lie on a straight line. In fact, the equation of this line is

$$-2x + y = 1$$

Any point lies on this line if its x and y coordinates satisfy this equation. For example, (2, 5) lies on the line because when the values $x = 2$, $y = 5$ are substituted into the left-hand side of the equation we obtain

$$-2(2) + 5 = -4 + 5 = 1$$

which is the right-hand side of the equation. The other points can be checked similarly (See Table 1.1).

Table 1.1

Point	Check	
(1, 3)	$-2(1) + 3 = -2 + 3 = 1$	✓
(0, 1)	$-2(0) + 1 = 0 + 1 = 1$	✓
(−2, −3)	$-2(-2) - 3 = 4 - 3 = 1$	✓
(−3, −5)	$-2(-3) - 5 = 6 - 5 = 1$	✓

Example

Sketch the line

$$2x + y = 5$$

Solution

Setting $x = 0$ gives

$$2(0) + y = 5$$
$$0 + y = 5$$
$$y = 5$$

Hence (0, 5) lies on the line.
   Setting $y = 0$ gives

$$2x + 0 = 5$$
$$2x = 5$$
$$x = 5/2 \qquad \text{(divide both sides by 2)}$$

Hence (5/2, 0) lies on the line.
   The line $2x + y = 5$ is sketched in Figure 1.4. Notice how easy the algebra is using this approach. The two points themselves are also slightly more meaningful. They are the points where the line intersects the coordinate axes.

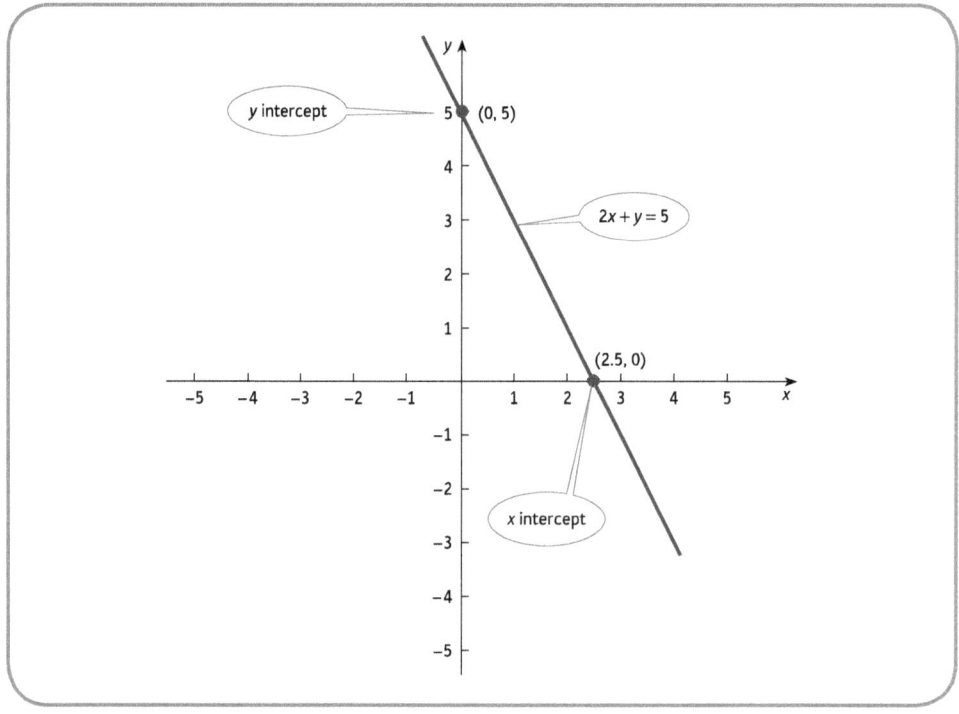

Figure 1.4

Practice Problem

4. Find the coordinates of the points where the line

$$x - 2y = 2$$

intersects the axes. Hence sketch its graph.

In economics it is sometimes necessary to handle more than one equation at the same time. For example, in supply and demand analysis we are interested in two equations, the supply equation and the demand equation. Both involve the same variables Q and P, so it makes sense to sketch them on the same diagram. This enables the market equilibrium quantity and price to be determined by finding the point of intersection of the two lines. We shall return to the analysis of supply and demand in Section 1.5. There are many other occasions in economics and business studies when it is necessary to determine the coordinates of points of intersection. The following is a straightforward example which illustrates the general principle.

Example

Find the point of intersection of the two lines

$$4x + 3y = 11$$
$$2x + y = 5$$

Solution

We have already seen how to sketch these lines in the previous two examples. We discovered that

$$4x + 3y = 11$$

passes through $(5, -3)$ and $(-1, 5)$, and that

$$2x + y = 5$$

passes through $(0, 5)$ and $(5/2, 0)$.

These two lines are sketched on the same diagram in Figure 1.5, from which the point of intersection is seen to be $(2, 1)$.

It is easy to verify that we have not made any mistakes by checking that $(2, 1)$ lies on both lines. It lies on

$$4x + 3y = 11 \text{ because } 4(2) + 3(1) = 8 + 3 = 11 \qquad ✓$$

$$\text{and lies on } 2x + y = 5 \text{ because } 2(2) + 1 = 4 + 1 = 5 \qquad ✓$$

For this reason, we say that $x = 2$, $y = 1$ is the solution of the **simultaneous linear equations**

$$4x + 3y = 11$$
$$2x + y = 5$$

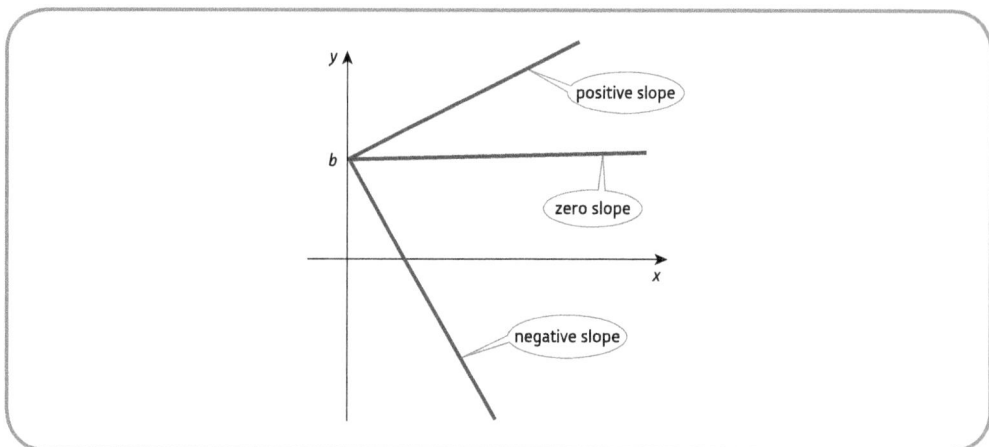

Figure 1.7

corresponding decrease in y, indicating that the line is downhill. If a is zero then the equation is just

$$y = b$$

indicating that y is fixed at b and the line is horizontal. The three cases are illustrated in Figure 1.7.

It is important to appreciate that in order to use the slope–intercept approach it is necessary for the equation to be written as

$$y = ax + b$$

If a linear equation does not have this form, it is usually possible to perform a preliminary rearrangement to isolate the variable y on the left-hand side.

For example, to use the slope–intercept approach to sketch the line

$$2x + 3y = 12$$

we begin by removing the x term from the left-hand side. Subtracting $2x$ from both sides gives

$$3y = 12 - 2x$$

and dividing both sides by 3 gives

$$y = 4 - \tfrac{2}{3}x$$

This is now in the required form with $a = -2/3$ and $b = 4$. The line is sketched in Figure 1.8. A slope of $-2/3$ means that, for every 1 unit along, we go 2/3 units down (or, equivalently, for every 3 units along, we go 2 units down). An intercept of 4 means that it passes through $(0, 4)$.

Practice Problem

6. Use the slope–intercept approach to sketch the lines

(a) $y = x + 2$

(b) $4x + 2y = 1$

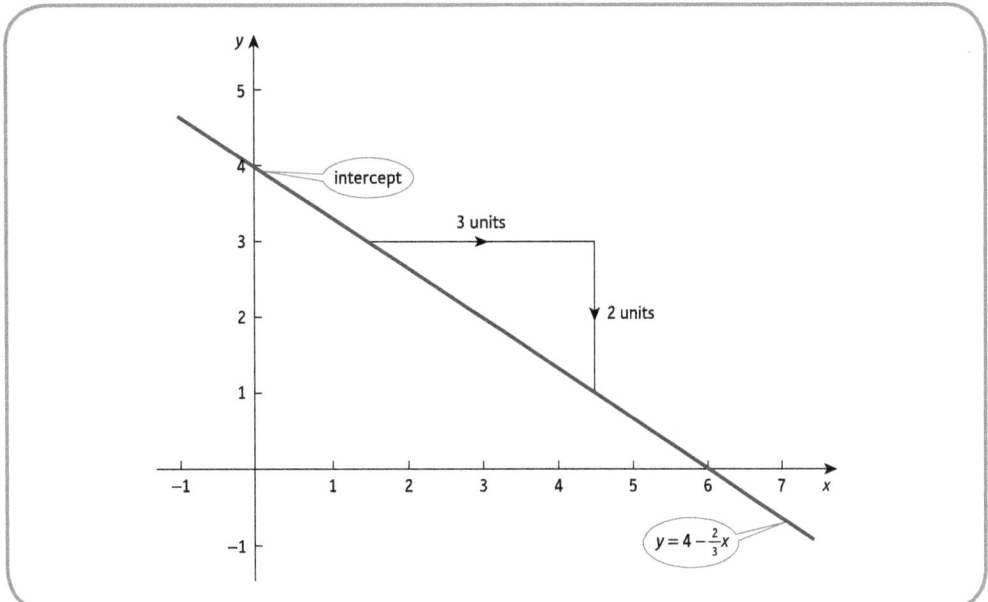

Figure 1.8

We conclude this section with two examples showing how linear graphs can be used in business.

Example

Two new models of a smartphone are launched on 1 January 2015. Predictions of sales are given by:

Model 1: $S_1 = 4 + 0.5n$ Model 2: $S_2 = 8 + 0.1n$

where S_i (in tens of thousands) denotes the monthly sales of model i after n months.

(a) State the values of the slope and intercept of each line and give an interpretation.

(b) Illustrate the sales of both models during the first year by drawing graphs on the same axes.

(c) Use the graph to find the month when sales of Model 1 overtake those of Model 2.

Solution

(a) The intercept for Model 1 is 4. There are 40 000 sales of this phone when the product is launched. The slope is 0.5 so each month sales increase by 5000. The corresponding figures for Model 2 are 8 and 0.1, respectively.

(b) The intercept for Model 1 is 4 so the line passes through $(0, 4)$. For every one-unit increase in n the value of S_1 increases by 0.5 so, for example, a two-unit increase in n results in a one-unit increase in S_1. The line passes through $(2, 5)$, $(4, 6)$ and so on. The line is sketched in Figure 1.9.

For Model 2, the line passes through $(0, 8)$ and since the slope is 0.1, it passes through $(10, 9)$.

(c) The graphs intersect at $(10, 9)$ so sales of Model 1 overtake sales of Model 2 after 10 months.

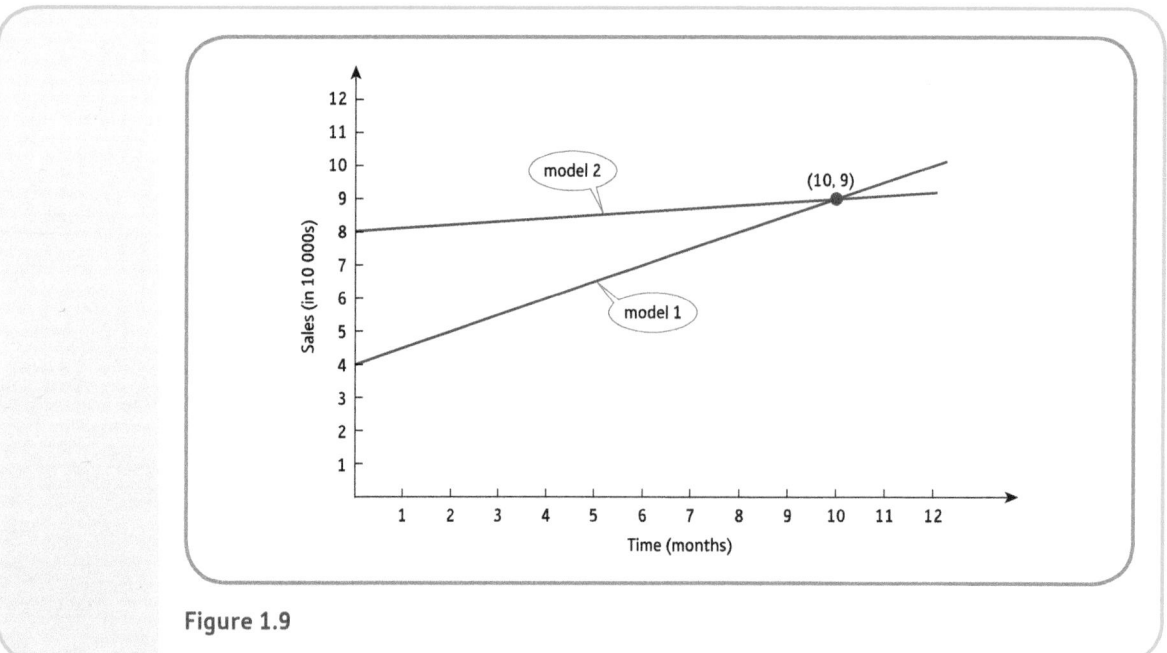

Figure 1.9

Example

Three companies can supply a university with some mathematical software. Each company has a different pricing structure:

Company 1 provides a site licence which costs $130 000 and can be used by anyone at the university;

Company 2 charges $1000 per user;

Company 3 charges a fixed amount of $40 000 for the first 60 users and $500 for each additional user.

(a) Draw a graph of each cost function on the same set of axes.

(b) What advice can you give the university about which company to use?

Solution

(a) If there are n users then the cost, C, from each supplier is:

Company 1: $C = 130\,000$. The graph is a horizontal line with intercept 130 000

Company 2: $C = 1000n$. The graph is a line passing through the origin with a slope 1000

Company 3: If $n \le 60$ then $C = 40\,000$

If $n > 60$ then $C = 40\,000 + 500(n - 60) = 500n + 10\,000$

The graph for company C is a horizontal line with intercept 40 000 until $n = 60$ after which the line bends upwards with a slope 500.

The graphs are sketched in Figure 1.10.

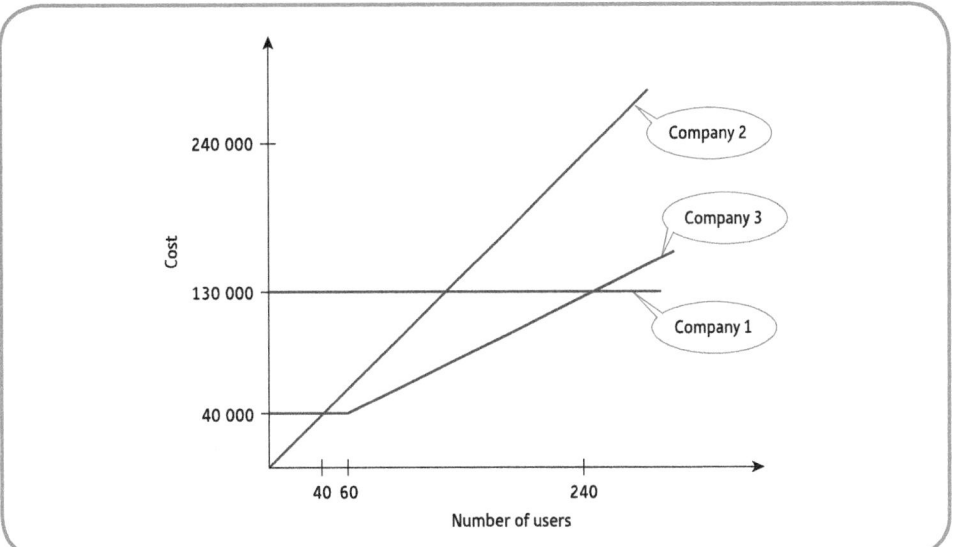

Figure 1.10

(b) The cheapest supplier depends on the number of users:

If $n \leq 40$ company 2 is the cheapest;

If $40 \leq n \leq 240$ company 3 is the cheapest;

If $n \geq 240$ company 1 is the cheapest.

Key Terms

Coefficient   A numerical multiplier of the variables in an algebraic term, such as the numbers 4 and 7 in the expression $4x + 7yz^2$.

Coordinates   A set of numbers that determine the position of a point relative to a set of axes.

Intercept   The point(s) where a graph crosses one of the coordinate axes.

Linear equation   An equation of the form $dx + ey = f$.

Origin   The point where the coordinate axes intersect.

Simultaneous linear equations   A set of linear equations in which there are (usually) the same number of equations and unknowns. The solution consists of values of the unknowns which satisfy all of the equations at the same time.

Slope of a line   Also known as the gradient, it is the change in the value of y when x increases by 1 unit.

x axis   The horizontal coordinate axis pointing from left to right.

y axis   The vertical coordinate axis pointing upwards.

Exercise 1.3

1. On graph paper draw axes with values of x and y between -3 and 10, and plot the following points:

    P(4, 0), Q(-2, 9), R(5, 8), S(-1, -2)

    Hence find the coordinates of the point of intersection of the line passing through P and Q, and the line passing through R and S.

2. An airline charges $300 for a flight of 2000 km and $700 for a flight of 4000 km.

    (a) Plot these points on graph paper with distance on the horizontal axis and cost on the vertical axis.

    (b) Assuming a linear model estimate

    (i) the cost of a flight of 3200 km

    (ii) the distance travelled on a flight costing $400.

3. By substituting values into the equation, decide which of the following points lie on the line, $x + 4y = 12$:

    A(12, 0), B(2, 2), C(4, 2), D(-8, 5), E(0, 3)

4. For the line $3x - 5y = 8$,

    (a) Find the value of x when $y = 2$.

    (b) Find the value of y when $x = 1$.

    Hence write down the coordinates of two points which lie on this line.

5. If $4x + 3y = 24$, complete the following table and hence sketch this line.

x	y
0	
	0
3	

6. Solve the following pairs of simultaneous linear equations graphically:

    (a) $-2x + y = 2$ (b) $3x + 4y = 12$ (c) $2x + y = 4$ (d) $x + y = 1$
        $2x + y = -6$ $x + 4y = 8$ $4x - 3y = 3$ $6x + 5y = 15$

7. State the value of the slope and y-intercept for each of the following lines:

    (a) $y = 5x + 9$ (b) $y = 3x - 1$ (c) $y = 13 - x$

    (d) $-x + y = 4$ (e) $4x + 2y = 5$ (f) $5x - y = 6$

8. Use the slope–intercept approach to produce a rough sketch of the following lines:

    (a) $y = -x$ (b) $x - 2y = 6$

9. A taxi firm charges a fixed cost of $4 plus a charge of $2.50 a mile.

    (a) Write down a formula for the cost, C, of a journey of x miles.

    (b) Plot a graph of C against x for $0 \le x \le 20$.

    (c) Hence, or otherwise, work out the distance of a journey which costs $24.

10. The number of people, N, employed in a chain of cafes is related to the number of cafes, n, by the equation:

$$N = 10n + 120$$

(a) Illustrate this relation by plotting a graph of N against n for $0 \le n \le 20$.

(b) Hence, or otherwise, calculate the number of

(i) employees when the company has 14 cafes;

(ii) cafes when the company employs 190 people.

(c) State the values of the slope and intercept of the graph and give an interpretation.

11. Monthly sales revenue, S (in \$), and monthly advertising expenditure, A (in \$), are modelled by the linear relation, $S = 9000 + 12A$.

(a) If the firm does not spend any money on advertising what is the expected sales revenue that month?

(b) If the firm spends \$800 on advertising one month what is the expected sales revenue?

(c) How much does the firm need to spend on advertising to achieve monthly sales revenue of \$15 000?

(d) If the firm increases monthly expenditure on advertising by \$1 what is the corresponding increase in sales revenue?

Exercise 1.3*

1. Which of the following points lie on the line $3x - 5y = 25$?

$(5, -2)$, $(10, 1)$, $(-5, 0)$ $(5, 10)$, $(-5, 10)$, $(0, -5)$

2. Solve the following pairs of simultaneous equations graphically:

(a) $y = 3x - 1$ **(b)** $2x + y = 6$ **(c)** $2x + 3y = 5$ **(d)** $3x + 4y = -12$

    $y = 2x + 1$ $x - y = -3$ $5x - 2y = -16$ $-2x + 3y = 25$

3. State the value of the slope and y-intercept for each of the following lines:

(a) $y = 7x - 34$ **(b)** $y = 1 - x$ **(c)** $3x - 2y = 6$ **(d)** $-4x + 2y = 5$

(e) $x - 5y = 0$ **(f)** $y = 2$ **(g)** $x = 4$

4. Identify the two lines in the following list which are parallel:

(a) $3x + 5y = 2$ **(b)** $5x - 3y = 1$ **(c)** $5x + 3y = 13$

(d) $10x - 6y = 9$ **(e)** $y = 0.6x + 2$

5. **(a)** The Wonderful Mobile Phone Company charges \$70 per month, and calls cost \$0.50 per minute. If I use my phone for x minutes in a month, write down an expression for the total cost in terms of x.

(b) Repeat part (a) for the Fantastic Mobile Phone Company, which charges \$20 per month and \$1 per minute.

(c) Plot both graphs on the same axes and hence find the call time per month which gives the same total cost for these two companies.

The coefficient of x in equation (1) is 4 and the coefficient of x in equation (2) is 2. If these numbers had turned out to be exactly the same then we could have eliminated the variable x by subtracting one equation from the other. However, we can arrange for this to be the case by multiplying the left-hand side of the second equation by 2. Of course, we must also remember to multiply the right-hand side of the second equation by 2 in order for this operation to be valid. The second equation then becomes

$$4x + 2y = 10 \tag{3}$$

We may now subtract equation (3) from (1) to get

$$y = 1$$

You may like to think of this in terms of the usual layout for the subtraction of two ordinary numbers: that is,

$$
\begin{aligned}
4x + 3y &= 11 \\
4x + 3y &= 10 \ - \\
\hline
y &= \ 1
\end{aligned}
$$

the xs cancel when you subtract

This number can now be substituted into one of the original equations to deduce x. From equation (1)

$$4x + 3(1) = 11 \quad \text{(substitute } y = 1\text{)}$$
$$4x + 3 = 11$$
$$4x = \ 8 \quad \text{(subtract 3 from both sides)}$$
$$x = \ 2 \quad \text{(divide both sides by 4)}$$

Hence the solution is $x = 2$, $y = 1$. As a check, substitution of these values into the other original equation (2) gives

$$2(2) + 1 = 5 \quad \checkmark$$

The method of elimination can be summarised as follows.

Step 1

Add/subtract a multiple of one equation to/from a multiple of the other to eliminate x.

Step 2

Solve the resulting equation for y.

Step 3

Substitute the value of y into one of the original equations to deduce x.

Step 4

Check that no mistakes have been made by substituting both x and y into the other original equation.

$$10x - 20y = 5$$
$$10x - 20y = 5 \ -$$
$$\overline{0 = 0}$$

everything cancels including the right-hand side!

Again, it is easy to explain this using graphs. The line $2x - 4y = 1$ passes through $(0, -1/4)$ and $(1/2, 0)$. The line $5x - 10y = 5/2$ passes through $(0, -1/4)$ and $(1/2, 0)$. Consequently, both equations represent the same line. From Figure 1.12 the lines intersect along the whole of their length and any point on this line is a solution. This particular system of equations has infinitely many solutions. This can also be deduced algebraically. The equation involving y in step 2 is

$$0y = 0$$

which is true for any value of y.

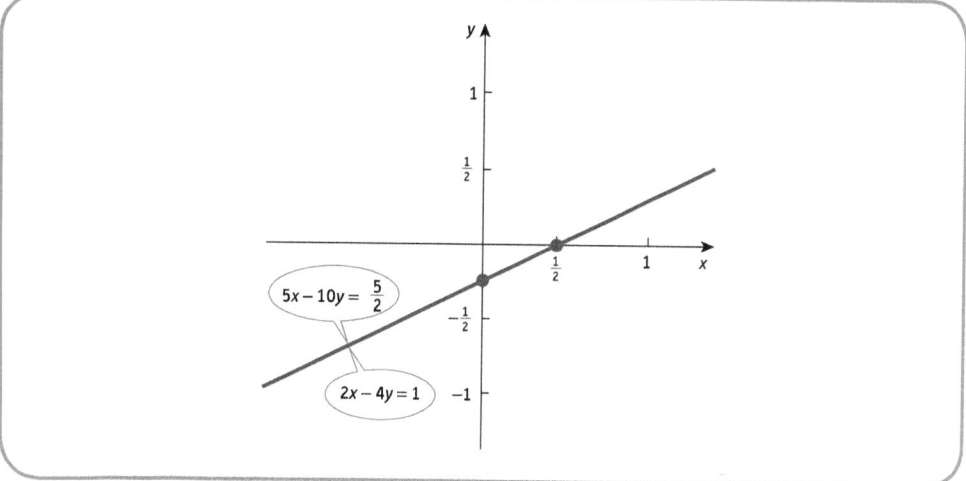

Figure 1.12

Practice Problem

2. Attempt to solve the following systems of equations:

(a) $3x - 6y = -2$ (b) $-5x + y = 4$
     $-4x + 8y = -1$ $10x - 2y = -8$

Comment on the nature of the solution in each case.

It is possible to identify when simultaneous equations fail to possess a unique solution by considering the general case:

$$ax + by = c$$
$$dx + ey = f$$

The variable y can be eliminated by multiplying the first equation by e, multiplying the second equation by b and subtracting:

$$aex + bey = ce$$
$$bdx + bey = bf \ -$$
$$\overline{(ae - bd)x = ce - bf}$$

Example

Solve the system of equations

$$3x + 2y = 1 \tag{1}$$
$$-2x + y = 2 \tag{2}$$

Solution

Step 1

The coefficients of x in equations (1) and (2) are 3 and -2 respectively. We can arrange for these to be the same size (but of opposite sign) by multiplying equation (1) by 2 and multiplying (2) by 3. The new equations will then have x coefficients of 6 and -6, so we can eliminate x this time by adding the equations together. The details are as follows.

Doubling the first equation produces

$$6x + 4y = 2 \tag{3}$$

Tripling the second equation produces

$$-6x + 3y = 6 \tag{4}$$

If equation (4) is added to equation (3) then

$$6x + 4y = 2$$
$$-6x + 3y = 6 \ +$$
$$\overline{7y = 8} \tag{5}$$

the xs cancel when you add

Step 2

Equation (5) can be solved by dividing both sides by 7 to get

$$y = 8/7$$

Step 3

If 8/7 is substituted for y in equation (1) then

$$3x + 2\left(\frac{8}{7}\right) = 1$$

$$3x + \frac{16}{7} = 1$$

$$3x = 1 - \frac{16}{7} \qquad \text{(subtract } 16/7 \text{ from both sides)}$$

$$3x = \frac{7 - 16}{7} \qquad \text{(put over a common denominator)}$$

$$3x = -\frac{9}{7}$$

$$x = \frac{1}{3} \times \left(-\frac{9}{7}\right) \qquad \text{(divide both sides by 3)}$$

$$x = -\frac{3}{7}$$

The solution is therefore $x = -3/7$, $y = 8/7$.

Step 4

As a check, equation (2) gives

$$-2\left(-\frac{3}{7}\right)+\frac{8}{7}=\frac{6}{7}+\frac{8}{7}=\frac{6+8}{7}=\frac{14}{7}=2 \quad \checkmark$$

Advice

In the general description of the method, we suggested that the variable x is eliminated in step 1. There is nothing special about x. We could equally well eliminate y at this stage and then solve the resulting equation in step 2 for x.

You might like to solve the above example using this alternative strategy. You need to double equation (2) and then subtract from (1).

Practice Problem

1. (a) Solve the equations

$$3x - 2y = 4$$
$$x - 2y = 2$$

by eliminating one of the variables.

(b) Solve the equations

$$3x + 5y = 19$$
$$-5x + 2y = -11$$

by eliminating one of the variables.

The following examples provide further practice in using the method and illustrate some special cases which may occur.

Example

Solve the system of equations

$$x - 2y = 1$$
$$2x - 4y = -3$$

Solution

The variable x can be eliminated by doubling the first equation and subtracting the second:

both the xs and the ys cancel!

$$\begin{aligned} 2x - 4y &= 2 \\ 2x - 4y &= -3 \;- \\ \hline 0 &= 5 \end{aligned}$$

The statement '0 = 5' is clearly nonsense and something has g understand what is going on here, let us try to solve this proble

The line $x - 2y = 1$ passes through the points (0, −1/2) and (1 $2x - 4y = -3$ passes through the points (0, 3/4) and (−3/2, 0) (che that these lines are parallel and so they do not intersect. It is th we were unable to find a solution using algebra, because this not have one. We could have deduced this before when subtr equation that only involves y in step 2 can be written as

$$0y = 5$$

and the problem is to find a value of y for which this equation is since

$$\text{zero} \times \text{any number} = \text{zero}$$

and so the original system of equations does not have a solution.

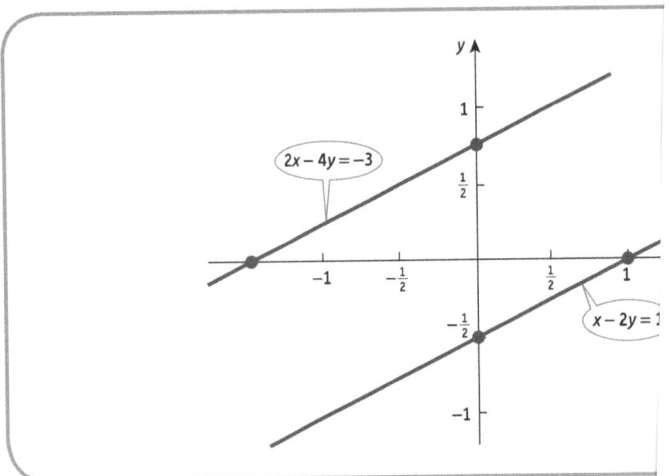

Figure 1.11

Example

Solve the equations

$$2x - 4y = 1$$
$$5x - 10y = 5/2$$

Solution

The variable x can be eliminated by multiplying the first e second equation by 2 and subtracting so that

$$x = \frac{ce - bf}{ae - bd}$$

In the same way it is possible to show that

$$y = \frac{af - cd}{ae - bd} \qquad \text{(see Exercise 1.4* Question 3).}$$

These formulae cannot be used when $ae = bd$ since it is impossible to divide by zero. In this case the system either has no solution or infinitely many solutions. You might like to check that this condition holds for both of the systems in Practice Problem 2.

We now show how the algebraic method can be used to solve three equations in three unknowns. As you might expect, the details are more complicated than for just two equations, but the principle is the same. We begin with a simple example to illustrate the general method. Consider the system

$$x + 3y - z = 4 \tag{1}$$
$$2x + y + 2z = 10 \tag{2}$$
$$3x - y + z = 4 \tag{3}$$

The objective is to find three numbers x, y and z which satisfy these equations simultaneously. Our previous work suggests that we should begin by eliminating x from all but one of the equations.

The variable x can be eliminated from the second equation by multiplying equation (1) by 2 and subtracting equation (2):

$$\begin{array}{r} 2x + 6y - 2z = 8 \\ 2x + y + 2z = 10 \ - \\ \hline 5y - 4z = -2 \end{array} \tag{4}$$

Similarly, we can eliminate x from the third equation by multiplying equation (1) by 3 and subtracting equation (3):

$$\begin{array}{r} 3x + 9y - 3z = 12 \\ 3x - y + z = 4 \ - \\ \hline 10y - 4z = 8 \end{array} \tag{5}$$

At this stage the first equation is unaltered but the second and third equations of the system have changed to equations (4) and (5) respectively, so the current equations are

$$x + 3y - z = 4 \tag{1}$$
$$5y - 4z = -2 \tag{4}$$
$$10y - 4z = 8 \tag{5}$$

Notice that the last two equations constitute a system of just two equations in two unknowns, y and z. This, of course, is precisely the type of problem that we already know how to solve. Once y and z have been calculated, the values can be substituted into equation (1) to deduce x.

We can eliminate y in the last equation by multiplying equation (4) by 2 and subtracting equation (5):

$$\begin{array}{r} 10y - 8z = -4 \\ 10y - 4z = 8 \ - \\ \hline -4z = -12 \end{array} \tag{6}$$

This produces a new system

$$4x + y + 3z = 8 \tag{1}$$
$$11y + 5z = 16 \tag{4}$$
$$-52z = -52 \tag{6}$$

Step 3

The last equation gives

$$z = \frac{-52}{-52} = 1 \qquad \text{(divide both sides by } -52)$$

If this is substituted into equation (4) then

$$11y + 5(1) = 16$$
$$11y + 5 = 16$$
$$11y = 11 \qquad \text{(subtract 5 from both sides)}$$
$$y = 1 \qquad \text{(divide both sides by 11)}$$

Finally, substituting $y = 1$ and $z = 1$ into equation (1) produces

$$4x + 1 + 3(1) = 8$$
$$4x + 4 = 8$$
$$4x = 4 \qquad \text{(subtract 5 from both sides)}$$
$$x = 1 \qquad \text{(divide both sides by 4)}$$

Hence the solution is $x = 1$, $y = 1$, $z = 1$.

Step 4

As a check the original equations (1), (2) and (3) give, respectively

$$4(1) + 1 + 3(1) = 8 \qquad \checkmark$$
$$-2(1) + 5(1) + 1 = 4 \qquad \checkmark$$
$$3(1) + 2(1) + 4(1) = 9 \qquad \checkmark$$

Practice Problem

3. Solve the following system of equations:

$$2x + 2y - 5z = -5 \tag{1}$$
$$x - y + z = 3 \tag{2}$$
$$-3x + y + 2z = -2 \tag{3}$$

As you might expect, it is possible for three simultaneous linear equations to have either no solution or infinitely many solutions. An illustration of this is given in Question 5 of Exercise 1.4*. The method described in this section has an obvious extension to larger systems of equations. However, the calculations are extremely tedious to perform by hand. Fortunately there are many computer packages available which are capable of solving large systems accurately and efficiently (a matter of a few seconds to solve 10 000 equations in 10 000 unknowns).

Advice

We shall return to the solution of simultaneous linear equations in Chapter 7 when we describe how matrix theory can be used to solve them. This does not depend on any subsequent chapters in this book, so you might like to read through this material now. Two techniques are suggested. A method based on inverse matrices is covered in Section 7.2 and an alternative using Cramer's rule can be found in Section 7.3.

Key Term

Elimination method   The method in which variables are removed from a system of simultaneous equations by adding (or subtracting) a multiple of one equation to (or from) a multiple of another.

Exercise 1.4

1. Use the elimination method to solve the following pairs of simultaneous linear equations:

    (a) $-2x + y = 2$ **(b)** $3x + 4y = 12$ **(c)** $2x + y = 4$ **(d)** $x + y = 1$

    $\ 2x + y = -6$ $\ x + 4y = 8$ $\ 4x - 3y = 3$ $\ 6x + 5y = 15$

2. The total annual sales of a book in either paper or electronic form are 3500. Each paper copy of the book costs \$30 and each e-book costs \$25. The total cost is \$97 500.

    (a) If x and y denote the number of copies in paper and electronic form, write down a pair of simultaneous equations.

    (b) Solve the equations to find the number of e-books sold.

3. Sketch the following lines on the same diagram:

    $$2x - 3y = 6, \quad 4x - 6y = 18, \quad x - \frac{3}{2}y = 3$$

    Hence comment on the nature of the solutions of the following systems of equations:

    (a) $2x - 3y = 6$ **(b)** $4x - 6y = 18$

    $\ x - \dfrac{3}{2}y = 3$ $\ x - \dfrac{3}{2}y = 3$

4. Use the elimination method to attempt to solve the following systems of equations. Comment on the nature of the solution in each case.

    (a) $-3x + 5y = 4$ **(b)** $6x - 2y = 3$

    $\ 9x - 15y = -12$ $\ 15x - 5y = 4$

5. If the following system of linear equations has infinitely many solutions, find the value of k.

    $$6x - 4y = 2$$
    $$-3x + 2y = k$$

Exercise 1.4*

1. Solve the following pairs of simultaneous equations:

   (a) $y = 3x - 1$ **(b)** $2x + y = 6$ **(c)** $2x + 3y = 5$ **(d)** $3x + 4y = -12$

       $y = 2x + 1$ $x - y = -3$ $5x - 2y = -16$ $-2x + 3y = 25$

2. Write down a possible set of values of the numbers a and b for which the simultaneous equations:

   (a) $2x + 3y = 4$ have infinitely many solutions

       $ax + 6y = b$

   (b) $4x - 6y = 1$ have no solutions

       $2x + ay = b$

3. By eliminating x from the system

   $$ax + by = c$$
   $$dx + ey = f$$

   show that

   $$y = \frac{af - cd}{ae - bd}$$

4. Solve the following systems of equations:

   (a) $x - 3y + 4z = 5$ (1)   **(b)** $3x + 2y - 2z = -5$ (1)

        $2x + y + z = 3$ (2) $4x + 3y + 3z = 17$ (2)

        $4x + 3y + 5z = 1$ (3) $2x - y + z = -1$ (3)

5. Attempt to solve the following systems of equations. Comment on the nature of the solution in each case.

   (a) $x - 2y + z = -2$ (1)   **(b)** $2x + 3y - z = 13$ (1)

        $x + y - 2z = 4$ (2) $x - 2y + 2z = -3$ (2)

        $-2x + y + z = 12$ (3) $3x + y + z = 10$ (3)

6. If the following system of equations has infinitely many solutions, find the value of the constant, k.

   $$x + 2y - 5z = 1$$
   $$2x - y + 3z = 4$$
   $$4x + 3y - 7z = k$$

   What can you say about the nature of the solution for other values of k?

7. A distribution centre sends three different types of parcels. One consignment has 6 small, 8 medium and 9 large parcels which cost \$173.20 to post. Another consignment has 7 small, 13 medium and 17 large parcels with total postage \$291.05. A large parcel costs twice as much to post as a small one. Work out the total cost of posting 3 small parcels, 9 medium parcels and 2 large parcels.

ation is also useful. It has the advantage that it involves the label f, which is e rule. If, in a piece of economic theory, there are two or more functions, we t labels to refer to each one. For example, a second function might be

10

ently identify the respective functions simply by referring to them by name: f or g.

ation also enables the information conveyed in Figure 1.13 to be written

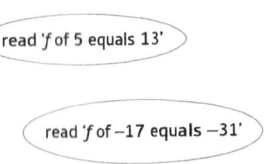

read 'f of 5 equals 13'

read 'f of -17 equals -31'

side the brackets is the incoming value, x, and the right-hand side is the outgoing value, y.

roblem

(b) $f(1)$ (c) $f(17)$ (d) $g(0)$ (e) $g(48)$ (f) $g(16)$

functions

$x + 50$
$2x + 25$

ce any connection between f and g?

ng and outgoing variables are referred to as the **independent** and **dependent** ctively. The value of y clearly 'depends' on the actual value of x that is fed into or example, in microeconomics the quantity demanded, Q, of a good depends price, P. We might express this as

n is called a **demand function**. Given any particular formula for $f(P)$ it is then a to produce a picture of the corresponding demand curve on graph paper. There difference of opinion between mathematicians and economists on how this e. If your quantitative methods lecturer is a mathematician then he or she is Q on the vertical axis and P on the horizontal axis. Economists, on the other y plot them the other way round with Q on the horizontal axis. In doing so, noting that since Q is related to P then, conversely, P must be related to Q, and nction of the form

tions, f and g, are said to be **inverse functions**: that is, f is the inverse of g tly, g is the inverse of f. We adopt the economists' approach in this book. In

SECTION 1.5

Supply and de

Objectives

At the end of this sect

- Use the function n
- Identify the endoge
- Identify and sketch
- Identify and sketch
- Determine the equ and algebraically.
- Determine the equ simultaneous linea

Microeconomics is co vidual firms and mark equilibrium, in which introduced in the pre quantity. However, b idea is central to near

A **function**, *f*, is a r going number, *y*. A f arithmetic calculation rule on two specific in

Unfortunately, suc alternative ways of ex

$y = 2x + 3$ or $f(x) =$

The first of these is fa number, *x*, the right-h

Figure 1.13

The second used to nam can use diff

$g(x) = -3.$

and we sub that is, as ei

The new

$f(5) = 13$

$f(-17) = -$

The numbe correspondi

Practice

1. Evaluate

(a) $f(25)$

for the t

$f(x) =$
$g(x) =$

Do you n

The inco variables res the function on the mark

$Q = f(P)$

Such a funct simple matt is, however, should be d likely to plo hand, norm we are mere so there is a

$P = g(Q)$

The two fu and, equiva

subsequent chapters we shall investigate other microeconomic functions such as total revenue, average cost and profit. It is conventional to plot each of these against Q (that is, with Q on the horizontal axis), so it makes sense to be consistent and to do the same here.

Written in the form $P = g(Q)$, the demand function tells us that P is a function of Q but it gives us no information about the precise relationship between these two variables. To find this we need to know the form of the function which can be obtained either from economic theory or from empirical evidence. For the moment we hypothesise that the function is linear so that

$$P = aQ + b$$

for some appropriate constants (called **parameters**), a and b. Of course, in reality, the relationship between price and quantity is likely to be much more complicated than this. However, the use of linear functions makes the mathematics nice and easy, and the result of any analysis at least provides a first approximation to the truth. The process of identifying the key features of the real world and making appropriate simplifications and assumptions is known as **modelling**. Models are based on economic laws and help to explain and predict the behaviour of real-world situations. Inevitably there is a conflict between mathematical ease and the model's accuracy. The closer the model comes to reality, the more complicated the mathematics is likely to be.

A graph of a typical linear demand function is shown in Figure 1.14. Elementary theory shows that demand usually falls as the price of a good rises and so the slope of the line is negative. Mathematically, P is then said to be a **decreasing function** of Q.

In symbols we write

$$a < 0 \qquad \text{read 'a is less than zero'}$$

It is also apparent from the graph that the intercept, b, is positive: that is,

$$b > 0 \qquad \text{read 'b is greater than zero'}$$

In fact, it is possible in theory for the demand curve to be horizontal with $a = 0$. This corresponds to perfect competition and we shall return to this special case in Chapter 4.

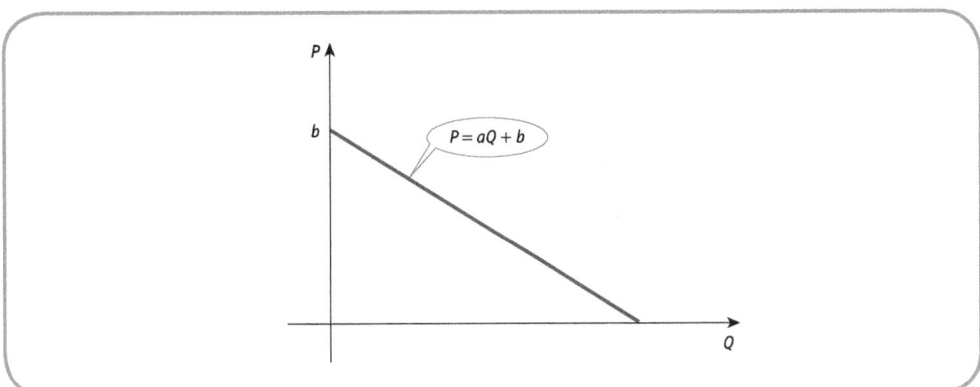

Figure 1.14

Example

Sketch a graph of the demand function

$$P = -2Q + 50$$

Hence, or otherwise, determine the value of

(a) P when $Q = 9$

(b) Q when $P = 10$

Solution

For the demand function

$$P = -2Q + 50$$

$a = -2$, $b = 50$, so the line has a slope of -2 and an intercept of 50. For every 1 unit along, the line goes down by 2 units, so it must cross the horizontal axis when $Q = 25$. (Alternatively, note that when $P = 0$ the equation reads $0 = -2Q + 50$, with solution $Q = 25$.) The graph is sketched in Figure 1.15.

(a) Given any quantity, Q, it is straightforward to use the graph to find the corresponding price, P. A line is drawn vertically upwards until it intersects the demand curve and the value of P is read off from the vertical axis. From Figure 1.15, when $Q = 9$ we see that $P = 32$. This can also be found by substituting $Q = 9$ directly into the demand function to get

$$P = -2(9) + 50 = 32$$

(b) Reversing this process enables us to calculate Q from a given value of P. A line is drawn horizontally until it intersects the demand curve and the value of Q is read off from the horizontal axis. Figure 1.15 indicates that $Q = 20$ when $P = 10$. Again this can be found by calculation. If $P = 10$ then the equation reads

$$10 = -2Q + 50$$
$$-40 = -2Q \qquad \text{(subtract 50 from both sides)}$$
$$20 = Q \qquad \text{(divide both sides by } -2\text{)}$$

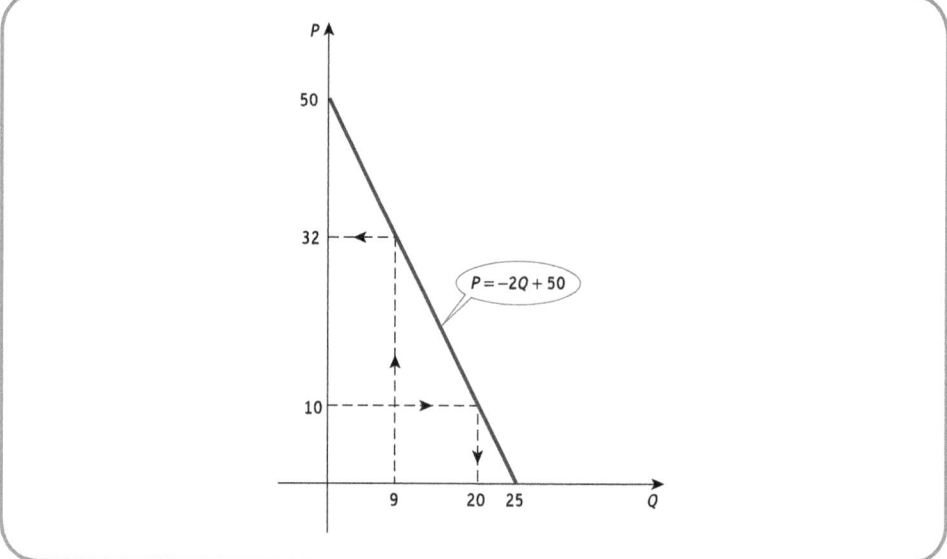

Figure 1.15

Practice Problem

2. Sketch a graph of the demand function

   $$P = -3Q + 75$$

   Hence, or otherwise, determine the value of

   (a) P when $Q = 23$
   (b) Q when $P = 18$

Example

A potter makes and sells ceramic bowls. It is observed that when the price is \$32 only 9 bowls are sold in a week but when the price decreases to \$10, weekly sales rise to 20. Assuming that demand can be modelled by a linear function

(a) obtain a formula for P in terms of Q

(b) sketch a graph of P against Q

(c) comment on the likely reliability of the model

Solution

(a) The general formula for a linear demand function is $P = aQ + b$, where a is the slope of the line. The values of the parameters a and b can be worked out in two different ways.

Method 1 – Calculate the slope of the line

Notice that weekly sales have gone up by 11 bowls as a result of a \$22 decrease in price. If the relationship is linear then a 1-unit increase in Q corresponds to a $22/11 = 2$-unit decrease in P so the graph has a slope of -2. The equation must be given by $P = -2Q + b$. To find b we can use the fact that when $Q = 9$, $P = 32$ so $32 = -2 \times 9 + b$ giving $b = 50$. The demand function is

$$P = -2Q + 50$$

Method 2 – Simultaneous equations

When $Q = 9$, we know that $P = 32$ so $9a + b = 32$

When $Q = 20$, we know that $P = 10$ so $20a + b = 10$

Subtracting the second equation from the first gives $-11a = 22$ so $a = -2$. This value can be substituted into either equation to get $b = 50$ as before.

(b) The graph is sketched in Figure 1.16 using the fact that the intercept is 50 and the slope is -2. Alternatively it could be sketched using the fact that it passes through $(9, 32)$ and $(20, 10)$.

(c) Although the assumption of a linear relationship may be valid in the middle of the range, it is unlikely to be true at the ends. If the potter were to give away the bowls for free it is unlikely that the demand would be limited to 25. Similarly at the other end it would be surprising if no-one buys a bowl the moment the price goes above \$50. In practice the graph will be curved at each end as shown by the dashed lines in Figure 1.16.

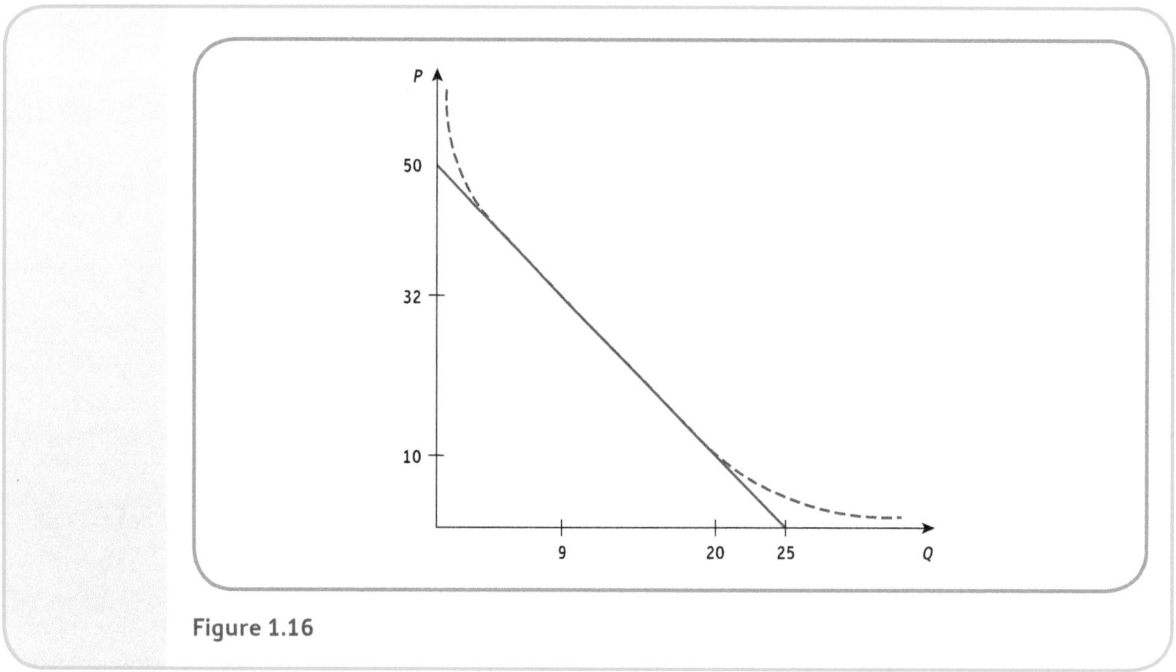

Figure 1.16

The model of consumer demand given so far is fairly crude in that it assumes that quantity depends solely on the price, P, of the good being considered. In practice, Q depends on other factors as well. These include the incomes of consumers, Y, the price of substitutable goods, P_S, the price of complementary goods, P_C, advertising expenditure, A, and consumers' tastes, T. A **substitutable good** is one that could be consumed instead of the good under consideration. For example, in the transport industry, buses and taxis could obviously be substituted for each other in urban areas. A **complementary good** is one that is used in conjunction with other goods. For example, laptops and printers are consumed together. Mathematically, we say that Q is a function of P, Y, P_S, P_C, A and T. This is written

$$Q = f(P, Y, P_S, P_C, A, T)$$

where the variables inside the brackets are separated by commas. In terms of a 'black box' diagram, this is represented with six incoming lines and one outgoing line as shown in Figure 1.17. In our previous discussion it was implicitly assumed that the variables Y, P_S, P_C, A and T are held fixed. We describe this situation by calling Q and P **endogenous variables**, since they are allowed to vary and are determined within the model. The remaining variables are called **exogenous**, since they are constant and are determined outside the model.

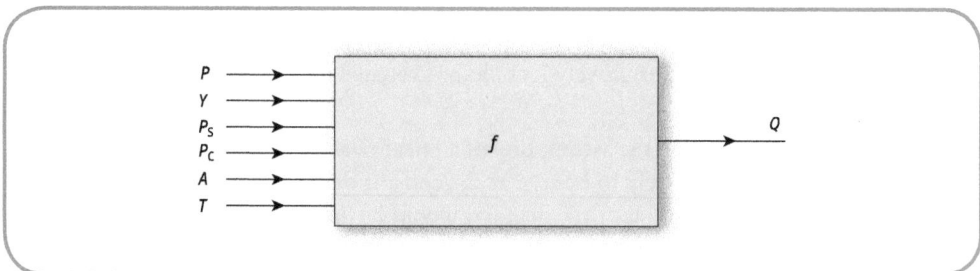

Figure 1.17

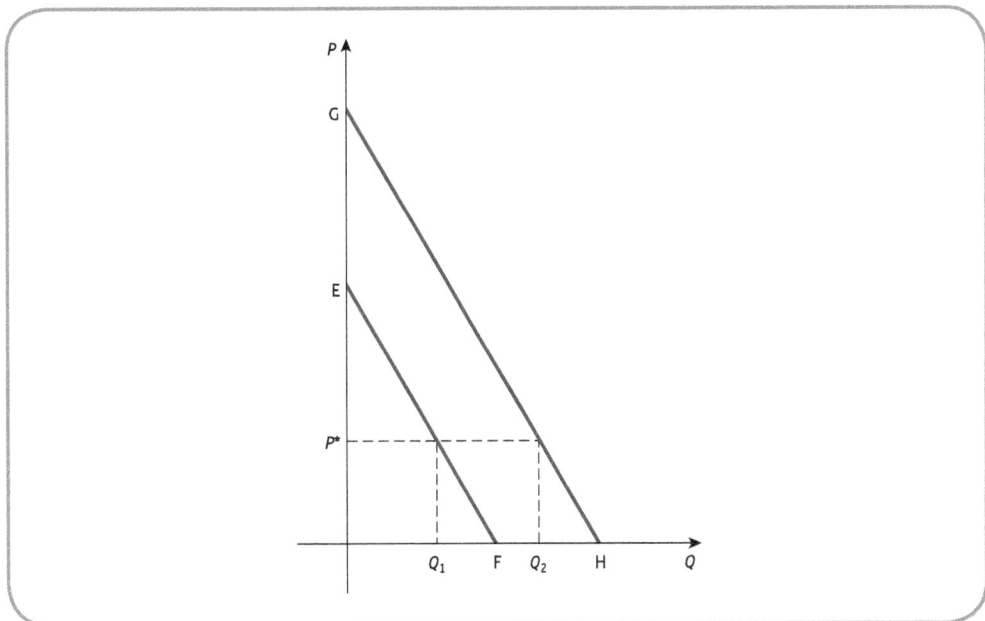

Figure 1.18

Let us return now to the standard demand curve shown in Figure 1.18 as the line EF. This is constructed on the assumption that Y, P_S, P_C, A and T are all constant. Notice that when the price is P^* the quantity demanded is Q_1. Now suppose that income, Y, increases. We would normally expect the demand to rise because the extra income buys more goods at price P^*. The effect is to shift the demand curve to the right because at price P^* consumers can afford the larger number of goods, Q_2. From Figure 1.18 we deduce that if the demand curve is

$$P = aQ + b$$

then a rise in income causes the intercept, b, to increase.

We conclude that if one of the exogenous variables changes then the whole demand curve moves, whereas if one of the endogenous variables changes, we simply move along the fixed curve.

Incidentally, it is possible that, for some goods, an increase in income actually causes the demand curve to shift to the left. In the 1960s and 1970s, most western economies saw a decline in the domestic consumption of coal as a result of an increase in income. In this case, higher wealth meant that more people were able to install central heating systems which use alternative forms of energy. Under these circumstances the good is referred to as an **inferior good**. On the other hand, a **normal good** is one whose demand rises as income rises. Cars and electrical goods are obvious examples of normal goods. Currently, concern about global warming is also reducing demand for coal. This factor can be incorporated as part of taste, although it is difficult to handle mathematically since it is virtually impossible to quantify taste and so to define T numerically.

The **supply** function is the relation between the quantity, Q, of a good that producers plan to bring to the market and the price, P, of the good. A typical linear supply curve is indicated in Figure 1.19. Economic theory indicates that, as the price rises, so does the supply. Mathematically, P is then said to be an **increasing function** of Q. A price increase encourages existing producers to raise output and entices new firms to enter the market. The line shown in Figure 1.19 has equation

$$P = aQ + b$$

It is possible to calculate these values using algebra. In equilibrium, $Q_D = Q_S$. If this common value is denoted by Q then the demand and supply equations become

$$P = -2Q + 50 \quad \text{and} \quad P = \tfrac{1}{2}Q + 25$$

This represents a pair of simultaneous equations for the two unknowns P and Q, and so could be solved using the elimination method described in the previous section. However, this is not strictly necessary because it follows immediately from the above equations that

$$-2Q + 50 = \tfrac{1}{2}Q + 25$$

since both sides are equal to P. This can be rearranged to calculate Q:

$$
\begin{aligned}
-2\tfrac{1}{2}Q + 50 &= 25 && \text{(subtract } \tfrac{1}{2}Q \text{ from both sides)} \\
-2\tfrac{1}{2}Q &= -25 && \text{(subtract 50 from both sides)} \\
Q &= 10 && \text{(divide both sides by } -2\tfrac{1}{2}\text{)}
\end{aligned}
$$

Finally, P can be found by substituting this value into either of the original equations. The demand equation gives

$$P = -2(10) + 50 = 30$$

As a check, the supply equation gives

$$P = \tfrac{1}{2}(10) + 25 = 30 \quad ✓$$

(b) If the government imposes a fixed tax of \$5 per good then the money that the firm actually receives from the sale of each good is the amount, P, that the consumer pays, less the tax, 5: that is, $P - 5$. Mathematically, this problem can be solved by replacing P by $P - 5$ in the supply equation to get the new supply equation

$$P - 5 = \tfrac{1}{2}Q_S + 25$$

that is,

$$P = \tfrac{1}{2}Q_S + 30$$

The remaining calculations proceed as before. In equilibrium, $Q_D = Q_S$. Again setting this common value to be Q gives

$$P = -2Q + 50$$
$$P = \tfrac{1}{2}Q + 30$$

Hence

$$-2Q + 50 = \tfrac{1}{2}Q + 30$$

which can be solved as before to give $Q = 8$. Substitution into either of the above equations gives $P = 34$. (Check the details.)

Graphically, the introduction of tax shifts the supply curve upwards by 5 units. Obviously the demand curve is unaltered. The dashed line in Figure 1.21 shows the new supply curve, from which the new equilibrium quantity is 8 and equilibrium price is 34. Note the effect that government taxation has on the market equilibrium price. This has risen to \$34 and so not all of the tax is passed on to the consumer. The consumer pays an additional \$4 per good. The remaining \$1 of tax must, therefore, be paid by the firm.

Practice Problem

3. The demand and supply functions of a good are given by

$$P = -4Q_D + 120$$
$$P = \tfrac{1}{3}Q_S + 29$$

where P, Q_D and Q_S denote the price, quantity demanded and quantity supplied respectively.

(a) Calculate the equilibrium price and quantity.

(b) Calculate the new equilibrium price and quantity after the imposition of a fixed tax of $13 per good. Who pays the tax?

We conclude this section by considering a more realistic model of supply and demand, taking into account substitutable and complementary goods. Let us suppose that there are two goods in related markets, which we call good 1 and good 2. The demand for either good depends on the prices of both good 1 and good 2. If the corresponding demand functions are linear then

$$Q_{D_1} = a_1 + b_1 P_1 + c_1 P_2$$
$$Q_{D_2} = a_2 + b_2 P_1 + c_2 P_2$$

where P_i and Q_{D_i} denote the price and demand for the ith good and a_i, b_i, c_i are parameters. For the first equation, $a_1 > 0$ because there is a positive demand when the prices of both goods are zero. Also, $b_1 < 0$ because the demand of a good falls as its price rises. The sign of c_1 depends on the nature of the goods. If the goods are substitutable then an increase in the price of good 2 would mean that consumers would switch from good 2 to good 1, causing Q_{D_1} to increase. Substitutable goods are therefore characterised by a positive value of c_1. On the other hand, if the goods are complementary then a rise in the price of either good would see the demand fall, so c_1 is negative. Similar results apply to the signs of a_2, b_2 and c_2. The calculation of the equilibrium price and quantity in a two-commodity market model is demonstrated in the following example.

Example

The demand and supply functions for two interdependent commodities are given by

$$Q_{D_1} = 10 - 2P_1 + P_2$$
$$Q_{D_2} = 5 + 2P_1 - 2P_2$$
$$Q_{S_1} = -3 + 2P_1$$
$$Q_{S_2} = -2 + 3P_2$$

where Q_{D_i}, Q_{S_i} and P_i denote the quantity demanded, quantity supplied and price of good i respectively. Determine the equilibrium price and quantity for this two-commodity model.

Solution

In equilibrium, we know that the quantity supplied is equal to the quantity demanded for each good, so that

$$Q_{D_1} = Q_{S_1} \quad \text{and} \quad Q_{D_2} = Q_{S_2}$$

Let us write these respective common values as Q_1 and Q_2. The demand and supply equations for good 1 then become

$$Q_1 = 10 - 2P_1 + P_2$$
$$Q_1 = -3 + 2P_1$$

Hence

$$10 - 2P_1 + P_2 = -3 + 2P_1$$

since both sides are equal to Q_1. It makes sense to tidy this equation up a bit by collecting all of the unknowns on the left-hand side and putting the constant terms on to the right-hand side:

$$10 - 4P_1 + P_2 = -3 \qquad \text{(subtract } 2P_1 \text{ from both sides)}$$
$$-4P_1 + P_2 = -13 \qquad \text{(subtract 10 from both sides)}$$

We can perform a similar process for good 2. The demand and supply equations become

$$Q_2 = 5 + 2P_1 - 2P_2$$
$$Q_2 = -2 + 3P_2$$

because $Q_{D_2} = Q_{S_2} = Q_2$ in equilibrium. Hence

$$5 + 2P_1 - 2P_2 = -2 + 3P_2$$
$$5 + 2P_1 - 5P_2 = -2 \qquad \text{(subtract } 3P_2 \text{ from both sides)}$$
$$2P_1 - 5P_2 = -7 \qquad \text{(subtract 5 from both sides)}$$

We have therefore shown that the equilibrium prices, P_1 and P_2, satisfy the simultaneous linear equations

$$-4P_1 + P_2 = -13 \tag{1}$$

$$2P_1 - 5P_2 = -7 \tag{2}$$

which can be solved by elimination. Following the steps described in Section 1.4 we proceed as follows.

Step 1

Double equation (2) and add to equation (1) to get

$$\begin{aligned} -4P_1 + \quad P_2 &= -13 \\ 4P_1 - 10P_2 &= -14 \; + \\ \hline -9P_2 &= -27 \end{aligned} \tag{3}$$

Step 2

Divide both sides of equation (3) by -9 to get $P_2 = 3$.

Step 3

If this is substituted into equation (1) then

$$-4P_1 + 3 = -13$$
$$-4P_1 = -16 \qquad \text{(subtract 3 from both sides)}$$
$$P_1 = 4 \qquad \text{(divide both sides by } -4)$$

Step 4

As a check, equation (2) gives

$$2(4) - 5(3) = -7 \quad \checkmark$$

Hence $P_1 = 4$ and $P_2 = 3$.

Finally, the equilibrium quantities can be deduced by substituting these values back into the original supply equations. For good 1,

$$Q_1 = -3 + 2P_1 = -3 + 2(4) = 5$$

For good 2,

$$Q_2 = -2 + 3P_2 = -2 + 3(3) = 7$$

As a check, the demand equations also give

$$Q_1 = 10 - 2P_1 + P_2 = 10 - 2(4) + 3 = 5 \quad \checkmark$$
$$Q_2 = 5 + 2P_1 - 2P_2 = 5 + 2(4) - 2(3) = 7 \quad \checkmark$$

Practice Problem

4. The demand and supply functions for two interdependent commodities are given by

$$Q_{D_1} = 40 - 5P_1 - P_2$$
$$Q_{D_2} = 50 - 2P_1 - 4P_2$$
$$Q_{S_1} = -3 + 4P_1$$
$$Q_{S_2} = -7 + 3P_2$$

where Q_{D_i}, Q_{S_i} and P_i denote the quantity demanded, quantity supplied and price of good i respectively. Determine the equilibrium price and quantity for this two-commodity model. Are these goods substitutable or complementary?

For a two-commodity market the equilibrium prices and quantities can be found by solving a system of two simultaneous equations. Exactly the same procedure can be applied to a three-commodity market, which requires the solution of a system of three simultaneous equations.

Advice

An example of a three-commodity model can be found in Question 6 of Exercise 1.5*. Alternative methods and further examples are described in Chapter 7. In general, with *n* goods it is necessary to solve *n* equations in *n* unknowns and, as pointed out in Section 1.4, this is best done using a computer package whenever *n* is large.

Key Terms

Complementary goods   A pair of goods consumed together. As the price of either goes up, the demand for both goods goes down.

Decreasing function   A function, $y = f(x)$, in which y decreases as x increases.

Demand function   A relationship between the quantity demanded and various factors that affect demand, including price.

Dependent variable   A variable whose value is determined by that taken by the independent variables; in $y = f(x)$, the dependent variable is y.

Endogenous variable   A variable whose value is determined within a model.

Equilibrium (market)   This state occurs when quantity supplied and quantity demanded are equal.

Exogenous variable   A variable whose value is determined outside a model.

Function   A rule that assigns to each incoming number, x, a uniquely defined outgoing number, y.

Increasing function   A function, $y = f(x)$, in which y increases as x increases.

Independent variable   A variable whose value determines that of the dependent variable; in $y = f(x)$, the independent variable is x.

Inferior good   A good whose demand decreases as income increases.

Inverse function   A function, written f^{-1}, which reverses the effect of a given function, f, so that $x = f^{-1}(y)$ when $y = f(x)$.

Modelling   The creation of piece of mathematical theory which represents (a simplification of) some aspect of practical economics.

Normal good   A good whose demand increases as income increases.

Parameter   A constant whose value affects the specific values but not the general form of a mathematical expression, such as the constants a, b and c in $ax^2 + bx + c$.

Substitutable goods   A pair of goods that are alternatives to each other. As the price of one of them goes up, the demand for the other rises.

Supply function   A relationship between the quantity supplied and various factors that affect supply, including price.

Exercise 1.5

1. If $f(x) = 3x + 15$ and $g(x) = \frac{1}{3}x - 5$, evaluate

   (a) $f(2)$ **(b)** $f(10)$ **(c)** $f(0)$ **(d)** $g(21)$ **(e)** $g(45)$ **(f)** $g(15)$

   What word describes the relationship between f and g?

2. Sketch a graph of the supply function

   $$P = \frac{1}{3}Q + 7$$

   Hence, or otherwise, determine the value of

   (a) P when $Q = 12$

   (b) Q when $P = 10$

   (c) Q when $P = 4$

3. The demand function of a good is

$$Q = 100 - P + 2Y + \tfrac{1}{2}A$$

where Q, P, Y and A denote quantity demanded, price, income and advertising expenditure respectively.

(a) Calculate the demand when $P = 10$, $Y = 40$ and $A = 6$. Assuming that price and income are fixed, calculate the additional advertising expenditure needed to raise demand to 179 units.

(b) Is this good inferior or normal?

4. The demand, Q, for a certain good depends on its own price, P, and the price of an alternative good, P_A, according to

$$Q = 30 - 3P + P_A$$

(a) Find Q if $P = 4$ and $P_A = 5$.

(b) Is the alternative good substitutable or complementary? Give a reason for your answer.

(c) Determine the value of P if $Q = 23$ and $P_A = 11$.

5. The demand for a good priced at \$50 is 420 units, and when the price is \$80 demand is 240 units. Assuming that the demand function takes the form $Q = aP + b$, find the values of a and b.

6. (a) Copy and complete the following table of values for the supply function

$$P = \tfrac{1}{2}Q + 20$$

Q	0		50
P		25	

Hence, or otherwise, draw an accurate sketch of this function using axes with values of Q and P between 0 and 50.

(b) On the same axes draw the graph of the demand function

$$P = 50 - Q$$

and hence find the equilibrium quantity and price.

(c) The good under consideration is normal. Describe the effect on the equilibrium quantity and price when income rises.

7. The demand and supply functions of a good are given by

$$P = -3Q_D + 48$$
$$P = \tfrac{1}{2}Q_S + 23$$

Find the equilibrium quantity if the government imposes a fixed tax of \$4 on each good.

8. The demand and supply functions for two interdependent commodities are given by

$$Q_{D_1} = 100 - 2P_1 + P_2$$
$$Q_{D_2} = 5 + 2P_1 - 3P_2$$
$$Q_{S_1} = -10 + P_1$$
$$Q_{S_2} = -5 + 6P_2$$

where Q_D, Q_S, and P_i denote the quantity demanded, quantity supplied and price of good i respectively. Determine the equilibrium price and quantity for this two-commodity model.

9. A demand function of a certain good is given by

$$Q = -20P + 0.04Y + 4T + 3P_r$$

where Q and P denote the quantity and price of the good, Y is income, T is taste, and P_r is the price of a related good.

(a) Calculate Q when $P = 8$, $Y = 1000$, $T = 15$ and $P_r = 30$.

(b) Is the related good substitutable or complementary? Give a reason for your answer.

(c) Find the value of P when $Q = 235$, $Y = 8000$, $T = 30$ and $P_r = 25$.

(d) The exogenous variables are now fixed at $Y = 2000$, $T = 10$ and $P_r = 5$. State the values of the slope and vertical intercept when the demand function is sketched with

  (i) P on the horizontal axis and Q on the vertical axis

  (ii) Q on the horizontal axis and P on the vertical axis.

Exercise 1.5*

1. Describe the effect on the demand curve due to an increase in

   (a) the price of substitutable goods

   (b) the price of complementary goods

   (c) advertising expenditure.

2. If the line, $P = {}^{-2}/_3Q + 6$, is sketched with P on the horizontal axis, and Q on the vertical axis, find the gradient, m, and the vertical intercept, c.

3. If the demand function of a good is

$$2P + 3Q_D = 60$$

where P and Q_D denote price and quantity demanded respectively, find the largest and smallest values of P for which this function is economically meaningful.

4. The demand and supply functions of a good are given by

$$P = -5Q_D + 80$$
$$P = 2Q_S + 10$$

where P, Q_D and Q_S denote price, quantity demanded and quantity supplied respectively.

(1) Find the equilibrium price and quantity

   (a) graphically

   (b) algebraically

(2) If the government deducts, as tax, 15% of the market price of each good, determine the new equilibrium price and quantity.

5. The supply and demand functions of a good are given by

    $$P = Q_S + 8$$
    $$P = -3Q_D + 80$$

    where P, Q_S and Q_D denote price, quantity supplied and quantity demanded respectively.

    (a) Find the equilibrium price and quantity if the government imposes a fixed tax of $36 on each good.

    (b) Find the corresponding value of the government's tax revenue.

6. The demand and supply functions for three interdependent commodities are

    $$Q_{D_1} = 15 - P_1 + 2P_2 + P_3$$
    $$Q_{D_2} = 9 + P_1 - P_2 - P_3$$
    $$Q_{D_3} = 8 + 2P_1 - P_2 - 4P_3$$
    $$Q_{S_1} = -7 + P_1$$
    $$Q_{S_2} = -4 + 4P_2$$
    $$Q_{S_3} = -5 + 2P_3$$

    where Q_{D_i}, Q_{S_i} and P_i denote the quantity demanded, quantity supplied and price of good i respectively. Determine the equilibrium price and quantity for this three-commodity model.

7. The demand and supply functions of a good are given by

    $$P = -3Q_D + 60$$
    $$P = 2Q_S + 40$$

    respectively. If the government decides to impose a tax of t per good, show that the equilibrium quantity is given by

    $$Q = 4 - \tfrac{1}{5}t$$

    and write down a similar expression for the equilibrium price.

    (a) If it is known that the equilibrium quantity is 3, work out the value of t. How much of this tax is paid by the firm?

    (b) If, instead of imposing a tax, the government provides a subsidy of $5 per good, find the new equilibrium price and quantity.

8. The linear supply and demand functions for a good are given by

    $$P = aQ + b \quad \text{and} \quad P = cQ + d$$

    (a) State whether each of the values of the parameters a, b, c and d are positive or negative.

    (b) Find expressions, simplified as far as possible, for equilibrium price and quantity.

SECTION 1.6
Transposition of formulae

Objectives

At the end of this section you should be able to:

- Manipulate formulae.
- Draw a flow chart representing a formula.
- Use a reverse flow chart to transpose a formula.
- Change the subject of a formula involving several letters.

Mathematical modelling involves the use of formulae to represent the relationship between economic variables. In microeconomics we have already seen how useful supply and demand formulae are. These provide a precise relationship between price and quantity. For example, the connection between price, P, and quantity, Q, might be modelled by

$$P = -4Q + 100$$

Given any value of Q it is trivial to deduce the corresponding value of P by merely replacing the symbol Q by a number. A value of $Q = 2$, say, gives

$$P = -4 \times 2 + 100$$
$$= -8 + 100$$
$$= 92$$

On the other hand, given P, it is necessary to solve an equation to deduce Q. For example, when $P = 40$, the equation is

$$-4Q + 100 = 40$$

which can be solved as follows:

$$-4Q = -60 \quad \text{(subtract 100 from both sides)}$$
$$Q = 15 \quad \text{(divide both sides by } -4\text{)}$$

This approach is reasonable when only one or two values of P are given. However, if we are given many values of P, it is clearly tedious and inefficient for us to solve the equation each time to find Q. The preferred approach is to **transpose** the formula for P. In other words, we rearrange the formula

$$P = \text{an expression involving } Q$$

into

$$Q = \text{an expression involving } P$$

Written this way round, the formula enables us to find Q by replacing P by a number. For the specific formula

$$-4Q + 100 = P$$

the steps are

$$-4Q = P - 100 \quad \text{(subtract 100 from both sides)}$$

$$Q = \frac{P - 100}{-4} \quad \text{(divide both sides by } -4\text{)}$$

Notice that

$$\frac{P - 100}{-4} = \frac{P}{-4} - \frac{100}{-4}$$

$$= -\tfrac{1}{4}P + 25$$

so the rearranged formula simplifies to

$$Q = -\tfrac{1}{4}P + 25$$

If we now wish to find Q when $P = 40$, we immediately get

$$Q = -\tfrac{1}{4} \times 40 + 25$$

$$= -10 + 25$$

$$= 15$$

The important thing to notice about the algebra is that the individual steps are identical to those used previously for solving the equation

$$-4Q + 100 = 40$$

i.e. the operations are again

'subtract 100 from both sides'

followed by

'divide both sides by −4'

Practice Problem

1. **(a)** Solve the equation

   $$\tfrac{1}{2}Q + 13 = 17$$

   State clearly exactly what operation you have performed to both sides at each stage of your solution.

   (b) By performing the same operations as part (a), rearrange the formula

   $$\tfrac{1}{2}Q + 13 = P$$

   into the form

   $$Q = \text{an expression involving } P$$

   (c) By substituting $P = 17$ into the formula derived in part (b), check that this agrees with your answer to part (a).

The algebraic details are as follows:

$$\frac{4}{2x+1} = y$$

$$\frac{1}{2x+1} = \frac{y}{4} \qquad \text{(divide both sides by 4)}$$

$$2x+1 = \frac{4}{y} \qquad \text{(reciprocate both sides)}$$

$$2x = \frac{4}{y} - 1 \qquad \text{(subtract 1 from both sides)}$$

$$= \frac{1}{2}\left(\frac{4}{y} - 1\right) \qquad \text{(divide both sides by 2)}$$

which can be simplified, by multiplying out the brackets, to give

$$x = \frac{2}{y} - \frac{1}{2}$$

Again, the reverse flow chart can be used directly to obtain

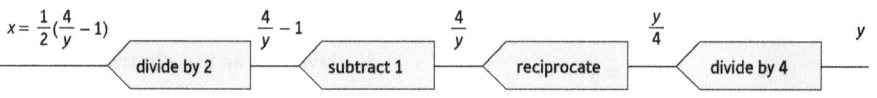

Practice Problem

2. Use flow charts to make x the subject of the following formulae:

(a) $y = 6x^2$ (b) $y = \dfrac{1}{7x-1}$

The following example contains two difficult instances of transposition. In both cases the letter x appears more than once on the right-hand side. If this happens, the technique based on flow charts cannot be used. However, it may still be possible to perform the manipulation even if some of the steps may not be immediately obvious.

Example

Transpose the following formulae to express x in terms of y:

(a) $ax = bx + cy + d$ (b) $y = \dfrac{x+1}{x-2}$

Solution

(a) In the formula

$$ax = bx + cy + d$$

there are terms involving x on both sides and since we are hoping to rearrange this into the form

$x =$ an expression involving y

it makes sense to collect the xs on the left-hand side. To do this we subtract bx from both sides to get

$$ax - bx = cy + d$$

Notice that x is a common factor of the left-hand side, so the distributive law can be applied 'in reverse' to take the x outside the brackets: that is,

$$(a - b)x = cy + d$$

Finally, both sides are divided by $a - b$ to get

$$x = \frac{cy + d}{a - b}$$

which is of the desired form.

(b) It is difficult to see where to begin with the formula

$$y = \frac{x + 1}{x - 2}$$

because there is an x in both the numerator and the denominator. Indeed, the thing that is preventing us getting started is precisely the fact that the expression is a fraction. We can, however, remove the fraction simply by multiplying both sides by the denominator to get

$$(x - 2)y = x + 1$$

and if we multiply out the brackets then

$$xy - 2y = x + 1$$

We want to rearrange this into the form

$x =$ an expression involving y

so we collect the xs on the left-hand side and put everything else on to the right-hand side. To do this we first add $2y$ to both sides to get

$$xy = x + 1 + 2y$$

and then subtract x from both sides to get

$$xy - x = 1 + 2y$$

The distributive law can now be applied 'in reverse' to take out the common factor of x: that is,

$$(y - 1)x = 1 + 2y$$

Finally, dividing through by $y - 1$ gives

$$x = \frac{1 + 2y}{y - 1}$$

Advice

This example contains some of the hardest algebraic manipulation seen so far in this book. I hope that you managed to follow the individual steps. However, it all might appear as if we have 'pulled rabbits out of hats'. You may feel that, if left on your own, you are never going to be able to decide what to do at each stage. Unfortunately there is no watertight strategy that always works, although the following five-point plan is worth considering if you get stuck.

To transpose a given formula of the form

$y =$ an expression involving x

into a formula of the form

$x =$ an expression involving y

you proceed as follows:

Step 1   Remove fractions.
Step 2   Multiply out the brackets.
Step 3   Collect all of the x's on to the left-hand side.
Step 4   Take out a factor of x.
Step 5   Divide by the coefficient of x.

You might find it helpful to look back at the previous example in the light of this strategy. In part (b) it is easy to identify each of the five steps. Part (a) also used this strategy, starting with the third step.

Example

Make x the subject of

$$y = \sqrt{\frac{ax+b}{cx+d}}$$

Solution

In this formula there is a square root symbol surrounding the right-hand side. This can be removed by squaring both sides to get

$$y^2 = \frac{ax+b}{cx+d}$$

We now apply the five-step strategy:

Step 1 $(cx + d)y^2 = ax + b$
Step 2 $cxy^2 + dy^2 = ax + b$
Step 3 $cxy^2 - ax = b - dy^2$
Step 4 $(cy^2 - a)x = b - dy^2$
Step 5 $x = \dfrac{b - dy^2}{cy^2 - a}$

Practice Problem

3. Transpose the following formulae to express x in terms of y:

(a) $x - ay = cx + y$

(b) $y = \dfrac{x-2}{x+4}$

Key Terms

Flow chart   A diagram consisting of boxes of instructions indicating a sequence of operations and their order.

Reverse flow chart   A flow chart indicating the inverse of the original sequence of operations in reverse order.

Transpose a formula   The rearrangement of a formula to make one of the other letters the subject.

Exercise 1.6

1. Make Q the subject of

$$P = 2Q + 8$$

Hence find the value of Q when $P = 52$.

2. Write down the formula representing each of the following flow charts

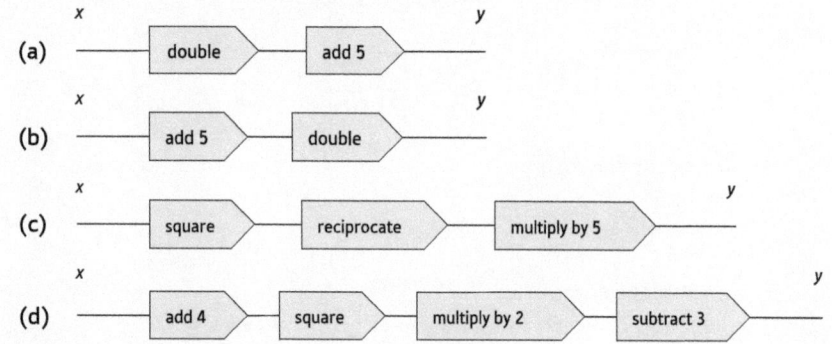

(a) x — double — add 5 — y

(b) x — add 5 — double — y

(c) x — square — reciprocate — multiply by 5 — y

(d) x — add 4 — square — multiply by 2 — subtract 3 — y

3. Draw flow charts for each of the following formulae:

(a) $y = 5x + 3$ (b) $y = 5(x + 3)$ (c) $y = 6x - 9$ (d) $y = 4x^2 - 6$

(e) $y = \dfrac{x}{2} + 7$ (f) $y = \dfrac{2}{x}$ (g) $y = \dfrac{1}{x+3}$

4. Make x the subject of each of the following formulae:

(a) $y = 9x - 6$ (b) $y = (x + 4)/3$ (c) $y = \dfrac{x}{2}$

(d) $y = \dfrac{x}{5} + 8$ (e) $y = \dfrac{1}{x+2}$ (f) $y = \dfrac{4}{3x - 7}$

5. Transpose the formulae:

   (a) $Q = aP + b$ to express P in terms of Q

   (b) $Y = aY + b + I$ to express Y in terms of I

   (c) $Q = \dfrac{1}{aP + b}$ to express P in terms of Q

6. Make x the subject of the formula

   $$y = \dfrac{3}{x} - 2$$

7. In business, the economic order quantity is $Q = \sqrt{\dfrac{2DR}{H}}$.

   (a) Make D the subject of this formula.

   (b) Make H the subject of this formula.

Exercise 1.6*

1. (1) Draw flow charts for each of the following formulae:

   (a) $y = 9x + 1$ (b) $y = 3 - x$ (c) $y = 5x^2 - 8$

   (d) $y = (3x + 5)$ (e) $y = \dfrac{4}{x^2 + 8}$

   (2) Hence, or otherwise, express x in terms of y in each case.

2. Make x the subject of the following formulae:

   (a) $\dfrac{a}{x} + b = \dfrac{c}{x}$ (b) $a - x = \dfrac{b + x}{a}$ (c) $e + \sqrt{x + f} = g$

   (d) $a\sqrt{\left(\dfrac{x - n}{m}\right)} = \dfrac{a^2}{b}$ (e) $\dfrac{\sqrt{x - m}}{n} = \dfrac{1}{m}$ (f) $\dfrac{\sqrt{x} + a}{\sqrt{x} - b} = \dfrac{b}{a}$

3. Transpose the formula

   $$V = \dfrac{5t + 1}{t - 1}$$

   to express t in terms of V.

   Hence, or otherwise, find the value of t when $V = 5.6$.

4. Make r the subject of the formula

   $$S = P\left(1 + \dfrac{r}{100}\right)^n$$

5. Rearrange the formula

   $$Y = \dfrac{-aT + b + I + G}{1 - a + at}$$

   to make each of the following letters the subject:

   (a) G (b) T (c) t (d) a

SECTION 1.7
National income determination

Objectives

At the end of this section you should be able to:

- Identify and sketch linear consumption functions.
- Identify and sketch linear savings functions.
- Set up simple macroeconomic models.
- Calculate equilibrium national income.
- Analyse IS and LM schedules.

Macroeconomics is concerned with the analysis of economic theory and policy at a national level. In this section we focus on one particular aspect known as national income determination. We describe how to set up simple models of the national economy which enable equilibrium levels of income to be calculated. Initially we assume that the economy is divided into two sectors, households and firms. Firms use resources such as land, capital, labour and raw materials to produce goods and services. These resources are known as **factors of production** and are taken to belong to households. **National income** represents the flow of income from firms to households given as payment for these factors. Households can then spend this money in one of two ways. Income can be used for the consumption of goods produced by firms or it can be put into savings. Consumption, C, and savings, S, are therefore functions of income, Y: that is,

$$C = f(Y)$$
$$S = g(Y)$$

for some appropriate consumption function, f, and savings function, g. Moreover, C and S are normally expected to increase as income rises, so f and g are both increasing functions.

We begin by analysing the **consumption function**. As usual we need to quantify the precise relationship between C and Y. If this relationship is linear then a graph of a typical consumption function is shown in Figure 1.22. It is clear from this graph that if

$$C = aY + b$$

then $a > 0$ and $b > 0$. The intercept b is the level of consumption when there is no income (that is, when $Y = 0$) and is known as **autonomous consumption**. The slope, a, is the change in C brought about by a 1 unit increase in Y and is known as the **marginal propensity to consume** (MPC). As previously noted, income is used up in consumption and savings so that

$$Y = C + S$$

It follows that only a proportion of the 1 unit increase in income is consumed; the rest goes into savings. Hence the slope, a, is generally smaller than 1: that is, $a < 1$. It is standard practice in mathematics to collapse the two separate inequalities $a > 0$ and $a < 1$ into the single inequality

$$0 < a < 1$$

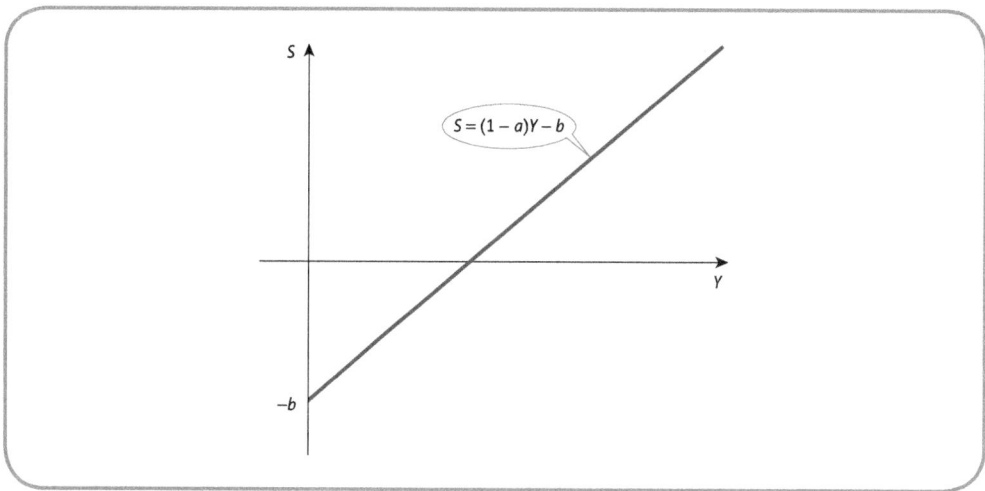

Figure 1.25

The simplest model of the national economy is illustrated in Figure 1.26, which shows the circular flow of income and expenditure. This is fairly crude, since it fails to take into account government activity or foreign trade. In this diagram **investment**, I, is an injection into the circular flow in the form of spending on capital goods.

Let us examine this more closely and represent the diagrammatic information in symbols. Consider first the box labelled 'Households'. The flow of money entering this box is Y and the flow leaving it is $C + S$. Hence we have the familiar relation

$Y = C + S$

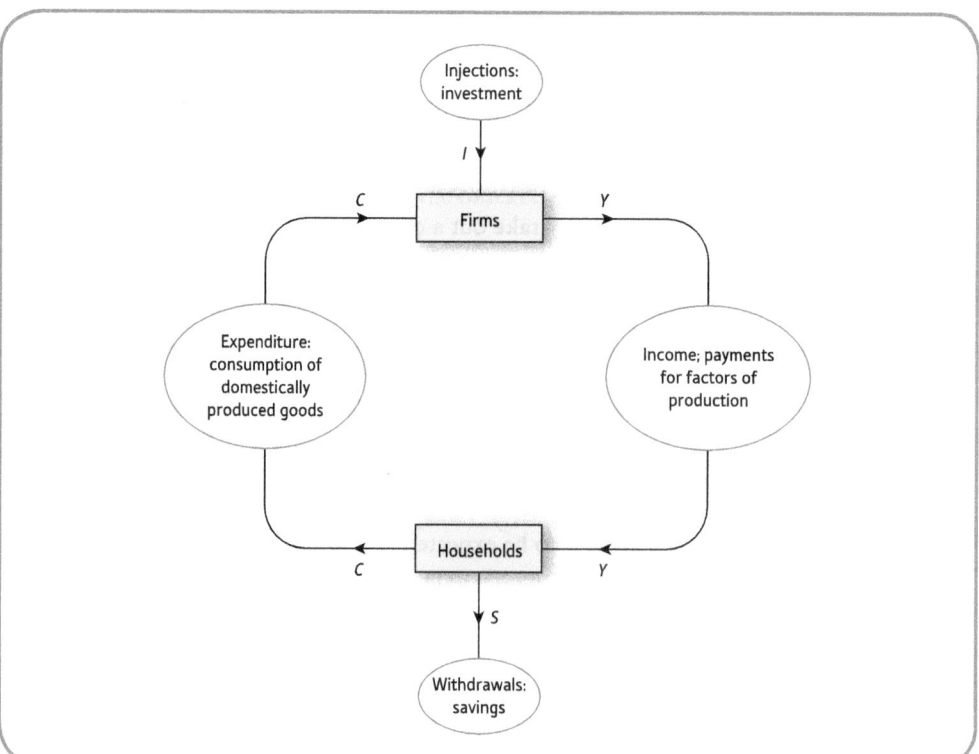

Figure 1.26

For the box labelled 'Firms' the flow entering it is $C + I$ and the flow leaving it is Y, so

$$Y = C + I$$

Suppose that the level of investment that firms plan to inject into the economy is known to be some fixed value, I^*. If the economy is in equilibrium, the flow of income and expenditure balance so that

$$Y = C + I^*$$

From the assumption that the consumption function is

$$C = aY + b$$

for given values of a and b these two equations represent a pair of simultaneous equations for the two unknowns Y and C. In these circumstances C and Y can be regarded as endogenous variables, since their precise values are determined within the model, whereas I^* is fixed outside the model and is exogenous.

Example

Find the equilibrium level of income and consumption if the consumption function is

$$C = 0.6Y + 10$$

and planned investment $I = 12$.

Solution

We know that

$Y = C + I$	(from theory)
$C = 0.6Y + 10$	(given in problem)
$I = 12$	(given in problem)

If the value of I is substituted into the first equation then

$$Y = C + 12$$

The expression for C can also be substituted to give

$$Y = 0.6Y + 10 + 12$$
$$Y = 0.6Y + 22$$
$$0.4Y = 22 \quad \text{(subtract } 0.6Y \text{ from both sides)}$$
$$Y = 55 \quad \text{(divide both sides by 0.4)}$$

The corresponding value of C can be deduced by putting this level of income into the consumption function to get

$$C = 0.6(55) + 10 = 43$$

The equilibrium income can also be found graphically by plotting expenditure against income. In this example the aggregate expenditure, $C + I$, is given by $0.6Y + 22$. This is sketched in Figure 1.27 using the fact that it passes through $(0, 22)$ and $(80, 70)$. Also sketched is the '45° line', so called because it makes an angle of 45° with the horizontal. This line passes through the points $(0, 0)$, $(1, 1)$, . . . , $(50, 50)$ and so on. In other words, at any point on this line expenditure and income are in balance. The equilibrium income can therefore be found by inspecting the point of intersection of this line and the aggregate expenditure line, $C + I$. From Figure 1.27 this occurs when $Y = 55$, which is in agreement with the calculated value.

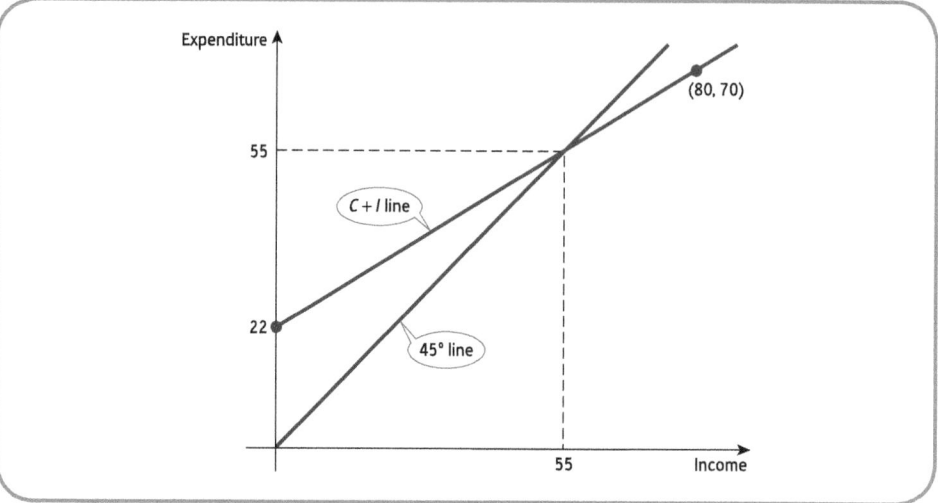

Figure 1.27

Practice Problem

2. Find the equilibrium level of income if the consumption function is

   $$C = 0.8Y + 25$$

   and planned investment $I = 17$. Calculate the new equilibrium income if planned investment rises by 1 unit.

To make the model more realistic let us now include **government expenditure**, G, and **taxation**, T, in the model. The injections box in Figure 1.26 now includes government expenditure in addition to investment, so

$$Y = C + I + G$$

We assume that planned government expenditure and planned investment are autonomous with fixed values G^* and I^* respectively, so that in equilibrium

$$Y = C + I^* + G^*$$

The withdrawals box in Figure 1.26 now includes taxation. This means that the income that households have to spend on consumer goods is no longer Y but rather $Y - T$ (income less tax), which is called **disposable income**, Y_d. Hence

$$C = aY_d + b$$

inate C by substituting equation (9) into (7) to get

5

$+ 47.5 + 55$

$+ 102.5$

ing for Y gives

02.5 (subtract $0.72Y$ from both sides)

66 (divide both sides by 0.28)

Problem

nat

$+ 25$

$+ 10$

e the equilibrium level of national income.

lude this section we return to the simple two-sector model:

_

b

the investment, I, was taken to be constant. It is more realistic to assume that
vestment depends on the rate of interest, r. As the interest rate rises, so investment
e have a relationship

1

0 and $d > 0$. Unfortunately, this model consists of three equations in the four
Y, C, I and r, so we cannot expect it to determine national income uniquely. The
ι do is to eliminate C and I, say, and to set up an equation relating Y and r. This
ily understood by an example. Suppose that

$+ 100$

$+ 1000$

chat the commodity market is in equilibrium when

I

ιn of the given expressions for C and I into this equation gives

$Y + 100) + (-20r + 1000)$

$- 20r + 1100$

with

$$Y_d = Y - T$$

In practice, the tax will eith
of national income ($T = tY$

Example

Given that

$$G = 20$$
$$I = 35$$
$$C = 0.9Y_d + 70$$
$$T = 0.2Y + 25$$

calculate the equilibrium le

Solution

At first sight this problem
variables. However, all we
stitute systematically one e
  We know that

$Y = C + I + G$	(from
$G = 20$	(give
$I = 35$	(give
$C = 0.9Y_d + 70$	(give
$T = 0.2Y + 25$	(give
$Y_d = Y - T$	(from

This represents a system of
put the fixed values of G an

$$Y = C + 35 + 20 = C + 55$$

This has at least removed
left to eliminate. We can rer

$$Y_d = Y - (0.2Y + 25)$$
$$= Y - 0.2Y - 25$$
$$= 0.8Y - 25$$

and then remove Y_d by subs

$$C = 0.9(0.8Y - 25) + 70$$
$$= 0.72Y - 22.5 + 70$$
$$= 0.72Y + 47.5$$

We can e

$$Y = C$$
$$= 0.7$$
$$= 0.7$$

Finally, s

$$0.28Y$$
$$Y$$

Practi

3. Giver

$$G = 40$$
$$I = 55$$
$$C = 0.8$$
$$T = 0.$$

calcul

To co

$$Y = C$$
$$C = aY$$

Previousl
planned
falls and

$$I = cr$$

where c
unknown
best we
is most e

$$C = 0.9$$
$$I = -2$$

We know

$$Y = C$$

Substitut

$$Y = (0.$$
$$= 0.8$$

which rearranges as

$$0.2Y + 20r = 1100$$

This equation, relating national income, Y, and interest rate, r, is called the IS schedule.

We obviously need some additional information before we can pin down the values of Y and r. This can be done by investigating the equilibrium of the money market. The money market is said to be in equilibrium when the supply of money, M_S, matches the demand for money, M_D: that is, when

$$M_S = M_D$$

There are many ways of measuring the money supply. In simple terms it can be thought of as consisting of the notes and coins in circulation, together with money held in bank deposits. The level of M_S is assumed to be controlled by the central bank and is taken to be autonomous, so that

$$M_S = M_S^*$$

for some fixed value M_S^*.

The demand for money comes from three sources: transactions, precautions and speculations. The transactions demand is used for the daily exchange of goods and services, whereas the precautionary demand is used to fund any emergencies requiring unforeseen expenditure. Both are assumed to be proportional to national income. Consequently, we lump these together and write

$$L_1 = k_1 Y$$

where L_1 denotes the aggregate transaction–precautionary demand and k_1 is a positive constant. The speculative demand for money is used as a reserve fund in case individuals or firms decide to invest in alternative assets such as government bonds. In Chapter 3 we show that, as interest rates rise, speculative demand falls. We model this by writing

$$L_2 = k_2 r + k_3$$

where L_2 denotes speculative demand, k_2 is a negative constant and k_3 is a positive constant. The total demand, M_D, is the sum of the transaction–precautionary demand and speculative demand: that is,

$$\begin{aligned} M_D &= L_1 + L_2 \\ &= k_1 Y + k_2 r + k_3 \end{aligned}$$

If the money market is in equilibrium then

$$M_S = M_D$$

that is,

$$M_S^* = k_1 Y + k_2 r + k_3$$

This equation, relating national income, Y, and interest rate, r, is called the LM schedule. If we assume that equilibrium exists in both the commodity and money markets then the IS and LM schedules provide a system of two equations in two unknowns, Y and r. These can easily be solved either by elimination or by graphical methods.

Example

Determine the equilibrium income and interest rate given the following information about the commodity market:

$$C = 0.8Y + 100$$

$$I = -20r + 1000$$

and the money market:

$$M_S = 2375$$

$$L_1 = 0.1Y$$

$$L_2 = -25r + 2000$$

What effect would a decrease in the money supply have on the equilibrium levels of Y and r?

Solution

The IS schedule for these particular consumption and investment functions has already been obtained in the preceding text. It was shown that the commodity market is in equilibrium when

$$0.2Y + 20r = 1100 \tag{1}$$

For the money market we see that the money supply is

$$M_S = 2375$$

and that the total demand for money (that is, the sum of the transaction–precautionary demand, L_1, and the speculative demand, L_2) is

$$M_D = L_1 + L_2 = 0.1Y - 25r + 2000$$

The money market is in equilibrium when

$$M_S = M_D$$

that is,

$$2375 = 0.1Y - 25r + 2000$$

The LM schedule is therefore given by

$$0.1Y - 25r = 375 \tag{2}$$

Equations (1) and (2) constitute a system of two equations for the two unknowns Y and r. The steps described in Section 1.4 can be used to solve this system:

Step 1

Double equation (2) and subtract from equation (1) to get

$$
\begin{array}{r}
0.2Y + 20r = 1100 \\
\underline{0.2Y - 50r = \ \ 750} - \\
70r = \ \ 350
\end{array}
\tag{3}
$$

Step 2

Divide both sides of equation (3) by 70 to get

$$r = 5$$

Step 3

Substitute $r = 5$ into equation (1) to get

$$0.2Y + 100 = 1100$$
$$0.2Y = 1000 \quad \text{(subtract 100 from both sides)}$$
$$Y = 5000 \quad \text{(divide both sides by 0.2)}$$

Step 4

As a check, equation (2) gives

$$0.1(5000) - 25(5) = 375 \quad \checkmark$$

The equilibrium levels of Y and r are therefore 5000 and 5 respectively.

To investigate what happens to Y and r as the money supply falls, we could just take a smaller value of M_S such as 2300 and repeat the calculations. However, it is more instructive to perform the investigation graphically. Figure 1.28 shows the IS and LM curves plotted on the same diagram with r on the horizontal axis and Y on the vertical axis. These lines intersect at (5, 5000), confirming the equilibrium levels of interest rate and income obtained by calculation. Any change in the money supply will obviously have no effect on the IS curve. On the other hand, a change in the money supply does affect the LM curve. To see this, let us return to the general LM schedule

$$k_1Y + k_2r + k_3 = M_S^*$$

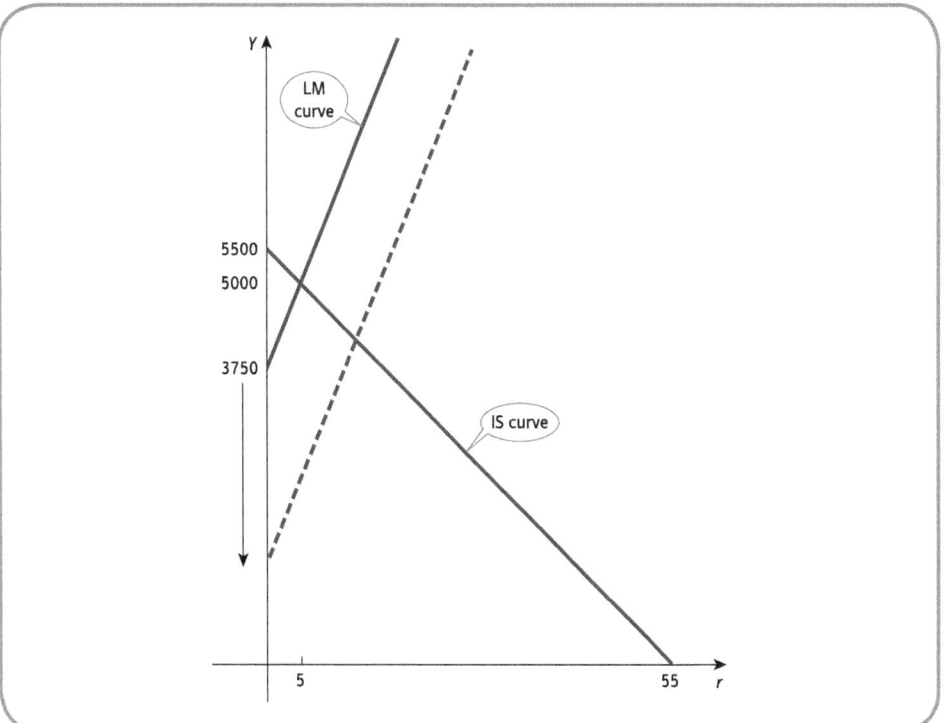

Figure 1.28

and transpose it to express Y in terms of r:

$k_1Y = -k_2r - k_3 + M_S^*$ (subtract $k_2r + k_3$ from both sides)

$Y = \left(\dfrac{-k_2}{k_1}\right)r + \dfrac{-k_3 + M_S^*}{k_1}$ (divide both sides by k_1)

Expressed in this form, we see that the LM schedule has slope $-k_2/k_1$ and intercept $(-k_3 + M_S^*)/k_1$.

Any decrease in M_S^* therefore decreases the intercept (but not the slope) and the LM curve shifts downwards. This is indicated by the dashed line in Figure 1.28. The point of intersection shifts both downwards and to the right. We deduce that, as the money supply falls, interest rates rise and national income decreases (assuming that both the commodity and money markets remain in equilibrium).

Advice

It is possible to produce general formulae for the equilibrium level of income in terms of various parameters used to specify the model. As you might expect, the algebra is a little harder but it does allow for a more general investigation into the effects of varying these parameters. We will return to this in Section 5.3.

Practice Problem

4. Determine the equilibrium income, Y, and interest rate, r, given the following information about the commodity market

   $C = 0.7Y + 85$

   $I = -50r + 1200$

   and the money market

   $M_S = 500$

   $L_1 = 0.2Y$

   $L_2 = -40r + 30$

   Sketch the IS and LM curves on the same diagram. What effect would an increase in the value of autonomous investment have on the equilibrium values of Y and r?

Key Terms

Autonomous consumption   The level of consumption when there is no income.

Autonomous savings   The withdrawals from savings when there is no income.

Consumption function   The relationship between national income and consumption.

Disposable income   Household income after the deduction of taxes and the addition of benefits.

Factors of production   The inputs to the production of goods and services: land, capital, labour and raw materials.

Government expenditure   The total amount of money spent by government on defence, education, health, police, etc.

Investment   The creation of output not for immediate consumption.

IS schedule   The equation relating national income and interest rate based on the assumption of equilibrium in the goods market.

LM schedule   The equation relating national income and interest rate based on the assumption of equilibrium in the money market.

Marginal propensity to consume   The fraction of a rise in national income which goes on consumption. It is the slope of the consumption function.

Marginal propensity to save   The fraction of a rise in national income which goes into savings. It is the slope of the savings function.

Money supply   The notes and coins in circulation together with money held in bank deposits.

National income   The flow of money from firms to households.

Precautionary demand for money   Money held in reserve by individuals or firms to fund unforeseen future expenditure.

Speculative demand for money   Money held back by firms or individuals for the purpose of investing in alternative assets, such as government bonds, at some future date.

Taxation   Money paid to government based on an individual's income and wealth (direct taxation) together with money paid by suppliers of goods or services based on expenditure (indirect taxation).

Transactions demand for money   Money used for everyday transactions of goods and services.

Exercise 1.7

1. If the consumption function is given by $C = 4200 + 0.75Y$ state the marginal propensity to consume and deduce the marginal propensity to save.

2. If the national income, Y, is 1000 units then consumption, C, is 800 units. Also whenever income rises by 100, consumption increases by 70. Assuming that the consumption function is linear:

   (a) state the marginal propensity to consume and deduce the marginal propensity to save;

   (b) find an expression for C in terms of Y.

3. If the consumption function is given by

   $$C = 0.7Y + 40$$

   state the values of

(a) autonomous consumption

(b) marginal propensity to consume.

Transpose this formula to express Y in terms of C and hence find the value of Y when $C = 110$.

4. Write down expressions for the savings function given that the consumption function is

(a) $C = 0.9Y + 72$ (b) $C = 0.8Y + 100$

5. For a closed economy with no government intervention the consumption function is

$C = 0.6Y + 30$

and planned investment is

$I = 100$

Calculate the equilibrium level of

(a) national income

(b) consumption

(c) savings.

6. A consumption function is given by $C = aY + b$.

It is known that when $Y = 10$, the value of C is 28, and that when $Y = 30$, the value of C is 44.

By solving a pair of simultaneous equations, find the values of a and b, and deduce that the corresponding savings function is given by

$S = 0.2Y - 20$

Determine the equilibrium level of income when planned investment $I = 13$.

7. Given that

$G = 50$

$I = 40$

$C = 0.75Y_d + 45$

$T = 0.2Y + 80$

calculate the equilibrium level of national income.

Exercise 1.7*

1. Write down an expression for the savings function, simplified as far as possible, given that the consumption function is

(a) $C = 0.7Y + 30$ (b) $C = \dfrac{Y^2 + 500}{Y + 10}$

2. If

$$C = aY + b$$
$$Y = C + I$$
$$I = I^*$$

show that

$$Y = \frac{b + I^*}{1 - a}$$

and obtain a similar expression for C in terms of a, b and I^*.

3. Transpose the formula

$$Y = \frac{b + I^*}{1 - a}$$

to express a in terms of Y, b and I^*.

4. An open economy is in equilibrium when

$$Y = C + I + G + X - M$$

where

Y = national income

C = consumption

I = investment

G = government expenditure

X = exports

M = imports

Determine the equilibrium level of income given that

$C = 0.8Y + 80$

$I = 70$

$G = 130$

$X = 100$

$M = 0.2Y + 50$

5. Given that

consumption,	$C = 0.8Y + 60$
investment,	$I = -30r + 740$
money supply,	$M_S = 4000$
transaction–precautionary demand for money,	$L_1 = 0.15Y$
speculative demand for money,	$L_2 = -20r + 3825$

determine the values of national income, Y, and interest rate, r, on the assumption that both the commodity and the money markets are in equilibrium.

6. Consider the national income model

$$Y = C + I$$
$$C = aY_d + 50$$
$$I = 24$$
$$Y_d = Y - T$$
$$T = 20$$

Show that the equilibrium level of national income is given by

$$Y = \frac{74 - 20a}{1 - a}$$

Transpose this equation to express a in terms of Y.

Hence, or otherwise, find the value of a for which $Y = 155$ and find the value of C.

7. Consider the national income model

$$Y = C + I^* + G^*$$
$$C = a(Y - T), \qquad 0 < a < 1$$
$$T = tY, \qquad\quad 0 < t < 1$$

Show that

$$Y = \frac{I^* + G^*}{1 + a(t - 1)}$$

and hence state what happens to Y when

(a) G^* increases   **(b)** t increases

Formal mathematics

The approach adopted in this textbook is very informal. Emphasis is placed throughout on making both the mathematics and economic applications as accessible as possible. Hopefully this will help you to understand and enjoy the subject. However, it could well be that your lecturers use more formal language and notation. For this reason we conclude each chapter with a brief discussion of more rigorous mathematical language and ideas which provide the framework for more advanced courses which you may take in future years.

In Section 1.2 a number line was used to represent the solutions of linear inequalities. The set of all numbers which lie between two values on the number line is called an **interval** and the notation that we use is summarised in the following table:

Interval	Notation
$a \le x \le b$	[a, b]
$a < x < b$	(a, b)
$a \le x < b$	[a, b)
$a < x \le b$	(a, b]

The first interval, which includes both end points, is called a **closed interval** and the second which excludes the end points, is called an **open interval**. Using this notation we would write [2, 5] as an abbreviation for $2 \le x \le 5$ and (3, 9] as an abbreviation for $3 < x \le 9$. It is also possible to use this notation to include intervals which are unbounded. For example, the interval $x \ge 6$, which consists of all numbers to the right of 6 on the number line (including 6 itself), can be written as [6, ∞). The symbol ∞ (infinity) is not a number but merely indicates that the interval goes on forever without an upper limit. In this notation we could write the complete set of numbers as (−∞, ∞).

It is often convenient in mathematics to ignore the sign of a number and deliberately make it positive. This is called the **absolute value** or **modulus** of a number, x, and is written $|x|$. In this notation we have

$$|-5| = 5 \text{ and } |4| = 4$$

If a number is negative we change the sign to make it positive whereas if the number is already positive it is unchanged, so we have

$$|x| = -x \text{ if } x < 0 \quad \text{and} \quad |x| = x \text{ if } x \ge 0$$

Example

Solve the following inequalities giving your answer using interval notation.

(a) $|x| \le 6$ (b) $|2x - 1| < 3$

→

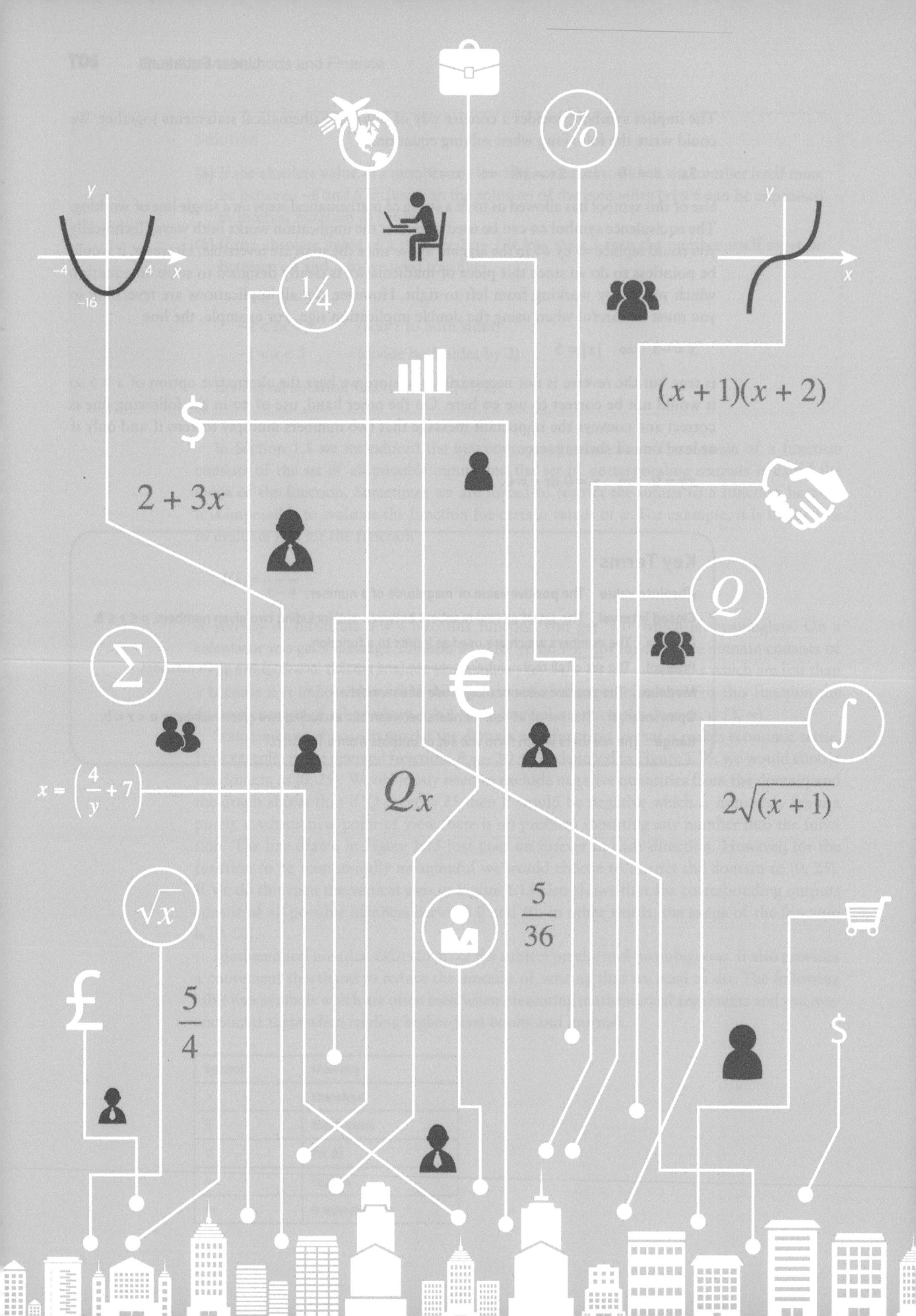

CHAPTER 2
Non-linear Equations

The main aim of this chapter is to describe the mathematics of non-linear equations. The approach is similar to that of Chapter 1. There are four sections. Section 2.1 should be read before Section 2.2, and Section 2.3 should be read before Section 2.4.

The first section investigates the simplest non-linear equation, known as a quadratic. A quadratic equation can easily be solved either by factorising it as the product of two linear factors or by using a special formula. You are also shown how to sketch the graphs of quadratic functions. The techniques are illustrated by finding the equilibrium price and quantity for quadratic supply and demand functions.

Section 2.2 introduces additional functions in microeconomics, including revenue and profit. There is very little new material in this section. It mainly consists of applying the ideas of Section 2.1 to sketch graphs of quadratic revenue and profit functions and to find their maximum values.

Finally, the topic of algebra, which we started in Chapter 1, is completed by investigating the rules of indices and logarithms. The basic concepts are covered in Section 2.3. The notation and rules of indices are extremely important and are used frequently in subsequent chapters. Section 2.4 focuses on two specific functions, namely the exponential and natural logarithm functions. If you run into difficulty, or are short of time, then this section could be omitted for the time being, particularly if you do not intend to study the next chapter on the mathematics of finance.

SECTION 2.1
Quadratic functions

Objectives

At the end of this section you should be able to:

- Solve a quadratic equation using 'the formula'.
- Solve a quadratic equation given its factorisation.
- Sketch the graph of a quadratic function using a table of function values.
- Sketch the graph of a quadratic function by finding the coordinates of the intercepts.
- Solve quadratic inequalities using graphs.
- Solve inequalities using sign diagrams.
- Determine equilibrium price and quantity given a pair of quadratic demand and supply functions.

The first chapter considered the topic of linear mathematics. In particular, we described how to sketch the graph of a linear function and how to solve a linear equation (or system of simultaneous linear equations). It was also pointed out that not all economic functions are of this simple form. In assuming that the demand and supply graphs are straight lines, we are certainly making the mathematical analysis easy, but we may well be sacrificing realism. It may be that the demand and supply graphs are curved and, in these circumstances, it is essential to model them using more complicated functions. The simplest non-linear function is known as a **quadratic function** and takes the form

$$f(x) = ax^2 + bx + c$$

for some parameters a, b and c. (In fact, even if the demand function is linear, functions derived from it, such as total revenue and profit, turn out to be quadratic. We investigate these functions in the next section.) For the moment we concentrate on the mathematics of quadratics and show how to sketch graphs of quadratic functions and how to solve quadratic equations.

Consider the elementary equation

$$x^2 - 9 = 0$$ x^2 is an abbreviation for $x \times x$

It is easy to see that the expression on the left-hand side is a special case of the above with $a = 1$, $b = 0$ and $c = -9$. To solve this equation we add 9 to both sides to get

$$x^2 = 9$$

so we need to find a number, x, which when multiplied by itself produces the value 9. A moment's thought should convince you that there are exactly two numbers that work, namely 3 and -3 because

$$3 \times 3 = 9 \quad \text{and} \quad (-3) \times (-3) = 9$$

These two solutions are called the **square roots** of 9. The symbol $\sqrt{}$ is reserved for the positive square root, so in this notation the solutions are $\sqrt{9}$ and $-\sqrt{9}$. These are usually combined and written $\pm\sqrt{9}$. The equation

$$x^2 - 9 = 0$$

is trivial to solve because the number 9 has obvious square roots. In general, it is necessary to use a calculator to evaluate square roots. For example, the equation

$$x^2 - 2 = 0$$

can be written as

$$x^2 = 2$$

and so has solutions $x = \pm\sqrt{2}$. My calculator gives 1.414 213 56 (correct to 8 decimal places) for the square root of 2, so the above equation has solutions

1.414 213 56   and   −1.414 213 56

Example

Solve the following quadratic equations:

(a) $5x^2 - 80 = 0$ **(b)** $x^2 + 64 = 0$ **(c)** $(x + 4)^2 = 81$

Solution

(a) $5x^2 - 80 = 0$

$$5x^2 = 80 \quad \text{(add 80 to both sides)}$$
$$x^2 = 16 \quad \text{(divide both sides by 5)}$$
$$x = \pm 4 \quad \text{(square root both sides)}$$

(b) $x^2 + 64 = 0$

$$x^2 = -64 \quad \text{(subtract 64 from both sides)}$$

This equation does not have a solution because you cannot square a real number and get a negative answer.

(c) $(x + 4)^2 = 81$

$$x + 4 = \pm 9 \quad \text{(square root both sides)}$$

The two solutions are obtained by taking the + and − signs separately. Taking the + sign,

$$x + 4 = 9 \quad \text{so} \quad x = 9 - 4 = 5$$

Taking the − sign,

$$x + 4 = -9 \quad \text{so} \quad x = -9 - 4 = -13$$

The two solutions are 5 and −13.

Practice Problem

1. Solve the following quadratic equations. (Round your solutions to 2 decimal places if necessary.)

   (a) $x^2 - 100 = 0$ (b) $2x^2 - 8 = 0$ (c) $x^2 - 3 = 0$ (d) $x^2 - 5.72 = 0$

   (e) $x^2 + 1 = 0$ (f) $3x^2 + 6.21 = 0$ (g) $x^2 = 0$

All of the equations considered in Practice Problem 1 are of the special form

$$ax^2 + c = 0$$

in which the coefficient of x is zero. To solve more general quadratic equations we use a formula that enables the solutions to be calculated in a few lines of working. It can be shown that

$$ax^2 + bx + c = 0$$

has solutions

$$x = \frac{-b \pm \sqrt{(b^2 - 4ac)}}{2a}$$

The following example describes how to use this formula. It also illustrates the fact (which you have already discovered in Practice Problem 1) that a quadratic equation can have two solutions, one solution or no solutions.

Example

Solve the quadratic equations

(a) $2x^2 + 9x + 5 = 0$ (b) $x^2 - 4x + 4 = 0$ (c) $3x^2 - 5x + 6 = 0$

Solution

(a) For the equation

$$2x^2 + 9x + 5 = 0$$

we have $a = 2$, $b = 9$ and $c = 5$. Substituting these values into the formula

$$x = \frac{-b \pm \sqrt{(b^2 - 4ac)}}{2a}$$

gives

$$x = \frac{-9 \pm \sqrt{(9^2 - 4(2)(5))}}{2(2)}$$

$$= \frac{-9 \pm \sqrt{(81 - 40)}}{4}$$

$$= \frac{-9 \pm \sqrt{41}}{4}$$

The two solutions are obtained by taking the + and − signs separately: that is,

$$\frac{-9+\sqrt{41}}{4} = -0.649 \quad \text{(correct to 3 decimal places)}$$

$$\frac{-9-\sqrt{41}}{4} = -3.851 \quad \text{(correct to 3 decimal places)}$$

It is easy to check that these are solutions by substituting them into the original equation. For example, putting $x = -0.649$ into

$$2x^2 + 9x + 5$$

gives

$$2(-0.649)^2 + 9(-0.649) + 5 = 0.001\ 402$$

which is close to zero, as required. We cannot expect to produce an exact value of zero because we rounded $\sqrt{41}$ to 3 decimal places. You might like to check for yourself that −3.851 is also a solution.

(b) For the equation

$$x^2 - 4x + 4 = 0$$

we have $a = 1$, $b = -4$ and $c = 4$. Substituting these values into the formula

$$x = \frac{-b \pm \sqrt{(b^2 - 4ac)}}{2a}$$

gives

$$x = \frac{-(-4) \pm \sqrt{((-4)^2 - 4(1)(4))}}{2(1)}$$

$$= \frac{4 \pm \sqrt{(16 - 16)}}{2}$$

$$= \frac{4 \pm \sqrt{0}}{2}$$

$$= \frac{4 \pm 0}{2}$$

Clearly we get the same answer irrespective of whether we take the + or the − sign here. In other words, this equation has only one solution, $x = 2$. As a check, substitution of $x = 2$ into the original equation gives

$$(2)^2 - 4(2) + 4 = 0$$

(c) For the equation

$$3x^2 - 5x + 6 = 0$$

we have $a = 3$, $b = -5$ and $c = 6$. Substituting these values into the formula

$$x = \frac{-b \pm \sqrt{(b^2 - 4ac)}}{2a}$$

or

$x + 2 = 0$ with solution $x = -2$

The quadratic equation

$x^2 + 3x + 2 = 0$

therefore has two solutions, $x = -1$ and $x = -2$.

The difficulty with this approach is that it is impossible, except in very simple cases, to work out the factorisation from any given quadratic, so the preferred method is to use the formula. However, if you are lucky enough to be given the factorisation, or perhaps clever enough to spot the factorisation for yourself, then it does provide a viable alternative.

One important feature of linear functions is that their graphs are always straight lines. Obviously the intercept and slope vary from function to function, but the shape is always the same. It turns out that a similar property holds for quadratic functions. Now, whenever you are asked to produce a graph of an unfamiliar function, it is often a good idea to tabulate the function, to plot these points on graph paper and to join them up with a smooth curve. The precise number of points to be taken depends on the function but, as a general rule, between 5 and 10 points usually produce a good picture.

A table of values for the simple square function

$f(x) = x^2$

is given by

x	-3	-2	-1	0	1	2	3
$f(x)$	9	4	1	0	1	4	9

The first row of the table gives a selection of 'incoming' numbers, x, while the second row shows the corresponding 'outgoing' numbers, y. Points with coordinates (x, y) are then plotted on graph paper to produce the curve shown in Figure 2.1. For convenience, different scales are used on the x and y axes.

Mathematicians call this curve a **parabola**, whereas economists refer to it as **U-shaped**. Notice that the graph is symmetric about the y axis with a minimum point at the origin; if a mirror is placed along the y axis then the left-hand part is the image of the right-hand part.

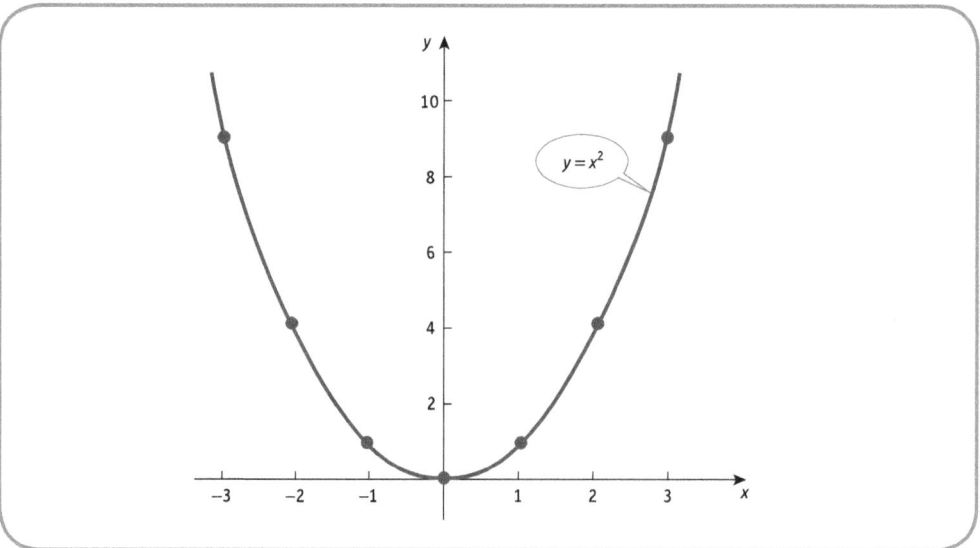

Figure 2.1

Advice

The following problem is designed to give you an opportunity to tabulate and sketch graphs of more general quadratic functions. Please remember that when you substitute numbers into a formula you must use BIDMAS to decide the order of the operations. For example, in part (a) you need to substitute $x = -1$ into $4x^2 - 12x + 5$. You get

$4(-1)^2 - 12(-1) + 5$

$= 4 + 12 + 5$

$= 21$

Note also that when using a calculator you must use brackets when squaring negative numbers. In this case a possible sequence of key presses might be

$$4 \quad (\quad (-) \quad 1 \quad) \quad x^2 \quad - \quad 12 \quad \times \quad (-) \quad 1 \quad + \quad 5 \quad =$$

Practice Problem

3. Complete the following tables of function values and hence sketch a graph of each quadratic function.

(a) $f(x) = 4x^2 - 12x + 5$

x	−1	0	1	2	3	4
$f(x)$						

(b) $f(x) = -x^2 + 6x - 9$

x	0	1	2	3	4	5	6
$f(x)$							

(c) $f(x) = -2x^2 + 4x - 6$

x	−2	−1	0	1	2	3	4
$f(x)$							

The results of Practice Problem 3 suggest that the graph of a quadratic is always parabolic. Furthermore, whenever the coefficient of x^2 is positive, the graph bends upwards and is a 'happy' parabola (U shape). A selection of U-shaped curves is shown in Figure 2.2. Similarly, when the coefficient of x^2 is negative, the graph bends downwards and is a 'sad' parabola (inverted U shape). A selection of inverted U-shaped curves is shown in Figure 2.3.

The task of sketching graphs from a table of function values is extremely tedious, particularly if only a rough sketch is required. It is usually more convenient just to determine a few key points on the curve. The obvious points to find are the intercepts with the coordinate axes, since these enable us to 'tether' the parabola down in the various positions shown in Figures 2.2 and 2.3. The curve crosses the y axis when $x = 0$. Evaluating the function

$$f(x) = ax^2 + bx + c$$

at $x = 0$ gives

$$f(0) = a(0)^2 + b(0) + c = c$$

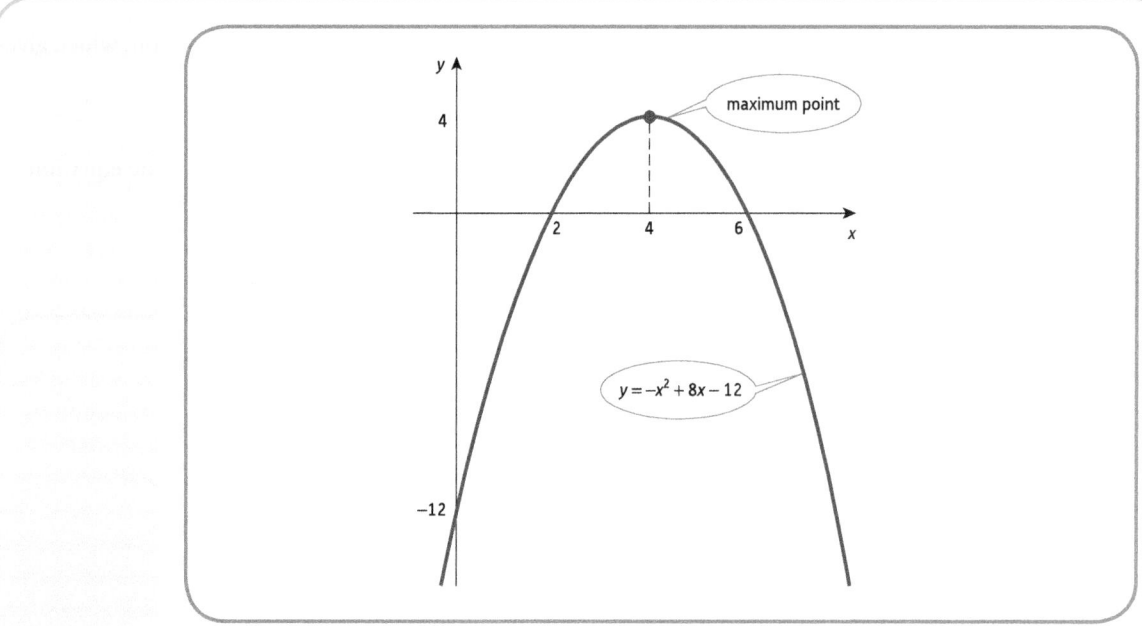

Figure 2.4

In fact, we can go even further in this case and locate the coordinates of the turning point – that is, the maximum point – on the curve. By symmetry, the x coordinate of this point occurs exactly halfway between $x = 2$ and $x = 6$: that is, at

$$x = \tfrac{1}{2}(2 + 6) = 4$$

The corresponding y coordinate is found by substituting $x = 4$ into the function to get

$$f(4) = -(4)^2 + 8(4) - 12 = 4$$

The maximum point on the curve therefore has coordinates $(4, 4)$.

Practice Problem

4. Use the three-step strategy to produce rough graphs of the following quadratic functions:

    (a) $f(x) = 2x^2 - 11x - 6$ **(b)** $f(x) = x^2 - 6x + 9$

One useful by-product of our work on sketching graphs is that it enables us to solve quadratic inequalities with no extra effort.

Example

Solve the following quadratic inequalities

    (a) $-x^2 + 8x - 12 > 0$ **(b)** $-x^2 + 8x - 12 \leq 0$

Solution

The graph of the function $f(x) = -x^2 + 8x - 12$ has already been sketched in Figure 2.4.

The parabola lies above the x axis (that is, the line $y = 0$) between 2 and 6 and is below the x axis outside these values.

(a) The quadratic function takes positive values when the graph is above the x axis so the inequality has solution, $2 < x < 6$. The values of 2 and 6 must be excluded from the solution since we require the quadratic to be strictly greater than zero.

(b) The graph is on or below the x axis at or to the left of 2, and at or to the right of 6, so the complete solution is $x \leq 2$ and $x \geq 6$.

Practice Problem

5. Use your answers to Practice Problem 4 to write down the solution to each of the following quadratic inequalities:

   (a) $2x^2 - 11x - 6 \leq 0$ (b) $x^2 - 6x + 9 > 0$

If the quadratic is in factorised form then there is an alternative method which can be used to solve the associated inequality. This is based on a sign diagram. It avoids the need to draw a graph and the method has the added advantage that it can be used to solve other inequalities. We illustrate the technique in the following example.

Example

Use a sign diagram to solve the following inequalities

(a) $(x - 2)(x + 3) \geq 0$ (b) $\dfrac{x}{x + 2} < 0$

Solution

(a) We know that the factor $x - 2$ is zero at $x = 2$. If x is smaller than 2 the factor is negative (for example, when $x = 1$, the factor takes the value, $-1 < 0$) and when x is bigger than 2 the factor is positive (for example, when $x = 4$, the factor takes the value, $2 > 0$). These results are illustrated on the number line:

$(x - 2)$ – – – – – – – – – – – – – – – 0 + + + +
    −5 −4 −3 −2 −1 0 1 2 3 4

The second factor, $x + 3$, takes the value zero at $x = -3$, is negative to the left of −3 and is positive to the right of −3. This is illustrated in the number line diagram:

$(x + 3)$ – – – – – 0 + + + + + + + + + + + + + +
    −5 −4 −3 −2 −1 0 1 2 3 4

The expression $(x - 2)(x + 3)$ is the product of the two factors. To the left of -3 the number lines show that both factors are negative so their product is positive. Between -3 and 2 one factor is negative and the other positive so their product is negative. Of course, if one factor is zero the product is automatically zero, irrespective of the sign of the second factor. The complete sign diagram for the product is shown below

$$(x - 2)(x + 3) \quad + \; + \; + \; + \; 0 \; - \; - \; - \; - \; - \; - \; - \; - \; 0 \; + \; + \; + \; +$$

$$-5 \quad -4 \quad -3 \quad -2 \quad -1 \quad 0 \quad 1 \quad 2 \quad 3 \quad 4$$

The diagram shows immediately that the inequality $(x - 2)(x + 3) \geq 0$ is satisfied by $x \leq -3$, $x \geq 2$.

(b) The factor $(x + 2)$ is zero at $x = -2$, negative to the left of $x = -2$, and positive to the right of this. The factor x is obviously zero at $x = 0$, negative to the left of $x = 0$, and positive to the right of this. The complete sign diagram is shown below:

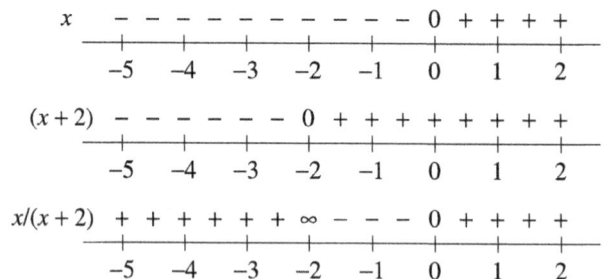

The rules for dividing negative numbers are the same as those for multiplying so the diagram is completed in the same way as before. The only exception occurs at $x = -2$ because we cannot divide by zero. This is indicated on the diagram by putting the symbol ∞ (infinity) at this position on the line. This diagram shows that the inequality $\dfrac{x}{x+2} < 0$ is satisfied by $-2 < x < 0$.

Practice Problem

6. Use a sign diagram to solve the following inequalities:

(a) $(x - 1)(x - 4) \leq 0$ **(b)** $\dfrac{x-1}{x+2} \geq 0$

We conclude this section by solving a particular problem in microeconomics. In Section 1.5 the concept of market equilibrium was introduced and in each of the problems the supply and demand functions were always given to be linear. The following example shows this to be an unnecessary restriction and indicates that it is almost as easy to manipulate quadratic supply and demand functions.

Example

Given the supply and demand functions

$$P = Q_S^2 + 14Q_S + 22$$
$$P = -Q_D^2 - 10Q_D + 150$$

calculate the equilibrium price and quantity.

Solution

In equilibrium, $Q_S = Q_D$, so if we denote this equilibrium quantity by Q, the supply and demand functions become

$$P = Q^2 + 14Q + 22$$
$$P = -Q^2 - 10Q + 150$$

Hence

$$Q^2 + 14Q + 22 = -Q^2 - 10Q + 150$$

since both sides are equal to P. Collecting like terms gives

$$2Q^2 + 24Q - 128 = 0$$

which is just a quadratic equation in the variable Q. Before using the formula to solve this it is a good idea to divide both sides by 2 to avoid large numbers. This gives

$$Q^2 + 12Q - 64 = 0$$

and so

$$Q = \frac{-12 \pm \sqrt{((12^2) - 4(1)(-64))}}{2(1)}$$
$$= \frac{-12 \pm \sqrt{(400)}}{2}$$
$$= \frac{-12 \pm 20}{2}$$

The quadratic equation has solutions $Q = -16$ and $Q = 4$. Now the solution $Q = -16$ can obviously be ignored because a negative quantity does not make sense. The equilibrium quantity is therefore 4. The equilibrium price can be calculated by substituting this value into either the original supply or demand equation.

From the supply equation,

$$P = 4^2 + 14(4) + 22 = 94$$

As a check, the demand equation gives

$$P = -(4)^2 - 10(4) + 150 = 94 \quad \checkmark$$

You might be puzzled by the fact that we actually obtain two possible solutions, one of which does not make economic sense. The supply and demand curves are sketched in Figure 2.5. This shows that there are indeed two points of intersection, confirming the mathematical solution. However, in economics the quantity and price are both positive, so the functions are only defined in the top right-hand (that is, positive) quadrant. In this region there is just one point of intersection, at (4, 94).

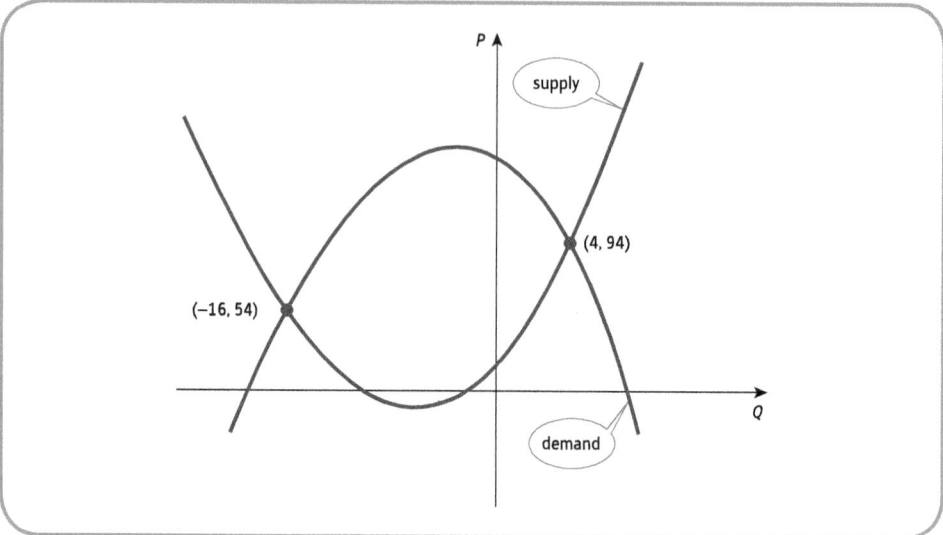

Figure 2.5

Practice Problem

7. Given the supply and demand functions

$$P = 2Q_S^2 + 10Q_S + 10$$
$$P = -Q_D^2 - 5Q_D + 52$$

calculate the equilibrium price and quantity.

Key Terms

Discriminant   The number $b^2 - 4ac$, which is used to indicate the number of solutions of the quadratic equation $ax^2 + bx + c = 0$.

Parabola   The shape of the graph of a quadratic function.

Quadratic function   A function of the form $f(x) = ax^2 + bx + c$ where $a \neq 0$.

Square root   A number that when multiplied by itself equals a given number; the solutions of the equation $x^2 = c$ which are written $\pm\sqrt{c}$.

U-shaped curve   A term used by economists to describe a curve, such as a parabola, which bends upwards, like the letter U.

Exercise 2.1

1. Solve the following quadratic equations:

   (a) $x^2 = 81$ (b) $x^2 = 36$ (c) $2x^2 = 8$

   (d) $(x - 1)^2 = 9$ (e) $(x + 5)^2 = 16$

2. Write down the solutions of the following equations:

   (a) $(x - 1)(x + 3) = 0$ (b) $(2x - 1)(x + 10) = 0$ (c) $x(x + 5) = 0$

   (d) $(3x + 5)(4x - 9) = 0$ (e) $(5 - 4x)(x - 5) = 0$

3. Use 'the formula' to solve the following quadratic equations. (Round your answers to 2 decimal places.)

   (a) $x^2 - 5x + 2 = 0$ (b) $2x^2 + 5x + 1 = 0$ (c) $-3x^2 + 7x + 2 = 0$

   (d) $x^2 - 3x - 1 = 0$ (e) $2x^2 + 8x + 8 = 0$ (f) $x^2 - 6x + 10 = 0$

4. Solve the equation $f(x) = 0$ for each of the following quadratic functions:

   (a) $f(x) = x^2 - 16$ (b) $f(x) = x(100 - x)$ (c) $f(x) = -x^2 + 22x - 85$

   (d) $f(x) = x^2 - 18x + 81$ (e) $f(x) = 2x^2 + 4x + 3$

5. Sketch the graphs of the quadratic functions given in Question 4.

6. Use the results of Question 5 to solve each of the following inequalities:

   (a) $x^2 - 16 \geq 0$ (b) $x(100 - x) > 0$ (c) $-x^2 + 22x - 85 \geq 0$

   (d) $x^2 - 18x + 81 \leq 0$ (e) $2x^2 + 4x + 3 > 0$

7. The production levels of coffee in Mexico, Q (in suitable units) depends on the average summer temperature, T (in °C).

   A statistical model of recent data shows that $Q = -0.046T^2 + 2.3T + 27.6$.

   (a) Complete the table of values and hence draw a graph of Q against T in the range, $23 \leq T \leq 30$.

T	23	24	25	26	27	28	29	30
Q								

   (b) Average summer temperatures over the last few decades have been about 25°C. However, some climate change models predict that this could rise by several degrees over the next 50 years. Use your graph to comment on the likely impact that this may have on coffee growers in Mexico.

8. Use a sign diagram to solve the following inequalities

   (a) $x(x - 3) > 0$ (b) $(x - 1)(x + 1) \geq 0$ (c) $\dfrac{x + 4}{x - 2} < 0$

9. Given the quadratic supply and demand functions

   $$P = Q_S^2 + 2Q_S + 12$$
   $$P = -Q_D^2 - 4Q_D + 68$$

   determine the equilibrium price and quantity.

10. Given the supply and demand functions

$$P = Q_S^2 + 2Q_S + 7$$

$$P = -Q_D + 25$$

determine the equilibrium price and quantity.

11. A clothing supplier sells t-shirts to retailers for $7 each. If a store agrees to buy more than 30 the supplier is willing to reduce the unit price by 3 cents for each shirt bought above 30, with a maximum single order of 100 shirts.

(a) How much does an order of 40 shirts cost?

(b) If the total cost of an order is $504.25 how many t-shirts did the store buy altogether?

Exercise 2.1*

1. Solve the following quadratic equations:

(a) $x^2 = 169$ 　　　　　(b) $(x - 5)^2 = 64$ 　　　　　(c) $(2x - 7)^2 = 121$

2. Find the solutions (in terms of d) of the quadratic equation

$$x^2 + 6dx - 7d^2 = 0$$

3. Write down the solutions of the following equations:

(a) $(x - 3)(x + 8) = 0$ 　　　(b) $(3x - 2)(2x + 9) = 0$ 　　　(c) $x(4x - 3) = 0$

(d) $(6x - 1)^2 = 0$ 　　　　　(e) $(x - 2)(x + 1)(4 - x) = 0$

4. Solve the following quadratic equations, rounding your answers to 2 decimal places, if necessary:

(a) $x^2 - 15x + 56 = 0$ 　　　(b) $2x^2 - 5x + 1 = 0$ 　　　(c) $4x^2 - 36 = 0$

(d) $x^2 - 14x + 49 = 0$ 　　　(e) $3x^2 + 4x + 7 = 0$ 　　　(f) $x^2 - 13x + 200 = 16x + 10$

5. Solve the following inequalities:

(a) $x^2 \geq 64$ 　　　　　　　(b) $x^2 - 10x + 9 \leq 0$ 　　　(c) $2x^2 + 15x + 7 < 0$

(d) $-3x^2 + 2x + 5 \geq 0$ 　　(e) $x^2 + 2x + 1 \leq 0$

6. One solution of the quadratic equation

$$x^2 - 8x + c = 0$$

is known to be $x = 2$. Find the second solution.

7. Find the value of k so that the equation

$$x^2 - 10x + 2k = 8x - k$$

has exactly one root.

8. Use a sign diagram to solve the following inequalities.

(a) $(x + 3)(x - 4) \geq 0$ (b) $(2 - x)(x + 1) > 0$ (c) $(x - 1)(x - 2)(x - 3) \leq 0$

(d) $\dfrac{(x - 2)}{(x - 3)(x - 5)} \geq 0$

9. A firm's monthly cost for paying cleaners' wages is \$47 250. Under a new pay deal each cleaner earns \$375 more each month. If the new pay deal goes through, the firm realises that it will need to reduce the number of cleaners by 3 if it is to cover its costs within the existing budget. What is the monthly salary of a cleaner before the pay rise?

10. Given the supply and demand functions

$$P = Q_S^2 + 10Q_S + 30$$
$$P = -Q_D^2 - 8Q_D + 200$$

calculate the equilibrium price, correct to 2 decimal places.

11. A pottery can make B bowls and P plates in a week according to the relation

$$2B^2 + 5B + 25P = 525$$

(a) If it makes 5 bowls, how many plates can it make in a week?

(b) What is the maximum number of bowls that it can produce in a week?

12. A city centre tour guide currently charges \$34 for a full day's tour. The average number of customers is 48. Market research suggests that for every \$1 increase in tour price, the guide can expect to lose 2 customers per tour.

(a) Show that if the price increase is \x then the expected revenue from each tour is

$$-2x^2 - 20x + 1632$$

(b) The guide needs to ensure that the expected revenue is at least \$1440. By solving a quadratic inequality, find the range of prices that need to be charged.

(c) What price should be charged to maximise expected revenue?

13. Given the supply and demand functions

$$Q_S = (P + 8)\sqrt{P + 20}$$
$$Q_D = \frac{460 - 12P - 3P^2}{\sqrt{P + 20}}$$

calculate the equilibrium price and quantity.

SECTION 2.2
Revenue, cost and profit

Objectives

At the end of this section you should be able to:

- Sketch the graphs of the total revenue, total cost, average cost and profit functions.
- Find the level of output that maximises total revenue.
- Find the level of output that maximises profit.
- Find the break-even levels of output.

The main aim of this section is to investigate one particular function in economics, namely profit. By making reasonable simplifying assumptions, the profit function is shown to be quadratic and so the methods developed in Section 2.1 can be used to analyse its properties. We describe how to find the levels of output required for a firm to break even and to maximise profit. The **profit** function is denoted by the Greek letter π (pi, pronounced 'pie') and is defined to be the difference between total revenue, TR, and total cost, TC: that is,

$$\pi = TR - TC$$

This definition is entirely sensible because TR is the amount of money received by the firm from the sale of its goods and TC is the amount of money that the firm has to spend to produce these goods. We begin by considering the total revenue and total cost functions in turn.

The **total revenue** received from the sale of Q goods at price P is given by

$$TR = PQ$$

For example, if the price of each good is $70 and the firm sells 300 then the revenue is

$$\$70 \times 300 = \$21\ 000$$

Given any particular demand function, expressing P in terms of Q, it is a simple matter to obtain a formula for TR solely in terms of Q. A graph of TR against Q can then be sketched.

Example

Given the demand function

$$P = 100 - 2Q$$

express TR as a function of Q and hence sketch its graph.

(a) For what values of Q is TR zero?

(b) What is the maximum value of TR?

Solution

Total revenue is defined by

$$TR = PQ$$

and, since $P = 100 - 2Q$, we have

$$TR = (100 - 2Q)Q = 100Q - 2Q^2$$

This function is quadratic and so its graph can be sketched using the strategy described in Section 2.1.

Step 1

The coefficient of Q^2 is negative, so the graph has an inverted U shape.

Step 2

The constant term is zero, so the graph crosses the TR axis at the origin.

Step 3

To find where the curve crosses the horizontal axis, we could use 'the formula'. However, this is not necessary, since it follows immediately from the factorisation

$$TR = (100 - 2Q)Q$$

that TR = 0 when either $100 - 2Q = 0$ or $Q = 0$. In other words, the quadratic equation has two solutions, $Q = 0$ and $Q = 50$.

The total revenue curve is shown in Figure 2.6.

(a) From Figure 2.6 the total revenue is zero when $Q = 0$ and $Q = 50$.

(b) By symmetry, the parabola reaches its maximum halfway between 0 and 50, that is at $Q = 25$. The corresponding total revenue is given by

$$TR = 100(25) - 2(25)^2 = 1250$$

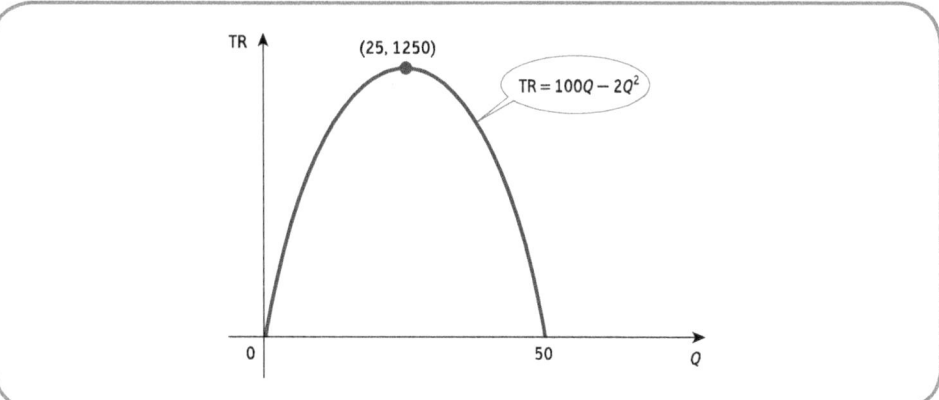

Figure 2.6

Practice Problem

1. Given the demand function

$$P = 1000 - Q$$

express TR as a function of Q and hence sketch a graph of TR against Q. What value of Q maximises total revenue and what is the corresponding price?

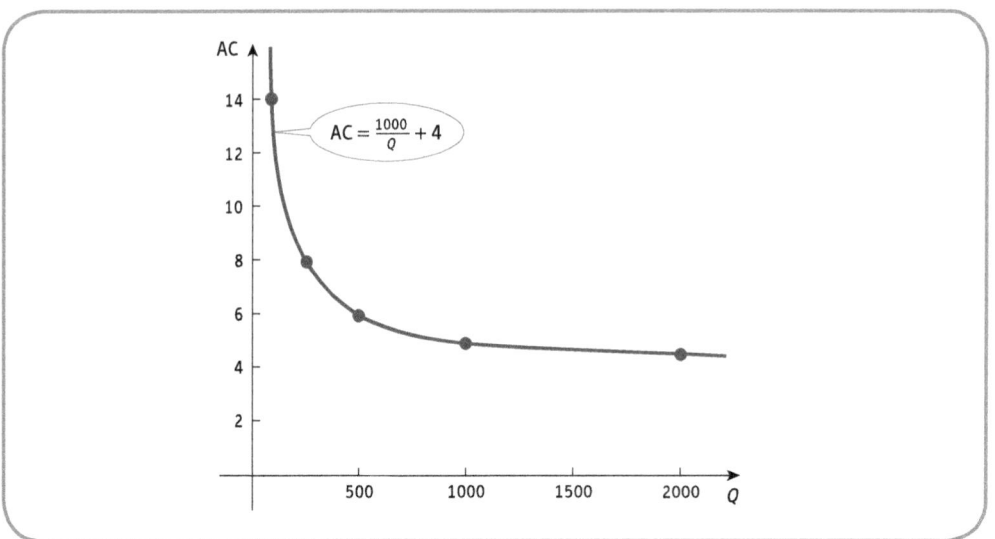

Figure 2.8

Practice Problem

2. Given that fixed costs are 100 and that variable costs are 2 per unit, express TC and AC as functions of Q. Hence sketch their graphs.

In general, whenever the variable cost, VC, is a constant the total cost function,

$$TC = FC + (VC)Q$$

is linear. The intercept is FC and the slope is VC. For the average cost function

$$AC = \frac{FC}{Q} + VC$$

note that if Q is small, then FC/Q is large, so the graph bends sharply upwards as Q approaches zero. As Q increases, FC/Q decreases and eventually tails off to zero for large values of Q. The AC curve therefore flattens off and approaches VC as Q gets larger and larger. This phenomenon is hardly surprising, since the fixed costs are shared between more and more goods, so have little effect on AC for large Q. The graph of AC therefore has the basic L shape shown in Figure 2.9. This effect, in which the average cost decreases as the number of units produced increases, is one reason for economies of scale, which encourage the growth of large organisations. This discussion assumes that VC is a constant. In practice, this may not be the case and VC might depend on Q. The TC graph is then no longer linear and the AC graph becomes U-shaped rather than L-shaped. An example of this can be found in Question 5 in Exercise 2.2 at the end of this section.

Figure 2.10 shows typical TR and TC graphs sketched on the same diagram. These are drawn on the assumption that the demand function is linear (which leads to a quadratic total revenue function) and that the variable costs are constant (which leads to a linear total cost function). The horizontal axis represents quantity, Q. Strictly speaking the label Q means different things for the two functions. For the revenue function, Q denotes the quantity of goods actually sold, whereas for the cost function it denotes the quantity produced. In

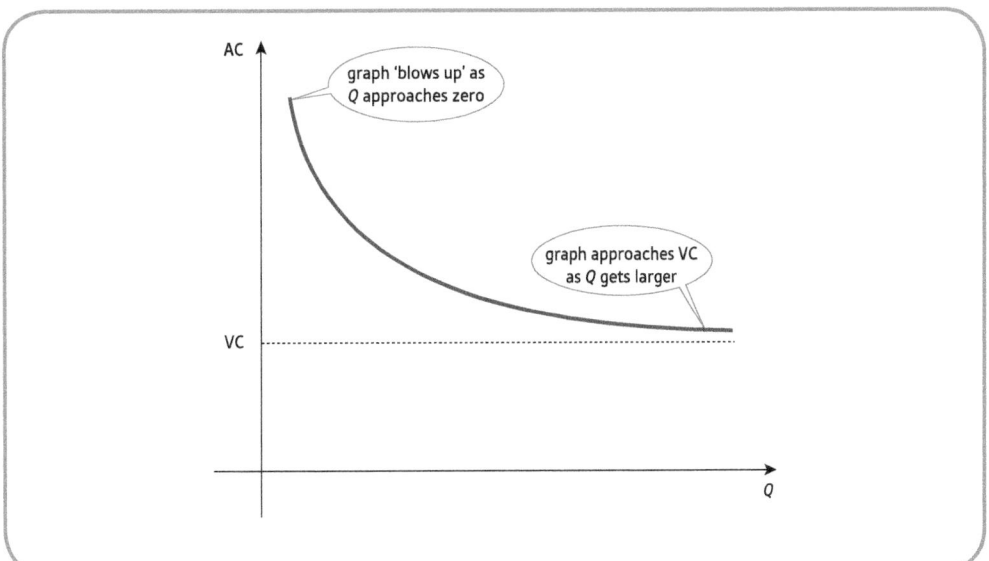

Figure 2.9

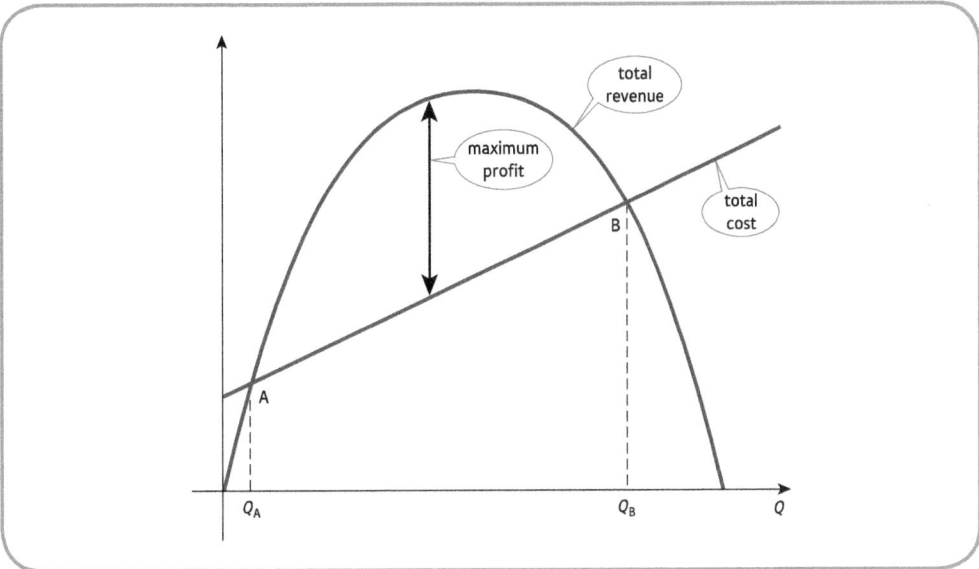

Figure 2.10

sketching both graphs on the same diagram we are implicitly assuming that these two values are the same and that the firm sells all of the goods that it produces.

The two curves intersect at precisely two points, A and B, corresponding to output levels Q_A and Q_B. At these points the cost and revenue are equal and the firm breaks even. If $Q < Q_A$ or $Q > Q_B$ then the TC curve lies above that of TR, so cost exceeds revenue. For these levels of output the firm makes a loss. If $Q_A < Q < Q_B$ then revenue exceeds cost and the firm makes a profit which is equal to the vertical distance between the revenue and cost curves. The maximum profit occurs where the gap between them is largest. The easiest way of calculating maximum profit is to obtain a formula for profit directly in terms of Q using the defining equation

$$\pi = TR - TC$$

Example

If fixed costs are 4, variable costs per unit are 1 and the demand function is

$$P = 10 - 2Q$$

obtain an expression for π in terms of Q and hence sketch a graph of π against Q.

(a) For what values of Q does the firm break even?

(b) What is the maximum profit?

Solution

We begin by obtaining expressions for the total cost and total revenue. For this problem, FC = 4 and VC = 1, so

$$TC = FC + (VC)Q = 4 + Q$$

The given demand function is $P = 10 - 2Q$
so TR = PQ = $(10 - 2Q)Q = 10Q - 2Q^2$
Hence the profit is given by

$$\begin{aligned}
\pi &= TR - TC \\
&= (10Q - 2Q^2) - (4 + Q) \\
&= 10Q - 2Q^2 - 4 - Q \\
&= -2Q^2 + 9Q - 4
\end{aligned}$$

To sketch a graph of the profit function we follow the strategy described in Section 2.1.

Step 1

The coefficient of Q^2 is negative, so the graph has an inverted U shape.

Step 2

The constant term is –4, so the graph crosses the vertical axis when $\pi = -4$.

Step 3

The graph crosses the horizontal axis when $\pi = 0$, so we need to solve the quadratic equation

$$-2Q^2 + 9Q - 4 = 0$$

This can be done using 'the formula' to get

$$Q = \frac{-9 \pm \sqrt{81 - 32}}{2(-2)} = \frac{-9 \pm 7}{-4}$$

so $Q = 0.5$ and $Q = 4$.
   The profit curve is sketched in Figure 2.11.

(a) From Figure 2.11 we see that profit is zero when $Q = 0.5$ and $Q = 4$.

(b) By symmetry, the parabola reaches its maximum halfway between 0.5 and 4: that is, at

$$Q = \tfrac{1}{2}(0.5 + 4) = 2.25$$

   The corresponding profit is given by

$$\pi = -2(2.25)^2 + 9(2.25) - 4 = 6.125$$

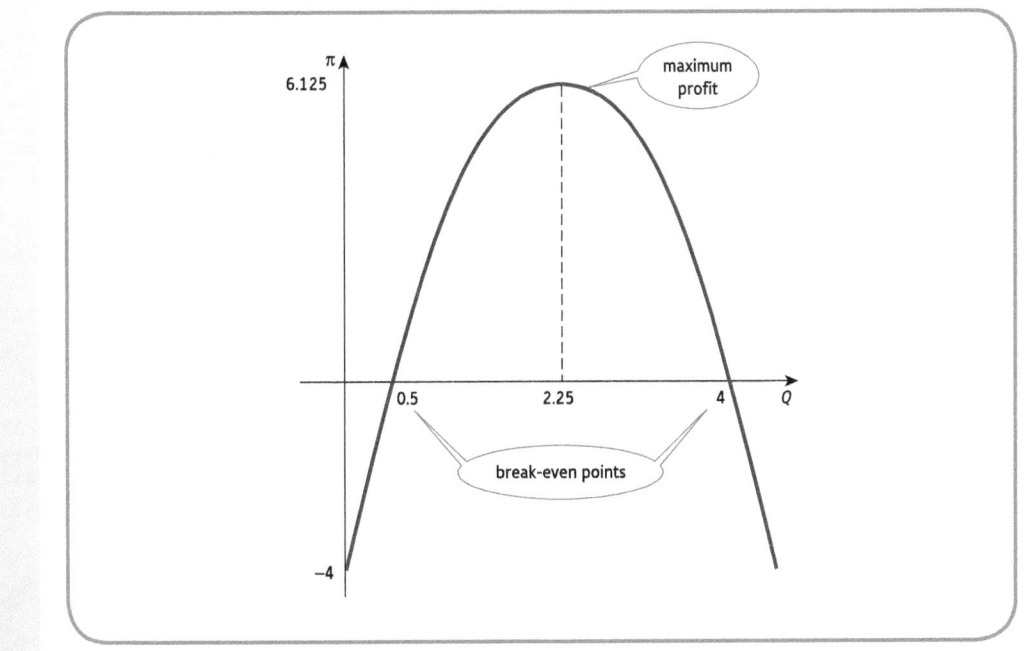

Figure 2.11

Advice

It is important to notice the use of brackets in the previous derivation of π. A common student mistake is to forget to include the brackets and just to write down

$\pi = TR - TC$

$= 10Q - 2Q^2 - 4 + Q$

$= -2Q^2 + 11Q - 4$

This cannot be right, since the whole of the total cost needs to be subtracted from the total revenue, not just the fixed costs. You might be surprised to learn that many economics students make this sort of blunder, particularly under examination conditions.

Practice Problem

3. If fixed costs are 25, variable costs per unit are 2 and the demand function is

$P = 20 - Q$

obtain an expression for π in terms of Q and hence sketch its graph.

(a) Find the levels of output which give a profit of 31.

(b) Find the maximum profit and the value of Q at which it is achieved.

Key Terms

Average cost   Total cost per unit of output: AC = TC/Q.

Fixed costs   Total costs that are independent of output.

L-shaped curve   A term used by economists to describe the graph of a function, such as $f(x) = a + \dfrac{b}{x}$, which bends roughly like the letter L.

Profit   Total revenue minus total cost: $\pi = TR - TC$.

Rectangular hyperbola   A term used by mathematicians to describe the graph of a function, such as $f(x) = a + \dfrac{b}{x}$, which is a hyperbola with horizontal and vertical asymptotes.

Total cost   The sum of the total variable and fixed costs: TC = TVC + FC.

Total revenue   A firm's total earnings from the sales of a good: TR = PQ.

Variable costs   Total costs that change according to the amount of output produced.

Exercise 2.2

1. **(a)** If the demand function of a good is given by

    $$P = 80 - 3Q$$

    find the price when $Q = 10$, and deduce the total revenue.

    (b) If fixed costs are 100 and variable costs are 5 per unit find the total cost when $Q = 10$.

    (c) Use your answers to parts (a) and (b) to work out the corresponding profit.

2. Given the following demand functions, express TR as a function of Q and hence sketch the graphs of TR against Q:

    (a) $P = 4$ **(b)** $P = 7/Q$ **(c)** $P = 10 - 4Q$

3. Given the following total revenue functions, find the corresponding demand functions:

    (a) TR = $50Q - 4Q^2$ **(b)** TR = 10

4. Given that fixed costs are 500 and that variable costs are 10 per unit, express TC and AC as functions of Q. Hence sketch their graphs.

5. Given that fixed costs are 1 and that variable costs are $Q + 1$ per unit, express TC and AC as functions of Q. Hence sketch their graphs.

6. The total cost, TC, of producing 100 units of a good is 600 and the total cost of producing 150 units is 850. Assuming that the total cost function is linear, find an expression for TC in terms of Q, the number of units produced.

7. The total cost of producing 500 items a day in a factory is $40 000, which includes a fixed cost of $2000.

    (a) Work out the variable cost per item.

    (b) Work out the total cost of producing 600 items a day.

8. A taxi firm charges a fixed cost of $10 together with a variable cost of $3 per mile.

(a) Work out the average cost per mile for a journey of 4 miles.

(b) Work out the minimum distance travelled if the average cost per mile is to be less than $3.25.

9. Find an expression for the profit function given the demand function

$$2Q + P = 25$$

and the average cost function

$$AC = \frac{32}{Q} + 5$$

Find the values of Q for which the firm

(a) breaks even

(b) makes a loss of 432 units

(c) maximises profit.

10. Sketch, on the same diagram, graphs of the total revenue and total cost functions,

$$TR = -2Q^2 + 14Q$$
$$TC = 2Q + 10$$

(1) Use your graphs to estimate the values of Q for which the firm

(a) breaks even

(b) maximises profit.

(2) Confirm your answers to part (1) using algebra.

11. The demand function for a firm's product is given by $P = 60 - Q$.
Fixed costs are 100, and the variable costs per good are $Q + 6$.

(a) Write down an expression for total revenue, TR, in terms of Q and sketch a graph of TR against Q, indicating clearly the intercepts with the coordinate axes.

(b) Write down an expression for total costs, TC, in terms of Q and deduce that the average cost function is given by

$$AC = Q + 6 + \frac{100}{Q}$$

Copy and complete the following table of function values:

Q	2	5	10	15	20
AC	58				

Draw an accurate graph of AC against Q and state the value of Q that minimises average cost.

(c) Show that the profit function is given by

$$\pi = 2(2 - Q)(Q - 25)$$

State the values of Q for which the firm breaks even and determine the maximum profit.

Exercise 2.2*

1. If fixed costs are 30, variable costs per unit are $Q + 3$, and the demand function is

    $$P + 2Q = 50$$

    show that the associated profit function is

    $$\pi = -3Q^2 + 47Q - 30.$$

    Find the break-even values of Q and deduce the maximum profit.

2. The profit function of a firm is of the form

    $$\pi = aQ^2 + bQ + c$$

    If it is known that $\pi = 9$, 34 and 19 when $Q = 1$, 2 and 3 respectively, write down a set of three simultaneous equations for the three unknowns, a, b and c. Solve this system to find a, b and c. Hence find the profit when $Q = 4$.

3. A firm's average cost function is given by

    $$AC = \frac{800}{Q} + 2Q + 18$$

    (a) Find, to the nearest whole number, the value of Q at the lowest point on the graph of AC plotted against Q, in the interval, $0 \le Q \le 30$.

    (b) State the value of the fixed costs.

4. If the demand equation is $aP + bQ = c$, fixed costs are d, and variable costs are e per unit, find expressions, in terms of Q, for each of the following economic functions:

    (a) total revenue   (b) total cost   (c) average cost   (d) profit

5. The Ennerdale Bank charges its customers for every withdrawal: $0.50 for each online transfer and $0.25 for each cash machine withdrawal. The North Borsetshire Bank charges customers a fixed annual charge of $15 and each debit (online or machine) costs a further $0.30. You may assume that there are no other withdrawals, that the account never goes overdrawn and that any interest due is negligible.

    (a) The proportion of withdrawals that are via online transfers is a and the total number of withdrawals made during the year is N. If the cost of operating the two accounts is the same, show that

    $$a = \frac{1}{5} + \frac{60}{N}$$

    Sketch the graph of this relationship.

    (b) What advice can you offer new customers if at least 60% of the customer's annual withdrawals are from cash machines?

SECTION 2.3
Indices and logarithms

Objectives

At the end of this section you should be able to:

- Evaluate b^n in the case when n is positive, negative, a whole number or a fraction.
- Simplify algebraic expressions using the rules of indices.
- Investigate the returns to scale of a production function.
- Evaluate logarithms in simple cases.
- Use the rules of logarithms to solve equations in which the unknown occurs as a power.

Advice

This section is quite long, with some important ideas. If you are comfortable using the rules of indices and already know what a logarithm is, you should be able to read through the material in one sitting, concentrating on the applications. However, if your current understanding is hazy (or non-existent), you should consider studying this topic on separate occasions. To help with this, the material in this section has been split into the following convenient sub-sections:

- index notation
- rules of indices
- logarithms
- summary.

2.3.1 Index notation

We have already used b^2 as an abbreviation for $b \times b$. In this section we extend the notation to b^n for any value of n, positive, negative, whole number or fraction. In general, if

$$M = b^n$$

we say that b^n is the **exponential form** of M to base b. The number n is then referred to as the **index, power** or **exponent**. An obvious way of extending

$$b^2 = b \times b$$

to other positive whole number powers, n, is to define

$$b^3 = b \times b \times b$$
$$b^4 = b \times b \times b \times b$$

and, in general,

$$b^n = b \times b \times b \times b \times \ldots \times b$$

a total of n
bs multiplied
together

To include the case of negative powers, consider the following table of values of 2^n:

2^{-3}	2^{-2}	2^{-1}	2^0	2^1	2^2	2^3	2^4
?	?	?	?	2	4	8	16

To work from left to right along the completed part of the table, all you have to do is to multiply each number by 2. Equivalently, if you work from right to left, you simply divide by 2. It makes sense to continue this pattern beyond $2^1 = 2$. Dividing this by 2 gives

$$2^0 = 2 \div 2 = 1$$

and dividing again by 2 gives

$$2^{-1} = 1 \div 2 = {}^1\!/_2$$

and so on. The completed table is then

2^{-3}	2^{-2}	2^{-1}	2^0	2^1	2^2	2^3	2^4
$\frac{1}{8}$	$\frac{1}{4}$	$\frac{1}{2}$	1	2	4	8	16

Notice that

$$2^{-1} = \frac{1}{2} = \frac{1}{2^1}$$

$$2^{-2} = \frac{1}{4} = \frac{1}{2^2}$$

$$2^{-3} = \frac{1}{8} = \frac{1}{2^3}$$

In other words, negative powers are evaluated by taking the reciprocal of the corresponding positive power. Motivated by this particular example, we define

$$b^0 = 1$$

and

$$b^{-n} = \frac{1}{b^n}$$

where n is any positive whole number.

Example

Evaluate

(a) 3^2 (b) 4^3 (c) 7^0 (d) 5^1 (e) 5^{-1}

(f) $(-2)^6$ (g) 3^{-4} (h) $(-2)^{-3}$ (i) $(1.723)^0$

Solution

Using the definitions

$$b^n = b \times b \times b \times \ldots \times b$$
$$b^0 = 1$$
$$b^{-n} = \frac{1}{b^n}$$

we obtain

(a) $3^2 = 3 \times 3 = 9$

(b) $4^3 = 4 \times 4 \times 4 = 64$

(c) $7^0 = 1$

because any number raised to the power of zero equals 1.

(d) $5^1 = 5$

(e) $5^{-1} = \dfrac{1}{5^1} = \dfrac{1}{5}$

(f) $(-2)^6 = (-2) \times (-2) \times (-2) \times (-2) \times (-2) \times (-2) = 64$

where the answer is positive because there are an even number of minus signs.

(g) $3^{-4} = \dfrac{1}{3^4} = \dfrac{1}{3 \times 3 \times 3 \times 3} = \dfrac{1}{81}$

(h) $(-2)^{-3} = \dfrac{1}{(-2)^3} = \dfrac{1}{(-2) \times (-2) \times (-2)} = -\dfrac{1}{8}$

where the answer is negative because there are an odd number of minus signs.

(i) $(1.723)^0 = 1$

Practice Problem

1. **(1)** Without using a calculator evaluate

   (a) 10^2 **(b)** 10^1 **(c)** 10^0 **(d)** 10^{-1} **(e)** 10^{-2} **(f)** $(-1)^{100}$

   (g) $(-1)^{99}$ **(h)** 7^{-3} **(i)** $(-9)^2$ **(j)** $(72\ 101)^1$ **(k)** $(2.718)^0$

   (2) Confirm your answer to part (1) using a calculator.

We handle fractional powers in two stages. We begin by defining b^m where m is a reciprocal such as $^1/_2$ or $^1/_8$ and then consider more general fractions such as $^3/_4$ or $^3/_8$ later. Assuming that n is a positive whole number, we define

$$b^{1/n} = n\text{th root of } b$$

By this we mean that $b^{1/n}$ is a number which, when raised to the power n, produces b. In symbols, if $c = b^{1/n}$ then $c^n = b$. Using this definition,

$$9^{1/2} = \text{square root of } 9 \quad = 3 \quad (\text{because } 3^2 = 9)$$
$$8^{1/3} = \text{cube root of } 8 \quad = 2 \quad (\text{because } 2^3 = 8)$$
$$625^{1/4} = \text{fourth root of } 625 \ = 5 \quad (\text{because } 5^4 = 625)$$

Of course, the nth root of a number may not exist. There is no number c satisfying $c^2 = -4$, for example, and so $(-4)^{1/2}$ is not defined. It is also possible for some numbers to have more than one nth root. For example, there are two values of c which satisfy $c^4 = 16$, namely $c = 2$ and $c = -2$. In these circumstances it is standard practice to take the positive root, so $16^{1/4} = 2$.

so replacing b by 10^2 we have

$$(10^2)^3 = 10^2 \times 10^2 \times 10^2 = (10 \times 10) \times (10 \times 10) \times (10 \times 10) = 10^6$$

because there are six 10s multiplied together: that is,

$$(10^2)^3 = 10^6 = 10^{2 \times 3}$$

This confirms rule 3, which tells you that if you take a 'power of a power', all you have to do is to multiply the indices.

Rule 4

Suppose we want to raise 2×3 to the power 4. By definition,

$$b^4 = b \times b \times b \times b$$

so replacing b by 2×3 gives

$$(2 \times 3)^4 = (2 \times 3) \times (2 \times 3) \times (2 \times 3) \times (2 \times 3)$$

and, because it does not matter in which order numbers are multiplied, this can be written as

$$(2 \times 2 \times 2 \times 2) \times (3 \times 3 \times 3 \times 3)$$

that is,

$$(2 \times 3)^4 = 2^4 \times 3^4$$

This confirms rule 4, which tells you that if you take the power of a product of two numbers, all you have to do is to take the power of each number separately and multiply.

A word of warning is in order regarding these laws. Notice that in rules 1 and 2 the bases of the numbers involved are the same. These rules do not apply if the bases are different. For example, rule 1 gives no information about

$$2^4 \times 3^5$$

Similarly, please notice that in rule 4 the numbers a and b are multiplied together. For some strange reason, some business and economics students seem to think that rule 4 also applies to addition, so that

$$(a + b)^n = a^n + b^n \qquad \text{This statement is NOT true}$$

It would make algebraic manipulation a whole lot easier if it were true, but I am afraid to say that it is definitely false! If you need convincing of this, note, for example, that

$$(1 + 2)^3 = 3^3 = 27$$

which is not the same as

$$1^3 + 2^3 = 1 + 8 = 9$$

One variation of rule 4 which is true is

$$\left(\frac{a}{b}\right)^n = \frac{a^n}{b^n} \quad (b \neq 0)$$

This is all right because division (unlike addition or subtraction) is the same sort of operation as multiplication. In fact,

$$\left(\frac{a}{b}\right)^n$$

can be thought of as

$$\left(a \times \frac{1}{b}\right)^n$$

so applying rule 4 to this product gives

$$a^n\left(\frac{1}{b}\right)^n = \frac{a^n}{b^n}$$

as required.

Advice

There might be occasions (such as in examinations!) when you only half remember a rule or perhaps think that you have discovered a brand new rule for yourself. If you are ever worried about whether some rule is legal or not, you should always check it out by trying numbers, just as we did for $(a + b)^n$. Obviously, one numerical example which actually works does not prove that the rule will always work. However, one example which fails is good enough to tell you that your supposed rule is rubbish.

The following example demonstrates how rules 1–4 are used to simplify algebraic expressions.

Example

Simplify

(a) $x^{1/4} \times x^{3/4}$ **(b)** $\dfrac{x^2 y^3}{x^4 y}$ **(c)** $(x^2 y^{-1/3})^3$

Solution

(a) The expression

$$x^{1/4} \times x^{3/4}$$

represents the product of two numbers in exponential form with the same base. From rule 1 we may add the indices to get

$$x^{1/4} \times x^{3/4} = x^{1/4+3/4} = x^1$$

which is just x.

(b) The expression

$$\frac{x^2 y^3}{x^4 y}$$

is more complicated than that in part (a) since it involves numbers in exponential form with two different bases, x and y. From rule 2,

$$\frac{x^2}{x^4}$$

may be simplified by subtracting indices to get

$$x^2 \div x^4 = x^{2-4} = x^{-2}$$

Similarly,

$$\frac{y^3}{y} = y^3 \div y^1 = y^{3-1} = y^2$$

Hence

$$\frac{x^2 y^3}{x^4 y} = x^{-2} y^2$$

It is not possible to simplify this any further, because x^{-2} and y^2 have different bases. However, if you prefer, this can be written as

$$\frac{y^2}{x^2}$$

because negative powers denote reciprocals.

(c) An obvious first step in the simplification of

$$(x^2 y^{-1/3})^3$$

is to apply rule 4, treating x^2 as the value of a and $y^{-1/3}$ as b to get

$$(x^2 y^{-1/3})^3 = (x^2)^3 (y^{-1/3})^3$$

Rule 3 then allows us to write

$$(x^2)^3 = x^{2 \times 3} = x^6$$
$$(y^{-1/3})^3 = y^{(-1/3) \times 3} = y^{-1}$$

Hence

$$(x^2 y^{-1/3})^3 = x^6 y^{-1}$$

As in part (b), if you think it looks neater, you can write this as

$$\frac{x^6}{y}$$

because negative powers denote reciprocals.

Practice Problem

3. Simplify

(a) $(x^{3/4})^8$ (b) $\dfrac{x^2}{x^{3/2}}$ (c) $(x^2 y^4)^3$ (d) $\sqrt{x}(x^{5/2} + y^3)$

[Hint: in part (d) note that $\sqrt{x} = x^{1/2}$ and multiply out the brackets.]

There are occasions throughout this book when we use the rules of indices and definitions of b^n. For the moment, we concentrate on one specific application where we see these ideas in action. The output, Q, of any production process depends on a variety of inputs, known as **factors of production**. These comprise land, capital, labour and enterprise. For simplicity we restrict our attention to capital and labour. **Capital**, K, denotes all man-made aids to production such as buildings, tools and plant machinery. **Labour**, L, denotes all paid work in the production process. The dependence of Q on K and L may be written

$$Q = f(K, L)$$

which is called a **production function**. Once this relationship is made explicit, in the form of a formula, it is straightforward to calculate the level of production from any given combination of inputs. For example, if

$$Q = 100K^{1/3}L^{1/2}$$

then the inputs $K = 27$ and $L = 100$ lead to an output

$$Q = 100(27)^{1/3}(100)^{1/2}$$
$$= 100(3)(10)$$
$$= 3000$$

Of particular interest is the effect on output when inputs are scaled in some way. If capital and labour both double, does the production level also double, does it go up by more than double or does it go up by less than double? For the particular production function,

$$Q = 100K^{1/3}L^{1/2}$$

we see that, when K and L are replaced by $2K$ and $2L$, respectively,

$$Q = 100(2K)^{1/3}(2L)^{1/2}$$

Now, by rule 4,

$$(2K)^{1/3} = 2^{1/3}K^{1/3} \text{ and } (2L)^{1/2} = 2^{1/2}L^{1/2}$$

so

$$Q = 100(2^{1/3}K^{1/3})(2^{1/2}L^{1/2})$$
$$= (2^{1/3}2^{1/2})(100K^{1/3}L^{1/2})$$

The second term, $100K^{1/3}L^{1/2}$, is just the original value of Q, so we see that the output is multiplied by

$$2^{1/3}2^{1/2}$$

Using rule 1, this number may be simplified by adding the indices to get

$$2^{1/3}2^{1/2} = 2^{5/6}$$

Moreover, because 5/6 is less than 1, the scale factor is smaller than 2. In fact, my calculator gives

$$2^{5/6} = 1.78 \text{ (to 2 decimal places)}$$

so output goes up by just less than double.

It is important to notice that the above argument does not depend on the particular value, 2, that is taken as the scale factor. Exactly the same procedure can be applied if the inputs, K and L, are scaled by a general number λ (where λ is a Greek letter pronounced 'lambda'). Replacing K and L by λK and λL respectively in the formula

$$Q = 100K^{1/3}L^{1/2}$$

gives

$$Q = 100(\lambda K)^{1/3}(\lambda L)^{1/2}$$
$$= 100\lambda^{1/3}K^{1/3}\lambda^{1/2}L^{1/2} \qquad \text{(rule 4)}$$
$$= (\lambda^{1/3}\lambda^{1/2})(100K^{1/3}L^{1/2})$$
$$= \lambda^{5/6}(100K^{1/3}L^{1/2}) \qquad \text{(rule 1)}$$

We see that the output gets scaled by $\lambda^{5/6}$, which is smaller than λ since the power, 5/6, is less than 1. We describe this by saying that the production function exhibits decreasing returns to scale.

In general, a function

$$Q = f(K, L)$$

is said to be **homogeneous** if

$$f(\lambda K, \lambda L) = \lambda^n f(K, L)$$

for some number, n. This means that when both variables K and L are multiplied by λ we can pull out all of the λs as a common factor, λ^n. The power, n, is called the **degree of homogeneity**. In the previous example we showed that

$$f(\lambda K, \lambda L) = \lambda^{5/6} f(K, L)$$

and so it is homogeneous of degree 5/6. In general, if the degree of homogeneity, n, satisfies:

- $n < 1$, the function is said to display **decreasing returns to scale**
- $n = 1$, the function is said to display **constant returns to scale**
- $n > 1$, the function is said to display **increasing returns to scale**.

Example

Show that the following production function is homogeneous and find its degree of homogeneity:

$$Q = 2K^{1/2}L^{3/2}$$

Does this function exhibit decreasing returns to scale, constant returns to scale or increasing returns to scale?

Solution

We are given that

$$f(K, L) = 2K^{1/2}L^{3/2}$$

so replacing K by λK and L by λL gives

$$f(\lambda K, \lambda L) = 2(\lambda K)^{1/2}(\lambda L)^{3/2}$$

We can pull out all of the λs by using rule 4 to get

$$2\lambda^{1/2}K^{1/2}\lambda^{3/2}L^{3/2}$$

and then use rule 1 to get

$$\lambda^2(2K^{1/2}L^{3/2})$$

$$\lambda^{1/2}\lambda^{3/2} = \lambda^{1/2+3/2}$$
$$= \lambda^2$$

We have therefore shown that

$$f(\lambda K, \lambda L) = \lambda^2 f(K, L)$$

and so the function is homogeneous of degree 2. Moreover, since $2 > 1$ we deduce that it has increasing returns to scale.

Practice Problem

4. Show that the following production functions are homogeneous and comment on their returns to scale:

(a) $Q = 7KL^2$ (b) $Q = 50K^{1/4}L^{3/4}$

You may well have noticed that all of the production functions considered so far are of the form

$$Q = AK^{\alpha}L^{\beta}$$

for some positive constants, A, α and β. (The Greek letters α and β are pronounced 'alpha' and 'beta' respectively.) Such functions are called **Cobb–Douglas production functions**. It is easy to see that they are homogeneous of degree $\alpha + \beta$ because if

$$f(K, L) = AK^{\alpha}L^{\beta}$$

then

$$\begin{aligned} f(\lambda K, \lambda L) &= A(\lambda K)^{\alpha}(\lambda L)^{\beta} \\ &= A\lambda^{\alpha}K^{\alpha}\lambda^{\beta}L^{\beta} && \text{(rule 4)} \\ &= \lambda^{\alpha+\beta}(AK^{\alpha}L^{\beta}) && \text{(rule 1)} \\ &= \lambda^{\alpha+\beta}f(K, L) \end{aligned}$$

Consequently, Cobb–Douglas production functions exhibit

- decreasing returns to scale, if $\alpha + \beta < 1$
- constant returns to scale, if $\alpha + \beta = 1$
- increasing returns to scale, if $\alpha + \beta > 1$.

By the way, not all production functions are of this type. Indeed, it is not even necessary for a production function to be homogeneous. Some examples illustrating these cases are given in Question 5 in Exercise 2.3 at the end of this section. We shall return to the topic of production functions in Chapter 5.

2.3.3 Logarithms

At the beginning of this section we stated that if a number, M, is expressed as

$$M = b^n$$

Example

Use the rules of logarithms to express each of the following as a single logarithm:

(a) $\log_b x + \log_b y - \log_b z$ **(b)** $2\log_b x - 3\log_b y$

Solution

(a) The first rule of logs shows that the *sum* of two logs can be written as the log of a *product*, so

$$\log_b x + \log_b y - \log_b z = \log_b(xy) - \log_b z$$

Also, according to rule 2, the *difference* of two logs is the log of a *quotient*, so we can simplify further to get

$$\log_b\left(\frac{xy}{z}\right)$$

(b) Given any combination of logs such as

$$2\log_b x - 3\log_b y$$

the trick is to use the third rule to 'get rid' of the coefficients. Since

$$2\log_b x = \log_b x^2 \quad \text{and} \quad 3\log_b y = \log_b y^3$$

we see that

$$2\log_b x - 3\log_b y = \log_b x^2 - \log_b y^3$$

Only now can we use the second rule of logs, which allows us to write the expression as the single logarithm

$$\log_b\left(\frac{x^2}{y^3}\right)$$

Practice Problem

6. Use the rules of logs to express each of the following as a single logarithm:

(a) $\log_b x - \log_b y + \log_b z$ **(b)** $4\log_b x + 2\log_b y$

Before we continue with this topic a word of warning is in order. Be careful to learn the rules of logs correctly. A common mistake is to misread rule 1 as

$$\log_b(x + y) = \log_b x + \log_b y \qquad \text{This is NOT true}$$

Remember that logs are just a posh way of thinking about indices and it is when you *multiply* numbers together that you end up adding the indices, so the correct version has to be

$$\log_b(xy) = \log_b x + \log_b y$$

Example

Find the value of x which satisfies

(a) $200(1.1)^x = 20\,000$ **(b)** $5^x = 2(3)^x$

Solution

(a) An obvious first step in the solution of

$$200(1.1)^x = 20\,000$$

is to divide both sides by 200 to get

$$(1.1)^x = 100$$

In Chapter 1 it was pointed out that we can do whatever we like to an equation, provided that we do the same thing to both sides. In particular, we may take logarithms of both sides to get

$$\log(1.1)^x = \log(100)$$

Now by rule 3 we have

$$\log(1.1)^x = x \log(1.1)$$

so the equation becomes

$$x \log(1.1) = \log(100)$$

Notice the effect that rule 3 has on the equation. It brings the unknown down to the same level as the rest of the expression. This is the whole point of taking logarithms, since it converts an equation in which the unknown appears as a power into one which can be solved using familiar algebraic methods. Dividing both sides of the equation

$$x \log(1.1) = \log(100)$$

by $\log(1.1)$ gives

$$x = \frac{\log(100)}{\log(1.1)}$$

So far no mention has been made of the base of the logarithm. The above equation for x is true no matter what base is used. It makes sense to use logarithms to base 10 because all scientific calculators have this facility as one of their function keys. Using base 10, my calculator gives

$$x = \frac{\log(100)}{\log(1.1)} = \frac{2}{0.041\,395\,685} = 48.32$$

> check this using
> your own calculator

to 2 decimal places.

As a check, if this number is substituted back into the original equation, then

$$200(1.1)^x = 200(1.1)^{48.32} = 20\,004 \quad \checkmark$$

We cannot expect to obtain the exact answer, because we rounded x to only two decimal places.

(b) To solve

$$5^x = 2(3)^x$$

we take logarithms of both sides to get

$$\log(5^x) = \log(2 \times 3^x)$$

The right-hand side is the logarithm of a product and, according to rule 1, can be written as the sum of the logarithms, so the equation becomes

$$\log(5^x) = \log(2) + \log(3^x)$$

As in part (a) the key step is to use rule 3 to 'bring down the powers'. If rule 3 is applied to both $\log(5^x)$ and $\log(3^x)$ then the equation becomes

$$x \log(5) = \log(2) + x \log(3)$$

This is now the type of equation that we know how to solve. We collect x's on the left-hand side to get

$$x \log(5) - x \log(3) = \log(2)$$

and then pull out a common factor of x to get

$$x[\log(5) - \log(3)] = \log(2)$$

Now, by rule 2, the difference of two logarithms is the same as the logarithm of their quotient, so

$$\log(5) - \log(3) = \log(5 \div 3)$$

Hence the equation becomes

$$x \log\left(\frac{5}{3}\right) = \log(2)$$

so

$$x = \frac{\log(2)}{\log(5/3)}$$

Finally, taking logarithms to base 10 using a calculator gives

$$x = \frac{0.301\,029\,996}{0.221\,848\,750} = 1.36$$

to 2 decimal places.

As a check, the original equation

$$5^x = 2(3)^x$$

becomes

$$5^{1.36} = 2(3)^{1.36}$$

that is,

$$8.92 = 8.91 \quad \checkmark$$

Again the slight discrepancy is due to rounding errors in the value of x.

Key Terms

Capital   Man-made assets used in the production of goods and services.

Cobb–Douglas production function   A production function of the form: $Q = AK^{\alpha}L^{\beta}$.

Constant returns to scale   Exhibited by a production function when a given percentage increase in input leads to the same percentage increase in output: $f(\lambda K, \lambda L) = \lambda f(K, L)$.

Decreasing returns to scale   Exhibited by a production function when a given percentage increase in input leads to a smaller percentage increase in output: $f(\lambda K, \lambda L) = \lambda^n f(K, L)$ where $0 < n < 1$.

Degree of homogeneity   The number n in the relation $f(\lambda K, \lambda L) = \lambda^n f(K, L)$.

Exponent   A superscript attached to a variable; the number 5 is the exponent in the expression, $2x^5$.

Exponential form   A representation of a number which is written using powers. For example, 2^5 is the exponential form of the number 32.

Factors of production   The inputs into the production of goods and services: labour, land, capital and raw materials.

Homogeneous function   A function with the property that when all of the inputs are multiplied by a constant, λ, the output is multiplied by λ^n where n is the degree of homogeneity.

Increasing returns to scale   Exhibited by a production function when a given percentage increase in input leads to a larger percentage increase in output: $f(\lambda K, \lambda L) = \lambda^n f(K, L)$ where $n > 1$.

Index   Another word for exponent.

Labour   All forms of human input to the production process.

Logarithm   The power to which a base must be raised to yield a particular number.

Power   Another word for exponent. If this is a positive integer then it gives the number of times a number is multiplied by itself.

Production function   The relationship between the output of a good and the inputs used to produce it.

Exercise 2.3

1. (1) Without using your calculator evaluate

    (a) 8^2 (b) 2^1 (c) 3^{-1} (d) 17^0 (e) $1^{1/5}$ (f) $36^{1/2}$ (g) $8^{2/3}$ (h) $49^{-3/2}$

    (2) Confirm your answer to part (1) using a calculator.

2. Use the rules of indices to simplify

    (a) $a^3 \times a^8$ (b) $\dfrac{b^7}{b^2}$ (c) $(c^2)^3$ (d) $\dfrac{x^4 y^5}{x^2 y^3}$ (e) $(xy^2)^3$

    (f) $y^3 \div y^7$ (g) $(x^{1/2})^8$ (h) $f^2 \times f^4 \times f$ (i) $\sqrt{(y^6)}$ (j) $\dfrac{x^3}{x^{-2}}$

3. Write the following expressions using index notation

    (a) $\sqrt{x}$ (b) $\dfrac{1}{x^2}$ (c) $\sqrt[3]{x}$ (d) $\dfrac{1}{x}$ (e) $\dfrac{1}{\sqrt{x}}$ (f) $x\sqrt{x}$

4. For the production function, $Q = 200K^{1/4}L^{2/3}$ find the output when

    (a) $K = 16, L = 27$ (b) $K = 10\ 000, L = 1000$

5. Which of the following production functions are homogeneous? For those functions which are homogeneous write down their degrees of homogeneity and comment on their returns to scale.

Practice Problem

7. Solve the following equations for x:

(a) $3^x = 7$ (b) $5(2)^x = 10^x$

Advice

In this section we have met a large number of definitions and rules concerning indices and logarithms. For convenience, we have collected these together in the form of a summary. The facts relating to indices are particularly important and you should make every effort to memorise these before proceeding with the rest of this book.

2.3.4 Summary

Indices

If n is a positive whole number then

$$b^n = b \times b \times \ldots \times b$$
$$b^0 = 1$$
$$b^{-n} = 1/b^n$$
$$b^{1/n} = n\text{th root of } b$$

Also, if p and q are whole numbers with $q > 0$ then

$$b^{p/q} = (b^p)^{1/q} = (b^{1/q})^p$$

The four rules of indices are:

Rule 1 $b^m \times b^n = b^{m+n}$

Rule 2 $b^m \div b^n = b^{m-n}$

Rule 3 $(b^m)^n = b^{mn}$

Rule 4 $(ab)^n = a^n b^n$

Logarithms

If $M = b^n$ then $n = \log_b M$. The three rules of logarithms are:

Rule 1 $\log_b(x \times y) = \log_b x + \log_b y$

Rule 2 $\log_b(x \div y) = \log_b x - \log_b y$

Rule 3 $\log_b x^m = m \log_b x$

(a) $Q = 500K^{1/3}L^{1/4}$

(b) $Q = 3LK + L^2$

(c) $Q = L + 5L^2K^3$

6. Write down the values of x which satisfy each of the following equations:

   (a) $5^x = 25$ (b) $3^x = \dfrac{1}{3}$ (c) $2^x = \dfrac{1}{8}$

   (d) $2^x = 64$ (e) $100^x = 10$ (f) $8^x = 1$

7. Write down the value of

   (a) $\log_b b^2$ (b) $\log_b b$ (c) $\log_b 1$ (d) $\log_b \sqrt{b}$ (e) $\log_b(1/b)$

8. Use the rules of logs to express each of the following as a single log:

   (a) $\log_b x + \log_b z$

   (b) $3\log_b x - 2\log_b y$

   (c) $\log_b y - 3\log_b z$

9. Express the following in terms of $\log_b x$ and $\log_b y$:

   (a) $\log_b x^2 y$

   (b) $\log_b\left(\dfrac{x}{y^2}\right)$

   (c) $\log_b x^2 y^7$

10. Solve the following equations for x. Give your answers to 2 decimal places.

    (a) $5^x = 8$ (b) $10^x = 50$ (c) $1.2^x = 3$ (d) $1000 \times 1.05^x = 1500$

11. (1) State the values of

    (a) $\log_2 32$ (b) $\log_9\left(\dfrac{1}{3}\right)$

    (2) Use the rules of logs to express

    $\quad 2\log_b x - 4\log_b y$

    as a single logarithm.

    (3) Use logs to solve the equation

    $\quad 10(1.05)^x = 300$

    Give your answer correct to 1 decimal place.

12. (1) State the values of x that satisfy the following equations:

    (a) $81 = 3^x$ (b) $\dfrac{1}{25} = 5^x$ (c) $16^{1/2} = 2^x$

    (2) Use the rules of indices to simplify:

    (a) $\dfrac{x^6 y^9}{x^3 y^8}$ (b) $(x^3 y)^5$ (c) $\sqrt{\dfrac{x^9 y^4}{x^5}}$

13. The number of complaints, N, received by a small company each month can be modelled by

$$N = 80\log_{10}(7 + 10t)$$

where t denotes the number of months since the company's launch.

(a) Estimate the number of complaints received by the company each month for the first six months of trading.

(b) Plot a graph of N against t and hence comment on how N varies with t.

14. If two firms A and B use the same labour input, L, their output in the short-term is given by $Q_A = 108\sqrt{L}$ and $Q_B = 4L^2$, respectively. Find the non-zero value of L which produces the same level of output for these two firms.

Exercise 2.3*

1. **(1)** Evaluate the following without using a calculator

   (a) $32^{3/5}$ **(b)** $64^{-5/6}$ **(c)** $\left(\dfrac{1}{125}\right)^{-4/3}$ **(d)** $\left(3\dfrac{3}{8}\right)^{2/3}$ **(e)** $\left(2\dfrac{1}{4}\right)^{-1/2}$

   (2) Confirm your answer to part (1) using a calculator.

2. Use the rules of indices to simplify

   (a) $y^{3/2} \times y^{1/2}$ **(b)** $\dfrac{x^2 y}{xy^{-1}}$ **(c)** $(xy^{1/2})^4$

   (d) $(p^2)^{1/3} \div (p^{1/3})^2$ **(e)** $(24q)^{1/3} \div (3q)^{1/3}$ **(f)** $(25p^2q^4)^{1/2}$

3. Write the following expressions using index notation

   (a) $\dfrac{1}{x^7}$ **(b)** $\sqrt[4]{x}$ **(c)** $\dfrac{1}{x\sqrt{x}}$ **(d)** $2x^5\sqrt{x}$ **(e)** $\dfrac{8}{x(\sqrt[3]{x})}$

4. If $a = \dfrac{2\sqrt{x}}{y^3}$ and $b = 3x^4y$, simplify $\dfrac{4b}{a^2}$

5. Show that the production function

   $$Q = A[bK^\alpha + (1 - b)L^\alpha]^{1/\alpha}$$

   is homogeneous and displays constant returns to scale.

6. Solve the following equations:

   (a) $2^{3x} = 4$ **(b)** $4 \times 2^x = 32$ **(c)** $8^x = 2 \times \left(\dfrac{1}{2}\right)^x$

7. Use the rules of logs to express each of the following as a single log:

   (a) $\log_b(xy) - \log_b x - \log_b y$

   (b) $3\log_b x - 2\log_b y$

   (c) $\log_b y + 5\log_b x - 2\log_b z$

   (d) $2 + 3\log_b x$

8. Express the following in terms of $\log_b x$, $\log_b y$ and $\log_b z$:

(a) $\log_b(x^2y^3z^4)$ (b) $\log_b\left(\dfrac{x^4}{y^2z^5}\right)$ (c) $\log_b\left(\dfrac{x}{\sqrt{yz}}\right)$

9. If $\log_b 2 = p$, $\log_b 3 = q$ and $\log_b 10 = r$, express the following in terms of p, q and r:

(a) $\log_b\left(\dfrac{1}{3}\right)$ (b) $\log_b 12$ (c) $\log_b 0.000\,3$ (d) $\log_b 600$

10. Solve the following equations. Round your answers to 2 decimal places.

(a) $10(1.07)^x = 2000$ (b) $10^{x-1} = 3$ (c) $5^{x-2} = 5$ (d) $2(7)^{-x} = 3^x$

11. Solve the inequalities giving the bounds to 3 decimal places:

(a) $3^{2x+1} \le 7$ (b) $0.8^x < 0.04$

12. Solve the equation

$$\log_{10}(x+2) + \log_{10}x - 1 = \log_{10}\left(\frac{3}{2}\right)$$

13. (1) Define the term *homogeneous* when used to describe a production function $f(K, L)$.

(2) If the production function

$$f(K, L) = 4K^mL^{1/3} + 3K$$

is homogeneous, state the value of m.

Does the function display decreasing, constant or increasing returns to scale?

14. (1) State the values of x that satisfy the following equations:

(a) $4 = 8^x$ (b) $5 = \left(\dfrac{1}{25}\right)^x$

(2) Express y in terms of x:

$$2\log_a x = \log_a 7 + \log_a y$$

15. Show that $2\log_{10}x - \dfrac{1}{2}\log_{10}y - \dfrac{1}{3}\log_{10}1000$ can be simplified to

$$\log_{10}\left(\sqrt{\frac{x^4}{y}}\right) - 1$$

16. Transpose each of the following production functions for L:

(a) $Q = AK^{\alpha}L^{\beta}$ (b) $Q = A[bK^{\alpha} + (1 - b)L^{\alpha}]^{1/\alpha}$

17. Show that each of these functions is homogeneous and state the degree of homogeneity:

(a) $f(K,L) = \dfrac{K^2 + L^2}{K + L}$

(b) $f(K,L) = KL\ln\left(\dfrac{K^2 + L^2}{KL}\right)$

(c) $f(K,L) = A[aK^m + bL^m]^{n/m}$

(d) $f(K,L) = KL^2 g(L/K)$ where g is a general function.

SECTION 2.4
The exponential and natural logarithm functions

Objectives

At the end of this section you should be able to:

- Sketch graphs of general exponential functions.
- Understand how the number e is defined.
- Use the exponential function to model growth and decay.
- Use log graphs to find unknown parameters in simple models.
- Use the natural logarithm function to solve equations.

In the previous section we described how to define numbers of the form b^x, and discussed the idea of a logarithm, $\log_b x$. It turns out that there is one base (the number e = 2.718 281 . . .) that is particularly important in mathematics. The purpose of this present section is to introduce you to this strange number and to consider a few simple applications.

We begin by investigating the graphs of the functions,

$$f(x) = 2^x \quad \text{and} \quad g(x) = 2^{-x}$$

As we pointed out in Section 2.3, a number such as 2^x is said to be in exponential form. The number 2 is called the base and x is called the exponent. Values of this function are easily found either by pressing the power key x^y on a calculator or by using the definition of b^n given in Section 2.3. A selection of these is given in the following table:

x	−3	−2	−1	0	1	2	3	4	5
2^x	0.125	0.25	0.5	1	2	4	8	16	32

A graph of $f(x)$ based on this table is sketched in Figure 2.12. Notice that the graph approaches the x axis for large negative values of x and it rises rapidly as x increases.

A graph of the negative exponential, $g(x) = 2^{-x}$, shown in Figure 2.13 is based on the following table of values:

x	−5	−4	−3	−2	−1	0	1	2	3
2^{-x}	32	16	8	4	2	1	0.5	0.25	0.125

This function is sketched in Figure 2.13. It is worth noticing that the numbers appearing in the table of 2^{-x} are the same as those of 2^x but arranged in reverse order. Hence the graph of 2^{-x} is obtained by reflecting the graph of 2^x in the y axis.

Figure 2.12 displays the graph of a particular exponential function, 2^x. Quite generally, the graph of any exponential function

$$f(x) = b^x$$

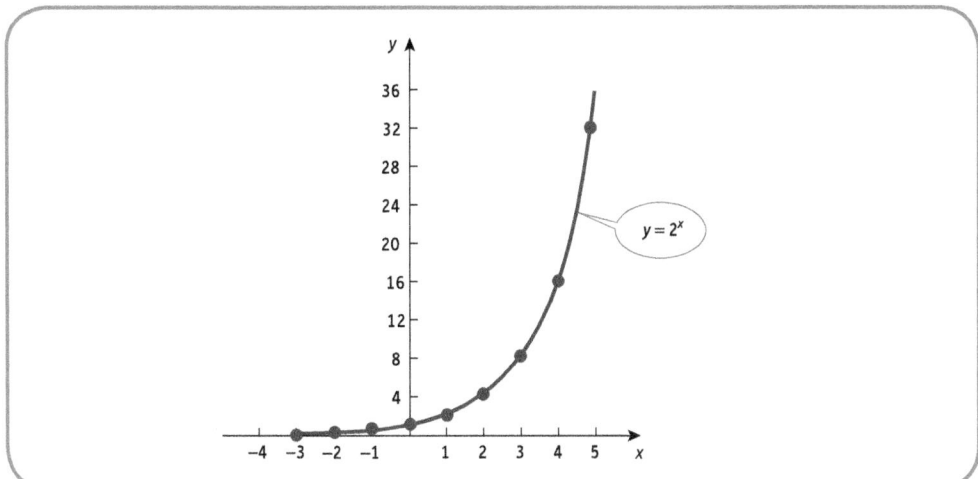

Figure 2.12

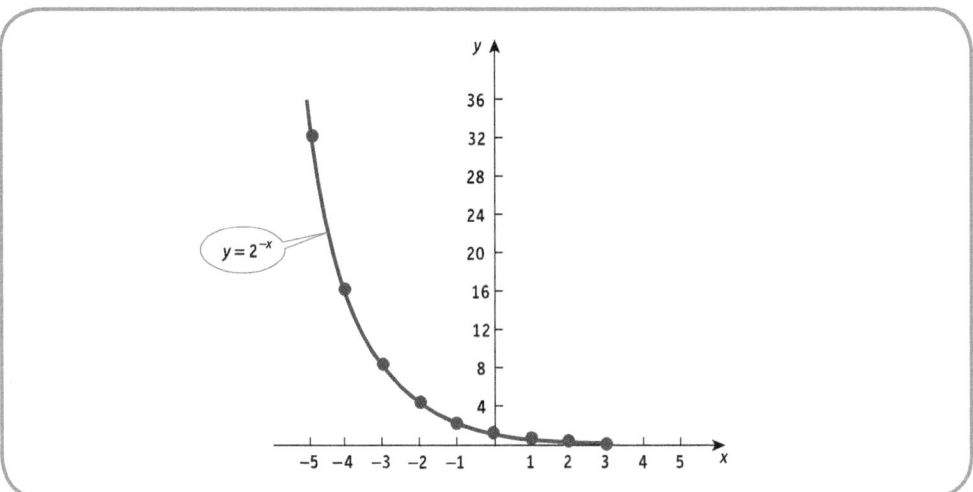

Figure 2.13

has the same basic shape provided $b > 1$. The only difference is that larger values of b produce steeper curves. A similar comment applies to the negative exponential, b^{-x}.

Practice Problem

1. Complete the following table of function values of 3^x and 3^{-x} and hence sketch their graphs.

x	-3	-2	-1	0	1	2	3
3^x							
3^{-x}							

Obviously there is a whole class of functions, each corresponding to a different base, b. Of particular interest is the case when b takes the value

2.718 281 828 459 . . .

This number is written as e and the function

$$f(x) = e^x$$

is referred to as *the* **exponential function**. In fact, it is not necessary for you to understand where this number comes from. All scientific calculators have an e^x button and you may simply wish to accept the results of using it. However, it might help your confidence if you have some appreciation of how it is defined. To this end, consider the following example and subsequent problem.

Example

Evaluate the expression

$$\left(1+\frac{1}{m}\right)^m$$

where $m = 1, 10, 100$ and 1000, and comment briefly on the behaviour of this sequence.

Solution

Substituting the values $m = 1, 10, 100$ and 1000 into

$$\left(1+\frac{1}{m}\right)^m$$

gives

$$\left(1+\frac{1}{1}\right)^1 = 2^1 = 2$$

$$\left(1+\frac{1}{10}\right)^{10} = (1.1)^{10} = 2.593\,742\,460$$

$$\left(1+\frac{1}{100}\right)^{100} = (1.01)^{100} = 2.704\,813\,829$$

$$\left(1+\frac{1}{1000}\right)^{1000} = (1.001)^{1000} = 2.716\,923\,932$$

The numbers are clearly getting bigger as m increases. However, the rate of increase appears to be slowing down, suggesting that numbers are converging to some fixed value.

The following problem gives you an opportunity to continue the sequence and to discover for yourself the limiting value.

Practice Problem

2. (a) Use the power key x^y on your calculator to evaluate

$$\left(1+\frac{1}{m}\right)^m$$

where $m = 10\ 000$, $100\ 000$ and $1\ 000\ 000$.

(b) Use your calculator to evaluate e^1 and compare with your answer to part (a).

Hopefully, the results of Practice Problem 2 should convince you that as m gets larger, the value of

$$\left(1+\frac{1}{m}\right)^m$$

approaches a limiting value of $2.718\ 281\ 828\ldots$, which we choose to denote by the letter e. In symbols we write

$$e = \lim_{m\to\infty}\left(1+\frac{1}{m}\right)^m$$

The significance of this number can only be fully appreciated in the context of calculus, which we study in Chapter 4. However, it is useful at this stage to consider some preliminary examples. These will give you practice in using the e^x button on your calculator and will give you some idea how this function can be used in modelling.

Advice

The number e has a similar status in mathematics as the number π and is just as useful. It arises in the mathematics of finance, which we discuss in the next chapter. You might like to glance through Section 3.2 now if you need convincing of the usefulness of e.

Example

The percentage, y, of households possessing refrigerators, t years after they have been introduced in a developed country, is modelled by

$$y = 100 - 95e^{-0.15t}$$

(1) Find the percentage of households that have refrigerators

   (a) at their launch

   (b) after 1 year

   (c) after 10 years

   (d) after 20 years.

(2) What is the market saturation level?

(3) Sketch a graph of y against t and hence give a qualitative description of the growth of refrigerator ownership over time.

Solution

(1) To calculate the percentage of households possessing refrigerators now and in 1, 10 and 20 years' time, we substitute $t = 0, 1, 10$ and 20 into the formula

$$y = 100 - 95e^{-0.15t}$$

to get

(a) $y(0) = 100 - 95e^0 = 5\%$

(b) $y(1) = 100 - 95e^{-0.15} = 18\%$

(c) $y(10) = 100 - 95e^{-1.5} = 79\%$

(d) $y(20) = 100 - 95e^{-3.0} = 95\%$

check these numbers
on your own calculator

(2) To find the saturation level we need to investigate what happens to y as t gets ever larger. We know that the graph of a negative exponential function has the basic shape shown in Figure 2.13. Consequently, the value of $e^{-0.15t}$ will eventually approach zero as t increases. The market saturation level is therefore given by

$$y = 100 - 95(0) = 100\%$$

(3) A graph of y against t, based on the information obtained in parts (1) and (2), is sketched in Figure 2.14.

This shows that y grows rapidly to begin with, but slows down as the market approaches saturation level. An economic variable which increases over time but approaches a fixed value like this is said to display **limited growth**. A saturation level of 100% indicates that eventually all households are expected to possess refrigerators, which is not surprising given the nature of the product.

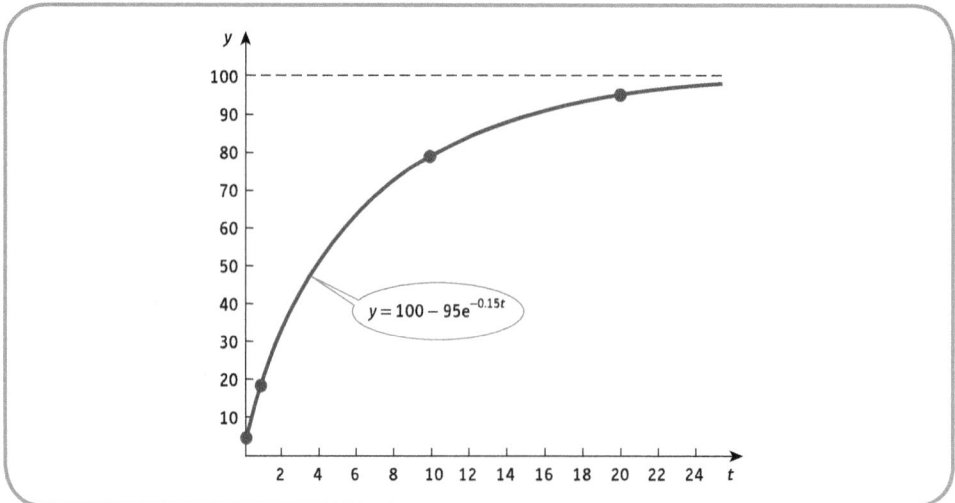

Figure 2.14

Practice Problem

3. The percentage, y, of households possessing microwave ovens t years after they have been launched is modelled by

$$y = \frac{55}{1 + 800e^{-0.3t}}$$

(1) Find the percentage of households that have microwaves

   (a) at their launch
   (b) after 10 years
   (c) after 20 years
   (d) after 30 years.

(2) What is the market saturation level?

(3) Sketch a graph of y against t and hence give a qualitative description of the growth of microwave ownership over time.

In Section 2.3 we noted that if a number M can be expressed as b^n then n is called the logarithm of M to base b. In particular, for base e,

   if $M = e^n$ then $n = \log_e M$

We call logarithms to base e **natural logarithms**. These occur sufficiently frequently to warrant their own notation. Rather than writing $\log_e M$ we simply put $\ln M$ instead. The three rules of logs can then be stated as

$$\textit{Rule 1} \quad \ln(x \times y) = \ln x + \ln y$$
$$\textit{Rule 2} \quad \ln(x \div y) = \ln x - \ln y$$
$$\textit{Rule 3} \quad \ln x^m = m \ln x$$

Example

Use the rules of logs to express

(a) $\ln\left(\dfrac{x}{\sqrt{y}}\right)$ in terms of $\ln x$ and $\ln y$

(b) $3 \ln p + \ln q - 2 \ln r$ as a single logarithm.

Solution

(a) In this part we need to 'expand', so we read the rules of logs from left to right:

$$\ln\left(\frac{x}{\sqrt{y}}\right) = \ln x - \ln\sqrt{y} \qquad \text{(rule 2)}$$

$$= \ln x - \ln y^{1/2} \qquad \text{(fractional powers denote roots)}$$

$$= \ln x - \frac{1}{2}\ln y \qquad \text{(rule 3)}$$

Example

The values of GNP, g, measured in billions of dollars, over a period of t years was observed to be

t (years)	2	5	10	20
g (billions of dollars)	12	16	27	74

Model the growth of GNP using a formula of the form

$$g = Be^{At}$$

for appropriate values of A and B. Hence estimate the value of GNP after 15 years.

Solution

Figure 2.15 shows the four points plotted with g on the vertical axis and t on the horizontal axis. The basic shape of the curve joining these points certainly suggests that an exponential function is likely to provide a reasonable model, but it gives no information about what values to use for the parameters A and B. However, since one of the unknown parameters, A, occurs as a power in the relation

$$g = Be^{At}$$

it is a good idea to take natural logs of both sides to get

$$\ln g = \ln(Be^{At})$$

The rules of logs enable us to expand the right-hand side to get

$$\ln(Be^{At}) = \ln B + \ln(e^{At}) \quad \text{(rule 1)}$$
$$= \ln B + At \quad \text{(definition of a log to base e)}$$

Hence

$$\ln g = At + \ln B$$

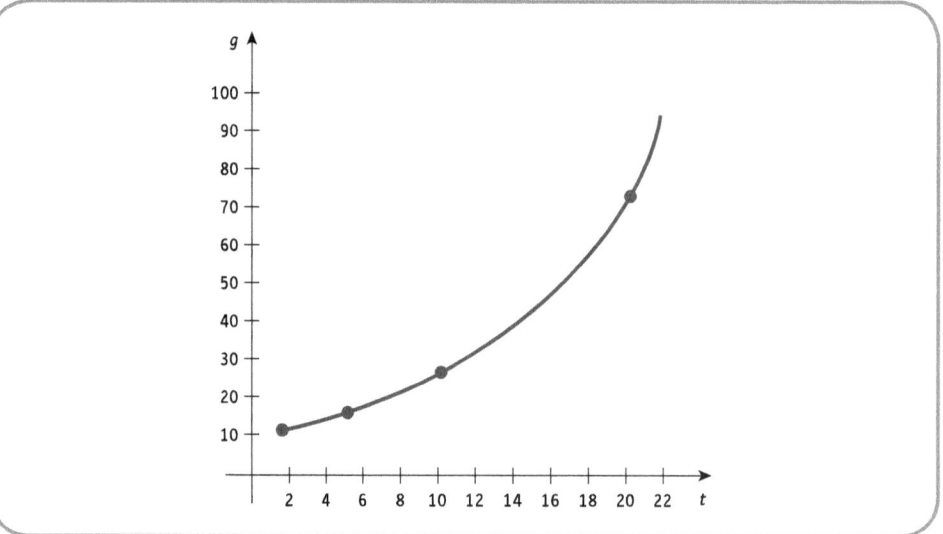

Figure 2.15

Although this does not look like it at first sight, this relation is actually the equation of a straight line! To see this recall that the usual equation of a line is $y = ax + b$. The log equation is indeed of this form if we put

$$y = \ln g \quad \text{and} \quad x = t$$

The equation then becomes

$$y = Ax + \ln B$$

so a graph of $\ln g$ plotted on the vertical axis with t plotted on the horizontal axis should produce a straight line with slope A and with an intercept on the vertical axis of $\ln B$.

Figure 2.16 shows this graph based on the table of values

$x = t$	2	5	10	20
$y = \ln g$	2.48	2.77	3.30	4.30

As one might expect, the points do not exactly lie on a straight line, since the formula is only a model. However, the line sketched in Figure 2.16 is a remarkably good fit. The slope can be calculated as

$$A = \frac{4 - 3}{18.6 - 7.6} = 0.09$$

and the vertical intercept can be read off the graph as 2.25. This is $\ln B$ and so

$$B = e^{2.25} = 9.49$$

Hence the formula for the approximate relation between g and t is

$$g = 9.49e^{0.09t}$$

An estimate of the GNP after 15 years can be obtained by substituting $t = 15$ into this formula to get

$$g = 36.6 \quad \text{(billion dollars)}$$

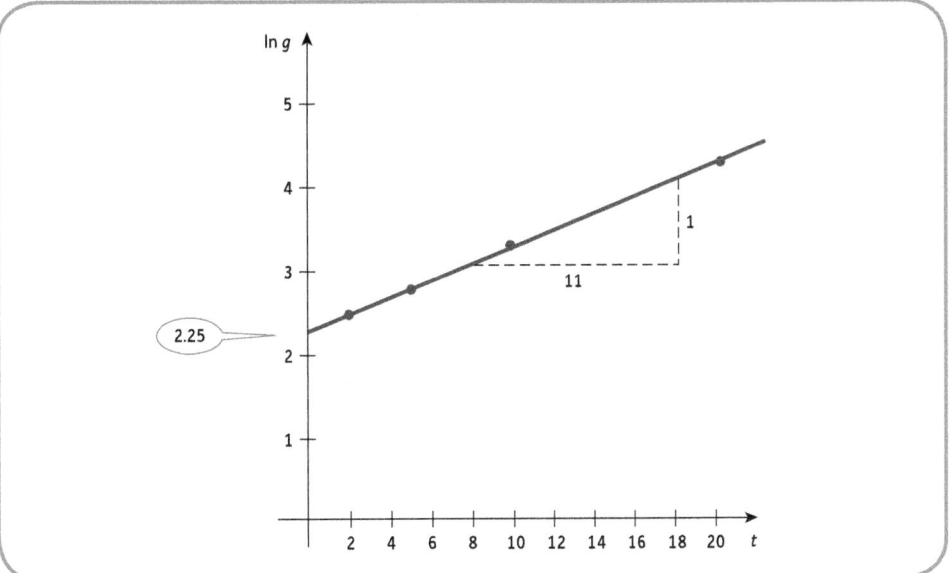

Figure 2.16

Practice Problem

6. Immediately after the launch of a new product, the monthly sales figures (in thousands) are as follows:

t (months)	1	3	6	12
s (sales)	1.8	2.7	5.0	16.5

(1) Complete the following table of values of ln s:

t	1	3	6	12
ln s	0.59		1.61	

(2) Plot these points on graph paper with the values of ln s on the vertical axis and t on the horizontal axis. Draw a straight line passing close to these points. Write down the value of the vertical intercept and calculate the slope.

(3) Use your answers to part (2) to estimate the values of A and B in the relation $s = Be^{At}$.

(4) Use the exponential model derived in part (3) to estimate the sales when

(a) $t = 9$ (b) $t = 60$

Which of these estimates would you expect to be the more reliable? Give a reason for your answer.

Key Terms

Exponential function   The function, $f(x) = e^x$; an exponential function in which the base is the number e = 2.718 281....

Limited growth   Used to describe an economic variable which increases over time but which tends to a fixed quantity.

Natural logarithm   A logarithm to base e; if $M = e^n$ then n is the natural logarithm of M and we write, $n = \ln M$.

Unlimited growth   Used to describe an economic variable which increases without bound.

Exercise 2.4

1. The number of items, N, produced each day by an assembly-line worker, t days after an initial training period, is modelled by

$$N = 100 - 100e^{-0.4t}$$

(1) Calculate the number of items produced daily

(a) 1 day after the training period

(b) 2 days after the training period

(c) 10 days after the training period.

(2) What is the worker's daily production in the long run?

(3) Sketch a graph of N against t and explain why the general shape might have been expected.

2. Use the rules of logs to expand each of the following:

   (a) $\ln xy$ **(b)** $\ln xy^4$ **(c)** $\ln (xy)^2$

   (d) $\ln \dfrac{x^5}{y^7}$ **(e)** $\ln \sqrt{\dfrac{x}{y}}$ **(f)** $\ln \sqrt{\dfrac{xy^3}{z}}$

3. Use the rules of logs to express each of the following as a single logarithm:

   (a) $\ln x + 2 \ln x$ **(b)** $4 \ln x - 3 \ln y + 5 \ln z$

4. Solve each of the following equations. (Round your answer to 2 decimal places.)

   (a) $e^x = 5.9$ **(b)** $e^x = 0.45$ **(c)** $e^x = -2$

   (d) $e^{3x} = 13.68$ **(e)** $e^{-5x} = 0.34$ **(f)** $4e^{2x} = 7.98$

5. The value of a second-hand car reduces exponentially with age, so that its value $\$y$ after t years can be modelled by the formula

   $$y = Ae^{-ax}$$

   If the car was \$50 000 when new and was worth \$38 000 after 2 years, find the values of A and a, correct to 3 decimal places.
   Use this model to predict the value of the car

   (a) when the car is 5 years old

   (b) in the long run.

6. Solve the following equations

   (a) $\ln x = 5$ **(b)** $\ln x = 0$

7. Future sales of two products A and B are given by $S_A = 5e^{0.01t}$ and $S_B = 2e^{0.02t}$. Find the time, t, when sales of the two products are the same.

8. Show that the following production function is homogeneous and state whether it displays decreasing, increasing or constant returns to scale.

   $$f(K,L) = (K^2 + L^2)e^{K/L}$$

Exercise 2.4*

1. The value (in cents) of shares, t years after their flotation on the stock market, is modelled by

   $$V = 6e^{0.8t}$$

   Find the increase in the value of these shares, 4 years and 2 months later. Give your answer to the nearest cent.

2. Solve each of the following equations, correct to 2 decimal places:

   (a) $6e^{-2x} = 0.62$ **(b)** $5 \ln(4x) = 9.84$ **(c)** $3 \ln(5x) - 2 \ln(x) = 7$

3. A team of financial advisers guiding the launch of a national newspaper has modelled the future circulation of the newspaper by the equation

$$N = c(1 - e^{-kt})$$

where N is the daily circulation after t days of publication, and c and k are positive constants. Transpose this formula to show that

$$t = \frac{1}{k} \ln\left(\frac{c}{c - N}\right)$$

When the paper is launched, audits show that

$$c = 700\,000 \quad \text{and} \quad k = \ln 2$$

(a) Calculate the daily circulation after 30 days of publication.

(b) After how many days will the daily circulation first reach 525 000?

(c) What advice can you give the newspaper proprietor if it is known that the paper will break even only if the daily circulation exceeds 750 000?

4. A Cobb–Douglas production function is given by

$$Q = 3L^{1/2}K^{1/3}$$

Find an expression for $\ln Q$ in terms of $\ln L$ and $\ln K$.

If a graph were to be sketched of $\ln Q$ against $\ln K$ (for varying values of Q and K but with L fixed), explain briefly why the graph will be a straight line and state its slope and vertical intercept.

5. The following table gives data relating a firm's output, Q and labour, L:

L	1	2	3	4	5
Q	0.50	0.63	0.72	0.80	0.85

The firm's short-run production function is believed to be of the form

$$Q = AL^n$$

(a) Show that

$$\ln Q = n \ln L + \ln A$$

(b) Using the data supplied, copy and complete the following table:

$\ln L$		0.69		1.39	
$\ln Q$	−0.69		−0.33		−0.16

Plot these points with $\ln L$ on the horizontal axis and $\ln Q$ on the vertical axis. Draw a straight line passing as close as possible to all five points.

(c) By finding the slope and vertical intercept of the line sketched in part (b), estimate the values of the parameters n and A.

6. (a) Multiply out the brackets

$$(3y - 1)(y + 5)$$

(b) Solve the equation

$$3e^{2x} + 13e^x = 10$$

Give your answer correct to 3 decimal places.

7. **(a)** Make y the subject of the equation

$$x = ae^{by}$$

(b) Make x the subject of the equation

$$y = \ln(3 + e^{2x})$$

8. Solve the following equations for x

(a) $\ln(x - 5) = 0$ **(b)** $\ln(x^2 - x - 1) = 0$ **(c)** $x \ln(\sqrt{x} - 4) = 0$

(d) $e^{5x+1} = 10$ **(e)** $e^{-x^2/2} = 0.25$

9. The demand and supply functions of a good are given by

$$Q_D = Ae^{-k_1 P} \quad \text{and} \quad Q_S = Be^{k_2 P} \text{ respectively}$$

where A, B, k_1 and k_2 are positive constants.

Find the equilibrium price and show that the equilibrium quantity is given by

$$(A^{k_2} B^{k_1})^{\frac{1}{k_2 + k_1}}.$$

Formal mathematics

The quadratic functions that we have been investigating in this chapter have an obvious extension to cubic functions:

$$f(x) = ax^3 + bx^2 + cx + d$$

Linear, quadratic and cubic functions are all examples of a general class of functions called **polynomials** which are defined by

$$f(x) = a_n x^n + a_{n-1} x^{n-1} + \ldots + a_0$$

The coefficients, a_i, are constants and the highest power of x is called the **degree** of the polynomial. A quadratic is a polynomial of degree 2 and a cubic has degree 3. Functions such as $f(x) = \dfrac{1}{x} + 4$ and $f(x) = \dfrac{1}{x^2 - 2x + 1}$, however, are not polynomials.

One property of functions that is important is that of continuity. A simple way of understanding this is to imagine drawing the graph of a function. If this can be done without taking your pen off the page the function is described as being **continuous** everywhere. An example of such a function is shown in Figure 2.17(a). Polynomials are examples of functions which are continuous at all values of their domain. On the other hand, if the graph has jumps or breaks in it then the function is **discontinuous** at those points. Figure 2.17(b) shows the graph of a function which is undefined at $x = 2$ and the graph separates into two different branches either side of $x = 2$. Functions involving reciprocals are examples of functions of this type. Indeed the graph in Figure 2.17(a) is that of the specific function, $f(x) = \dfrac{1}{x - 2}$. The graph in Figure 2.17(c) also illustrates a function which is discontinuous at $x = 2$ because it has a jump at this point. For values of $x < 2$ the function takes the constant value of 3, whereas when $x \geq 2$ the function takes the constant value of 5. In other words,

$$f(x) = \begin{cases} 3, & x < 2 \\ 5, & x \geq 2 \end{cases}$$

A function which is defined in separate bits like this is said to be defined piecewise.

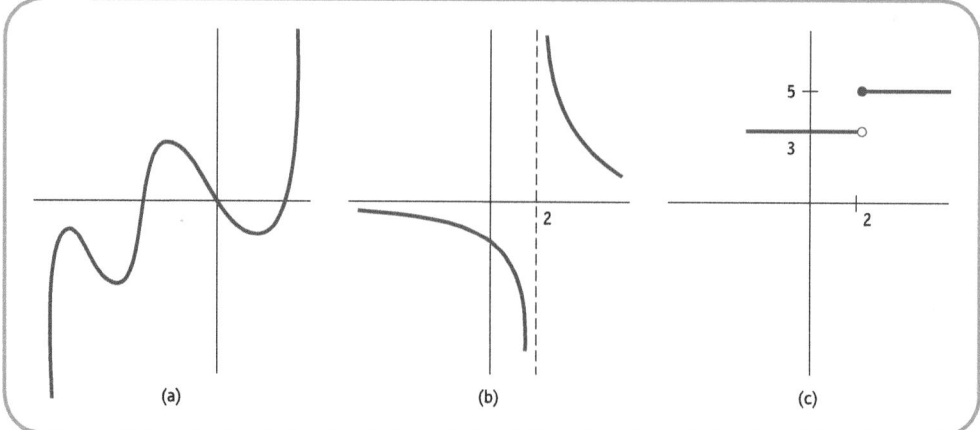

(a)   (b)   (c)

Figure 2.17

The majority of functions in economics are continuous, reflecting the fact that usually there are gradual fluctuations in economic variables without any sudden changes. However, sometimes there are catastrophic events which lead to sudden jumps. For example, the outbreak of war (or rumour of one) can lead to dramatic changes in prices of commodities such as oil or gold.

The above description of continuous functions is easy to visualise but is not very precise. In order to give a formal definition of a continuous function we need the concept of a limit. We write

$$\lim_{x \to a} f(x)$$ (read 'the limit of f of x, as x tends to a')

for the value that the function gets ever closer to, as x approaches a value a. This is most easily understood via an example.

Example

Find $\lim_{x \to 0} \dfrac{e^x - 1}{x}$

Solution

If we attempt to evaluate the function $f(x) = \dfrac{e^x - 1}{x}$ at $x = 0$ we are faced with $f(0) = \dfrac{0}{0}$ which is undefined. However, if we start with, say, $x = \pm 1$, and allow x to approach 0 from either direction, we can see that the value is in fact 1. This is illustrated in the table of values below, which shows that as x gets closer and closer to 0 (through both positive and negative values) the function approaches 1. In symbols, $\lim_{x \to 0} \dfrac{e^x - 1}{x} = 1$

x	1	0.1	0.01	0.001
$f(x)$	1.71828	1.05171	1.00501	1.00050

x	−1	−0.1	−0.01	−0.001
$f(x)$	0.63212	0.95163	0.99502	0.99950

A graph of $f(x)$ is sketched in Figure 2.18. Although the function is undefined at $x = 0$ the graph shows that it is possible to 'plug the hole' by defining $f(0) = 1$.

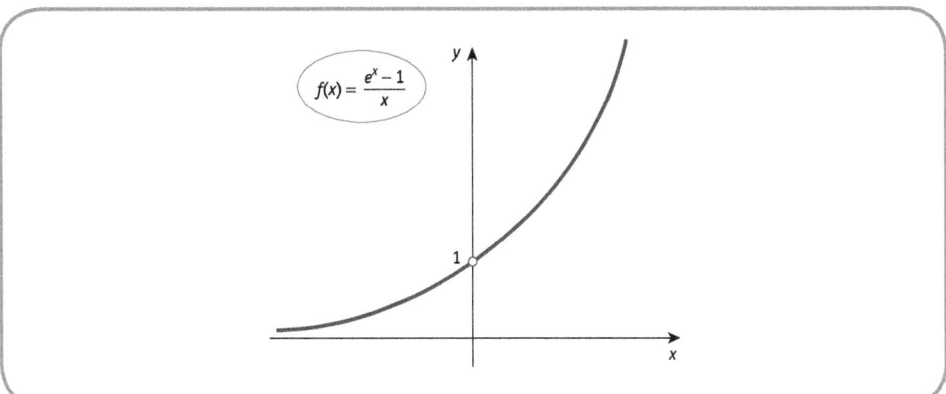

Figure 2.18

Definition A function f is continuous at $x = a$ if $\lim_{x \to a} f(x) = f(a)$

In other words, a function is continuous at $x = a$ provided the function can be evaluated at $x = a$ (so that $f(a)$ exists), and that the limit also exists and equals $f(a)$.

Referring to the functions illustrated in Figure 2.17 and 2.18 we see that:

- The function in Figure 2.17(b) is discontinuous because f is undefined at $x = 2$.
- The function in Figure 2.17(c) is discontinuous because the $\lim_{x \to 2} f(x)$ does not exist (it gives a value 5 as x approaches 2 from the right but a different value of 3 as x approaches 2 from the left).
- The function in Figure 2.18 is discontinuous because f is undefined at $x = 0$.

It is possible to remove the discontinuity for the function, $f(x) = \dfrac{e^x - 1}{x}$. As we saw in the previous example, $\lim_{x \to 0} \dfrac{e^x - 1}{x} = 1$. If we are prepared to define the function piecewise as

$$f(x) = \begin{cases} \dfrac{e^x - 1}{x} & \text{if } x \neq 0 \\ 1 & \text{if } x = 0 \end{cases}$$

then the function is now defined at $x = 0$ and the value of the limit and the function both give the value of 1 at this point.

Continuous functions have many important properties. In particular, it is necessary for a function to be continuous in order even to consider the idea of differentiability which we will investigate in Chapter 4.

Key Terms

Continuous   The name given to a function which can be drawn without taking a pen off the paper. More formally when $\lim_{x \to a} f(x) = f(a)$ at all points in the domain.

Degree   The highest power in a polynomial.

Discontinuous   The name given to a function which is not continuous everywhere. The graph of the function has jumps or gaps.

Polynomial   A function of the form $a_n x^n + a_{n-1} x^{n-1} + \ldots + a_0$.

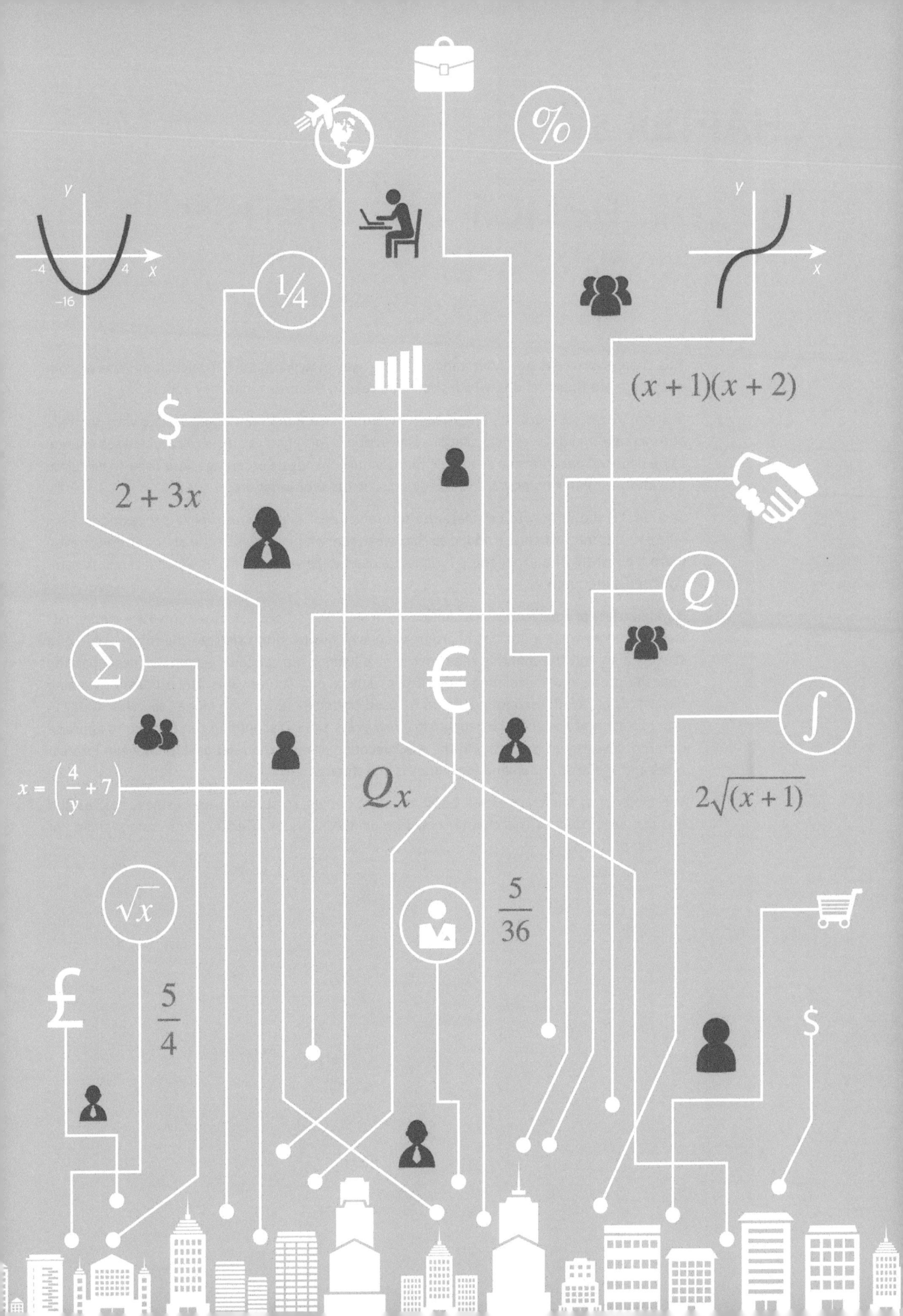

CHAPTER 3
Mathematics of Finance

This chapter provides an understanding of the way in which financial calculations are worked out. There are four sections, which should be read in the order that they appear.

Section 3.1 revises work on percentages. In particular, a quick method of dealing with percentage increase and decrease calculations is described. This enables an overall percentage change to be deduced easily from a sequence of individual changes. Percentages are used to calculate and interpret index numbers, and to adjust value data for inflation.

Section 3.2 shows how to calculate the future value of a lump sum which is invested to earn interest. This interest can be added to the investment annually, semi-annually, quarterly or even more frequently. The exponential function is used to solve problems in which interest is compounded continuously.

A wide variety of applications are considered in Sections 3.3 and 3.4. In Section 3.3 a mathematical device known as a geometric progression, which is used to calculate the future value of a savings plan and the monthly repayments of a loan, is introduced. Section 3.4 describes the opposite problem of calculating the present value given a future value. The process of working backwards is called discounting. It can be used to decide how much money to invest today in order to achieve a specific target sum in a few years' time. Discounting can be used to appraise different investment projects. On the macroeconomic level, the relationship between interest rates and speculative demand for money is investigated.

The material in this chapter will be of greatest benefit to students on business studies and management courses. This chapter could be omitted without affecting your understanding of the rest of this book.

SECTION 3.1
Percentages

Objectives

At the end of this section you should be able to:

- Understand what a percentage is.
- Solve problems involving a percentage increase or decrease.
- Write down scale factors associated with percentage changes.
- Work out overall percentage changes.
- Calculate and interpret index numbers.
- Adjust value data for inflation.

Advice

The first part of this section provides a leisurely revision of the idea of a percentage as well as reminding you about how to use scale factors to cope with percentage changes. These ideas are crucial to any understanding of financial mathematics. However, if you are already confident in using percentages, you may wish to miss this out and move straight on to the applications covered in subsections 3.1.1 and 3.1.2.

In order to be able to handle financial calculations, it is necessary to use percentages proficiently. The word 'percentage' literally means 'per cent', i.e. per hundredth, so that whenever we speak of $r\%$ of something, we simply mean the fraction $(r/100)$ ths of it.

For example,

$$25\% \text{ is the same as } \quad \frac{25}{100} = \frac{1}{4}$$

$$30\% \text{ is the same as } \quad \frac{30}{100} = \frac{3}{10}$$

$$50\% \text{ is the same as } \quad \frac{50}{100} = \frac{1}{2}$$

Example

Calculate

(a) 15% of 12

(b) 150% of 290

Solution

(a) 15% of 12 is the same as

$$\frac{15}{100} \times 12 = 0.15 \times 12 = 1.8$$

(b) 150% of 290 is the same as

$$\frac{150}{100} \times 290 = 1.5 \times 290 = 435$$

Practice Problem

1. Calculate

   (a) 10% of $2.90   (b) 75% of $1250   (c) 24% of $580

Whenever any numerical quantity increases or decreases, it is customary to refer to this change in percentage terms. The following example serves to remind you how to perform calculations involving percentage changes.

Example

(a) An investment rises from $2500 to $3375. Express the increase as a percentage of the original.
(b) At the beginning of a year, the population of a small village is 8400. If the annual rise in population is 12%, find the population at the end of the year.
(c) In a sale, all prices are reduced by 20%. Find the sale price of a good originally costing $580.

Solution

(a) The rise in the value of the investment is

$$3375 - 2500 = 875$$

As a fraction of the original this is

$$\frac{875}{2500} = 0.35$$

This is the same as 35 hundredths, so the percentage rise is 35%.

(b) As a fraction

$$12\% \text{ is the same as } \frac{12}{100} = 0.12$$

so the rise in population is

$$0.12 \times 8400 = 1008$$

Hence the final population is

$$8400 + 1008 = 9408$$

(c) As a fraction

$$20\% \text{ is the same as } \frac{20}{100} = 0.2$$

so the fall in price is

$$0.2 \times 580 = 116$$

Hence the final price is

$$580 - 116 = \$464$$

Practice Problem

2. **(a)** A firm's annual sales rise from 50 000 to 55 000 from one year to the next. Express the rise as a percentage of the original.

   (b) The government imposes a 15% tax on the price of a good. How much does the consumer pay for a good priced by a firm at $1360?

   (c) Investments fall during the course of a year by 7%. Find the value of an investment at the end of the year if it was worth $9500 at the beginning of the year.

In the previous example and in Practice Problem 2, the calculations were performed in two separate stages. The actual rise or fall was first worked out, and these changes were then applied to the original value to obtain the final answer. It is possible to obtain this answer in a single calculation, and we now describe how this can be done. Not only is this new approach quicker, but it also enables us to tackle more difficult problems. To be specific, let us suppose that the price of a good is set to rise by 9%, and that its current price is $78. The new price consists of the original (which can be thought of as 100% of the $78) plus the increase (which is 9% of $78). The final price is therefore

$$100\% + 9\% = 109\% \text{ (of the \$78)}$$

which is the same as

$$\frac{109}{100} = 1.09$$

(c) The scale factor is

$$\frac{\text{new value}}{\text{old value}} = \frac{174\,989}{190\,205} = 0.92$$

which can be thought of as

$$1 - \frac{8}{100}$$

so the fall is 8%.

Practice Problem

4. **(a)** Current monthly output from a factory is 25 000. In a recession, this is expected to fall by 65%. Estimate the new level of output.

(b) As a result of a modernisation programme, a firm is able to reduce the size of its workforce by 24%. If it now employs 570 workers, how many people did it employ before restructuring?

(c) Shares originally worth $10.50 fall in a stock market crash to $2.10. Find the percentage decrease.

The final application of scale factors that we consider is to the calculation of overall percentage changes. It is often the case that over various periods of time the price of a good is subject to several individual percentage changes. It is useful to be able to replace these by an equivalent single percentage change spanning the entire period. This can be done by simply multiplying together successive scale factors.

Example

(a) Share prices rise by 32% during the first half of the year and rise by a further 10% during the second half. What is the overall percentage change?

(b) Find the overall percentage change in the price of a good if it rises by 5% in a year but is then reduced by 30% in a sale.

Solution

(a) To find the value of shares at the end of the first 6 months we would multiply by

$$1 + \frac{32}{100} = 1.32$$

and at the end of the year we would multiply again by the scale factor

$$1 + \frac{10}{100} = 1.1$$

The net effect is to multiply by their product

$$1.32 \times 1.1 = 1.452$$

which can be thought of as

$$1 + \frac{45.2}{100}$$

so the overall change is 45.2%.

Notice that this is not the same as

$$32\% + 10\% = 42\%$$

This is because during the second half of the year we not only get a 10% rise in the original value, but we also get a 10% rise on the gain accrued during the first 6 months.

(b) The individual scale factors are 1.05 and 0.7, so the overall scale factor is

$$1.05 \times 0.7 = 0.735$$

The fact that this is less than 1 indicates that the overall change is a decrease. Writing

$$0.735 = 1 - 0.265 = 1 - \frac{26.5}{100}$$

we see that this scale factor represents a 26.5% decrease.

Practice Problem

5. Find the single percentage increase or decrease equivalent to

(a) an increase of 30% followed by an increase of 40%

(b) a decrease of 30% followed by a decrease of 40%

(c) an increase of 10% followed by a decrease of 50%.

We conclude this section by describing two applications of percentages in macroeconomics:

- index numbers
- inflation.

We consider each of these in turn.

3.1.1 Index numbers

Economic data often take the form of a **time series**; values of economic indicators are available on an annual, quarterly or monthly basis, and we are interested in analysing the rise and fall of these numbers over time. **Index numbers** enable us to identify trends and relationships in the data. The following example shows you how to calculate index numbers and how to interpret them.

Example

Table 3.1 shows the values of household spending (in billions of dollars) during a 5-year period. Calculate the index numbers when 2011 is taken as the base year and give a brief interpretation.

Table 3.1

	Year				
	2010	**2011**	**2012**	**2013**	**2014**
Household spending	686.9	697.2	723.7	716.6	734.5

Solution

When finding index numbers, a base year is chosen and the value of 100 is allocated to that year. In this example, we are told to take 2011 as the base year, so the index number of 2011 is 100. To find the index number of the year 2012 we work out the scale factor associated with the change in household spending from the base year, 2011 to 2012, and then multiply the answer by 100.

$$\text{index number} = \text{scale factor from base year} \times 100$$

In this case, we get

$$\frac{723.7}{697.2} \times 100 = 103.8$$

This shows that the value of household spending in 2012 was 103.8% of its value in 2011. In other words, household spending increased by 3.8% during 2012.

For the year 2013, the value of household spending was 716.6, giving an index number

$$\frac{716.6}{697.2} \times 100 = 102.8$$

This shows that the value of household spending in 2013 was 102.8% of its value in 2011. In other words, household spending increased by 2.8% between 2011 and 2013. Notice that this is less than that calculated for 2012, reflecting the fact that spending actually fell slightly during 2013. The remaining two index numbers are calculated in a similar way and are shown in Table 3.2.

Table 3.2

	Year				
	2010	**2011**	**2012**	**2013**	**2014**
Household spending	686.9	697.2	723.7	716.6	734.5
Index number	98.5	100	103.8	102.8	105.3

Practice Problem

6. Calculate the index numbers for the data shown in Table 3.1, this time taking 2010 as the base year.

Index numbers themselves have no units. They merely express the value of some quantity as a percentage of a base number. This is particularly useful, since it enables us to compare how values of quantities, of varying magnitudes, change in relation to each other. Table 3.3 shows the rise and fall of two share prices during an 8-month period. The prices (in dollars) listed for each share are taken on the last day of each month. Share A is exceptionally cheap. Investors often include this type of share in their portfolio, since they can occasionally make spectacular gains. This was the case with many dot.com shares at the end of the 1990s. The second share is more expensive and corresponds to a larger, more established firm.

Table 3.3

Month	Jan	Feb	Mar	Apr	May	Jun	Jul	Aug
Share A	0.31	0.28	0.31	0.34	0.40	0.39	0.45	0.52
Share B	6.34	6.40	6.45	6.52	6.57	6.43	6.65	7.00

The index numbers have been listed in Table 3.4, taking April as the base month. Notice that both shares are given the same index number of 100 in April. This is despite the fact that the values of the two shares are very different. This creates 'a level playing-field', enabling us to monitor the relative performance of the two shares. The index numbers show quite clearly that share A has outperformed share B during this period. Indeed, if an investor had spent $1000 on shares of type A in January, they could have bought 3225 of them, which would be worth $1677 in August, making a profit of $677. The corresponding profit for share B is only $103.

Table 3.4

Month	Jan	Feb	Mar	Apr	May	Jun	Jul	Aug
Index of share price A (April = 100)	91.2	82.3	91.2	100	117.6	114.7	132.4	152.9
Index of share price B (April = 100)	97.2	98.2	98.9	100	100.8	98.6	102.0	107.4

Incidentally, if the only information you have about the time series is the set of index numbers, then it is possible to work out the percentage changes between any pair of values. Table 3.5 shows the index numbers of the output of a particular firm for the years 2013 and 2014.

Table 3.5

	Output							
	13Q1	13Q2	13Q3	13Q4	14Q1	14Q2	14Q3	14Q4
Index	89.3	98.1	105.0	99.3	100	106.3	110.2	105.7

The table shows that the base quarter is the first quarter of 2014 because the index number is 100 in 14Q1. It is, of course, easy to find the percentage change from this quarter to any subsequent quarter. For example, the index number associated with the third quarter of 2014 is 110.2, so we know immediately that the percentage change in output from 14Q1 to 14Q3 is 10.2%. However, it is not immediately obvious what the percentage change is from, say, 13Q2 to 14Q2. To work this out, note that the scale factor of this change is

$$\frac{106.3}{98.1} = 1.084$$

which corresponds to an 8.4% increase.

Similarly, the scale factor of the change from 13Q3 to 14Q1 is

$$\frac{100}{105} = 0.952$$

This is less than 1, reflecting the fact that output has fallen. To find the percentage change we write the scale factor as

$$1 - 0.048$$

which shows that the percentage decrease is 4.8%.

Practice Problem

7. Use the index numbers listed in Table 3.5 to find the percentage change in output from

   (a) 14Q1 to 14Q4
   (b) 13Q1 to 14Q4
   (c) 13Q1 to 14Q1

It is possible to create sensible index numbers to measure the variation of a bundle of goods over time. To be specific suppose that a firm buys three products. Table 3.6 shows the number of each type bought in 2014 together with the unit prices of each item in 2014 and 2015.

Table 3.6

Product	Number bought in 2014	Unit price in 2014	Unit price in 2015
A	20	8	10
B	35	18	23
C	10	6	5

The total purchase cost in 2014 is worked out by multiplying the quantities by the corresponding prices which gives

$$20 \times 8 + 35 \times 18 + 10 \times 6 = 850$$

If we assume that the firm buys the same number of each type in 2015 the total cost would be

$$20 \times 10 + 35 \times 23 + 10 \times 5 = 1055$$

Taking the base year as 2014 we see that the index number in 2014 is 100 and the index number in 2015 is

$$\frac{1055}{850} \times 100 = 124.1$$

In this calculation we have created a weighted index which assumes that the quantities purchased in 2015 are the same as the base year. This is referred to as a base-weighted index (or **Laspeyres index**). It provides a good indication to the firm of changing costs, although it becomes unreliable if the firm changes the amount it buys over time. If figures are available for the quantities purchased each year then it is possible to work out an index based on current values. For example, if the quantities bought in 2015 are those shown in Table 3.7 then the current weighted index in 2015 is

$$\frac{17 \times 10 + 38 \times 23 + 12 \times 5}{850} \times 100 = \frac{1104}{850} \times 100 = 129.9$$

Table 3.7

Product	Number bought in 2015
A	17
B	38
C	12

This is referred to as the **Paasche index**. It has the obvious advantage of reflecting changes in the actual purchases made by the firm. On the downside it is necessary to know the precise amounts of each item bought every year and, strictly speaking, since the calculations change each year you are not comparing like quantities.

3.1.2 Inflation

Over a period of time, the prices of many goods and services usually increase. The annual rate of **inflation** is the average percentage change in a given selection of these goods and services, over the previous year. Seasonal variations are taken into account, and the particular basket of goods and services is changed periodically to reflect changing patterns of household expenditure. The presence of inflation is particularly irritating when trying to interpret a time series that involves a monetary value. It is inevitable that this will be influenced by inflation during any year, and what is of interest is the fluctuation of a time series 'over and above' inflation. Economists deal with this by distinguishing between nominal and real data. **Nominal data** are the original, raw data such as those listed in tables in the previous subsection. These are based on the prices that prevailed at the time. **Real data** are the values that have been adjusted to take inflation into account. The standard way of doing this is to pick a year and then convert the values for all other years to the level that they would have had in this base year. This may sound rather complicated, but the idea and calculations involved are really quite simple as the following example demonstrates.

Example

Table 3.8 shows the price (in thousands of dollars) of an average house in a certain town during a 5-year period. The price quoted is the value of the house at the end of each year. Use the annual rates of inflation given in Table 3.9 to adjust the prices to those prevailing at the end of 1991. Compare the rise in both the nominal and real values of house prices during this period.

Table 3.8

	Year				
	1990	**1991**	**1992**	**1993**	**1994**
Average house price	72	89	93	100	106

Table 3.9

	Year			
	1991	**1992**	**1993**	**1994**
Annual rate of inflation	10.7%	7.1%	3.5%	2.3%

Solution

The raw figures shown in Table 3.8 give the impression that houses increased steadily in value throughout this period, with a quite substantial gain during the first year. However, if inflation had been very high then the gain in real terms would have been quite small. Indeed, if the rate of inflation were to exceed the percentage rise of these nominal data, then the price of a house would actually fall in real terms. To analyse this situation we will use Table 3.9, which shows the rates of inflation during this period. Notice that since the house prices listed in Table 3.9 are quoted at the end of each year, we are not interested in the rate of inflation during 1990.

We are told in the question to choose 1991 as the base year and calculate the value of the house at '1991 prices'. The value of the house at the end of 1991 is obviously $89 000, since no adjustment needs to be made. At the end of 1992, the house is worth $93 000. However, during that year inflation was 7.1%. To adjust this price to '1991 prices' we simply divide by the scale factor 1.071, since we are going backwards in time. We get

$$\frac{93\,000}{1.071} = 86\,835$$

In real terms the house has fallen in value by over $2000.

To adjust the price of the house in 1993 we first need to divide by 1.035 to backtrack to the year 1992, and then divide again by 1.071 to reach 1991. We get

$$\frac{100\,000}{1.035 \times 1.071} = 90\,213$$

In real terms there has at least been some gain during 1993. However, this is less than impressive, and from a purely financial point of view, there would have been more lucrative ways of investing this capital.

For the 1994 price, the adjusted value is

$$\frac{106\,000}{1.023 \times 1.035 \times 1.071} = 93\,476$$

and, for 1990, the adjusted value is

$$72\,000 \times 1.107 = 79\,704$$ going forward in time so multiply

Table 3.10 lists both the nominal and the 'constant 1991' values of the house (rounded to the nearest thousand) for comparison. It shows quite clearly that, apart from the gain during 1991, the increase in value has, in fact, been quite modest.

Table 3.10

	Year				
	1990	**1991**	**1992**	**1993**	**1994**
Nominal house price	72	89	94	100	106
1991 house price	80	89	87	90	93

Practice Problem

8. Table 3.11 shows the average annual salary (in thousands of dollars) of employees in a small firm, together with the annual rate of inflation for that year. Adjust these salaries to the prices prevailing at the end of 2001 and so give the real values of the employees' salaries at constant '2001 prices'. Comment on the rise in earnings during this period.

Table 3.11

	Year				
	2000	2001	2002	2003	2004
Salary	17.3	18.1	19.8	23.5	26.0
Inflation		4.9	4.3	4.0	3.5

Key Terms

Index number   The scale factor of a variable measured from the base year multiplied by 100.

Inflation   The percentage increase in the level of prices over a 12-month period.

Laspeyre index   An index number for groups of data which are weighted by the quantities used in the base year.

Nominal data   Monetary values prevailing at the time that they were measured.

Paasche index   An index number for groups of data which are weighted by the quantities used in the current year.

Real data   Monetary values adjusted to take inflation into account.

Scale factor   The multiplier that gives the final value in percentage problems.

Time series   A sequence of numbers indicating the variation of data over time.

Exercise 3.1

1. Express the following percentages as fractions in their simplest form:

   (a) 35%   (b) 88%   (c) 250%   (d) $17^1/_2$%   (e) 0.2%

2. Calculate each of the following:

   (a) 5% of 24   (b) 8% of 88   (c) 48% of 4563   (d) 112% of 56

3. A firm has 132 female and 88 male employees.

   (a) What percentage of staff are female?

   (b) During the next year 8 additional female staff are employed. If the percentage of female staff is now 56%, how many additional male staff were recruited during the year?

4. Write down the scale factors corresponding to

  (a) an increase of 19%

  (b) an increase of 250%

  (c) a decrease of 2%

  (d) a decrease of 43%.

5. Write down the percentage changes corresponding to the following scale factors:

  (a) 1.04   **(b)** 1.42   **(c)** 0.86

  (d) 3.45   **(e)** 1.0025   **(f)** 0.04

6. Find the new quantities when

  (a) $16.25 is increased by 12%

  (b) the population of a town, currently at 113 566, rises by 5%

  (c) a good priced by a firm at $87.90 is subject to a sales tax of 15%

  (d) a good priced at $2300 is reduced by 30% in a sale

  (e) a car, valued at $23 000, depreciates by 32%.

7. A student discount card reduces a bill in a restaurant from $124 to $80.60. Work out the percentage discount.

8. A shop sells books at '20% below the recommended retail price (r.r.p.)'. If it sells a book for $12.40 find

  (a) the r.r.p.

  (b) the cost of the book after a further reduction of 15% in a sale

  (c) the overall percentage discount obtained by buying the book from the shop in the sale compared with the manufacturer's r.r.p.

9. A TV costs $900 including 20% sales tax. Find the new price if tax is reduced to 15%.

10. An antiques dealer tries to sell a vase at 45% above the $18 000 which the dealer paid at auction.

  (a) What is the new sale price?

  (b) By what percentage can the dealer now reduce the price before making a loss?

11. Find the single percentage increase or decrease equivalent to

  (a) a 10% increase followed by a 25% increase

  (b) a 34% decrease followed by a 65% increase

  (c) a 25% increase followed by a 25% decrease.

Explain in words why the overall change in part (c) is not 0%.

12. Table 3.12 gives the annual rate of inflation during a 5-year period.

Table 3.12

	2000	2001	2002	2003	2004
Annual rate of inflation	1.8%	2.1%	2.9%	2.4%	2.7%

If a nominal house price at the end of 2000 was $10.8 million, find the real house price adjusted to prices prevailing at the end of the year 2003. Round your answer to three significant figures.

13. The price of a good during the last five years is:

$25 $30 $36 $43 $50

Calculate the index numbers using the last year as the base year and hence comment on the rise in prices during this period.

14. Table 3.13 shows the monthly index of sales of a good during the first four months of the year.

Table 3.13

Month	Jan	Feb	Mar	Apr
Index	100	120	145	150

(a) Which month is chosen as the base year?

(b) If sales in February are 3840, what are the sales in April?

(c) What is the index number in May if sales are 4256?

15. Table 3.14 shows the index numbers associated with transport costs during a 20-year period. The public transport costs reflect changes to bus and train fares, whereas private transport costs include purchase, service, petrol, tax and insurance costs of cars.

Table 3.14

	Year				
	1985	1990	1995	2000	2005
Public transport	100	130	198	224	245
Private transport	100	125	180	199	221

(1) Which year is chosen as the base year?

(2) Find the percentage increases in the cost of public transport from

   (a) 1985 to 1990   (b) 1990 to 1995   (c) 1995 to 2000   (d) 2000 to 2005

(3) Repeat part (2) for private transport.

(4) Comment briefly on the relative rise in public and private transport costs during this 20-year period.

16. Table 3.15 shows the number of items (in thousands) produced from a factory production line during the course of a year. Taking the second quarter as the base quarter, calculate the associated index numbers. Suggest a possible reason for the fluctuations in output.

Table 3.15

	Quarter			
	Q1	Q2	Q3	Q4
Output	13.5	1.4	2.5	10.5

17. Table 3.16 shows the prices of a good for each year between 2009 and 2014.

Table 3.16

Year	2009	2010	2011	2012	2013	2014
Price ($)	40	48	44	56	60	71

(a) Work out the index numbers, correct to 1 decimal place, taking 2010 as the base year.

(b) If the index number for 2015 is 135, calculate the corresponding price. You may assume that the base year is still 2010.

(c) If the index number in 2011 is approximately 73, find the year that is used as the base year.

Exercise 3.1*

1. Total revenue from daily ticket sales to a theme park is $1 352 400. A total of 12 000 tickets were sold and 65% of these were child's tickets with a 30% discount off the adult price. Work out the cost of an adult ticket.

2. The cost of a computer is $6000 including 20% sales tax. In a generous gesture, the government decides to reduce the rate to just 17.5%. Find the cost of the computer after the tax has changed.

3. A coat originally costing $150 is reduced by 25% in a sale and, since nobody bought the coat, a further reduction of 20% of the sale price is applied.

(a) Find the final cost of the coat after both reductions.

(b) Find the overall percentage reduction and explain why this is not the same as a single reduction of 45%.

4. A furniture store has a sale of 40% on selected items.
A sales assistant, Carol, reduces the price of a sofa originally costing $1200.

(a) What is the new price?
The manager does not want this sofa to be in the sale and the following day tells another sales assistant, Michael, to restore the sofa back to the original price. He does not know what the original price was and decides to show off his mathematical knowledge by taking the answer to part (a) and multiplying it by 1.4.

(b) Explain carefully why this does not give the correct answer of $1200.

(c) Suggest an alternative calculation that would give the right answer.

5. During 2014 the price of a good increased by 8%. In the sales on 1 January 2015 all items are reduced by 25%.

(a) If the sale price of the good is $688.50, find the original price at the beginning of 2014.

(b) Find the overall percentage change.

(c) What percentage increase would be needed to restore the cost to the original price prevailing on 1 January 2014? Give your answer to 1 decimal place.

6. Table 3.17 shows government expenditure (in billions of dollars) on education for four consecutive years, together with the rate of inflation for each year.

    (a) Taking 2004 as the base year, work out the index numbers of the nominal data given in the third row of the table.

    (b) Find the values of expenditure at constant 2004 prices and hence recalculate the index numbers of real government expenditure.

    (c) Give an interpretation of the index numbers calculated in part (b).

    Table 3.17

	Year			
	2004	**2005**	**2006**	**2007**
Spending	236	240	267	276
Inflation		4.7	4.2	3.4

7. Index numbers associated with the growth of unemployment during an 8-year period are shown in Table 3.18.

    (a) What are the base years for the two indices?

    (b) If the government had not switched to index 2, what would be the values of index 1 in years 7 and 8?

    (c) What values would index 2 have been in years 1, 2, 3, 4 and 5?

    (d) If unemployment was 1.2 million in year 4, how many people were unemployed in years 1 and 8?

    Table 3.18

	Year							
	1	**2**	**3**	**4**	**5**	**6**	**7**	**8**
Index 1	100	95	105	110	119	127		
Index 2						100	112	118

8. The prices of a good at the end of each year between 2003 and 2008 are listed in Table 3.19, which also shows the annual rate of inflation.

    Table 3.19

Year	**2003**	**2004**	**2005**	**2006**	**2007**	**2008**
Price	230	242	251	257	270	284
Inflation		4%	3%	2.5%	2%	2%

    (a) Find the values of the prices adjusted to the end of year 2004, correct to 2 decimal places. Hence, calculate the index numbers of the real data with 2004 as the base year. Give your answers correct to 1 decimal place.

    (b) If the index number of the real price for 2009 is 109 and the rate of inflation for that year is 2.5%, work out the nominal value of the price in 2009. Give your answer rounded to the nearest whole number.

    (c) If the index number of the real data in 2002 is 95.6 and the nominal price is $215, find the rate of inflation for 2002. Give your answer correct to 1 decimal place.

9. A firm buys three goods. The number of each type bought in 2013 is shown in Table 3.20 together with the unit prices for three consecutive years.

Table 3.20

Product	Number bought in 2013	Unit price in 2013	Unit price in 2014	Unit Price in 2015
A	56	34	36	42
B	40	24	24	23
C	122	13	11	14

(a) Calculate a base-weighted index (Laspeyres) for these data using 2013 as the base year.

(b) Comment on the values obtained in part (a).

10. The number of goods bought by the firm in Q9 vary over time. Figures for 2014 and 2015 are shown in Table 3.21.

Table 3.21

Product	Number bought in 2014	Number bought in 2015
A	62	96
B	44	46
C	134	102

(a) Calculate a current-weighted index (Paasche) for these data using 2013 as the base year.

(b) Compare the values with those obtained in Q9.

SECTION 3.2
Compound interest

Objectives

At the end of this section you should be able to:

- Understand the difference between simple and compound interest.
- Calculate the future value of a principal under annual compounding.
- Calculate the future value of a principal under continuous compounding.
- Determine the annual percentage rate of interest given a nominal rate of interest.

Today, businesses and individuals are faced with a bewildering array of loan facilities and investment opportunities. In this section we explain how these financial calculations are carried out to enable an informed choice to be made between the various possibilities available. We begin by considering what happens when a single lump sum is invested and show how to calculate the amount accumulated over a period of time.

Suppose that someone gives you the option of receiving $500 now or $500 in 3 years' time. Which of these alternatives would you accept? Most people would take the money now, partly because they may have an immediate need for it, but also because they recognise that $500 is worth more today than in 3 years' time. Even if we ignore the effects of inflation, it is still better to take the money now, since it can be invested and will increase in value over the 3-year period. In order to work out this value we need to know the rate of interest and the basis on which it is calculated. Let us begin by assuming that the $500 is invested for 3 years at 10% interest compounded annually. What exactly do we mean by '10% interest compounded annually'? Well, at the end of each year, the interest is calculated and is added on to the amount currently invested. If the original amount is $500 then after 1 year the interest is 10% of $500, which is

$$\frac{10}{100} \times \$500 = \frac{1}{10} \times \$500 = \$50$$

so the amount rises by $50 to $550.

What happens to this amount at the end of the second year? Is the interest also $50? This would actually be the case with **simple interest**, when the amount of interest received is the same for all years. However, with **compound interest**, we get 'interest on the interest'. Nearly all financial investments use compound rather than simple interest, because investors need to be rewarded for not taking the interest payment out of the fund each year. Under annual compounding the interest obtained at the end of the second year is 10% of the amount invested at the start of that year. This not only consists of the original $500, but also the $50 already received as interest on the first year's investment. Consequently, we get an additional

$$\frac{1}{10} \times \$550 = \$55$$

raising the sum to $605. Finally, at the end of the third year, the interest is

$$\frac{1}{10} \times \$605 = \$60.50$$

so the investment is $665.50. You are therefore $165.50 better off by taking the $500 now and investing it for 3 years. The calculations are summarised in Table 3.22.

Table 3.22

End of year	Interest ($)	Investment ($)
1	50	550
2	55	605
3	60.50	665.50

The calculations in Table 3.22 were performed by finding the interest earned each year and adding it on to the amount accumulated at the beginning of the year. This approach is rather laborious, particularly if the money is invested over a long period of time. What is really needed is a method of calculating the investment after, say, 10 years without having to determine the amount for the 9 intermediate years. This can be done using the scale factor approach discussed in the previous section. To illustrate this, let us return to the problem of investing $500 at 10% interest compounded annually. The original sum of money is called the **principal** and is denoted by P, and the final sum is called the **future value** and is denoted by S. The scale factor associated with an increase of 10% is

$$1 + \frac{10}{100} = 1.1$$

so at the end of 1 year the total amount invested is $P(1.1)$.

After 2 years we get

$$P(1.1) \times (1.1) = P(1.1)^2$$

and after 3 years the future value is

$$S = P(1.1)^2 \times (1.1) = P(1.1)^3$$

Setting $P = 500$, we see that

$$S = 500(1.1)^3 = \$665.50$$

which is, of course, the same as the amount calculated previously.

In general, if the interest rate is $r\%$ compounded annually then the scale factor is

$$1 + \frac{r}{100}$$

so, after n years,

$$S = P\left(1 + \frac{r}{100}\right)^n$$

Given the values of r, P and n it is simple to evaluate S using the power key x^y on a calculator.

Example

Find the value, in 4 years' time, of \$10 000 invested at 5% interest compounded annually.

Solution

In this problem, $P = 10\ 000$, $r = 5$ and $n = 4$, so the formula $S = P\left(1 + \dfrac{r}{100}\right)^n$ gives

$$S = 10\ 000\left(1 + \frac{5}{100}\right)^4 = 10\ 000(1.05)^4 = \$12\ 155.06$$

Practice Problem

1. Use the formula

$$S = P\left(1 + \frac{r}{100}\right)^n$$

to find the value, in 10 years' time, of \$1000 invested at 8% interest compounded annually.

The compound interest formula derived previously involves four variables, r, n, P and S. Provided that we know any three of these, we can use the formula to determine the remaining variable. This is illustrated in the following example.

Example

A principal of \$25 000 is invested at 12% interest compounded annually. After how many years will the investment first exceed \$250 000?

Solution

We want to save a total of \$250 000 starting with an initial investment of \$25 000. The problem is to determine the number of years required for this on the assumption that the interest is fixed at 12% throughout this time. The formula for compound interest is

$$S = P\left(1 + \frac{r}{100}\right)^n$$

We are given that

$$P = 25\ 000, \quad S = 250\ 000, \quad r = 12$$

so we need to solve the equation

$$250\,000 = 25\,000\left(1+\frac{12}{100}\right)^n$$

for n.

One way of doing this would just be to keep on guessing values of n until we find the one that works. However, a more mathematical approach is to use logarithms, because we are being asked to solve an equation in which the unknown occurs as a power. Following the method described in Section 2.3, we first divide both sides by 25 000 to get

$$10 = (1.12)^n$$

Taking logarithms of both sides gives

$$\log(10) = \log(1.12)^n$$

and if you apply rule 3 of logarithms you get

$$\log(10) = n\log(1.12) \qquad \boxed{\log_b x^m = m\log_b x}$$

Hence

$$n = \frac{\log(10)}{\log(1.12)}$$

$$= \frac{1}{0.49\,218\,023} \quad \text{(taking logarithms to base 10)}$$

$$= 20.3 \qquad \text{(to 1 decimal place)}$$

Now we know that n must be a whole number because interest is only added on at the end of each year. We assume that the first interest payment occurs exactly 12 months after the initial investment and every 12 months thereafter. The answer, 20.3, tells us that after only 20 years the amount is less than $250 000, so we need to wait until 21 years have elapsed before it exceeds this amount. In fact, after 20 years

$$S = \$25\,000(1.12)^{20} = \$241\,157.33$$

and after 21 years

$$S = \$25\,000(1.12)^{21} = \$270\,096.21$$

In this example we calculated the time taken for $25 000 to increase by a factor of 10. It can be shown that this time depends only on the interest rate and not on the actual value of the principal. To see this, note that if a general principal, P, increases tenfold then its future value is $10P$. If the interest rate is 12%, then we need to solve

$$10P = P\left(1+\frac{12}{100}\right)^n$$

for n. The Ps cancel (indicating that the answer is independent of P) to produce the equation

$$10 = (1.12)^n$$

This is identical to the equation obtained in the previous example and, as we have just seen, has the solution $n = 20.3$.

Practice Problem

2. A firm estimates that its sales will rise by 3% each year and that it needs to sell at least 10 000 goods each year in order to make a profit. Given that its current annual sales are only 9000, how many years will it take before the firm breaks even?

You may have noticed that in all of the previous problems it is assumed that the interest is compounded annually. It is possible for interest to be added to the investment more frequently than this. For example, suppose that a principal of $500 is invested for 3 years at 10% interest compounded quarterly. What do we mean by '10% interest compounded quarterly'? Well, it does *not* mean that we get 10% interest every 3 months. Instead, the 10% is split into four equal portions, one for each quarter. Every 3 months the interest accrued is

$$\frac{10\%}{4} = 2.5\%$$

so after the first quarter the investment gets multiplied by 1.025 to give

$$500(1.025)$$

and after the second quarter it gets multiplied by another 1.025 to give

$$500(1.025)^2$$

and so on. Moreover, since there are exactly twelve 3-month periods in 3 years we deduce that the future value is

$$500(1.025)^{12} = \$672.44$$

Notice that this is greater than the sum obtained at the start of this section under annual compounding. (Why is this?)

This example highlights the fact that the compound interest formula

$$S = P\left(1 + \frac{r}{100}\right)^n$$

derived earlier for annual compounding can also be used for other types of compounding. All that is needed is to reinterpret the symbols r and n. The variable r now represents the rate of interest per time period and n represents the total number of periods.

Example

A principal of $10 is invested at 12% interest for 1 year. Determine the future value if the interest is compounded

(a) annually   **(b)** semi-annually   **(c)** quarterly   **(d)** monthly   **(e)** weekly

Solution

The formula for compound interest gives

$$S = P\left(1 + \frac{r}{100}\right)^n$$

Practice Problems

3. **(1)** A principal, $30, is invested at 6% interest for 2 years. Determine the future value if the interest is compounded

(a) annually   **(b)** semi-annually   **(c)** quarterly

(d) monthly   **(e)** weekly   **(f)** daily

(2) Use the formula

$$S = Pe^{rt/100}$$

to determine the future value of $30 invested at 6% interest compounded continuously for 2 years. Confirm that it is in agreement with the results of part (1).

4. Determine the rate of interest required for a principal of $1000 to produce a future value of $4000 after 10 years compounded continuously.

Given that there are so many ways of calculating compound interest, people often find it difficult to appraise different investment opportunities. What is needed is a standard 'benchmark' that enables an individual to compare different forms of savings or credit schemes on an equal basis. The one that is commonly used is annual compounding. All firms offering investment or loan facilities are required to provide the effective annual rate. This is often referred to as the **annual percentage rate**, which is abbreviated to APR. The APR is the rate of interest which, when compounded annually, produces the same yield as the nominal (that is, the stated) rate of interest. The phrase 'annual equivalent rate' (AER) is frequently used when applied to savings.

Example

Determine the annual equivalent rate of interest of a deposit account that has a nominal rate of 6.6% compounded monthly.

Solution

The AER is the overall rate of interest, which can be calculated using scale factors. If the account offers a return of 6.6% compounded monthly then each month the interest is

$$\frac{6.6}{12} = 0.55\%$$

of the amount invested at the beginning of that month. The monthly scale factor is

$$1 + \frac{0.55}{100} = 1.0055$$

so in a whole year the principal gets multiplied by

$$(1.0055)^{12} = 1.068$$

which can be written as

$$1 + \frac{6.8}{100}$$

so the AER is 6.8%.

Practice Problem

5. Determine the annual percentage rate of interest if the nominal rate is 12% compounded quarterly.

Although the aim of this chapter is to investigate the mathematics of finance, the mathematical techniques themselves are more widely applicable. We conclude this section with two examples to illustrate this.

Example

A country's annual GNP (gross national product), currently at $25 000 million, is predicted to grow by 3.5% each year. The population is expected to increase by 2% a year from its current level of 40 million. After how many years will GNP per capita (that is, GNP per head of population) reach $700?

Solution

The per capita value of GNP is worked out by dividing GNP by the size of the population. Initially, this is

$$\frac{25\,000\,000\,000}{40\,000\,000} = \$625$$

During the next few years, GNP is forecast to grow at a faster rate than the population so this value will increase.

The scale factor associated with a 3.5% increase is 1.035, so after n years GNP (in millions of dollars) will be

$$\text{GNP} = 25\,000 \times (1.035)^n$$

Similarly, the population (also in millions) will be

$$\text{population} = 40 \times (1.02)^n$$

Hence GNP per capita is

$$\frac{25\,000 \times (1.035)^n}{40 \times (1.02)^n} = \frac{25\,000}{40} \times \frac{(1.035)^n}{(1.02)^n} = 625 \times \left(\frac{1.035}{1.02}\right)^n$$

We want to find the number of years required for this to reach 700, so we need to solve the equation

$$625 \times \left(\frac{1.035}{1.02}\right)^n = 700$$

for n. Dividing both sides by 625 gives

$$\left(\frac{1.035}{1.02}\right)^n = 1.12$$

and after taking logs of both sides we get

$$\log\left(\frac{1.035}{1.02}\right)^n = \log(1.12)$$

$$n\log\left(\frac{1.035}{1.02}\right)^n = \log(1.12) \quad \text{(rule 3 of logs)}$$

so that

$$n = \frac{\log(1.12)}{\log(1.035/1.02)} = 7.76$$

We deduce that the target figure of $700 per capita will be achieved after 8 years.

Example

A firm decides to increase output at a constant rate from its current level of 50 000 to 60 000 during the next 5 years. Calculate the annual rate of increase required to achieve this growth.

Solution

If the rate of increase is $r\%$ then the scale factor is $1 + \dfrac{r}{100}$ so, after 5 years, output will be

$$50\,000\left(1 + \frac{r}{100}\right)^5$$

To achieve a final output of 60 000, the value of r is chosen to satisfy the equation

$$50\,000\left(1 + \frac{r}{100}\right)^5 = 60\,000$$

Dividing both sides by 50 000 gives

$$\left(1 + \frac{r}{100}\right)^5 = 1.2$$

The difficulty in solving this equation is that the unknown, r, is trapped inside the brackets, which are raised to the power of 5. This is analogous to the problem of solving an equation such as

$$x^2 = 5.23$$

which we would solve by taking square roots of both sides to find x. This suggests that we can find r by taking fifth roots of both sides of

$$\left(1 + \frac{r}{100}\right)^5 = 1.2$$

to get

$$1 + \frac{r}{100} = (1.2)^{1/5} = 1.037$$

Hence $r = 3.7\%$.

Practice Problem

6. The turnover of a leading supermarket chain, A, is currently $560 million and is expected to increase at a constant rate of 1.5% a year. Its nearest rival, supermarket B, has a current turnover of $480 million and plans to increase this at a constant rate of 3.4% a year. After how many years will supermarket B overtake supermarket A?

Key Terms

Annual percentage rate   The equivalent annual interest paid for a loan, taking into account the compounding over a variety of time periods.

Compound interest   The interest which is added on to the initial investment, so that this will itself gain interest in subsequent time periods.

Continuous compounding   The limiting value when interest is compounded with ever-increasing frequency.

Future value   The final value of an investment after one or more time periods.

Principal   The value of the original sum invested.

Simple interest   The interest which is paid direct to the investor instead of being added to the original amount.

Exercise 3.2

1. A bank offers a return of 7% interest compounded annually. Find the future value of a principal of $4500 after 6 years. What is the overall percentage rise over this period?

2. Find the future value of $20 000 in 2 years' time if compounded quarterly at 8% interest.

3. The value of an asset, currently priced at $100 000, is expected to increase by 20% a year.

   (a) Find its value in 10 years' time.

   (b) After how many years will it be worth $1 million?

4. How long will it take for a sum of money to double if it is invested at 5% interest compounded annually?

5. A piece of machinery depreciates in value by 5% a year. Determine its value in 3 years' time if its current value is $50 000.

6. A principal, $7000, is invested at 9% interest for 8 years. Determine its future value if the interest is compounded

   (a) annually   (b) semi-annually   (c) monthly   (d) continuously

7. Which of the following savings accounts offers the greater return?

   Account A: an annual rate of 8.05% paid semi-annually

   Account B: an annual rate of 7.95% paid monthly

8. Find the future value of $100 compounded continuously at an annual rate of 6% for 12 years.

9. How long will it take for a sum of money to triple in value if invested at an annual rate of 3% compounded continuously?

10. If a piece of machinery depreciates continuously at an annual rate of 4%, how many years will it take for the value of the machinery to halve?

11. A department store has its own credit card facilities, for which it charges interest at a rate of 2% each month. Explain briefly why this is not the same as an annual rate of 24%. What is the annual percentage rate?

12. Determine the APR if the nominal rate is 7% compounded continuously.

13. Current annual consumption of energy is 78 billion units and this is expected to rise at a fixed rate of 5.8% each year. The capacity of the industry to supply energy is currently 104 billion units.

    (a) Assuming that the supply remains steady, after how many years will demand exceed supply?

    (b) What constant rate of growth of energy production would be needed to satisfy demand for the next 50 years?

14. Find the value, in 2 years time, of $4000 invested at 5% compounded annually. In the following 2 years, the interest rate is expected to rise to 8%. Find the final value of the investment at the end of the 4-year period, and find the overall percentage increase. Give your answers correct to 2 decimal places.

15. Find the APR of a loan if the monthly interest rate is 1.65%. Give your answer correct to 2 decimal places.

16. The future value S of principal P invested for n years with an interest rate r% compounded annually may be calculated using the formula

    $$S = P\left(1 + \frac{r}{100}\right)^n$$

    Rearrange this formula to express P in terms of S, r and n.

17. The number of rail passenger journeys made between England and Scotland in 2004 was 5.015 million. In 2011 the figure was 7.419 million. Work out the yearly percentage rate of growth (assumed constant) during this period.

18. Table 3.23 shows the depreciation in the value of two models of car.

    Table 3.23

Year	2011	2012
Car A	36 000	32 000
Car B	32 000	28 800

    (a) Assuming that the depreciation of Car A is linear estimate its value in 2013.

    (b) Assuming that the depreciation of Car B is exponential estimate its value in 2013.

    (c) Predict when Car A will be worth less than Car B.

Exercise 3.2*

1. A principal of $7650 is invested at a rate of 3.7% compounded annually. After how many years will the investment first exceed $12 250?

2. A principal of $70 000 is invested at 6% interest for 4 years. Find the difference in the future value if the interest is compounded quarterly compared to continuous compounding. Round your answer to 2 decimal places.

3. Midwest Bank offers a return of 5% compounded annually for each and every year. The rival BFB offers a return of 3% for the first year and 7% in the second and subsequent years (both compounded annually). Which bank would you choose to invest in if you decided to invest a principal for (a) 2 years; (b) 3 years?

4. A car depreciates by 40% in the first year, 30% in the second year and 20% thereafter. I buy a car for $14 700 when it is 2 years old.

   (a) How much did it cost when new?

   (b) After how many years will it be worth less than 25% of the amount that I paid for it?

5. The population of a country is currently at 56 million and is forecast to rise by 3.7% each year. It is capable of producing 2500 million units of food each year, and it is estimated that each member of the population requires a minimum of 65 units of food each year. At the moment, the extra food needed to satisfy this requirement is imported, but the government decides to increase food production at a constant rate each year, with the aim of making the country self-sufficient after 10 years. Find the annual rate of growth required to achieve this.

6. Simon decides to buy a new sofa which is available at each of three stores at the same fixed price. He decides to borrow the money using each store's credit facility.

   Store A has an effective rate of interest of 12.6%.
   Store B charges interest at a rate of 10.5% compounded continuously.
   Store C charges interest at a rate of 11.5% compounded quarterly.

   From which store should Simon buy his sofa to minimise the total cost?

7. If a principal, P, is invested at r% interest compounded annually then its future value, S, after n years is given by

$$S = P\left(1 + \frac{r}{100}\right)^n$$

   (a) Use this formula to show that if an interest rate of r% is compounded k times a year then after t years

$$S = P\left(1 + \frac{r}{100k}\right)^{tk}$$

   (b) Show that if $m = 100k/r$ then the formula in part (a) can be written as

$$S = P\left(\left(1 + \frac{1}{m}\right)^m\right)^{rt/100}$$

(c) Use the definition

$$e = \lim_{m \to \infty} \left(1 + \frac{1}{m} \right)^m$$

to deduce that if the interest is compounded with ever-increasing frequency (that is, continuously) then

$$S = Pe^{rt/100}$$

8. World oil reserves are currently estimated to be 600 billion units. If this quantity is reduced by 8% a year, after how many years will oil reserves drop below 100 billion units?

9. The nominal rate of interest of a store card is 18% compounded monthly.

   (a) State the monthly interest rate.

   (b) Find the equivalent annual rate of interest if the compounding is continuous. Round your answer to 2 decimal places.

10. Write down an expression for the annual percentage growth rate of a country whose GDP increases by a factor of g over a period of n years.

11. (a) A principal, P, is invested at a nominal rate of interest, of $r\%$ compounded n times a year. Show that the AER is given by the formula

$$\text{AER} = 100 \left(1 + \frac{r}{100n} \right)^n - 100$$

   (b) Find a formula for AER when the interest is compounded continuously.

SECTION 3.3
Geometric series

Objectives

At the end of this section you should be able to:

- Recognise a geometric progression.
- Evaluate a geometric series.
- Calculate the total investment obtained from a regular savings plan.
- Calculate the instalments needed to repay a loan.

Consider the following sequence of numbers:

2, 6, 18, 54, . . .

One obvious question, often asked in intelligence tests, is what is the next term in the sequence? All that is required is for you to spot the pattern so that it can be used to generate the next term. In this case, successive numbers are obtained by multiplying by 3, so the fifth term is

$54 \times 3 = 162$

the sixth term is

$162 \times 3 = 486$

and so on. Any sequence in which terms are calculated by multiplying their predecessor by a fixed number is called a **geometric progression** and the multiplicative factor itself is called a **geometric ratio**. The sequence above is a geometric progression with geometric ratio 3. The reason for introducing these sequences is not to help you to answer intelligence tests, but rather to analyse compound interest problems. You may well have noticed that all of the problems given in the previous section produced such a sequence. For example, if a principal, $500, is invested at 10% interest compounded annually, then the future values in successive years are

$500(1.1), 500(1.1)^2, 500(1.1)^3, \ldots$

which we recognise as a geometric progression with geometric ratio 1.1.

Example

Which of the following sequences are geometric progressions? For those sequences that are of this type, write down their geometric ratios.

(a) 1000, −100, 10, −1, . . .   (b) 2, 4, 6, 8, . . .   (c) $a, ar, ar^2, ar^3, \ldots$

Solution

(a) 1000, −100, 10, −1, . . . is a geometric progression with geometric ratio, $-\dfrac{1}{10}$.

(b) 2, 4, 6, 8, . . . is not a geometric progression because to go from one term to the next you *add* 2. Such a sequence is called an **arithmetic progression** and is of little interest in business and economics.

(c) a, ar, ar^2, ar^3, . . . is a geometric progression with geometric ratio, r.

Practice Problem

1. Decide which of the following sequences are geometric progressions. For those sequences that are of this type, write down their geometric ratios.

(a) 3, 6, 12, 24, . . .   (b) 5, 10, 15, 20, . . .   (c) 1, −3, 9, −27, . . .

(d) 8, 4, 2, 1, $^1/_2$, . . .   (e) 500, 500(1.07), 500(1.07)^2, . . .

All of the problems considered in Section 3.2 involved a single lump-sum payment into an investment account. The task was simply to determine its future value after a period of time when it is subject to a certain type of compounding. In this section, we extend this to include multiple payments. This situation occurs whenever individuals save regularly or when businesses take out a loan that is paid back using fixed monthly or annual instalments. To tackle these problems we need to be able to sum (that is, to add together) consecutive terms of a geometric progression. Such an expression is called a **geometric series**. Suppose that we want to sum the first six terms of the geometric progression given by the sequence

2, 6, 18, 54, . . .   (1)

The easiest way of doing this is to write down these six numbers and add them together to get

$$2 + 6 + 18 + 54 + 162 + 486 = 728$$

There is, however, a special formula to sum a geometric series which is particularly useful when there are lots of terms or when the individual terms are more complicated to evaluate. It can be shown that the sum of the first n terms of a geometric progression in which the first term is a, and the geometric ratio is r, is equal to

$$a\left(\frac{r^n - 1}{r - 1}\right) \quad (r \neq 1)$$

Use of the symbol r to denote both the interest rate and the geometric ratio is unfortunate but fairly standard. In practice, it is usually clear from the context what this symbol represents, so no confusion should arise.

A proof of this formula is given in Question 7 in Exercise 3.3* at the end of this section. As a check, let us use it to determine the sum of the first six terms of sequence (1) above. In this case the first term $a = 2$, the geometric ratio $r = 3$ and the number of terms $n = 6$, so the geometric series is equal to

$$2\left(\frac{3^6 - 1}{3 - 1}\right) = 3^6 - 1 = 728$$

which agrees with the previous value found by summing the terms longhand. In this case there is no real benefit in using the formula. However, it would be tedious to evaluate the geometric series

$$500(1.1) + 500(1.1)^2 + 500(1.1)^3 + \ldots + 500(1.1)^{25}$$

longhand, whereas substituting, $a = 500(1.1)$, $r = 1.1$ and $n = 25$ into the formula immediately gives

$$500(1.1)\left(\frac{(1.1)^{25} - 1}{1.1 - 1}\right) = 54\ 090.88$$

Practice Problem

2. **(a)** Write down the next term in the sequence

$$1, 2, 4, 8, \ldots$$

and hence find the sum of the first five terms. Check that this agrees with the value obtained using

$$a\left(\frac{r^n - 1}{r - 1}\right)$$

(b) Evaluate the geometric series

$$100(1.07) + 100(1.07)^2 + \ldots + 100(1.07)^{20}$$

There are two particular applications of geometric series that we now consider, involving savings and loans. We begin by analysing savings plans. In the simplest case, an individual decides to invest a regular sum of money into a bank account. This is sometimes referred to as a **sinking fund** and is used to meet some future financial commitment. It is assumed that he or she saves an equal amount and that the money is put into the account at the same time each year (or month). We further assume that the interest rate does not change. The latter may not be an entirely realistic assumption, since it can fluctuate wildly in volatile market conditions. Indeed, banks offer a variety of rates of interest depending on the notice required for withdrawal and on the actual amount of money saved. Question 5 in Exercise 3.3* at the end of this section considers what happens when the interest rate rises as the investment goes above certain threshold levels.

Example

A person saves $100 in a bank account at the beginning of each month. The bank offers a return of 12% compounded monthly.

(a) Determine the total amount saved after 12 months.

(b) After how many months does the amount saved first exceed $2000?

Solution

(a) During the year a total of 12 regular savings of $100 are made. Each $100 is put into an account that gives a return of 12% compounded monthly, or equivalently, a return of 1% each month. However, each payment is invested for a different period of time. For example, the first payment is invested for the full 12 months, whereas the final payment is invested for 1 month only. We need to work out the future value of each payment separately and add them together.

The first payment is invested for 12 months, gaining a monthly interest of 1%, so its future value is

$$100(1.01)^{12}$$

The second payment is invested for 11 months, so its future value is

$$100(1.01)^{11}$$

Likewise, the third payment yields

$$100(1.01)^{10}$$

and so on. The last payment is invested for 1 month, so its future value is

$$100(1.01)^{1}$$

The total value of the savings at the end of 12 months is then

$$100(1.01)^{12} + 100(1.01)^{11} + \ldots + 100(1.01)^{1}$$

If we rewrite this series in the order of ascending powers, we then have the more familiar form

$$100(1.01)^{1} + \ldots + 100(1.01)^{11} + 100(1.01)^{12}$$

This is equal to the sum of the first 12 terms of a geometric progression in which the first term is $100(1.01)$ and the geometric ratio is 1.01. Its value can therefore be found by using

$$a\left(\frac{r^{n}-1}{r-1}\right)$$

with $a = 100(1.01)$, $r = 1.01$ and $n = 12$, which gives

$$\$100(1.01)\left(\frac{(1.01)^{12}-1}{1.01-1}\right) = \$1280.93$$

(b) In part (a) we showed that after 12 months the total amount saved is

$$100(1.01) + 100(1.01)^{2} + \ldots + 100(1.01)^{12}$$

Using exactly the same argument, it is easy to see that after n months the account contains

$$100(1.01) + 100(1.01)^{2} + \ldots + 100(1.01)^{n}$$

The formula for the sum of the first n terms of a geometric progression shows that this is the same as

$$100(1.01)\left(\frac{1.01^n - 1}{1.01 - 1}\right) = 10\,100(1.01^n - 1)$$

The problem here is to find the number of months needed for total savings to rise to $2000. Mathematically, this is equivalent to solving the equation

$$10\,100(1.01^n - 1) = 2000$$

for n. Following the strategy described in Section 2.3 gives

$$1.01^n - 1 = 0.198 \qquad \text{(divide both sides by 10\,100)}$$
$$1.01^n = 1.198 \qquad \text{(add 1 to both sides)}$$
$$\log(1.01)^n = \log(1.198) \qquad \text{(take logs of both sides)}$$
$$n\log(1.01) = \log(1.198) \qquad \text{(rule 3 of logs)}$$
$$n = \frac{\log(1.198)}{\log(1.01)} \qquad \text{(divide both sides by } \log(1.01))$$
$$= 18.2$$

It follows that after 18 months savings are less than $2000, whereas after 19 months savings exceed this amount. The target figure of $2000 is therefore reached at the end of the 19th month.

Practice Problem

3. An individual saves $1000 in a bank account at the beginning of each year. The bank offers a return of 8% compounded annually.

    (a) Determine the amount saved after 10 years.

    (b) After how many years does the amount saved first exceed $20 000?

We now turn our attention to loans. Many businesses finance their expansion by obtaining loans from a bank or other financial institution. Banks are keen to do this provided that they receive interest as a reward for lending money. Businesses pay back loans by monthly or annual repayments. The way in which this repayment is calculated is as follows. Let us suppose that interest is calculated on a monthly basis and that the firm repays the debt by fixed monthly instalments at the end of each month. The bank calculates the interest charged during the first month based on the original loan. At the end of the month, this interest is added on to the original loan and the repayment is simultaneously deducted to determine the amount owed. The bank then charges interest in the second month based on this new amount and the process is repeated. Provided that the monthly repayment is greater than the interest charged each month, the amount owed decreases and eventually the debt is cleared. In practice, the period during which the loan is repaid is fixed in advance and the monthly repayments are calculated to achieve this end.

Example

Determine the monthly repayments needed to repay a $100 000 loan which is paid back over 25 years when the interest rate is 8% compounded annually.

Solution

In this example the time interval between consecutive repayments is 1 month, whereas the period during which interest is charged is 1 year. This type of financial calculation typifies the way in which certain types of housing loan are worked out. The interest is compounded annually at 8%, so the amount of interest charged during the first year is 8% of the original loan: that is,

$$\frac{8}{100} \times 100\,000 = 8000$$

This amount is added on to the outstanding debt at the end of the first year. During this time, 12 monthly repayments are made, so if each instalment is x, the outstanding debt must decrease by $12x$. Hence, at the end of the first year, the amount owed is

$$100\,000 + 8000 - 12x = 108\,000 - 12x$$

In order to be able to spot a pattern in the annual debt, let us write this as

$$100\,000(1.08) - 12x$$

where the first part simply reflects the fact that 8% interest is added on to the original sum of $100 000. At the end of the second year, a similar calculation is performed. The amount owed rises by 8% to become

$$[100\,000(1.08) - 12x](1.08) = 100\,000(1.08)^2 - 12x(1.08)$$

and we deduct $12x$ for the repayments to get

$$100\,000(1.08)^2 - 12x(1.08) - 12x$$

This is the amount owed at the end of the second year. Each year we multiply by 1.08 and subtract $12x$, so at the end of the third year we owe

$$[100\,000(1.08)^2 - 12x(1.08) - 12x]\,(1.08) - 12x$$
$$= 100\,000(1.08)^3 - 12x(1.08)^2 - 12x(1.08) - 12x$$

and so on. These results are summarised in Table 3.24. If we continue the pattern, we see that after 25 years the amount owed is

$$100\,000(1.08)^{25} - 12x(1.08)^{24} - 12x(1.08)^{23} - \ldots - 12x$$
$$= 100\,000(1.08)^{25} - 12x[1 + 1.08 + (1.08)^2 + \ldots + (1.08)^{24}]$$

(Taking out a common factor of $12x$ and rewriting powers of 1.08 in ascending order.)

Table 3.24

End of year	Outstanding debt
1	$100\,000(1.08)^1 - 12x$
2	$100\,000(1.08)^2 - 12x(1.08)^1 - 12x$
3	$100\,000(1.08)^3 - 12x(1.08)^2 - 12x(1.08)^1 - 12x$

The first term is easily evaluated using a calculator to get

$$100\,000(1.08)^{25} = 684\,847.520$$

The geometric series inside the square brackets can be worked out from the formula

$$a\left(\frac{r^n - 1}{r - 1}\right)$$

The first term $a = 1$, the geometric ratio $r = 1.08$, and we are summing the first 25 terms, so $n = 25$. (Can you see why there are actually 25 terms in this series rather than 24?) Hence

$$[1 + 1.08 + (1.08)^2 + \cdots + (1.08)^{24}] = \frac{1.08^{25} - 1}{1.08 - 1} = 73.106$$

The amount owed at the end of 25 years is therefore

$$684\,847.520 - 12x(73.106) = 684\,847.520 - 877.272x$$

In this expression, x denotes the monthly repayment, which is chosen so that the debt is completely cleared after 25 years. This will be so if x is the solution of

$$684\,847.520 - 877.272x = 0$$

Hence

$$x = \frac{684\,847.520}{877.272} = \$780.66$$

The monthly repayment on a 25-year loan of $100\,000 is $780.66, assuming that the interest rate remains fixed at 8% throughout this period.

It is interesting to substitute this value of x into the expressions for the outstanding debt given in Table 3.24. The results are listed in Table 3.25. What is so depressing about these figures is that the debt only falls by about $1500 to begin with, in spite of the fact that over $9000 is being repaid each year!

Table 3.25

End of year	Outstanding debt
1	$98 632.08
2	$97 154.73
3	$95 559.18

Practice Problem

4. A person requests an immediate bank overdraft of $2000. The bank generously agrees to this, but insists that it should be repaid by 12 monthly instalments and charges 1% interest every month on the outstanding debt. Determine the monthly repayment.

The mathematics used in this section for problems on savings and loans can be used for other time series. Reserves of non-renewable commodities such as minerals, oil and gas continue to decline, and geometric series can be used to estimate the year in which these stocks are likely to run out.

Example

Total reserves of a non-renewable resource are 250 million tonnes. Annual consumption, currently at 20 million tonnes per year, is expected to rise by 2% a year. After how many years will stocks be exhausted?

Solution

In the first year, consumption will be 20 million tonnes. In the second year, this will rise by 2%, so consumption will be 20(1.02) million tonnes. In the third year, this will again rise by 2% to become $20(1.02)^2$ million tonnes. The total consumption (in millions of tonnes) during the next n years will be

$$20 + 20(1.02) + 20(1.02)^2 + \ldots + 20(1.02)^{n-1}$$

This represents the sum of n terms of a geometric series with first term $a = 20$ and geometric ratio $r = 1.02$, so is equal to

$$20\left(\frac{1.02^n - 1}{1.02 - 1}\right) = 1000(1.02^n - 1)$$

Reserves will run out when this exceeds 250 million, so we need to solve the equation

$$1000(1.02^n - 1) = 250$$

for n. This is easily solved using logarithms:

$$
\begin{array}{ll}
1.02^n - 1 = 0.25 & \text{(divide both sides by 1000)} \\
1.02^n = 1.25 & \text{(add 1 to both sides)} \\
\log(1.02)^n = \log(1.25) & \text{(take logs of both sides)} \\
n\log(1.02) = \log(1.25) & \text{(rule 3 of logs)} \\
n = \dfrac{\log(1.25)}{\log(1.02)} & \text{(divide both sides by } \log(1.02)) \\
= 11.27 &
\end{array}
$$

so the reserves will be completely exhausted after 12 years.

Practice Problem

5. It is estimated that world reserves of oil currently stand at 2625 billion units. Oil is currently extracted at an annual rate of 45.5 billion units and this is set to increase by 2.6% a year. After how many years will oil reserves run out?

Example

Current annual extraction of a non-renewable resource is 40 billion units and this is expected to fall at a rate of 5% each year. Estimate the current minimum level of reserves if this resource is to last in perpetuity (that is, for ever).

Solution

In the first year 40 billion units are extracted. In the second year this falls by 5% to 40(0.95) billion units. In the third year this goes down by a further 5% to $40(0.95)^2$. After n years the total amount extracted will be

$$40 + 40(0.95) + 40(0.95)^2 + \ldots + 40(0.95)^{n-1}$$

Using the formula for the sum of a geometric progression gives

$$40\left(\frac{0.95^n - 1}{0.95 - 1}\right) = 40\left(\frac{0.95^n - 1}{-0.05}\right) = 800(1 - 0.95^n)$$

To see what happens in perpetuity we need to investigate the behaviour 0.95^n as n tends to infinity. Now since the magnitude of 0.95 is less than unity, it is easy to see that 0.95^n converges to zero and so the total amount will be 800 billion units.

Key Terms

Arithmetic progression   A sequence of numbers with a constant difference between consecutive terms; the nth term takes the form, $a + bn$.

Geometric progression   A sequence of numbers with a constant ratio between consecutive terms; the nth term takes the form, ar^{n-1}.

Geometric ratio   The constant multiplier in a geometric series.

Geometric series   A sum of the consecutive terms of a geometric progression.

Sinking fund   A fixed sum of money saved at regular intervals which is used to fund some future financial commitment.

Exercise 3.3

1. Find the value of the geometric series

    $$1000 + 1000(1.03) + 1000(1.03)^2 + \ldots + 1000(1.03)^9$$

2. An individual saves $5000 in a bank account at the beginning of each year for 10 years. No further savings or withdrawals are made from the account. Determine the total amount saved if the annual interest rate is 8% compounded:

    (a) annually

    (b) semi-annually.

3. Determine the monthly repayments needed to repay a $125 000 loan which is paid back over 20 years when the interest rate is 7% compounded annually. Round your answer to 2 decimal places.

4. A prize fund is set up with a single investment of $5000 to provide an annual prize of $500. The fund is invested to earn interest at a rate of 7% compounded annually. If the first prize is awarded 1 year after the initial investment, find the number of years for which the prize can be awarded before the fund falls below $500.

5. The current extraction of a certain mineral is 12 million tonnes a year and this is expected to fall at a constant rate of 6% each year. Estimate the current minimum level of world reserves if the extraction is to last in perpetuity.

6. A person invests $5000 at the beginning of a year in a savings account that offers a return of 4.5% compounded annually. At the beginning of each subsequent year an additional $1000 is invested in the account. How much will there be in the account at the end of ten years?

7. A person borrows $100 000 at the beginning of a year and agrees to repay the loan in ten equal instalments at the end of each year. Interest is charged at a rate of 6% compounded annually.

    (a) Find the annual repayment.

    (b) Work out the total amount of interest paid and compare this with the total interest paid when repaying the loan in five equal annual instalments instead of ten.

8. A person wishes to save a regular amount at the beginning of each month in order to buy a car in 18 months' time. An account offers a return of 4.8% compounded monthly. Work out the monthly savings if the total amount saved at the end of 18 months is $18 000.

Exercise 3.3*

1. Find the sum of the of the geometric series,

    $$5 - 20 + 80 - 320 + \ldots - 20\ 971\ 520$$

2. A regular saving of $500 is made into a sinking fund at the start of each year for 10 years. Determine the value of the fund at the end of the tenth year on the assumption that the rate of interest is

    (a) 11% compounded annually

    (b) 10% compounded continuously.

3. Monthly sales figures for January are 5600. This is expected to fall for the following 9 months at a rate of 2% each month. Thereafter sales are predicted to rise at a constant rate of 4% each month. Estimate total sales for the next 2 years (including the first January).

4. Determine the monthly repayments needed to repay a $50 000 loan that is paid back over 25 years when the interest rate is 9% compounded annually. Calculate the increased monthly repayments needed in the case when

    (a) the interest rate rises to 10%

    (b) the period of repayment is reduced to 20 years.

5. A bank has three different types of account in which the interest rate depends on the amount invested. The 'ordinary' account offers a return of 6% and is available to every customer. The 'extra' account offers 7% and is available only to customers with $5000 or more to invest. The 'superextra' account offers 8% and is available only to customers with $20 000 or more to invest. In each case, interest is compounded annually and is added to the investment at the end of the year.

   A person saves $4000 at the beginning of each year for 25 years. Calculate the total amount saved on the assumption that the money is transferred to a higher-interest account at the earliest opportunity.

6. A business takes out a loan of $500 000 from a bank and agrees to repay the loan by paying a fixed amount of $60 000 at the end of each subsequent year. Once the debt falls below $60 000 the business pays off the outstanding debt as the final payment. Work out the final payment if the interest rate is 7.5% compounded annually.

7. If

   $$S_n = a + ar + ar^2 + \ldots + ar^{n-1}$$

   write down an expression for rS_n and deduce that

   $$rS_n - S_n = ar^n - a$$

   Hence show that the sum of the first n terms of a geometric progression with first term a and geometric ratio r is given by

   $$a\left(\frac{r^n - 1}{r - 1}\right)$$

   provided that $r \neq 1$.

8. At the beginning of a month, a customer owes a credit card company $8480. In the middle of the month, the customer repays A, where $A < \$8480$, and at the end of the month the company adds interest at a rate of 6% of the outstanding debt. This process is repeated with the customer continuing to pay off the same amount, A, each month.

   (a) Find the value of A for which the customer still owes $8480 at the start of each month.

   (b) If $A = 1000$, calculate the amount owing at the end of the eighth month.

   (c) Show that the value of A for which the whole amount owing is exactly paid off after the nth payment is given by

   $$A = \frac{8480R^{n-1}(R - 1)}{R^n - 1} \quad \text{where} \quad R = 1.06$$

   (d) Find the value of A if the debt is to be paid off exactly after 2 years.

SECTION 3.4
Investment appraisal

> ### Objectives
>
> At the end of this section you should be able to:
>
> - Calculate present values under discrete and continuous compounding.
> - Use net present values to appraise investment projects.
> - Calculate the internal rate of return.
> - Calculate the present value of an annuity.
> - Use discounting to compare investment projects.
> - Calculate the present value of government securities.

In Section 3.2 the following two formulas were used to solve compound interest problems

$$S = P\left(1 + \frac{r}{100}\right)^t \tag{1}$$

$$S = Pe^{rt/100} \tag{2}$$

The first of these can be applied to any type of compounding in which the interest is added on to the investment at the end of discrete time intervals. The second formula is used when the interest is added on continuously. Both formulas involve the variables

P = principal

S = future value

r = interest rate

t = time

In the case of discrete compounding, the letter t represents the number of time periods. (In Section 3.2 this was denoted by n.) For continuous compounding, t is measured in years. Given any three of these variables it is possible to work out the value of the remaining variable. Various examples were considered in Section 3.2. Of particular interest is the case where S, r and t are given, and P is the unknown to be determined. In this situation we know the future value, and we want to work backwards to calculate the original principal. This process is called **discounting** and the principal, P, is called the **present value**. The rate of interest is sometimes referred to as the **discount rate**. Equations (1) and (2) are easily rearranged to produce explicit formulas for the present value under discrete and continuous compounding:

$$P = \frac{S}{(1 + r/100)^t} = S\left(1 + \frac{r}{100}\right)^{-t}$$

reciprocals are denoted by negative powers

$$P = \frac{S}{e^{rt/100}} = Se^{-rt/100}$$

Example

Find the present value of $1000 in 4 years' time if the discount rate is 10% compounded

(a) semi-annually

(b) continuously

Solution

(a) The discount formula for discrete compounding is

$$P = S\left(1 + \frac{r}{100}\right)^{-t}$$

If compounding occurs semi-annually then $r = 5$ since the interest rate per 6 months is $10/2 = 5$, and $t = 8$ since there are eight 6-month periods in 4 years. We are given that the future value is $1000, so

$$P = \$1000(1.05)^{-8} = \$676.84$$

(b) The discount formula for continuous compounding is

$$P = Se^{-rt/100}$$

In this formula, r is the annual discount rate, which is 10, and t is measured in years, so is 4. Hence the present value is

$$P = \$1000e^{-0.4} = \$670.32$$

Notice that the present value in part (b) is smaller than that in part (a). This is to be expected because continuous compounding always produces a higher yield. Consequently, we need to invest a smaller amount under continuous compounding to produce the future value of $1000 after 4 years.

Practice Problem

1. Find the present value of $100 000 in 10 years' time if the discount rate is 6% compounded

   (a) annually   **(b)** continuously

Present values are a useful way of appraising investment projects. Suppose that you are invited to invest $600 today in a business venture that is certain to produce a return of $1000 in 5 years' time. If the discount rate is 10% compounded semi-annually then part (a) of the previous example shows that the present value of this return is $676.84. This exceeds the initial outlay of $600, so the venture is regarded as profitable. We quantify this profit by calculating the difference between the present value of the revenue and the present value of the costs, which is known as the **net present value** (NPV). In this example, the net present value is

$$\$676.84 - \$600 = \$76.84$$

Quite generally, a project is considered worthwhile when the NPV is positive. Moreover, if a decision is to be made between two different projects then the one with the higher NPV is the preferred choice.

An alternative way of assessing individual projects is based on the **internal rate of return** (IRR). This is the annual rate which, when applied to the initial outlay, yields the same return as the project after the same number of years. The investment is considered worthwhile provided the IRR exceeds the market rate. Obviously, in practice, other factors such as risk need to be considered before a decision is made.

The following example illustrates both NPV and IRR methods and shows how a value of the IRR itself can be calculated.

Example

A project requiring an initial outlay of $15 000 is guaranteed to produce a return of $20 000 in 3 years' time. Use the

(a) net present value

(b) internal rate of return

methods to decide whether this investment is worthwhile if the prevailing market rate is 5% compounded annually. Would your decision be affected if the interest rate were 12%?

Solution

(a) The present value of $20 000 in 3 years' time, based on a discount rate of 5%, is found by setting $S = 20\ 000$, $t = 3$ and $r = 5$ in the formula

$$P = S\left(1+\frac{r}{100}\right)^{-t}$$

This gives

$$P = \$20\ 000(1.05)^{-3} = \$17\ 276.75$$

The NPV is therefore

$$\$17\ 276.75 - \$15\ 000 = \$2276.75$$

The project is to be recommended because this value is positive.

(b) To calculate the IRR we use the formula

$$S = P\left(1+\frac{r}{100}\right)^{t}$$

We are given $S = 20\ 000$, $P = 15\ 000$ and $t = 3$, so we need to solve

$$20\ 000 = 15\ 000\left(1+\frac{r}{100}\right)^{3}$$

for r. An obvious first step is to divide both sides of this equation by 15 000 to get

$$\frac{4}{3} = \left(1+\frac{r}{100}\right)^{3}$$

We can extract r by taking cube roots of both sides of

$$\left(1+\frac{r}{100}\right)^3 = \frac{4}{3}$$

to get

$$1+\frac{r}{100} = \left(\frac{4}{3}\right)^{1/3} = 1.1$$

Hence

$$\frac{r}{100} = 1.1 - 1 = 0.1$$

and so the IRR is 10%. The project is therefore to be recommended because this value exceeds the market rate of 5%.

For the last part of the problem we are invited to consider whether our advice would be different if the market rate were 12%. Using the NPV method, we need to repeat the calculations, replacing 5 by 12. The corresponding net present value is then

$$\$20\,000(1.12)^{-3} - \$15\,000 = -\$764.40$$

This time the NPV is negative, so the project leads to an effective loss and is not to be recommended. The same conclusion can be reached more easily using the IRR method. We have already seen that the internal rate of return is 10% and can deduce immediately that you would be better off investing the $15 000 at the market rate of 12%, since this gives the higher yield.

Practice Problem

2. An investment project requires an initial outlay of $8000 and will produce a return of $17 000 at the end of 5 years. Use the

(a) net present value

(b) internal rate of return

methods to decide whether this is worthwhile if the capital could be invested elsewhere at 15% compounded annually.

Advice

This problem illustrates the use of two different methods for investment appraisal. It may appear at first sight that the method based on the IRR is the preferred approach, particularly if you wish to consider more than one interest rate. However, this is not usually the case. The IRR method can give wholly misleading advice when *comparing* two or more projects, and you must be careful when interpreting the results of this method. The following example highlights the difficulty.

Example

Suppose that it is possible to invest in only one of two different projects. Project A requires an initial outlay of $1000 and yields $1200 in 4 years' time. Project B requires an outlay of $30 000 and yields $35 000 after 4 years. Which of these projects would you choose to invest in when the market rate is 3% compounded annually?

Solution

Let us first solve this problem using net present values.

For Project A

$$\text{NPV} = \$1200(1.03)^{-4} - \$1000 = \$66.18$$

For Project B

$$\text{NPV} = \$35\,000(1.03)^{-4} - \$30\,000 = \$1097.05$$

Both projects are viable as they produce positive net present values. Moreover, the second project is preferred, since it has the higher value. You can see that this recommendation is correct by considering how you might invest $30 000. If you opt for Project A then the best you can do is to invest $1000 of this amount to give a return of $1200 in 4 years' time. The remaining $29 000 could be invested at the market rate of 3% to yield

$$\$29\,000(1.03)^4 = \$32\,639.76$$

The total return is then

$$\$1200 + \$32\,639.76 = \$33\,839.76$$

On the other hand, if you opt for Project B then the whole of the $30 000 can be invested to yield $35 000. In other words, in 4 years' time you would be

$$\$35\,000 - \$33\,839.76 = \$1160.24$$

better off by choosing Project B, which confirms the advice given by the NPV method.

However, this is contrary to the advice given by the IRR method. For Project A, the internal rate of return, r_A, satisfies

$$1200 = 1000\left(1 + \frac{r_A}{100}\right)^4$$

Dividing by 1000 gives

$$\left(1 + \frac{r_A}{100}\right)^4 = 1.2$$

and if we take fourth roots we get

$$1 + \frac{r_A}{100} = (1.2)^{1/4} = 1.047$$

so $r_A = 4.7\%$.

For Project B the internal rate of return, r_B, satisfies

$$35\,000 = 30\,000\left(1 + \frac{r_B}{100}\right)^4$$

This can be solved as before to get $r_B = 3.9\%$.

Project A gives the higher internal rate of return even though, as we have seen, Project B is the preferred choice.

The results of this example show that the IRR method is an unreliable way of comparing investment opportunities when there are significant differences between the amounts involved. This is because the IRR method compares percentages, and obviously a large percentage of a small sum could give a smaller profit than a small percentage of a larger sum.

Practice Problem

3. A firm needs to choose between two projects, A and B. Project A involves an initial outlay of $13 500 and yields $18 000 in 2 years' time. Project B requires an outlay of $9000 and yields $13 000 after 2 years. Which of these projects would you advise the firm to invest in if the annual market rate of interest is 7%?

So far in this section we have calculated the present value of a single future value. We now consider the case of a sequence of payments over time. The simplest cash flow of this type is an **annuity**, which is a sequence of regular equal payments. It can be thought of as the opposite of a sinking fund. This time a lump sum is invested and, subsequently, equal amounts of money are withdrawn at fixed time intervals. Provided that the payments themselves exceed the amount of interest gained during the time interval between payments, the fund will decrease and eventually become zero. At this point the payments cease. In practice, we are interested in the value of the original lump sum needed to secure a regular income over a known period of time. This can be done by summing the present values of the individual payments.

To be specific suppose that a person wishes to retire and receive a regular income of $10 000 at the end of each year for the next 10 years. If the interest rate is 7% compounded annually then the present values can be worked out using the formula

$$P = 10\,000\left(1 + \frac{7}{100}\right)^{-t}$$

The first payment is made at the end of the first year so its present value is

$$P = \$10\,000(1.07)^{-1} = \$9345.79$$

This means that if we want to take out $10 000 from the fund in 1 year's time then we need to invest $9345.79 today. The second payment of $10 000 is made at the end of the second year, so its present value is

$$\$10\,000(1.07)^{-2} = \$8734.39$$

This is the amount of money that needs to be invested now to cover the second payment from the fund. In general, the present value of $10 000 in t years' time is

$$10\,000(1.07)^{-t}$$

so the total present value is

$$10\,000(1.07)^{-1} + 10\,000(1.07)^{-2} + \ldots + 10\,000(1.07)^{-10}$$

This is a geometric series, so we may use the formula

$$a\left(\frac{r^n - 1}{r - 1}\right)$$

In this case, $a = 10\,000(1.07)^{-1}$, $r = 1.07^{-1}$ and $n = 10$, so the present value of the annuity is

$$\$10\,000(1.07)^{-1}\left(\frac{1.07^{-10}-1}{1.07^{-1}-1}\right) = \$70\,235.82$$

This represents the amount of money that needs to be invested now so that a regular annual income of $10 000 can be withdrawn from the fund for the next 10 years.

For many people there is a real fear that their pension will not provide an adequate income for the whole of their retirement. If the income stream is to continue for ever then we need to investigate what happens to the formula

$$a\left(\frac{r^n-1}{r-1}\right)$$

as n gets bigger and bigger. In this case $r = 1.07^{-1} < 1$, so as n increases, r^n decreases and tends towards zero. This behaviour can be seen clearly from the table:

n	1	10	100
1.07^{-n}	0.9346	0.5083	0.0012

Setting $r^n = 0$ in the formula for the sum of geometric series shows that if the series goes on for ever then eventually the sum approaches

$$\frac{a}{1-r}$$

so that the present value of the annuity in perpetuity is

$$\frac{10\,000(1.07)^{-1}}{1-1.07^{-1}} = \$142\,857.14$$

This compares with the figure of $70 235.82 calculated previously to secure the income for 10 years.

Practice Problem

4. Find the present value of an annuity that yields an income of $2000 at the end of each month for 10 years, assuming that the interest rate is 6% compounded monthly.

The argument used in the previous example can be used to calculate the net present value. For instance, suppose that a business requires an initial investment of $60 000, which is guaranteed to return a regular payment of $10 000 at the end of each year for the next 10 years. If the discount rate is 7% compounded annually then the previous example shows that the present value is $70 235.82. The net present value of the investment is therefore

$$\$70\,235.82 - \$60\,000 = \$10\,235.82$$

A similar procedure can be used when the payments are irregular, although it is no longer possible to use the formula for the sum of a geometric progression. Instead the present value of each individual payment is calculated and the values are then summed longhand.

Example

A small business has a choice of investing $20 000 in one of two projects. The revenue flows from the two projects during the next 4 years are listed in Table 3.26. If the interest rate is 11% compounded annually, which of these two projects would you advise the company to invest in?

Table 3.26

End of year	Revenue ($)	
	Project A	Project B
1	6 000	10 000
2	3 000	6 000
3	10 000	9 000
4	8 000	1 000
Total	27 000	26 000

Solution

If we simply add together all of the individual receipts, it appears that Project A is to be preferred, since the total revenue generated from Project A is $1000 greater than that from Project B. However, this naïve approach fails to take into account the time distribution.

From Table 3.26 we see that both projects yield a single receipt of $10 000. For Project A this occurs at the end of year 3, whereas for Project B this occurs at the end of year 1. This $10 000 is worth more in Project B because it occurs earlier in the revenue stream and, once received, could be invested for longer at the prevailing rate of interest. To compare these projects we need to discount the revenue stream to the present value. The present values obtained depend on the discount rate. Table 3.27 shows the present values based on the given rate of 11% compounded annually. These values are calculated using the formula

$$P = S(1.11)^{-t}$$

For example, the present value of the $10 000 revenue in Project A is given by

$$\$10\ 000(1.11)^{-3} = \$7311.91$$

The net present values for Project A and Project B are given by

$$\$20\ 422.04 - \$20\ 000 = \$422.04$$

and

$$\$21\ 109.19 - \$20\ 000 = \$1109.19$$

respectively. Consequently, if it is possible to invest in only one of these projects, the preferred choice is Project B.

Table 3.27

End of year	Discounted revenue ($)	
	Project A	Project B
1	5405.41	9000.01
2	2434.87	4869.73
3	7311.91	6580.72
4	5269.85	658.73
Total	20 422.04	21 109.19

Practice Problem

5. A firm has a choice of spending $10 000 today on one of two projects. The revenue obtained from these projects is listed in Table 3.28. Assuming that the discount rate is 15% compounded annually, which of these two projects would you advise the company to invest in?

Table 3.28

End of year	Revenue ($)	
	Project A	Project B
1	2000	1000
2	2000	1000
3	3000	2000
4	3000	6000
5	3000	4000

It is sometimes useful to find the internal rate of return of a project yielding a sequence of payments over time. However, as the following example demonstrates, this can be difficult to calculate, particularly when there are more than two payments.

Example

(a) Calculate the IRR of a project which requires an initial outlay of $20 000 and produces a return of $8000 at the end of year 1 and $15 000 at the end of year 2.

(b) Calculate the IRR of a project which requires an initial outlay of $5000 and produces returns of $1000, $2000 and $3000 at the end of years 1, 2 and 3, respectively.

Solution

(a) In the case of a single payment, the IRR is the annual rate of interest, r, which, when applied to the initial outlay, P, yields a known future payment, S. If this payment is made after t years then

$$S = P\left(1 + \frac{r}{100}\right)^t$$

or, equivalently

$$P = S\left(1 + \frac{r}{100}\right)^{-t}$$

Note that the right-hand side of this last equation is just the present value of S. Consequently, the IRR can be thought of as the rate of interest at which the present value of S equals the initial outlay P.

The present value of $8000 in 1 year's time is

$$8000\left(1 + \frac{r}{100}\right)^{-1}$$

where r is the annual rate of interest. Similarly, the present value of \$15 000 in 2 years' time is

$$15\,000\left(1+\frac{r}{100}\right)^{-2}$$

If r is to be the IRR then the sum of these present values must equal the initial investment of \$20 000. In other words, the IRR is the value of r that satisfies the equation

$$20\,000 = 8000\left(1+\frac{r}{100}\right)^{-1}+15\,000\left(1+\frac{r}{100}\right)^{-2}$$

The simplest way of solving this equation is to multiply both sides by $(1 + r/100)^2$ to remove all negative indices. This gives

$$20\,000\left(1+\frac{r}{100}\right)^{2} = 8000\left(1+\frac{r}{100}\right)+15\,000$$

$$b^m \times b^n = b^{m+n}$$
$$b^0 = 1$$

Now

$$\left(1+\frac{r}{100}\right)^{2} = \left(1+\frac{r}{100}\right)\left(1+\frac{r}{100}\right) = 1+\frac{r}{50}+\frac{r^2}{10\,000}$$

so if we multiply out the brackets, we obtain

$$20\,000 + 400r + 2r^2 = 8000 + 80r + 15\,000$$

Collecting like terms gives

$$2r^2 + 320r - 3000 = 0$$

This is a quadratic in r, so can be solved using the formula described in Section 2.1 to get

$$r = \frac{-320 \pm \sqrt{((320)^2 - 4(2)(-3000))}}{2(2)}$$

$$= \frac{-320 \pm 355.5}{4}$$

$$= 8.9\% \text{ or } -168.9\%$$

We can obviously ignore the negative solution, so can conclude that the IRR is 8.9%.

(b) If an initial outlay of \$5000 yields \$1000, \$2000 and \$3000 at the end of years 1, 2 and 3, respectively, then the internal rate of return, r, satisfies the equation

$$5000 = 1000\left(1+\frac{r}{100}\right)^{-1}+2000\left(1+\frac{r}{100}\right)^{-2}+3000\left(1+\frac{r}{100}\right)^{-3}$$

A sensible thing to do here might be to multiply through by $(1 + (r/100))^3$. However, this produces an equation involving r^3 (and lower powers of r), which is no easier to solve than the original. Indeed, a moment's thought should convince you that, in general, when dealing with a sequence of payments over n years, the IRR will satisfy an equation involving r^n (and lower powers of r). Under these circumstances it is virtually impossible to obtain the exact solution. The best way of proceeding would be to use a non-linear equation-solver routine on a computer, particularly if it is important that an accurate value of r is obtained. However, if all that is needed is a rough approximation then this can be done by systematic trial and error. We merely substitute likely solutions into the right-hand side of the equation until we find the one that works. For example, putting $r = 5$ gives

$$\frac{1000}{1.05} + \frac{200}{(1.05)^2} + \frac{3000}{(1.05)^3} = 5358$$

Other values of the expression

$$1000\left(1 + \frac{r}{100}\right)^{-1} + 2000\left(1 + \frac{r}{100}\right)^{-2} + 3000\left(1 + \frac{r}{100}\right)^{-3}$$

corresponding to $r = 6, 7, \ldots, 10$ are listed in the following table:

r	6	7	8	9	10
value	5242	5130	5022	4917	4816

Given that we are trying to find r so that this value is 5000, this table indicates that r is somewhere between 8% (which produces a value greater than 5000) and 9% (which produces a value less than 5000).

If a more accurate estimate of IRR is required then we simply try further values between 8% and 9%. For example, it is easy to check that putting $r = 8.5$ gives 4969, indicating that the exact value of r is between 8% and 8.5%. We conclude that the IRR is 8% to the nearest percentage.

Practice Problem

6. A project requires an initial investment of $12 000. It has a guaranteed return of $8000 at the end of year 1 and a return of $2000 each year at the end of years 2, 3 and 4.

    Estimate the IRR to the nearest percentage. Would you recommend that someone invests in this project if the prevailing market rate is 8% compounded annually?

Practice Problem 6 should have convinced you how tedious it is to calculate the internal rate of return 'by hand' when there are more than two payments in a revenue flow. A computer spreadsheet provides the ideal tool for dealing with this. Excel's Chart Wizard can be used to sketch a graph from which a rough estimate of IRR can be found. A more accurate value can be found using a 'finer' tabulation in the vicinity of this estimate.

We conclude this section by using the theory of discounting to explain the relationship between interest rates and the speculative demand for money. This was first introduced in Section 1.7 in the analysis of LM schedules. Speculative demand consists of money held in reserve to take advantage of changes in the value of alternative financial assets, such as government bonds. As their name suggests, these issues can be bought from the government at a certain price. In return, the government pays out interest on an annual basis for a prescribed number of years. At the end of this period the bond is redeemed and the purchaser is repaid the original sum. Now these bonds can be bought and sold at any point in their lifetime. The person who chooses to buy one of these bonds part-way through this period is entitled to all of the future interest payments, together with the final redemption payment. The value of existing securities clearly depends on the number of years remaining before redemption, together with the prevailing rate of interest.

Example

A 10-year bond is originally offered by the government at $5000 with an annual return of 9%. Assuming that the bond has 4 years left before redemption, calculate its present value assuming that the prevailing interest rate is

(a) 5%   **(b)** 7%   **(c)** 9%   **(d)** 11%   **(e)** 13%

Solution

The government pays annual interest of 9% on the $5000 bond, so agrees to pay the holder $450 every year for 10 years. At the end of the 10 years, the bond is redeemed by the government and $5000 is paid back to the purchaser. If there are just 4 years left between now and the date of redemption, the future cash flow that is paid on the bond is summarised in the second column of Table 3.29. This is similar to that of an annuity except that in the final year an extra payment of $5000 is received when the government pays back the original investment. The present value of this income stream is calculated in Table 3.29 using the given discount rates of 5%, 7%, 9%, 11% and 13% compounded annually. The total present value in each case is given in the last row of this table and varies from $5710 when the interest rate is 5% to $4405 when it is 13%.

Notice that the value of a bond falls as interest rates rise. This is entirely to be expected, since the formula we use to calculate individual present values is

$$P = \frac{S}{(1 + r/100)^t}$$

and larger values of r produce smaller values of P.

Table 3.29

End of year	Cash flow	Present values				
		5%	7%	9%	11%	13%
1	450	429	421	413	405	398
2	450	408	393	379	365	352
3	450	389	367	347	329	312
4	5450	4484	4158	3861	3590	3343
Total present value		5710	5339	5000	4689	4405

The effect of this relationship on financial markets can now be analysed. Let us suppose that the interest rate is high at, say, 13%. As you can see from Table 3.29, the price of the bond is relatively low. Moreover, one might reasonably expect that, in the future, interest rates are likely to fall, thereby increasing the present value of the bond. In this situation an investor would be encouraged to buy this bond in the expectation of not only receiving the cash flow from holding the bond but also receiving a capital gain on its present value. Speculative balances therefore decrease as a result of high interest rates because money is converted into securities. Exactly the opposite happens when interest rates are low. The corresponding present value is relatively high, and, with an expectation of a rise in interest rates and a possible capital loss, investors are reluctant to invest in securities, so speculative balances are high.

Practice Problem

7. A 10-year bond is originally offered by the government at $1000 with an annual return of 7%. Assuming that the bond currently has 3 years left before redemption and that the prevailing interest rate is 8% compounded annually, calculate its present value.

Key Terms

Annuity   A lump sum investment designed to produce a sequence of equal regular payments over time.

Discount rate   The interest rate that is used when going backwards in time to calculate the present value from a future value.

Discounting   The process of working backwards in time to find the present values from a future value.

Internal rate of return (IRR)   The interest rate for which the net present value is zero.

Net present value (NPV)   The present value of a revenue flow minus the original cost.

Present value   The amount that is invested initially to produce a specified future value after a given period of time.

Exercise 3.4

1. Determine the present value of $7000 in 2 years' time if the discount rate is 8% compounded

   (a) quarterly   (b) continuously

2. A small business promises a profit of $8000 on an initial investment of $20 000 after 5 years.

   (a) Calculate the internal rate of return.

   (b) Would you advise someone to invest in this business if the market rate is 6% compounded annually?

3. An investment company is considering one of two possible business ventures. Project 1 gives a return of $250 000 in 4 years' time whereas Project 2 gives a return of $350 000 in 8 years' time. Which project should the company invest in when the interest rate is 7% compounded annually?

4. The revenue of a firm (in $100 000s) at the end of each year for the next 5 years is listed in Table 3.30. Calculate the present value of the revenue stream if the annual discount rate is 8%.

   Table 3.30

Year	1	2	3	4	5
Revenue	-20	-14	5	39	64

5. A builder is offered one of two methods of payment:

   Option 1: A single sum of $73 000 to be paid now.
   Option 2: Five equal payments of $15 000 to be paid quarterly with the first instalment to be paid now.

   Advise the builder which offer to accept if the interest rate is 6% compounded quarterly.

6. A financial company invests £250 000 now and receives £300 000 in three years' time. Calculate the internal rate of return.

7. A company has the option of investing in a project and calculates the net present values shown in Table 3.31 at four different discount rates.

   Table 3.31

Discount rate	Net present values
3	$5510
4	$630
5	−$3980
6	−$8330

   (a) Estimate the internal rate of return of the project.

   (b) If the money could be invested elsewhere at 5.5% interest explain whether you would advise company to invest in this project.

8. You are given the opportunity of investing in one of three projects. Projects A, B and C require initial outlays of $20 000, $30 000 and $100 000 and are guaranteed to return $25 000, $37 000 and $117 000, respectively, in 3 years' time. Which of these projects would you invest in if the market rate is 5% compounded annually?

9. Determine the present value of an annuity that pays out $100 at the end of each year

   (a) for 5 years   (b) in perpetuity

   if the interest rate is 10% compounded annually.

10. An investor is given the opportunity to invest in one of two projects:

    Project A costs $10 000 now and pays back $15 000 at the end of 4 years.
    Project B costs $15 000 now and pays back $25 000 at the end of 5 years.
    The current interest rate is 9%.

    By calculating the net present values, decide which, if either, of these projects is to be recommended.

11. A proposed investment costs $130 000 today. The expected revenue flow is $40 000 at the end of year 1, and $140 000 at the end of year 2. Find the internal rate of return, correct to 1 decimal place.

Exercise 3.4*

1. Find the present value of $450 in 6 years' time if the discount rate is 9.5% compounded semi-annually. Round your answer to 2 decimal places.

2. A project requires an initial investment of $7000, and is guaranteed to yield a return of $1500 at the end of the first year, $2500 at the end of the second year and $x at the end of the third year. Find the value of x, correct to the nearest $, given that the net present value is $838.18 when the interest rate is 6% compounded annually.

3. Determine the present value of an annuity, if it pays out $2500 at the end of each year in perpetuity, assuming that the interest rate is 8% compounded annually.

4. A firm decides to invest in a new piece of machinery which is expected to produce an additional revenue of $8000 at the end of every year for 10 years. At the end of this period the firm plans to sell the machinery for scrap, for which it expects to receive $5000. What is the maximum amount that the firm should pay for the machine if it is not to suffer a net loss as a result of this investment? You may assume that the discount rate is 6% compounded annually.

5. During the next 3 years a business decides to invest $10 000 at the *beginning* of each year. The corresponding revenue that it can expect to receive at the *end* of each year is given in Table 3.32. Calculate the net present value if the discount rate is 4% compounded annually.

Table 3.32

End of year	Revenue ($)
1	5 000
2	20 000
3	50 000

6. A project requires an initial investment of $50 000. It produces a return of $40 000 at the end of year 1 and $30 000 at the end of year 2. Find the exact value of the internal rate of return.

7. A government bond that originally cost $500 with a yield of 6% has 5 years left before redemption. Determine its present value if the prevailing rate of interest is 15%.

8. An annuity pays out $20 000 per year in perpetuity. If the interest rate is 5% compounded annually, find

   (a) the present value of the whole annuity

   (b) the present value of the annuity for payments received, starting from the end of the 30th year

   (c) the present value of the annuity of the first 30 years.

9. An engineering company needs to decide whether or not to build a new factory. The costs of building the factory are $150 million initially, together with a further $100 million at the end of the next 2 years. Annual operating costs are $5 million commencing at the end of the third year. Annual revenue is predicted to be $50 million commencing at the end of the third year. If the interest rate is 6% compounded annually, find

   (a) the present value of the building costs

   (b) the present value of the operating costs at the end of n years ($n > 2$)

   (c) the present value of the revenue after n years ($n > 2$)

   (d) the minimum value of n for which the net present value is positive.

10. A project requires an initial outlay of $80 000 and produces a return of $20 000 at the end of year 1, $30 000 at the end of year 2, and $R at the end of year 3. Determine the value of R if the internal rate of return is 10%.

11. An annuity yields an income of $R at the end of each year for the next n years. If the interest rate is r% compounded annually, show that the present value is

$$\frac{100R[1+r/100]^{-n}}{r}$$

(a) Find the annual income if the interest rate is 6.5%, the present value is $14 000 and the annuity is paid for 15 years. Give your answer correct to 2 decimal places.

(b) Write down a general expression, in terms of r and R, for the present value if the annuity is to be paid in perpetuity.

12. A project requiring an initial outlay of $A produces a return of $a at the end of every year for n years.

(a) Show that the internal rate of return, r, satisfies the equation

$$A = \frac{100a}{r}\left[1-\left(1+\frac{r}{100}\right)^{-n}\right]$$

(b) Find the internal rate of return of a project which requires an initial outlay of $1 000 000 and gives a return of $10 000 in perpetuity.

Formal mathematics

The Greek letter Σ (sigma) is the equivalent of the letter S (for sum) and is used to express summations in a compact form. Given a sequence of numbers, $x_1, x_2, x_3, \ldots, x_n$ we define

$$\sum_{i=1}^{n} x_i = x_1 + x_2 + x_3 + \cdots + x_n$$

In this case we add together the terms x_i starting with $i = 1$, allowing the subscript to go up in integer steps, and finishing with $i = n$. The values of $i = 1$ and n which appear at the bottom and top of the sigma sign are called the **lower** and **upper limits** respectively. Using this notation we have:

$$\sum_{i=1}^{5} i^2 = 1^2 + 2^2 + 3^2 + 4^2 + 5^2$$

A typical term is i^2 so we need to add these together starting with $i = 1$ and running through all integer values until we reach $i = 5$.

Likewise:

$$\sum_{i=3}^{7} 2^i = 2^3 + 2^4 + 2^5 + 2^6 + 2^7$$

The lower limit is 3 so we begin by substituting $i = 3$ into the general term, 2^i to get 2^3. Subsequent terms are obtained by substituting consecutive integer values, $i = 4, 5, \ldots$ into the general term. The upper limit is 7 so we continue to add together all of the terms up to and including 2^7.

The notation clearly provides a convenient short-hand for what would otherwise be lengthy expressions and there are other advantages too. The following properties of sigma notation allow us to manipulate summations algebraically.

Property 1

$$\sum_{i=1}^{n} (x_i + y_i) = \sum_{i=1}^{n} x_i + \sum_{i=1}^{n} y_i$$

Property 2

$$\sum_{i=1}^{n} a x_i = a \sum_{i=1}^{n} x_i \quad \text{where } a \text{ is any constant}$$

These properties are easily checked by writing out the summations longhand. For Property 2 we have

$$\sum_{i=1}^{n} a x_i = a x_1 + a x_2 + \cdots + a x_n = a(x_1 + x_2 + \cdots + x_n) = a \sum_{i=1}^{n} x_i$$

As we have seen in this chapter, financial mathematics often involves the summation of series and the following example shows how to use it to express the sum of a geometric series using sigma notation.

Example

(a) A person saves \$2000 a year in a bank account at the beginning of the year for n years. If the bank offers a return of 4% a year, use sigma notation to write down an expression for the total amount saved.

(b) Use sigma notation to express the sum of the first n terms of a geometric series with first term a and geometric ratio r.

Solution

(a) During a period of n years the total amount saved is

$$2000(1.04) + 2000(1.04)^2 + 2000(1.04)^3 + \cdots + 2000(1.04)^n$$

which can be expressed succinctly as

$$\sum_{i=1}^{n} 2000(1.04)^i = 2000 \sum_{i=1}^{n} 1.04^i \quad \text{(using property 2 to take out the factor of 2000)}$$

(b) Using sigma notation the sum

$$a + ar + ar^2 + \cdots + ar^{n-1}$$

can be written as

$$\sum_{i=1}^{n} ar^{i-1} = a \sum_{i=1}^{n} r^{i-1} \quad \text{(again using property 2 to take out the factor of } a)$$

Key Terms

Lower limit   The number which appears at the bottom of the sigma notation to indicate the first term in a summation.

Upper limit   The number which appears at the top of the sigma notation to indicate the last term in a summation.

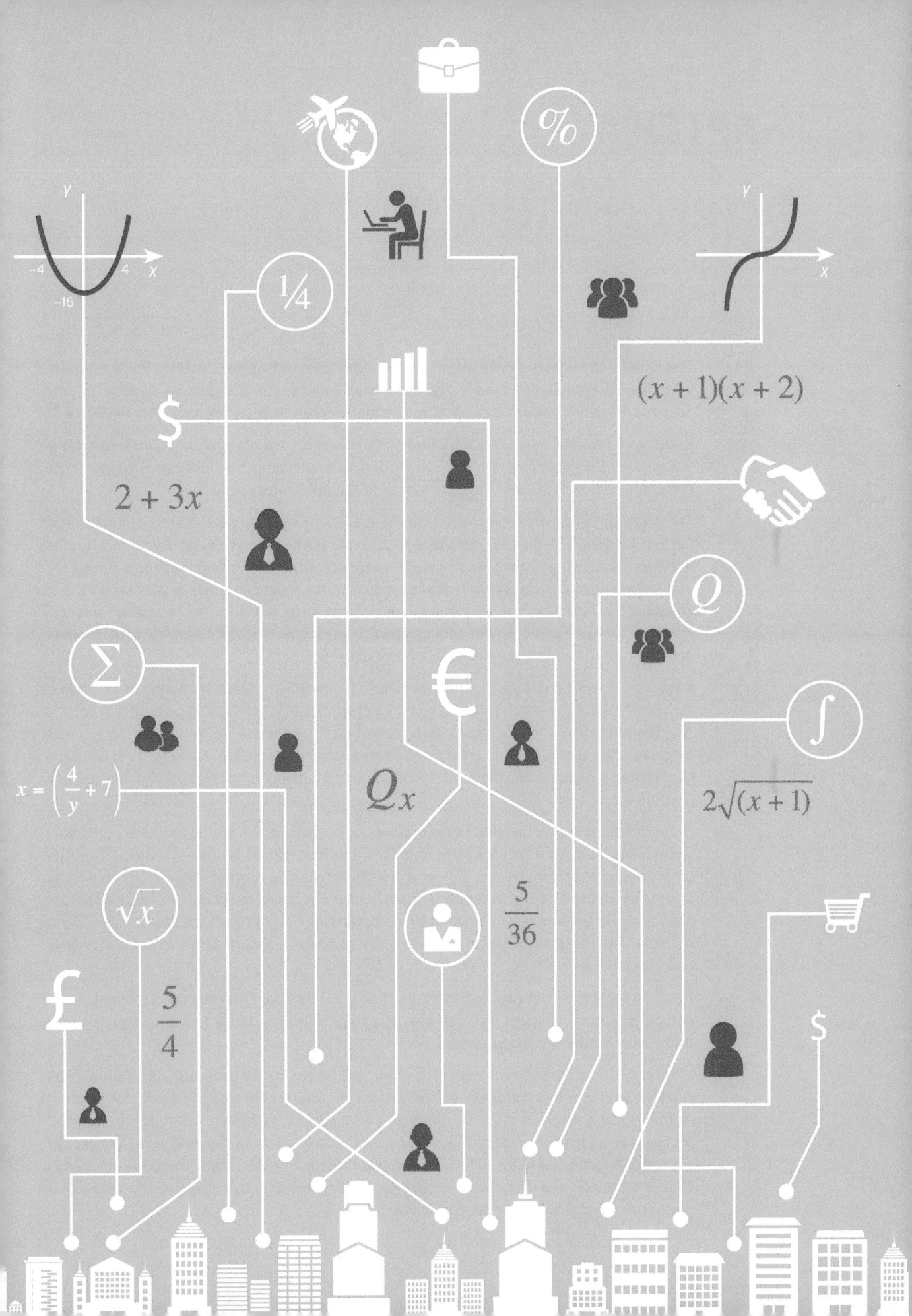

CHAPTER 4
Differentiation

This chapter provides a simple introduction to the general topic of calculus. There are eight sections, which should be read in the order that they appear. It should be possible to omit Sections 4.4 and 4.7 at a first reading and Section 4.6 can be read any time after Section 4.3.

Section 4.1 provides a leisurely introduction to the basic idea of differentiation. The material is explained using pictures, which will help you to understand the connection between the underlying mathematics and the economic applications in later sections.

There are six rules of differentiation, which are evenly split between Sections 4.2 and 4.4. Section 4.2 considers the easy rules that all students will need to know. However, if you are on a business studies or management course, the more advanced rules in Section 4.4 may not be of relevance and could be ignored. As far as possible, examples given in later sections and chapters are based on the easy rules only so that such students are not disadvantaged. However, the more advanced rules are essential to any proper study of mathematical economics and their use in deriving general results is unavoidable.

Sections 4.3 and 4.5 describe standard economic applications. Marginal functions associated with revenue, cost, production, consumption and savings functions are all discussed in Section 4.3. The important topic of elasticity is described in Section 4.5. The distinction is made between price elasticity along an arc and price elasticity at a point. Familiar results involving general linear demand functions and the relationship between price elasticity of demand and revenue are derived.

Sections 4.6 and 4.7 are devoted to the topic of optimisation, which is used to find the maximum and minimum values of economic functions. In the first half of Section 4.6 we concentrate on the mathematical technique. The second half contains four examination-type problems, all taken from economics and business, which are solved in detail. In Section 4.7, mathematics is used to derive general results relating to the optimisation of profit and production functions. A simple model of stock control in business is described and a general formula for the economic order quantity derived.

The final section revises two important mathematical functions, namely the exponential and natural logarithm functions. We describe how to differentiate these functions and illustrate their use in economics and business.

Differentiation is probably the most important topic in the whole book, and one that we shall continue in Chapters 5 and 6, since it provides the necessary background theory for much of mathematical economics. You are therefore advised to make every effort to attempt the problems given in each section. The prerequisites include an understanding of the concept of a function together with the ability to manipulate algebraic expressions. These are covered in Chapters 1 and 2, and if you have worked successfully through this material, you should find that you are in good shape to begin calculus.

SECTION 4.1
The derivative of a function

Objectives

At the end of this section you should be able to:

- Find the slope of a straight line given any two points on the line.
- Detect whether a line is uphill, downhill or horizontal using the sign of the slope.
- Recognise the notation $f'(x)$ and dy/dx for the derivative of a function.
- Estimate the derivative of a function by measuring the slope of a tangent.
- Differentiate power functions.

This introductory section is designed to get you started with differential calculus in a fairly painless way. There are really only three things that we are going to do. We discuss the basic idea of something called a derived function, give you two equivalent pieces of notation to describe it, and finally show you how to write down a formula for the derived function in simple cases.

In Chapter 1 the slope of a straight line was defined to be the change in the value of y brought about by a 1 unit increase in x. In fact, it is not necessary to restrict the change in x to a 1 unit increase. More generally, the **slope**, or **gradient**, of a line is taken to be the change in y divided by the corresponding change in x as you move between any two points on the line. It is customary to denote the change in y by Δy, where Δ is the Greek letter 'delta'. Likewise, the change in x is written Δx. In this notation we have

$$\text{slope} = \frac{\Delta y}{\Delta x}$$

Example

Find the slope of the straight line passing through

(a) A $(1, 2)$ and B $(3, 4)$ **(b)** A $(1, 2)$ and C $(4, 1)$ **(c)** A $(1, 2)$ and D $(5, 2)$

Solution

(a) Points A and B are sketched in Figure 4.1. As we move from A to B, the y coordinate changes from 2 to 4, which is an increase of 2 units, and the x coordinate changes from 1 to 3, which is also an increase of 2 units. Hence

$$\text{slope} = \frac{\Delta y}{\Delta x} = \frac{4-2}{3-1} = \frac{2}{2} = 1$$

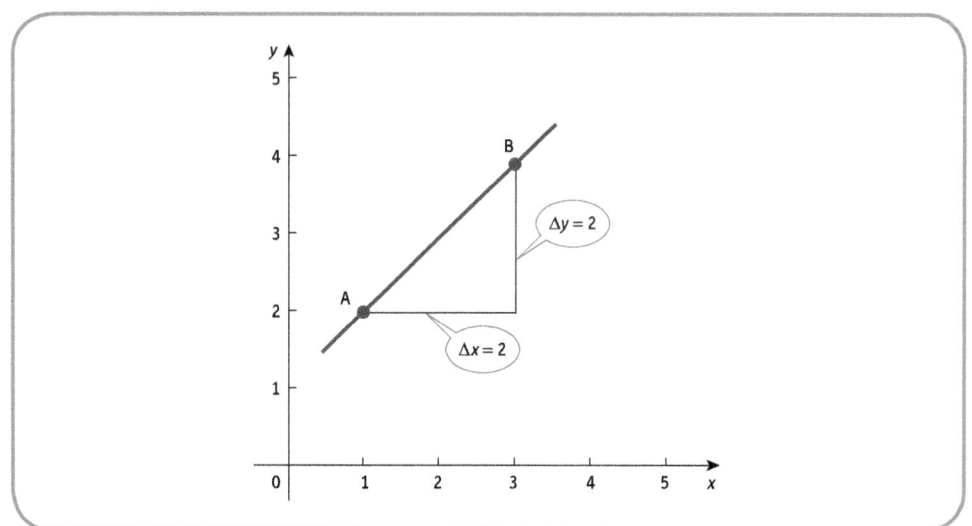

Figure 4.1

(b) Points A and C are sketched in Figure 4.2. As we move from A to C, the y coordinate changes from 2 to 1, which is a decrease of 1 unit, and the x coordinate changes from 1 to 4, which is an increase of 3 units. Hence

$$\text{slope} = \frac{\Delta y}{\Delta x} = \frac{1-2}{4-1} = \frac{-1}{3}$$

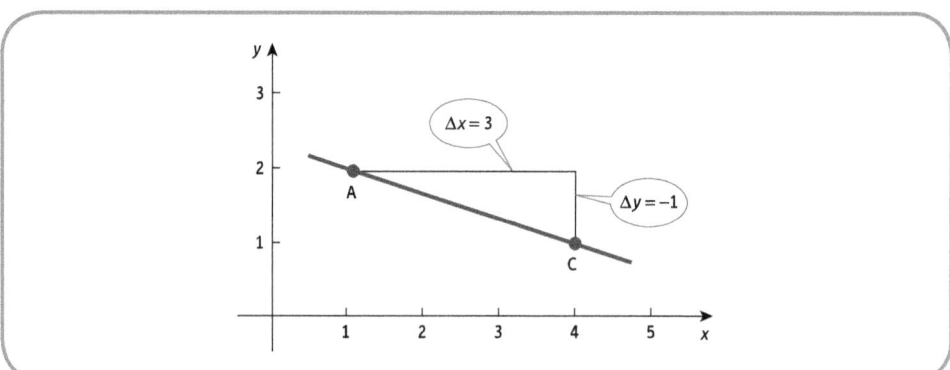

Figure 4.2

(c) Points A and D are sketched in Figure 4.3. As we move from A to D, the y coordinate remains fixed at 2, and the x coordinate changes from 1 to 5, which is an increase of 4 units. Hence

$$\text{slope} = \frac{\Delta y}{\Delta x} = \frac{2-2}{5-1} = \frac{0}{4} = 0$$

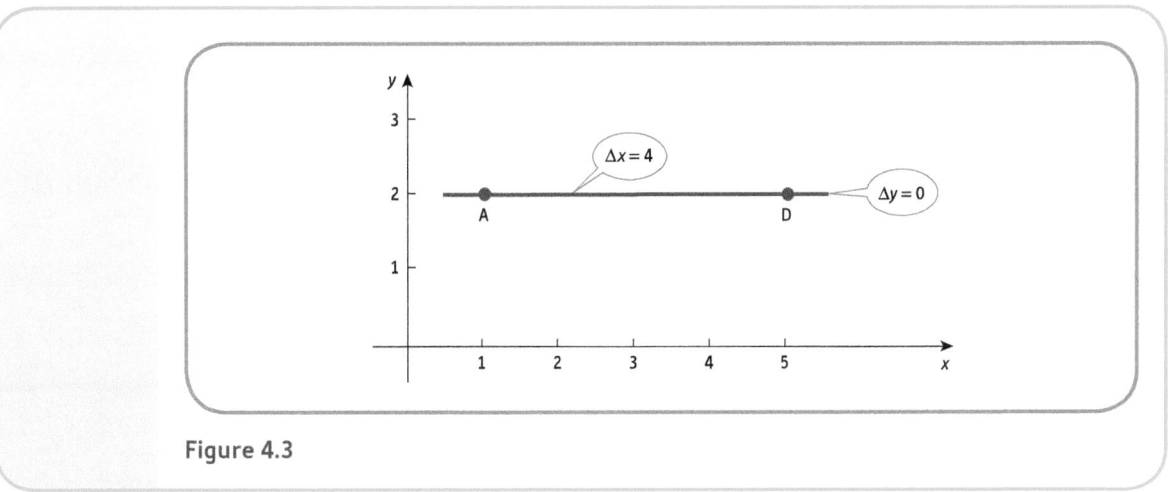

Figure 4.3

Practice Problem

1. Find the slope of the straight line passing through

   (a) E (−1, 3) and F (3, 11)   (b) E (−1, 3) and G (4, −2)   (c) E (−1, 3) and H (49, 3)

From these examples we see that the gradient is positive if the line is uphill, negative if the line is downhill and zero if the line is horizontal.

Unfortunately, not all functions in economics are linear, so it is necessary to extend the definition of slope to include more general curves. To do this we need the idea of a tangent, which is illustrated in Figure 4.4.

A straight line which passes through a point on a curve and which just touches the curve at this point is called a **tangent**. The slope, or gradient, of a curve at $x = a$ is then defined to be that of the tangent at $x = a$. Since we have already seen how to find the slope of a straight line, this gives us a precise way of measuring the slope of a curve. A simple curve together with a selection of tangents at various points is shown in Figure 4.5. Notice how each tangent passes through exactly one point on the curve and strikes a glancing blow. In this case, the slopes of the tangents increase as we move from left to right along the curve. This reflects the fact that the curve is flat at $x = 0$ but becomes progressively steeper further away.

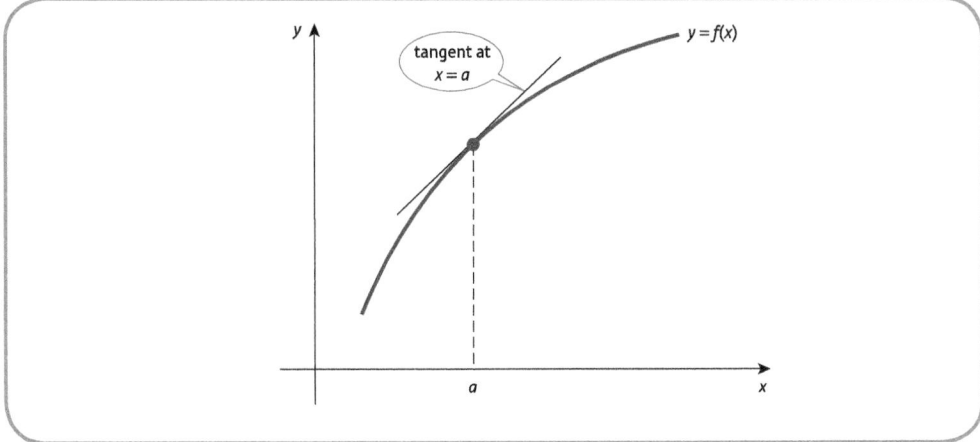

Figure 4.4

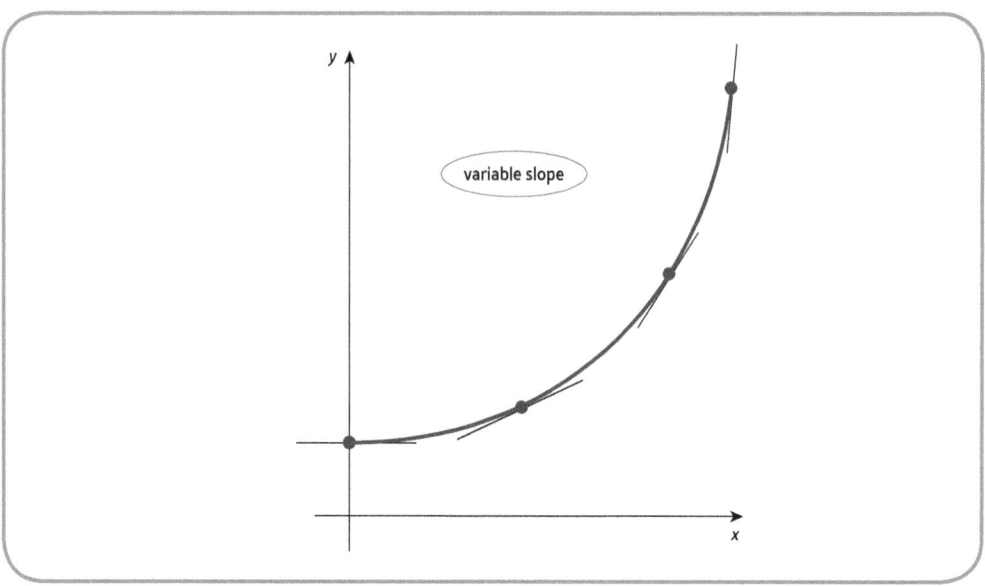

Figure 4.5

This highlights an important difference between the slope of a straight line and the slope of a curve. In the case of a straight line, the gradient is fixed throughout its length and it is immaterial which two points on a line are used to find it. For example, in Figure 4.6 all of the ratios $\Delta y/\Delta x$ have the value $\frac{1}{2}$. However, as we have just seen, the slope of a curve varies as we move along it. In mathematics we use the symbol

$$f'(a) \qquad \text{read 'f dashed of a'}$$

to represent the slope of the graph of a function f at $x = a$. This notation conveys the maximum amount of information with the minimum of fuss. As usual, we need the label f to denote which function we are considering. We certainly need the a to tell us at which point on the curve the gradient is being measured. Finally, the 'prime' symbol $'$ is used to distinguish the gradient from the function value. The notation $f(a)$ gives the height of the curve above the x axis at $x = a$, whereas $f'(a)$ gives the gradient of the curve at this point.

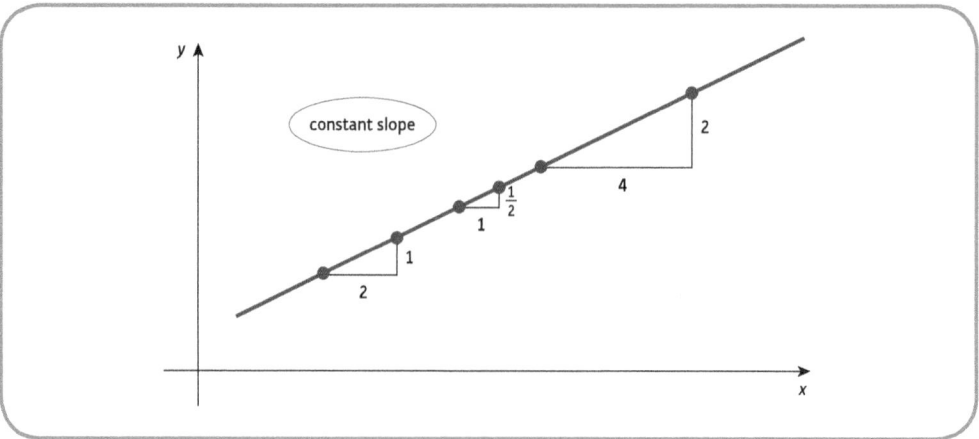

Figure 4.6

The slope of the graph of a function is called the **derivative** of the function. It is interesting to notice that corresponding to each value of x there is a uniquely defined derivative $f'(x)$. In other words, the rule 'find the slope of the graph of f at x' defines a function. This slope function is usually referred to as the **derived function**. An alternative notation for the derived function is

$$\frac{dy}{dx}$$ read 'dee y by dee x'

Historically, this symbol arose from the corresponding notation $\Delta y/\Delta x$ for the gradient of a straight line; the letter 'd' is the English equivalent of the Greek letter Δ. However, it is important to realise that

$$\frac{dy}{dx}$$

does not mean 'dy divided by dx'. It should be thought of as a single symbol representing the derivative of y with respect to x. It is immaterial which notation is used, although the context may well suggest which is more appropriate. For example, if we use

$$y = x^2$$

to identify the square function then it is natural to use

$$\frac{dy}{dx}$$

for the derived function. On the other hand, if we use

$$f(x) = x^2$$

then $f'(x)$ seems more appropriate.

A graph of the square function based on the table of values

x	−2.0	−1.5	−1.0	−0.5	0.0	0.5	1.0	1.5	2.0
$f(x)$	4	2.25	1	0.25	0	0.25	1	2.25	4

is sketched in Figure 4.7. From this graph we see that the slopes of the tangents are

$$f'(-1.5) = \frac{-15}{0.5} = -3$$

$$f'(-0.5) = \frac{-0.5}{0.5} = -1$$

$$f'(0) = 0$$

$$f'(0.5) = \frac{0.5}{0.5} = 1$$

$$f'(1.5) = \frac{1.5}{0.5} = 3$$

The value of $f'(0)$ is zero because the tangent is horizontal at $x = 0$. Notice that

$$f'(-1.5) = -f'(1.5) \qquad \text{and} \qquad f'(-0.5) = -f'(0.5)$$

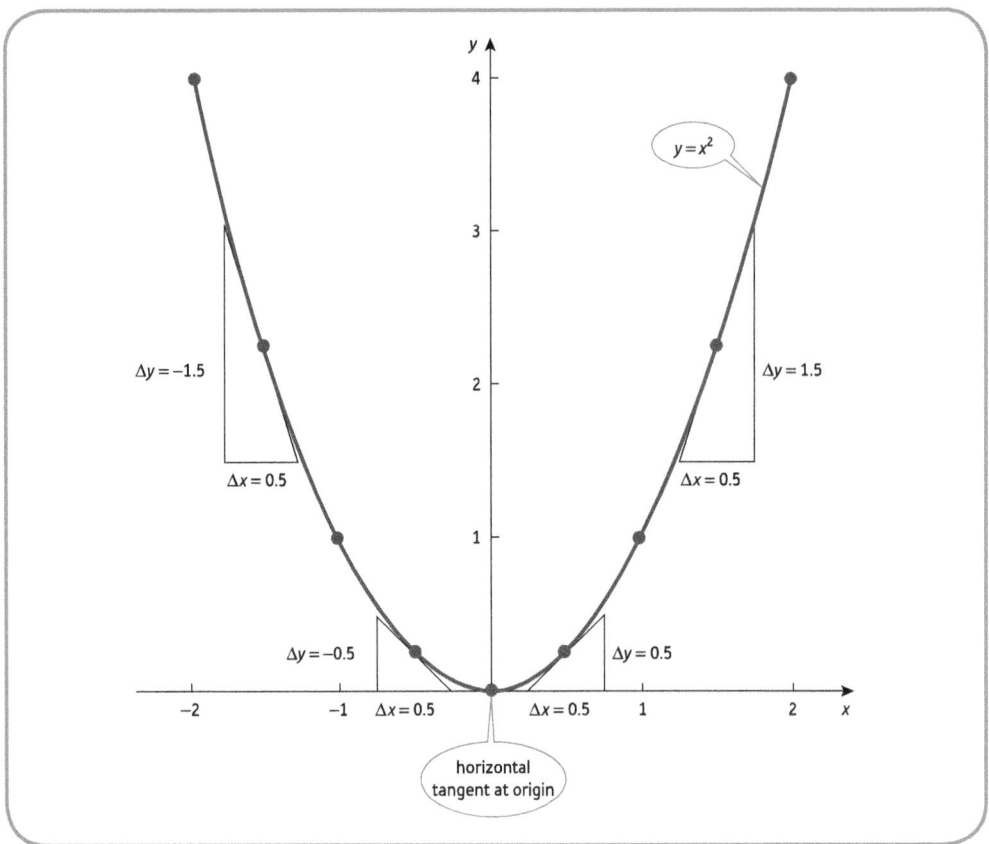

Figure 4.7

This is to be expected because the graph is symmetric about the y axis. The slopes of the tangents to the left of the y axis have the same size as those of the corresponding tangents to the right. However, they have opposite signs since the curve slopes downhill on one side and uphill on the other.

Practice Problem

2. Complete the following table of function values and hence sketch an accurate graph of $f(x) = x^3$.

x	−1.50	−1.25	−1.00	−0.75	−0.50	−0.25	0.00
$f(x)$		−1.95			−0.13		

x	0.25	0.50	0.75	1.00	1.25	1.50
$f(x)$		0.13			1.95	

Draw the tangents to the graph at $x = -1$, 0 and 1. Hence estimate the values of $f'(-1)$, $f'(0)$ and $f'(1)$.

Practice Problem 2 should convince you how hard it is in practice to calculate $f'(a)$ exactly using graphs. It is impossible to sketch a perfectly smooth curve using graph paper and pencil, and it is equally difficult to judge, by eye, precisely where the tangent should be. There is also the problem of measuring the vertical and horizontal distances required for the slope of the tangent. These inherent errors may compound to produce quite inaccurate values for $f'(a)$. Fortunately, there is a really simple formula that can be used to find $f'(a)$ when f is a power function. It can be proved that

if $f(x) = x^n$ then $f'(x) = nx^{n-1}$

or, equivalently,

if $y = x^n$ then $\dfrac{dy}{dx} = nx^{n-1}$

The process of finding the derived function symbolically (rather than using graphs) is known as **differentiation**. In order to differentiate x^n all that needs to be done is to bring the power down to the front and then to subtract 1 from the power:

x^n differentiates to nx^{n-1}

(subtract 1 from the power)

(bring down the power)

To differentiate the square function we set $n = 2$ in this formula to deduce that

$f(x) = x^2$ differentiates to $f'(x) = 2x^{2-1}$

(subtract 1)

(the 2 comes down)

that is,

$f'(x) = 2x^1 = 2x$

Using this result we see that

$f'(-1.5) = 2 \times (-1.5) = -3$
$f'(-0.5) = 2 \times (-0.5) = -1$
$f'(0) = 2 \times (0) = 0$
$f'(0.5) = 2 \times (0.5) = 1$
$f'(1.5) = 2 \times (1.5) = 3$

which are in agreement with the results obtained from the graph in Figure 4.7.

Practice Problem

3. If $f(x) = x^3$ write down a formula for $f'(x)$. Calculate $f'(-1), f'(0)$ and $f'(1)$. Confirm that these are in agreement with your rough estimates obtained in Practice Problem 2.

Example

Differentiate

(a) $y = x^4$ (b) $y = x^{10}$ (c) $y = x$ (d) $y = 1$ (e) $y = 1/x^4$ (f) $y = \sqrt{x}$

Solution

(a) To differentiate $y = x^4$ we bring down the power (that is, 4) to the front and then subtract 1 from the power (that is, $4 - 1 = 3$) to deduce that

$$\frac{dy}{dx} = 4x^3$$

(b) Similarly,

if $y = x^{10}$ then $\dfrac{dy}{dx} = 10x^9$

(c) To use the general formula to differentiate x we first need to express $y = x$ in the form $y = x^n$ for some number n. In this case $n = 1$ because $x^1 = x$, so

$$\frac{dy}{dx} = 1x^0 = 1 \quad \text{since} \quad x^0 = 1$$

This result is also obvious from the graph of $y = x$ sketched in Figure 4.8.

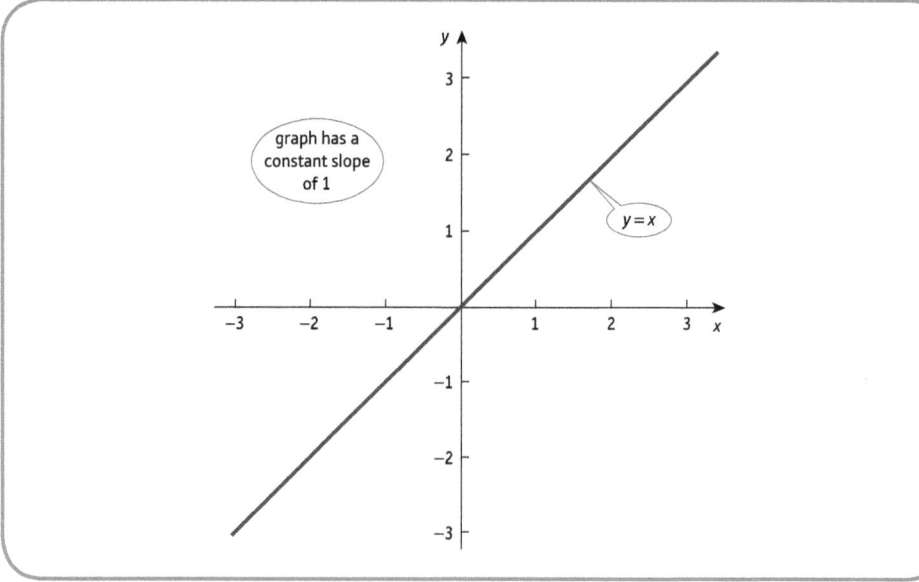

Figure 4.8

(d) Again, to differentiate 1 we need to express $y = 1$ in the form $y = x^n$. In this case $n = 0$ because $x^0 = 1$, so

$$\frac{dy}{dx} = 0x^{-1} = 0$$

This result is also obvious from the graph of $y = 1$ sketched in Figure 4.9.

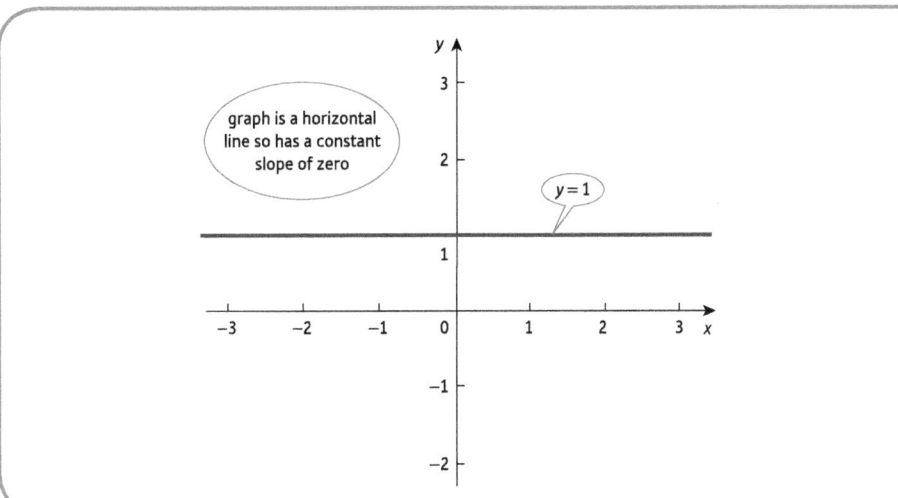

Figure 4.9

(e) Noting that $1/x^4 = x^{-4}$ it follows that

$$\text{if } y = \frac{1}{x^4} \quad \text{then} \quad \frac{\mathrm{d}y}{\mathrm{d}x} = -4x^{-5} = -\frac{4}{x^5}$$

The power has decreased to -5 because $-4 - 1 = -5$.

(f) Noting that $\sqrt{x} = x^{1/2}$ it follows that if

$$y = \sqrt{x} \quad \text{then} \quad \frac{\mathrm{d}y}{\mathrm{d}x} = \frac{1}{2}x^{-1/2}$$

$$= \frac{1}{2x^{1/2}} \qquad \text{\small negative powers denote reciprocals}$$

$$= \frac{1}{2\sqrt{x}} \qquad \text{\small fractional powers denote roots}$$

The power has decreased to $-\frac{1}{2}$ because $\frac{1}{2} - 1 = -\frac{1}{2}$.

Practice Problem

4. Differentiate

    (a) $y = x^5$ **(b)** $y = x^6$ **(c)** $y = x^{100}$ **(d)** $y = 1/x$ **(e)** $y = 1/x^2$

    [Hint: in parts (d) and (e) note that $1/x = x^{-1}$ and $1/x^2 = x^{-2}$]

> ## Key Terms
>
> **Derivative**   The gradient of the tangent to a curve at a point. The derivative at $x = a$ is written $f'(a)$.
>
> **Derived function**   The rule, f', which gives the gradient of a function, f, at a general point.
>
> **Differentiation**   The process or operation of determining the first derivative of a function.
>
> **Gradient**   The gradient of a line measures steepness and is the vertical change divided by the horizontal change between any two points on the line. The gradient of a curve at a point is that of the tangent at that point.
>
> **Slope**   An alternative word for gradient.
>
> **Tangent**   A line that just touches a curve at a point.

Exercise 4.1

1. Find the slope of the straight line passing through

   (a) (2, 5) and (4, 9)   **(b)** (3, −1) and (7, −5)   **(c)** (7, 19) and (4, 19)

2. Verify that the points (0, 2) and (3, 0) lie on the line

   $$2x + 3y = 6$$

   Hence find the slope of this line. Is the line uphill, downhill or horizontal?

3. Sketch the graph of the function

   $$f(x) = 5$$

   Explain why it follows from this that

   $$f'(x) = 0$$

4. Differentiate the function

   $$f(x) = x^7$$

   Hence calculate the slope of the graph of

   $$y = x^7$$

   at the point $x = 2$.

5. Differentiate

   (a) $y = x^8$ **(b)** $y = x^{50}$ **(c)** $y = x^{19}$ **(d)** $y = x^{999}$

6. Differentiate the following functions, giving your answer in a similar form, without negative or fractional indices:

   (a) $f(x) = \dfrac{1}{x^3}$ **(b)** $f(x) = \sqrt{x}$ **(c)** $f(x) = \dfrac{1}{\sqrt{x}}$ **(d)** $y = x\sqrt{x}$

7. Complete the following table of function values for the function, $f(x) = x^2 - 2x$:

x	−1	−0.5	0	0.5	1	1.5	2	2.5
$x^2 - 2x$								

   Sketch the graph of this function and, by measuring the slope of the tangents, estimate

   (a) $f'(-0.5)$ **(b)** $f'(1)$ **(c)** $f'(1.5)$

Exercise 4.1*

1. Verify that the points $(0, b)$ and $(1, a + b)$ lie on the line

   $$y = ax + b$$

   Hence show that this line has slope a.

2. Differentiate each of the following functions expressing your answer in a similar form:

   (a) x^{15} **(b)** $x^4\sqrt{x}$ **(c)** $\sqrt[3]{x}$ **(d)** $\dfrac{1}{\sqrt[4]{x}}$ **(e)** $\dfrac{\sqrt{x}}{x^7}$

3. For each of the graphs

   (a) $y = \sqrt{x}$ **(b)** $y = x\sqrt{x}$ **(c)** $y = \dfrac{1}{\sqrt{x}}$

   A is the point where $x = 4$, and B is the point where $x = 4.1$. In each case find

   (i) the y coordinates of A and B

   (ii) the gradient of the chord AB

   (iii) the value of $\dfrac{\mathrm{d}y}{\mathrm{d}x}$ at A.

   Compare your answers to parts (ii) and (iii).

4. Find the coordinates of the point(s) at which the curve has the specified gradient.

   (a) $y = x^{2/3}$ gradient $= \dfrac{1}{3}$ **(b)** $y = x^5$, gradient $= 405$

   (c) $y = \dfrac{1}{x^2}$, gradient $= 16$ **(d)** $y = \dfrac{1}{x\sqrt{x}}$, gradient $= -\dfrac{3}{64}$

SECTION 4.2
Rules of differentiation

Objectives

At the end of this section you should be able to:

- Use the constant rule to differentiate a function of the form $cf(x)$.
- Use the sum rule to differentiate a function of the form $f(x) + g(x)$.
- Use the difference rule to differentiate a function of the form $f(x) - g(x)$.
- Evaluate and interpret second-order derivatives.

Advice

In this section we consider three elementary rules of differentiation. Subsequent sections of this chapter describe various applications to economics. However, before you can tackle these successfully, you must have a thorough grasp of the basic techniques involved. The problems in this section are repetitive in nature. This is deliberate. Although the rules themselves are straightforward, it is necessary for you to practise them over and over again before you can become proficient in using them. In fact, you will not be able to get much further with the rest of this book until you have mastered the rules of this section.

Rule 1 The constant rule

If $h(x) = cf(x)$ then $h'(x) = cf'(x)$

for any constant c.

This rule tells you how to find the derivative of a constant multiple of a function:

differentiate the function and multiply by the constant

Example

Differentiate

(a) $y = 2x^4$ **(b)** $y = 10x$

Solution

(a) To differentiate $2x^4$ we first differentiate x^4 to get $4x^3$ and then multiply by 2. Hence

$$\text{if } y = 2x^4 \quad \text{then} \quad \frac{dy}{dx} = 2(4x^3) = 8x^3$$

(b) To differentiate $10x$ we first differentiate x to get 1 and then multiply by 10. Hence

$$\text{if } y = 10x \quad \text{then} \quad \frac{dy}{dx} = 10(1) = 10$$

Practice Problem

1. Differentiate

    (a) $y = 4x^3$ **(b)** $y = 2/x$

The constant rule can be used to show that

constants differentiate to zero

To see this, note that the equation

$y = c$

is the same as

$y = cx^0$

because $x^0 = 1$. By the constant rule we first differentiate x^0 to get $0x^{-1}$ and then multiply by c. Hence

if $y = c$ then $\dfrac{dy}{dx} = c(0x^{-1}) = 0$

This result is also apparent from the graph of $y = c$, sketched in Figure 4.10, which is a horizontal line c units away from the x axis. It is an important result and explains why lone constants lurking in mathematical expressions disappear when differentiated.

Rule 2 The sum rule

If $h(x) = f(x) + g(x)$ then $h'(x) = f'(x) + g'(x)$

This rule tells you how to find the derivative of the sum of two functions:

differentiate each function separately and add

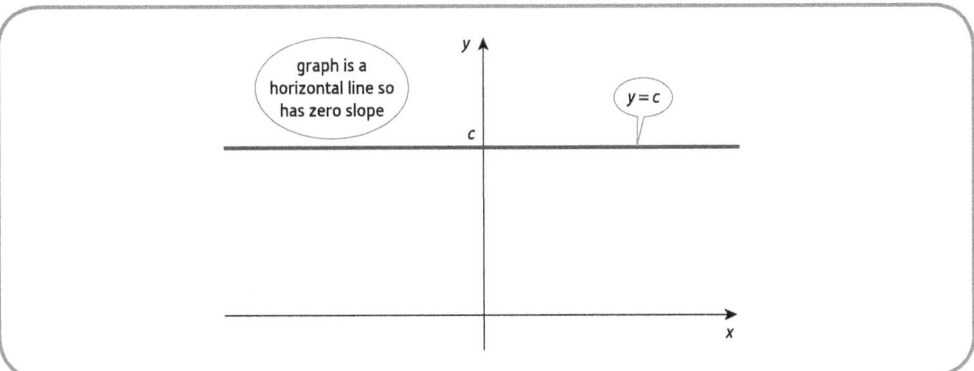

Figure 4.10

Example

Differentiate

(a) $y = x^2 + x^{50}$ **(b)** $y = x^3 + 3$

Solution

(a) To differentiate $x^2 + x^{50}$ we need to differentiate x^2 and x^{50} separately and add. Now

x^2 differentiates to $2x$

and

x^{50} differentiates to $50x^{49}$

so

if $y = x^2 + x^{50}$ then $\dfrac{dy}{dx} = 2x + 50x^{49}$

(b) To differentiate $x^3 + 3$ we need to differentiate x^3 and 3 separately and add. Now

x^3 differentiates to $3x^2$

and

3 differentiates to 0   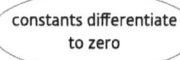 constants differentiate to zero

so

if $y = x^3 + 3$ then $\dfrac{dy}{dx} = 3x^2 + 0 = 3x^2$

Practice Problem

2. Differentiate

(a) $y = x^5 + x$ **(b)** $y = x^2 + 5$

Rule 3 The difference rule

If $h(x) = f(x) - g(x)$ then $h'(x) = f'(x) - g'(x)$

This rule tells you how to find the derivative of the difference of two functions:

differentiate each function separately and subtract

Example

Differentiate

(a) $y = x^5 - x^2$ **(b)** $y = x - \dfrac{1}{x^2}$

Solution

(a) To differentiate $x^5 - x^2$ we need to differentiate x^5 and x^2 separately and subtract. Now

x^5 differentiates to $5x^4$

and

x^2 differentiates to $2x$

so

if $y = x^5 - x^2$ then $\dfrac{dy}{dx} = 5x^4 - 2x$

(b) To differentiate $x - \dfrac{1}{x^2}$ we need to differentiate x and $\dfrac{1}{x^2}$ separately and subtract. Now

x differentiates to 1

and

$\dfrac{1}{x^2}$ differentiates to $-\dfrac{2}{x^3}$ x^{-2} differentiates to $-2x^{-3}$

so

if $y = x - \dfrac{1}{x^2}$ then $\dfrac{dy}{dx} = 1 - \left(-\dfrac{2}{x^3}\right) = 1 + \dfrac{2}{x^3}$

Practice Problem

3. Differentiate

(a) $y = x^2 - x^3$ **(b)** $y = 50 - \dfrac{1}{x^3}$

It is possible to combine these three rules and so to find the derivative of more involved functions, as the following example demonstrates.

Example

Differentiate

(a) $y = 3x^5 + 2x^3$ **(b)** $y = x^3 + 7x^2 - 2x + 10$ **(c)** $y = 2\sqrt{x} + \dfrac{3}{x}$

Solution

(a) The sum rule shows that to differentiate $3x^5 + 2x^3$ we need to differentiate $3x^5$ and $2x^3$ separately and add. By the constant rule

$3x^5$ differentiates to $3(5x^4) = 15x^4$

and

$2x^3$ differentiates to $2(3x^2) = 6x^2$

so

if $y = 3x^5 + 2x^3$ then $\dfrac{dy}{dx} = 15x^4 + 6x^2$

With practice you will soon find that you can just write the derivative down in a single line of working by differentiating term by term. For the function

$y = 3x^5 + 2x^3$

we could just write

$\dfrac{dy}{dx} = 3(5x^4) + 2(3x^2) = 15x^4 + 6x^2$

(b) So far we have only considered expressions comprising at most two terms. However, the sum and difference rules still apply to lengthier expressions, so we can differentiate term by term as before. For the function

$y = x^3 + 7x^2 - 2x + 10$

we get

$\dfrac{dy}{dx} = 3x^2 + 7(2x) - 2(1) + 0 = 3x^2 + 14x - 2$

(c) To differentiate

$y = 2\sqrt{x} + \dfrac{3}{x}$

we first rewrite it using the notation of indices as

$y = 2x^{1/2} + 3x^{-1}$

Differentiating term by term then gives

$\dfrac{dy}{dx} = 2\left(\dfrac{1}{2}\right)x^{-1/2} + 3(-1)x^{-2} = x^{-1/2} - 3x^{-2}$

which can be written in the more familiar form

$\dfrac{1}{\sqrt{x}} - \dfrac{3}{x^2}$

Practice Problem

4. Differentiate

(a) $y = 9x^5 + 2x^2$ (b) $y = 5x^8 - \dfrac{3}{x}$

(c) $y = x^2 + 6x + 3$ (d) $y = 2x^4 + 12x^3 - 4x^2 + 7x - 400$

Whenever a function is differentiated, the thing that you end up with is itself a function. This suggests the possibility of differentiating a second time to get the 'slope of the slope function'. This is written as

$f''(x)$ read '*f* double dashed of *x*'

or

$\dfrac{d^2y}{dx^2}$ read 'dee two *y* by dee *x* squared'

For example, if

$f(x) = 5x^2 - 7x + 12$

then differentiating once gives

$f'(x) = 10x - 7$

and if we now differentiate $f'(x)$ we get

$f''(x) = 10$

The function $f'(x)$ is called the **first-order derivative** and $f''(x)$ is called the **second-order derivative**.

Example

Evaluate $f''(1)$ where

$f(x) = x^7 + \dfrac{1}{x}$

Solution

To find $f''(1)$ we need to differentiate

$f(x) = x^7 + x^{-1}$

twice and put $x = 1$ into the end result. Differentiating once gives

$f'(x) = 7x^6 + (-1)x^{-2} = 7x^6 - x^{-2}$

and differentiating a second time gives

$f''(x) = 7(6x^5) - (-2)x^{-3} = 42x^5 + 2x^{-3}$

Finally, substituting $x = 1$ into

$f''(x) = 42x^5 + \dfrac{2}{x^3}$

gives

$f''(1) = 42 + 2 = 44$

It is possible to give a graphical interpretation of the sign of the second-order derivative. Remember that the first-order derivative, $f'(x)$, measures the gradient of a curve. If the derivative of $f'(x)$ is positive (that is, if $f''(x) > 0$) then $f'(x)$ is increasing so the graph gets steeper as you move from left to right. The curve bends upwards and the function is said to be **convex**. On the other hand, if $f''(x) < 0$, the gradient, $f'(x)$ must be decreasing, so the curve bends downwards. The function is said to be **concave**. It is perfectly possible for a curve to be convex for a certain range of values of x and concave for others. This is illustrated in Figure 4.11. For this function, $f''(x) < 0$ to the left of $x = a$, and $f''(x) > 0$ to the right of $x = a$. At $x = a$ itself, the curve changes from bending downwards to bending upwards and at this point, $f''(a) = 0$.

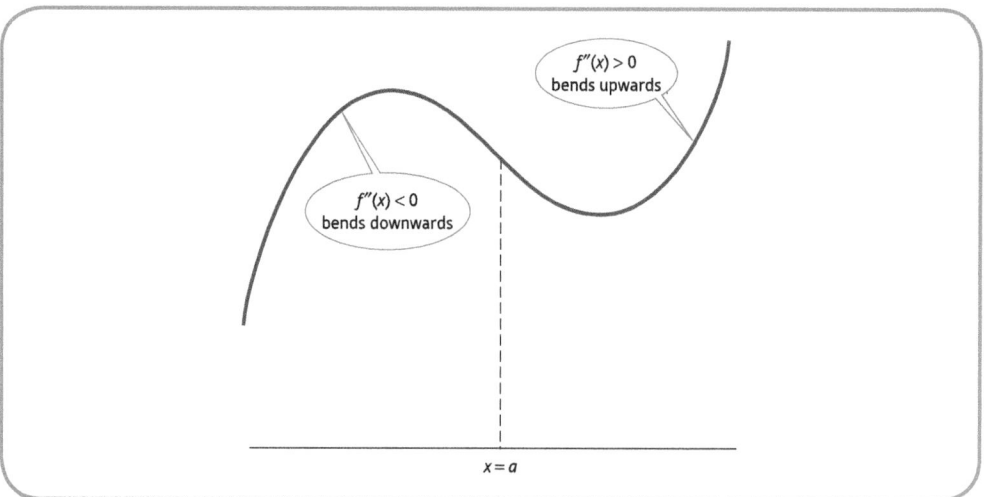

Figure 4.11

The second-order derivative can be used to confirm the convexity of the general quadratic function

$$f(x) = ax^2 + bx + c$$

The first- and second-order derivatives are $f'(x) = 2ax + b$ and $f''(x) = 2a$.

- If $a > 0$ then $f''(x) > 0$ so the parabola is convex.
- If $a < 0$ then $f''(x) < 0$ so the parabola is concave.

Of course, if $a = 0$ then $f(x) = bx + c$, which is the equation of a straight line, so the graph bends neither upwards nor downwards.

Throughout this section the functions have all been of the form $y = f(x)$, where the letters x and y denote the variables involved. In economic functions, different symbols are used. It should be obvious, however, that we can still differentiate such functions by applying the rules of this section. For example, if a supply function is given by

$$Q = P^2 + 3P + 1$$

and we need to find the derivative of Q with respect to P then we can apply the sum and difference rules to obtain

$$\frac{dQ}{dP} = 2P + 3$$

Key Terms

Concave   Graph bends downwards when $f''(x) < 0$.

Convex   Graph bends upwards when $f''(x) > 0$.

First-order derivative   The rate of change of a function with respect to its independent variable. It is the same as the 'derivative' of a function, $y = f(x)$, and is written as $f'(x)$ or dy/dx.

Second-order derivative   The derivative of the first-order derivative. The expression obtained when the original function, $y = f(x)$, is differentiated twice in succession and is written as $f''(x)$ or d^2y/dx^2.

Exercise 4.2

1. Differentiate

    (a) $y = 5x^2$

    (b) $y = \dfrac{3}{x}$

    (c) $y = 2x + 3$

    (d) $y = x^2 + x + 1$

    (e) $y = x^2 - 3x + 2$

    (f) $y = 3x - \dfrac{7}{x}$

    (g) $y = 2x^3 - 6x^2 + 49x - 54$

    (h) $y = ax + b$

    (i) $y = ax^2 + bx + c$

    (j) $y = 4x - \dfrac{3}{x} + \dfrac{7}{x^2}$

2. Evaluate $f'(x)$ for each of the following functions at the given point:

    (a) $f(x) = 3x^9$ at $x = 1$

    (b) $f(x) = x^2 - 2x$ at $x = 3$

    (c) $f(x) = x^3 - 4x^2 + 2x - 8$ at $x = 0$

    (d) $f(x) = 5x^4 - \dfrac{4}{x^4}$ at $x = -1$

    (e) $f(x) = \sqrt{x} - \dfrac{2}{x}$ at $x = 4$

3. By writing $x^2\left(x^2 + 2x - \dfrac{5}{x^2}\right) = x^4 + 2x^3 - 5$ differentiate $x^2\left(x^2 + 2x - \dfrac{5}{x^2}\right)$.

    Use a similar approach to differentiate

    (a) $x^2(3x - 4)$

    (b) $x(3x^3 - 2x^2 + 6x - 7)$

    (c) $(x + 1)(x - 6)$

    (d) $\dfrac{x^2 - 3}{x}$

    (e) $\dfrac{x - 4x^2}{x^3}$

    (f) $\dfrac{x^2 - 3x + 5}{x^2}$

4. Find expressions for d^2y/dx^2 in the case when

    (a) $y = 7x^2 - x$

    (b) $y = \dfrac{1}{x^2}$

    (c) $y = ax + b$

5. Evaluate $f''(2)$ for the function

    $$f(x) = x^3 - 4x^2 + 10x - 7$$

6. If $f(x) = x^2 - 6x + 8$, evaluate $f'(3)$. What information does this provide about the graph of $y = f(x)$ at $x = 3$?

7. By writing $\sqrt{4x} = \sqrt{4} \times \sqrt{x} = 2\sqrt{x}$, differentiate $\sqrt{4x}$.
    Use a similar approach to differentiate

    (a) $\sqrt{25x}$ (b) $\sqrt[3]{27x}$ (c) $\sqrt[4]{16x^3}$ (d) $\sqrt{\dfrac{25}{x}}$

8. Find expressions for

    (a) $\dfrac{dQ}{dP}$ for the supply function $Q = P^2 + P + 1$

    (b) $\dfrac{d(TR)}{dQ}$ for the total revenue function $TR = 50Q - 3Q^2$

    (c) $\dfrac{d(AC)}{dQ}$ for the average cost function $AC = \dfrac{30}{Q} + 10$

    (d) $\dfrac{dC}{dY}$ for the consumption function $C = 3Y + 7$

    (e) $\dfrac{dQ}{dL}$ for the production function $Q = 10\sqrt{L}$

    (f) $\dfrac{d\pi}{dQ}$ for the profit function $\pi = -2Q^3 + 15Q^2 - 24Q - 3$

Exercise 4.2*

1. Find the value of the first-order derivative of the function

$$y = 3\sqrt{x} - \frac{81}{x} + 13$$

when $x = 9$.

2. Find expressions for

(a) $\dfrac{dQ}{dP}$ for the supply function $Q = 2P^2 + P + 1$

(b) $\dfrac{d(TR)}{dQ}$ for the total revenue function $TR = 40Q - 3Q\sqrt{Q}$

(c) $\dfrac{d(AC)}{dQ}$ for the average cost function $AC = \dfrac{20}{Q} + 7Q + 25$

(d) $\dfrac{dC}{dY}$ for the consumption function $C = Y(2Y + 3) + 10$

(e) $\dfrac{dC}{dL}$ for the production function $Q = 200L - 4\sqrt[4]{L}$

(f) $\dfrac{d\pi}{dQ}$ for the profit function $\pi = -Q^3 + 20Q^2 - 7Q - 1$

3. Find the value of the second-order derivative of the following function at the point $x = 4$:

$$f(x) = -2x^3 + 4x^2 + x - 3$$

What information does this provide about the shape of the graph of $f(x)$ at this point?

4. Consider the graph of the function

$$f(x) = 2x^5 - 3x^4 + 2x^2 - 17x + 31$$

at $x = -1$.

Giving reasons for your answers,

(a) state whether the tangent slopes uphill, downhill or is horizontal

(b) state whether the graph is concave or convex at this point.

5. Use the second-order derivative to show that the graph of the cubic,

$$f(x) = ax^3 + bx^2 + cx + d \ (a > 0)$$

is convex when $x > -b/3a$ and concave when $x < -b/3a$.

6. Find the equation of the tangent to the curve

$$y = 4x^3 - 5x^2 + x - 3$$

at the point where it crosses the y axis.

7. A Pareto income distribution function is given by

$$f(x) = \frac{A}{x^a}, \quad x \geq 1$$

where A and a are positive constants and x is measured in \$100 000s.

(a) Find an expression for $f'(x)$ and hence comment on the slope of this function.

(b) Find an expression for $f''(x)$ and hence comment on the convexity of this function.

(c) Sketch a graph of $f(x)$.

(d) The area under the graph between $x = b$ and $x = c$ measures the proportion of people whose income is in the range, $b \leq x \leq c$. What does this graph indicate about the distributions of income above a threshold of \$100 000?

8. A utility function, $U(x)$, measures the amount of satisfaction gained by an individual who buys x units of a product or service. The Arrow–Pratt coefficient of relative risk aversion is defined by

$$r = -\frac{xU''(x)}{U'(x)}$$

Show that the coefficient of relative risk aversion is constant for the utility function

$$U(x) = \frac{x^{1-\gamma}}{1-\gamma}$$

SECTION 4.3
Marginal functions

Objectives

At the end of this section you should be able to:

- Calculate marginal revenue and marginal cost.
- Derive the relationship between marginal and average revenue for both a monopoly and perfect competition.
- Calculate marginal product of labour.
- State the law of diminishing marginal productivity using the notation of calculus.
- Calculate marginal propensity to consume and marginal propensity to save.

At this stage you may be wondering what on earth differentiation has got to do with economics. In fact, we cannot get very far with economic theory without making use of calculus. In this section we concentrate on three main areas that illustrate its applicability:

- revenue and cost
- production
- consumption and savings.

We consider each of these in turn.

4.3.1 Revenue and cost

In Chapter 2 we investigated the basic properties of the revenue function, TR. It is defined to be PQ, where P denotes the price of a good and Q denotes the quantity demanded. In practice, we usually know the demand function, which provides a relationship between P and Q. This enables a formula for TR to be written down solely in terms of Q. For example, if

$$P = 100 - 2Q$$

then

$$\text{TR} = PQ = (100 - 2Q)Q = 100Q - 2Q^2$$

The formula can be used to calculate the value of TR corresponding to any value of Q. Not content with this, we are also interested in the effect on TR of a change in the value of Q from some existing level. To do this we introduce the concept of marginal revenue. The **marginal revenue**, MR, of a good is defined by

$$\text{MR} = \frac{d(\text{TR})}{dQ}$$

marginal revenue is the derivative of total revenue with respect to demand

For example, the marginal revenue function corresponding to

$$TR = 100Q - 2Q^2$$

is given by

$$\frac{d(TR)}{dQ} = 100 - 4Q$$

If the current demand is 15, say, then

$$MR = 100 - 4(15) = 40$$

You may be familiar with an alternative definition often quoted in elementary economics textbooks. Marginal revenue is sometimes taken to be the change in TR brought about by a 1 unit increase in Q. It is easy to check that this gives an acceptable approximation to MR, although it is not quite the same as the exact value obtained by differentiation. For example, substituting $Q = 15$ into the total revenue function considered previously gives

$$TR = 100(15) - 2(15)^2 = 1050$$

An increase of 1 unit in the value of Q produces a total revenue

$$TR = 100(16) - 2(16)^2 = 1088$$

This is an increase of 38, which, according to the non-calculus definition, is the value of MR when Q is 15. This compares with the exact value of 40 obtained by differentiation.

It is instructive to give a graphical interpretation of these two approaches. In Figure 4.12 the point A lies on the TR curve corresponding to a quantity Q_0. The exact value of MR at this point is equal to the derivative

$$\frac{d(TR)}{dQ}$$

and so is given by the slope of the tangent at A. The point B also lies on the curve but corresponds to a 1 unit increase in Q. The vertical distance from A to B therefore equals the change in TR when Q increases by 1 unit. The slope of the line joining A and B (known as a **chord**) is

$$\frac{\Delta(TR)}{\Delta Q} = \frac{\Delta(TR)}{1} = \Delta(TR)$$

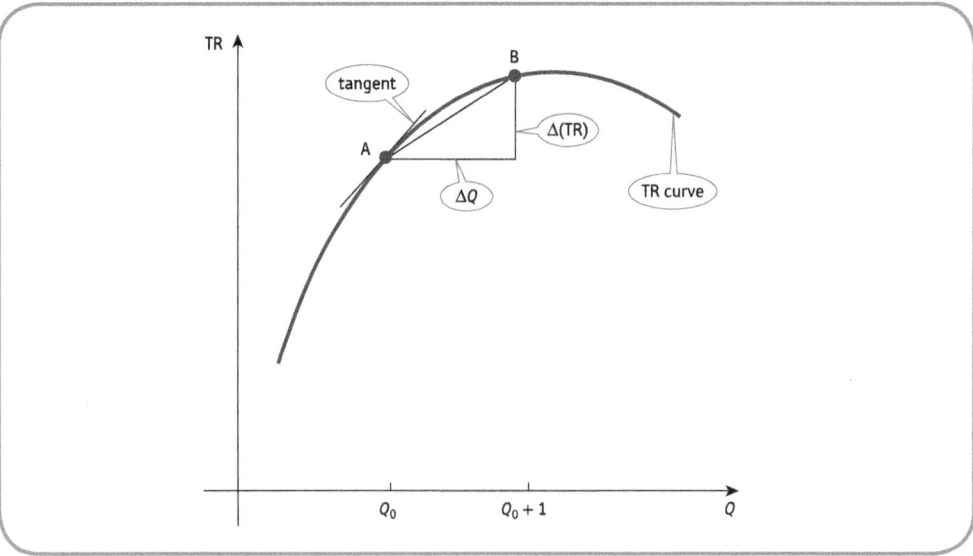

Figure 4.12

In other words, the slope of the chord is equal to the value of MR obtained from the non-calculus definition. Inspection of the diagram reveals that the slope of the tangent is approximately the same as that of the chord joining A and B. In this case the slope of the tangent is slightly the larger of the two, but there is not much in it. We therefore see that the 1 unit increase approach produces a reasonable approximation to the exact value of MR given by

$$\frac{d(TR)}{dQ}$$

Practice Problem

1. If the demand function is

   $$P = 60 - Q$$

   find an expression for TR in terms of Q.

   (1) Differentiate TR with respect to Q to find a general expression for MR in terms of Q. Hence write down the exact value of MR at $Q = 50$.

   (2) Calculate the value of TR when

   (a) $Q = 50$ **(b)** $Q = 51$

   and hence confirm that the 1 unit increase approach gives a reasonable approximation to the exact value of MR obtained in part (1).

The approximation indicated by Figure 4.12 holds for any value of ΔQ. The slope of the tangent at A is the marginal revenue, MR. The slope of the chord joining A and B is $\Delta(TR)/\Delta Q$. It follows that

$$MR \cong \frac{\Delta(TR)}{\Delta Q}$$

This equation can be transposed to give

$$\Delta(TR) \cong MR \times \Delta Q \qquad \left(\text{multiply both sides by } \Delta Q\right)$$

that is,

change in total revenue $\cong$ **marginal revenue** $\times$ **change in demand**

Moreover, Figure 4.12 shows that the smaller the value of ΔQ, the better the approximation becomes.

Example

If the total revenue function of a good is given by

$$100Q - Q^2$$

write down an expression for the marginal revenue function. If the current demand is 60, estimate the change in the value of TR due to a 2 unit increase in Q.

Solution

If

$$TR = 100Q - Q^2$$

then

$$MR = \frac{d(TR)}{dQ}$$
$$= 100 - 2Q$$

When $Q = 60$

$$MR = 100 - 2(60) = -20$$

If Q increases by 2 units, $\Delta Q = 2$ and the formula

$$\Delta(TR) \cong MR \times \Delta Q$$

shows that the change in total revenue is approximately

$$(-20) \times 2 = -40$$

A 2 unit increase in Q therefore leads to a decrease in TR of about 40.

Practice Problem

2. If the total revenue function of a good is given by

$$1000Q - 4Q^2$$

write down an expression for the marginal revenue function. If the current demand is 30, find the approximate change in the value of TR due to a

(a) 3 unit increase in Q

(b) 2 unit decrease in Q.

The simple model of demand, originally introduced in Section 1.5, assumed that price, P, and quantity, Q, are linearly related according to an equation

$$P = aQ + b$$

where the slope, a, is negative and the intercept, b, is positive. A downward-sloping demand curve such as this corresponds to the case of a **monopolist**. A single firm, or possibly a group

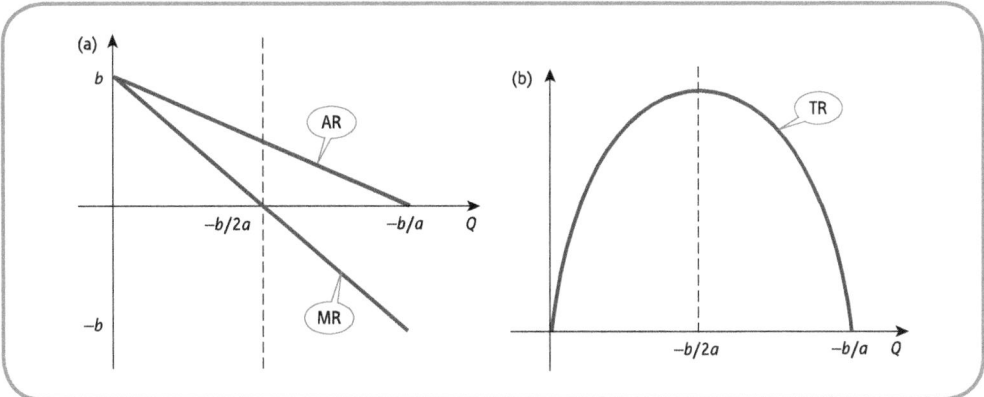

Figure 4.13

of firms forming a cartel, is assumed to be the only supplier of a particular product and so has control over the market price. As the firm raises the price, so demand falls. The associated total revenue function is given by

$$TR = PQ$$
$$= (aQ + b)Q$$
$$= aQ^2 + bQ$$

An expression for marginal revenue is obtained by differentiating TR with respect to Q to get

$$MR = 2aQ + b$$

It is interesting to notice that, on the assumption of a linear demand equation, the marginal revenue is also linear with the same intercept, b, but with slope $2a$. The marginal revenue curve slopes downhill exactly twice as fast as the demand curve. This is illustrated in Figure 4.13(a).

The **average revenue**, AR, is defined by

$$AR = \frac{TR}{Q}$$

and, since $TR = PQ$, we have

$$AR = \frac{PQ}{Q} = P$$

For this reason the demand curve is labelled average revenue in Figure 4.13(a). The above derivation of the result $AR = P$ is independent of the particular demand function. Consequently, the terms 'average revenue curve' and 'demand curve' are synonymous.

Figure 4.13(a) shows that the marginal revenue takes both positive and negative values. This is to be expected. The total revenue function is a quadratic and its graph has the familiar parabolic shape indicated in Figure 4.13(b). To the left of $-b/2a$ the graph is uphill, corresponding to a positive value of marginal revenue, whereas to the right of this point it is downhill, giving a negative value of marginal revenue. More significantly, at the maximum point of the TR curve, the tangent is horizontal with zero slope and so MR is zero.

At the other extreme from a monopolist is the case of **perfect competition**. For this model we assume that there are a large number of firms all selling an identical product and that

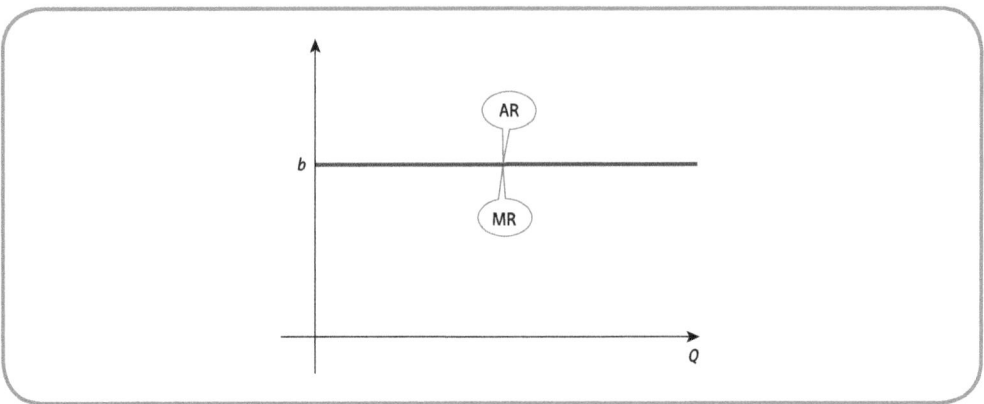

Figure 4.14

there are no barriers to entry into the industry. Since any individual firm produces a tiny proportion of the total output, it has no control over price. The firm can sell only at the prevailing market price and, because the firm is relatively small, it can sell any number of goods at this price. If the fixed price is denoted by b then the demand function is

$P = b$

and the associated total revenue function is

$\text{TR} = PQ = bQ$

An expression for marginal revenue is obtained by differentiating TR with respect to Q and, since b is just a constant, we see that

$\text{MR} = b$

In the case of perfect competition, the average and marginal revenue curves are the same. They are horizontal straight lines, b units above the Q axis as shown in Figure 4.14.

So far we have concentrated on the total revenue function. Exactly the same principle can be used for other economic functions. For instance, we define the **marginal cost**, MC, by

$$\text{MC} = \frac{d(\text{TC})}{dQ}$$

marginal cost is the derivative of total cost with respect to output

Again, using a simple geometrical argument, it is easy to see that if Q changes by a small amount ΔQ then the corresponding change in TC is given by

$\Delta(\text{TC}) \cong \text{MC} \times \Delta Q$

change in total cost $\cong$ marginal cost $\times$ change in output

In particular, putting $\Delta Q = 1$ gives

$\Delta(\text{TC}) \cong \text{MC}$

so that MC gives the approximate change in TC when Q increases by 1 unit.

Example

If the average cost function of a good is

$$AC = 2Q + 6 + \frac{13}{Q}$$

find an expression for MC. If the current output is 15, estimate the effect on TC of a 3 unit decrease in Q.

Solution

We first need to find an expression for TC using the given formula for AC. Now we know that the average cost is just the total cost divided by Q: that is,

$$AC = \frac{TC}{Q}$$

Hence

$$TC = (AC)Q$$

$$= \left(2Q + 6 + \frac{13}{Q}\right)Q$$

and, after multiplying out the brackets, we get

$$TC = 2Q^2 + 6Q + 13$$

In this formula the last term, 13, is independent of Q so must denote the fixed costs. The remaining part, $2Q^2 + 6Q$, depends on Q so represents the total variable costs. Differentiating gives

$$MC = \frac{d(TC)}{dQ}$$

$$= 4Q + 6$$

Notice that because the fixed costs are constant they differentiate to zero and so have no effect on the marginal cost. When $Q = 15$,

$$MC = 4(15) + 6 = 66$$

Also, if Q decreases by 2 units then $\Delta Q = -2$. Hence the change in TC is given by

$$\Delta(TC) \cong MC \times \Delta Q = 66 \times (-2) = -132$$

so TC decreases by 132 units approximately.

Practice Problem

3. Find the marginal cost given the average cost function

$$AC = \frac{100}{Q} + 2$$

Deduce that a 1 unit increase in Q will always result in a 2 unit increase in TC, irrespective of the current level of output.

4.3.2 Production

Production functions were introduced in Section 2.3. In the simplest case output, Q, is assumed to be a function of labour, L, and capital, K. Moreover, in the short run the input K can be assumed to be fixed, so Q is then only a function of one input L. (This is not a valid assumption in the long run and in general Q must be regarded as a function of at least two inputs. Methods for handling this situation are considered in the next chapter.) The variable L is usually measured in terms of the number of workers or possibly in terms of the number of worker hours. Motivated by our previous work, we define the **marginal product of labour**, MP_L, by

$$MP_L = \frac{dQ}{dL}$$

marginal product of labour is the derivative of output with respect to labour

As before, this gives the approximate change in Q that results from using 1 more unit of L.

It is instructive to work out numerical values of MP_L for the particular production function

$$Q = 300L^{1/2} - 4L$$

where L denotes the actual size of the workforce.

Differentiating Q with respect to L gives

$$\begin{aligned}
MP_L &= \frac{dQ}{dL} \\
&= 300(\tfrac{1}{2} L^{-1/2}) - 4 \\
&= 150L^{-1/2} - 4 \\
&= \frac{150}{\sqrt{L}} - 4
\end{aligned}$$

Substituting $L = 1, 9, 100$ and 2500 in turn into the formula for MP_L gives

(a) When $L = 1$

$$MP_L = \frac{150}{\sqrt{9}} - 4 = 146$$

(b) When $L = 9$

$$MP_L = \frac{150}{\sqrt{1}} - 4 = 46$$

(c) When $L = 100$

$$MP_L = \frac{150}{\sqrt{100}} - 4 = 11$$

(d) When $L = 2500$

$$MP_L = \frac{150}{\sqrt{2500}} - 4 = -1$$

Notice that the values of MP_L decline with increasing L. Part (a) shows that if the workforce consists of only one person then to employ two people would increase output by approximately 146. In part (b) we see that to increase the number of workers from 9 to 10 would result in about 46 additional units of output. In part (c) we see that a 1 unit increase in labour from a level of 100 increases output by only 11. In part (d) the situation is even worse. This indicates that to increase staff actually reduces output! The latter is a rather surprising result, but it is borne out by what occurs in real production processes. This may be due to problems of overcrowding on the shopfloor or to the need to create an elaborate administration to organise the larger workforce.

This production function illustrates the **law of diminishing marginal productivity** (sometimes called the **law of diminishing returns**). It states that the increase in output due to a 1 unit increase in labour will eventually decline. In other words, once the size of the workforce has reached a certain threshold level, the marginal product of labour will get smaller. For the production function

$$Q = 300L^{1/2} - 4L$$

the value of MP_L continually goes down with rising L. This is not always so. It is possible for the marginal product of labour to remain constant or to go up to begin with for small values of L. However, if it is to satisfy the law of diminishing marginal productivity then there must be some value of L above which MP_L decreases.

A typical product curve is sketched in Figure 4.15, which has slope

$$\frac{dQ}{dL} = MP_L$$

Between 0 and L_0 the curve bends upwards, becoming progressively steeper, and so the slope function, MP_L, increases. Mathematically, this means that the slope of MP_L is positive: that is,

$$\frac{d(MP_L)}{dQ} > 0$$

Now MP_L is itself the derivative of Q with respect to L, so we can use the notation for the second-order derivative and write this as

$$\frac{d^2Q}{dL^2} > 0$$

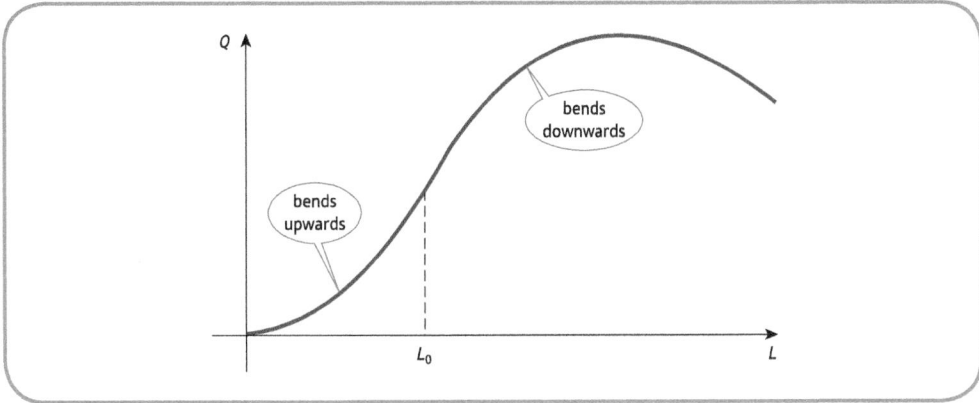

Figure 4.15

Similarly, if L exceeds the threshold value of L_0, then Figure 4.15 shows that the product curve bends downwards and the slope decreases. In this region, the slope of the slope function is negative, so that

$$\frac{d^2Q}{dL^2} < 0$$

The law of diminishing returns states that this must happen eventually: that is,

$$\frac{d^2Q}{dL^2} < 0$$

for sufficiently large L.

Practice Problem

4. A Cobb–Douglas production function is given by

$$Q = 5L^{1/2}K^{1/2}$$

Assuming that capital, K, is fixed at 100, write down a formula for Q in terms of L only. Calculate the marginal product of labour when

(a) $L = 1$ (b) $L = 9$ (c) $L = 10\ 000$

Verify that the law of diminishing marginal productivity holds in this case.

4.3.3 Consumption and savings

In Chapter 1 the relationship between consumption, C, savings, S, and national income, Y, was investigated. If we assume that national income is only used up in consumption and savings then

$$Y = C + S$$

Of particular interest is the effect on C and S due to variations in Y. Expressed simply, if national income rises by a certain amount, are people more likely to go out and spend their extra income on consumer goods or will they save it? To analyse this behaviour we use the concepts **marginal propensity to consume**, MPC, and **marginal propensity to save**, MPS, which are defined by

$$\text{MPC} = \frac{dC}{dY} \quad \text{and} \quad \text{MPS} = \frac{dS}{dY}$$

Marginal propensity to consume is the derivative of consumption with respect to income

Marginal propensity to save is the derivative of savings with respect to income

These definitions are consistent with those given in Section 1.7, where MPC and MPS were taken to be the slopes of the linear consumption and savings curves, respectively. At first sight it appears that, in general, we need to work out two derivatives in order to evaluate MPC and

MPS. However, this is not strictly necessary. Recall that we can do whatever we like to an equation provided we do the same thing to both sides. Consequently, we can differentiate both sides of the equation

$$Y = C + S$$

with respect to Y to deduce that

$$\frac{dY}{dY} = \frac{dC}{dY} + \frac{dS}{dY} = \text{MPC} + \text{MPS}$$

Now we are already familiar with the result that when we differentiate x with respect to x the answer is 1. In this case Y plays the role of x, so

$$\frac{dY}{dY} = 1$$

Hence

$$1 = \text{MPC} + \text{MPS}$$

This formula is identical to the result given in Section 1.7 for simple linear functions. In practice, it means that we need only work out one of the derivatives. The remaining derivative can then be calculated directly from this equation.

Example

If the consumption function is

$$C = 0.01Y^2 + 0.2Y + 50$$

calculate MPC and MPS when $Y = 30$.

Solution

In this example the consumption function is given, so we begin by finding MPC. To do this we differentiate C with respect to Y. If

$$C = 0.01Y^2 + 0.2Y + 50$$

then

$$\frac{dC}{dY} = 0.02Y + 0.2$$

so, when $Y = 30$,

$$\text{MPC} = 0.02(30) + 0.2 = 0.8$$

To find the corresponding value of MPS we use the formula

$$\text{MPC} + \text{MPS} = 1$$

which gives

$$\text{MPS} = 1 - \text{MPC} = 1 - 0.8 = 0.2$$

This indicates that when national income increases by 1 unit (from its current level of 30) consumption rises by approximately 0.8 units, whereas savings rise by only about 0.2 units. At this level of income the nation has a greater propensity to consume than it has to save.

Practice Problem

5. If the savings function is given by

$$S = 0.02Y^2 - Y + 100$$

calculate the values of MPS and MPC when $Y = 40$. Give a brief interpretation of these results.

Key Terms

Average revenue   Total revenue per unit of output: $AR = TR/Q = P$.

Chord   A straight line joining two points on a curve.

Law of diminishing marginal productivity (law of diminishing returns)   Once the size of the workforce exceeds a particular value, the increase in output due to a 1 unit increase in labour will decline: $d^2Q/dL^2 < 0$ for sufficiently large L.

Marginal cost   The cost of producing 1 more unit of output: $MC = d(TC)/dQ$.

Marginal product of labour   The extra output produced by 1 more unit of labour: $MP_L = dQ/dL$.

Marginal propensity to consume   The fraction of a rise in national income which goes into consumption: $MPC = dC/dY$.

Marginal propensity to save   The fraction of a rise in national income which goes into savings: $MPS = dS/dY$.

Marginal revenue   The extra revenue gained by selling 1 more unit of a good: $MR = d(TR)/dQ$.

Monopolist   The only firm in the industry.

Perfect competition   A situation in which there are no barriers to entry in an industry where there are many firms selling an identical product at the market price.

Exercise 4.3

1. If the demand function is

$$P = 100 - 4Q$$

find expressions for TR and MR in terms of Q. Hence estimate the change in TR brought about by a 0.3 unit increase in output from a current level of 12 units.

2. If the demand function is

$$P = 80 - 3Q$$

show that

$$MR = 2P - 80$$

3. A monopolist's demand function is given by

$$P + Q = 100$$

Write down expressions for TR and MR in terms of Q and sketch their graphs. Find the value of Q which gives a marginal revenue of zero and comment on the significance of this value.

4. If the average cost function of a good is

$$AC = \frac{15}{Q} + 2Q + 9$$

find an expression for TC. What are the fixed costs in this case? Write down an expression for the marginal cost function.

5. A firm's production function is

$$Q = 50L - 0.01L^2$$

where L denotes the size of the workforce. Find the value of MP_L in the case when

(a) $L = 1$ (b) $L = 10$ (c) $L = 100$ (d) $L = 1000$

Does the law of diminishing marginal productivity apply to this particular function?

6. If the consumption function is

$$C = 50 + 2\sqrt{Y}$$

calculate MPC and MPS when $Y = 36$ and give an interpretation of these results.

7. If the consumption function is

$$C = 0.02Y^2 + 0.1Y + 25$$

find the value of Y when $MPS = 0.38$.

8. The price of a company's shares, P, recorded in dollars at midday is a function of time, t, measured in days since the beginning of the year. Give an interpretation of the statement:

$$\frac{dP}{dt} = 0.25$$

when $t = 6$.

9. If the demand function is

$$P = 3000 - 2\sqrt{Q}$$

find expressions for TR and MR. Calculate the marginal revenue when $Q = 9$ and give an interpretation of this result.

Exercise 4.3*

1. A firm's demand function is given by

$$P = 100 - 4\sqrt{Q} - 3Q$$

(a) Write down an expression for total revenue, TR, in terms of Q.

(b) Find an expression for the marginal revenue, MR, and find the value of MR when $Q = 9$.

(c) Use the result of part (b) to *estimate* the change in TR when Q increases by 0.25 units from its current level of 9 units and compare this with the exact change in TR.

2. The consumption function is

    $$C = 0.01Y^2 + 0.8Y + 100$$

    (a) Calculate the values of MPC and MPS when $Y = 8$.

    (b) Use the fact that $C + S = Y$ to obtain a formula for S in terms of Y. By differentiating this expression find the value of MPS at $Y = 8$ and verify that this agrees with your answer to part (a).

3. The fixed costs of producing a good are 100 and the variable costs are $2 + Q/10$ per unit.

    (a) Find expressions for TC and MC.

    (b) Evaluate MC at $Q = 30$ and hence estimate the change in TC brought about by a 2 unit increase in output from a current level of 30 units.

    (c) At what level of output does MC = 22?

4. Show that the law of diminishing marginal productivity holds for the production function

    $$Q = 6L^2 - 0.2L^3$$

5. A firm's production function is given by

    $$Q = 5\sqrt{L} - 0.1L$$

    (a) Find an expression for the marginal product of labour, MP_L.

    (b) Solve the equation $\mathrm{MP}_L = 0$ and briefly explain the significance of this value of L.

    (c) Show that the law of diminishing marginal productivity holds for this function.

6. A firm's average cost function takes the form

    $$AC = 4Q + a + \frac{6}{Q}$$

    and it is known that MC = 35 when $Q = 3$. Find the value of AC when $Q = 6$.

7. The total cost of producing a good is given by

    $$TC = 250 + 20Q$$

    The marginal revenue is 18 at $Q = 219$. If production is increased from its current level of 219, would you expect profit to increase, decrease or stay the same? Give reasons for your answer.

8. Given the demand and total cost functions

    $$P = 150 - 2Q \quad \text{and} \quad TC = 40 + 0.5Q^2$$

    find the marginal profit when $Q = 25$ and give an interpretation of this result.

9. If the total cost function is given by $TC = aQ^2 + bQ + c$ show that

    $$\frac{d(AC)}{dQ} = \frac{MC - AC}{Q}$$

SECTION 4.4
Further rules of differentiation

> ## Objectives
>
> At the end of this section you should be able to:
>
> - Use the chain rule to differentiate a function of a function.
> - Use the product rule to differentiate the product of two functions.
> - Use the quotient rule to differentiate the quotient of two functions.
> - Differentiate complicated functions using a combination of rules.

Section 4.2 introduced you to the basic rules of differentiation. Unfortunately, not all functions can be differentiated using these rules alone. For example, we are unable to differentiate the functions

$$x\sqrt{(2x-3)} \quad \text{and} \quad \frac{x}{x^2+1}$$

using just the constant, sum or difference rules. The aim of the present section is to describe three further rules which allow you to find the derivative of more complicated expressions. Indeed, the totality of all six rules will enable you to differentiate any mathematical function. Although you may find that the rules described in this section take you slightly longer to grasp than before, they are vital to any understanding of economic theory.

The first rule that we investigate is called the chain rule and it can be used to differentiate functions such as

$$y = (2x+3)^{10} \quad \text{and} \quad y = \sqrt{(1+x^2)}$$

The distinguishing feature of these expressions is that they represent a 'function of a function'. To understand what we mean by this, consider how you might evaluate

$$y = (2x + 3)^{10}$$

on a calculator. You would first work out an intermediate number u, say, given by

$$u = 2x + 3$$

and then raise it to the power of 10 to get

$$y = u^{10}$$

This process is illustrated using the flow chart in Figure 4.16. Note how the incoming number x is first processed by the inner function, 'double and add 3'. The output u from this is then passed on to the outer function, 'raise to the power of 10', to produce the final outgoing number y.

The function

$$y = \sqrt{(1+x^2)}$$

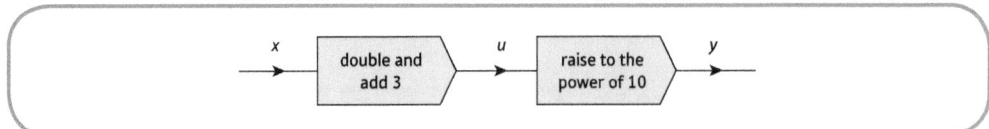

Figure 4.16

can be viewed in the same way. To calculate y you perform the inner function, 'square and add 1', followed by the outer function, 'take square roots'.

The chain rule for differentiating a function of a function may now be stated.

Rule 4 The chain rule

If y is a function of u, which is itself a function of x, then

$$\frac{dy}{dx} = \frac{dy}{du} \times \frac{du}{dx}$$

differentiate the outer function and multiply by the derivative of the inner function

To illustrate this rule, let us return to the function

$$y = (2x + 3)^{10}$$

in which

$$y = u^{10} \quad \text{and} \quad u = 2x + 3$$

Now

$$\frac{dy}{du} = 10u^9 = 10(2x + 3)^9$$

$$\frac{du}{dx} = 2$$

The chain rule then gives

$$\frac{dy}{dx} = \frac{dy}{du} \times \frac{du}{dx} = 10(2x + 3)^9 (2) = 20(2x + 3)^9$$

With practice it is possible to perform the differentiation without explicitly introducing the variable u. To differentiate

$$y = (2x + 3)^{10}$$

we first differentiate the outer power function to get

$$10(2x + 3)^9$$

and then multiply by the derivative of the inner function, $2x + 3$, which is 2, so

$$\frac{dy}{dx} = 20(2x + 3)^9$$

Example

Differentiate

(a) $y = (3x^2 - 5x + 2)^4$

(b) $y = \dfrac{1}{3x + 7}$

(c) $y = \sqrt{(1 + x^2)}$

Solution

(a) The chain rule shows that to differentiate $(3x^2 - 5x + 2)^4$ we first differentiate the outer power function to get

$$4(3x^2 - 5x + 2)^3$$

and then multiply by the derivative of the inner function, $3x^2 - 5x + 2$, which is $6x - 5$. Hence if

$$y = (3x^2 - 5x + 2)^4 \quad \text{then} \quad \frac{dy}{dx} = 4(3x^2 - 5x + 2)^3(6x - 5)$$

(b) To use the chain rule to differentiate

$$y = \frac{1}{3x + 7}$$

recall that reciprocals are denoted by negative powers, so that

$$y = (3x + 7)^{-1}$$

The outer power function differentiates to get

$$-(3x + 7)^{-2}$$

and the inner function, $3x + 7$, differentiates to get 3. By the chain rule we just multiply these together to deduce that

$$\text{if } y = \frac{1}{3x + 7} \quad \text{then} \quad \frac{dy}{dx} = -(3x + 7)^{-2}(3) = \frac{-3}{(3x + 7)^2}$$

(c) To use the chain rule to differentiate

$$y = \sqrt{(1 + x^2)}$$

recall that roots are denoted by fractional powers, so that

$$y = (1 + x^2)^{1/2}$$

The outer power function differentiates to get

$$\frac{1}{2}(1 + x^2)^{-1/2}$$

and the inner function, $1 + x^2$, differentiates to get $2x$. By the chain rule we just multiply these together to deduce that

$$\text{if } y = \sqrt{(1 + x^2)} \quad \text{then} \quad \frac{dy}{dx} = \frac{1}{2}(1 + x^2)^{-1/2}(2x) = \frac{x}{\sqrt{(1 + x^2)}}$$

Practice Problem

1. Differentiate

(a) $y = (3x - 4)^5$ (b) $y = (x^2 + 3x + 5)^3$ (c) $y = \dfrac{1}{2x - 3}$ (d) $y = \sqrt{(4x - 3)}$

The next rule is used to differentiate the product of two functions, $f(x)g(x)$. In order to give a clear statement of this rule, we write

$$u = f(x) \quad \text{and} \quad v = g(x)$$

Rule 5 The product rule

$$\text{If } y = uv \quad \text{then} \quad \frac{dy}{dx} = u\frac{dv}{dx} + v\frac{du}{dx}$$

This rule tells you how to differentiate the product of two functions:

multiply each function by the derivative of the other and add

Example

Differentiate

(a) $y = x^2(2x + 1)^3$ (b) $x\sqrt{(6x + 1)}$ (c) $y = \dfrac{x}{1 + x}$

Solution

(a) The function $x^2(2x + 1)^3$ involves the product of two simpler functions, namely x^2 and $(2x + 1)^3$, which we denote by u and v respectively. (It does not matter which function we label u and which we label v. The same answer is obtained if u is $(2x + 1)^3$ and v is x^2. You might like to check this for yourself later.) Now if

$$u = x^2 \quad \text{and} \quad v = (2x + 1)^3$$

then

$$\frac{du}{dx} = 2x \quad \text{and} \quad \frac{dv}{dx} = 6(2x + 1)^2$$

where we have used the chain rule to find dv/dx. By the product rule,

$$\frac{dy}{dx} = u\frac{dv}{dx} + v\frac{du}{dx}$$
$$= x^2[6(2x + 1)^2] + (2x + 1)^3(2x)$$

The first term is obtained by leaving u alone and multiplying it by the derivative of v. Similarly, the second term is obtained by leaving v alone and multiplying it by the derivative of u.

If desired, the final answer may be simplified by taking out a common factor of $2x(2x+1)^2$. This factor goes into the first term $3x$ times and into the second $2x+1$ times. Hence

$$\frac{dy}{dx} = 2x(2x+1)^2[3x+(2x+1)] = 2x(2x+1)^2(5x+1)$$

(b) The function $x\sqrt{(6x+1)}$ involves the product of the simpler functions

$$u = x \quad \text{and} \quad v = \sqrt{6x+1} = (6x+1)^{1/2}$$

for which

$$\frac{du}{dx} = 1 \quad \text{and} \quad \frac{dv}{dx} = \frac{1}{2}(6x+1)^{-1/2} \times 6 = 3(6x+1)^{-1/2}$$

where we have used the chain rule to find dv/dx. By the product rule,

$$\frac{dy}{dx} = u\frac{dv}{dx} + v\frac{du}{dx}$$

$$= x[3(6x+1)^{-1/2}] + (6x+1)^{1/2}(1)$$

$$= \frac{3x}{\sqrt{(6x+1)}} + \sqrt{(6x+1)}$$

If desired, this can be simplified by putting the second term over a common denominator

$$\sqrt{(6x+1)}$$

To do this we multiply the top and bottom of the second term by $\sqrt{6x+1}$ to get

$$\frac{(6x+1)}{\sqrt{(6x+1)}}$$

$\sqrt{(6x+1)} \times \sqrt{(6x+1)} = 6x+1$

Hence

$$\frac{dy}{dx} = \frac{3x+(6x+1)}{\sqrt{(6x+1)}} = \frac{9x+1}{\sqrt{(6x+1)}}$$

(c) At first sight it is hard to see how we can use the product rule to differentiate

$$\frac{x}{1+x}$$

since it appears to be the quotient and not the product of two functions. However, if we recall that reciprocals are equivalent to negative powers, we may rewrite it as

$$x(1+x)^{-1}$$

It follows that we can put

$$u = x \quad \text{and} \quad v = (1+x)^{-1}$$

which gives

$$\frac{du}{dx} = 1 \quad \text{and} \quad \frac{dv}{dx} = -(1+x)^{-2}$$

where we have used the chain rule to find dv/dx. By the product rule

$$\frac{dy}{dx} = u\frac{dv}{dx} + v\frac{du}{dx}$$

$$\frac{dy}{dx} = x[-(1+x)^{-2}] + (1+x)^{-1}(1)$$

$$= \frac{-x}{(1+x)^2} + \frac{1}{1+x}$$

If desired, this can be simplified by putting the second term over a common denominator

$$(1+x)^2$$

To do this we multiply the top and bottom of the second term by $1 + x$ to get

$$\frac{1+x}{(1+x)^2}$$

Hence

$$\frac{dy}{dx} = \frac{-x}{(1+x)^2} + \frac{1+x}{(1+x)^2} = \frac{-x+(1+x)}{(1+x)^2} = \frac{1}{(1+x)^2}$$

Practice Problem

2. Differentiate

(a) $y = x(3x-1)^6$ **(b)** $y = x^3\sqrt{(2x+3)}$ **(c)** $y = \dfrac{x}{x-2}$

Advice

You may have found the product rule the hardest of the rules so far. This may have been due to the algebraic manipulation that is required to simplify the final expression. If this is the case, do not worry about it at this stage. The important thing is that you can use the product rule to obtain some sort of an answer even if you cannot tidy it up at the end. This is not to say that the simplification of an expression is pointless. If the result of differentiation is to be used in a subsequent piece of theory, it may well save time in the long run if it is simplified first.

One of the most difficult parts of Practice Problem 2 is part (c), since this involves algebraic fractions. For this function, it is necessary to manipulate negative indices and to put two individual fractions over a common denominator. You may feel that you are unable to do either of these processes with confidence. For this reason we conclude this section with a rule that is specifically designed to differentiate this type of function. The rule itself is quite complicated. However, as will become apparent, it does the algebra for you, so you may prefer to use it rather than the product rule when differentiating algebraic fractions.

Rule 6 The quotient rule

$$\text{If } y = \frac{u}{v} \quad \text{then} \quad \frac{dy}{dx} = \frac{v\,du/dx - u\,dv/dx}{v^2}$$

This rule tells you how to differentiate the quotient of two functions:

bottom times derivative of top, minus top times derivative of bottom,
all over bottom squared

Example

Differentiate

(a) $y = \dfrac{x}{1+x}$ **(b)** $y = \dfrac{1+x^2}{2-x^3}$

Solution

(a) In the quotient rule, u is used as the label for the numerator and v is used for the denominator, so to differentiate

$$\frac{x}{1+x}$$

we must take

$$u = x \quad \text{and} \quad v = 1 + x$$

for which

$$\frac{du}{dx} = 1 \quad \text{and} \quad \frac{dv}{dx} = 1$$

By the quotient rule

$$\frac{dy}{dx} = \frac{v\,du/dx - u\,du/dx}{v^2}$$

$$= \frac{(1+x)(1) - x(1)}{(1+x^2)}$$

$$= \frac{1+x-x}{(1+x^2)}$$

$$= \frac{1}{(1+x^2)}$$

Notice how the quotient rule automatically puts the final expression over a common denominator. Compare this with the algebra required to obtain the same answer using the product rule in part (c) of the previous example.

(b) The numerator of the algebraic fraction

$$\frac{1+x^2}{2-x^3}$$

is $1 + x^2$ and the denominator is $2 - x^3$, so we take

$$u = 1 + x^2 \quad \text{and} \quad v = 2 - x^3$$

for which

$$\frac{du}{dx} = 2x \quad \text{and} \quad \frac{dv}{dx} = -3x^2$$

By the quotient rule

$$\frac{dy}{dx} = \frac{v\,du/dx - u\,dv/dx}{v^2}$$

$$= \frac{(2 - x^3)(2x) - (1 + x^2)(-3x^2)}{(2 - x^3)^3}$$

$$= \frac{4x - 2x^4 + 3x^2 + 3x^4}{(2 - x^3)^3}$$

$$= \frac{x^4 + 3x^2 + 4x}{(2 - x^3)^3}$$

Practice Problem

3. Differentiate

(a) $y = \dfrac{x}{x - 2}$ (b) $y = \dfrac{x - 1}{x + 1}$

[You might like to check that your answer to part (a) is the same as that obtained in Practice Problem 2(c).]

Advice

The product and quotient rules give alternative methods for the differentiation of algebraic fractions. It does not matter which rule you go for; use whichever rule is easiest for you.

Exercise 4.4

1. Use the chain rule to differentiate

   (a) $y = (5x + 1)^3$ **(b)** $y = (2x - 7)^8$ **(c)** $y = (x + 9)^5$

   (d) $y = (4x^2 - 7)^3$ **(e)** $y = (x^2 + 4x - 3)^4$ **(f)** $y = \sqrt{(2x+1)}$

   (g) $y = \dfrac{1}{3x+1}$ **(h)** $y = \dfrac{1}{(4x-3)^2}$ **(i)** $y = \dfrac{1}{\sqrt{(2x+5)}}$

2. Use the product rule to differentiate

   (a) $y = x(3x + 4)^2$ **(b)** $y = x^2(x - 2)^3$ **(c)** $y = x\sqrt{(x+2)}$

   (d) $y = (x - 1)(x + 6)^3$ **(e)** $y = (2x + 1)(x + 5)^3$ **(f)** $y = x^3(2x - 5)^4$

3. Use the quotient rule to differentiate

   (a) $y = \dfrac{x}{x-5}$ **(b)** $y = \dfrac{x}{(x+7)}$ **(c)** $y = \dfrac{x+3}{x-2}$

   (d) $y = \dfrac{2x+9}{3x+1}$ **(e)** $y = \dfrac{x}{(5x+6)}$ **(f)** $y = \dfrac{x+4}{3x-7}$

4. Differentiate

   $$y = (5x + 7)^2$$

   (a) by using the chain rule

   (b) by first multiplying out the brackets and then differentiating term by term.

5. Differentiate

   $$y = x^5(x + 2)^2$$

   (a) by using the product rule

   (b) by first multiplying out the brackets and then differentiating term by term.

6. Find expressions for marginal revenue in the case when the demand function is given by

   (a) $P = (100 - Q)^3$ **(b)** $P = \dfrac{1000}{Q+4}$

7. If the consumption function is

   $$C = \dfrac{300 + 2Y^2}{1+Y}$$

   calculate MPC and MPS when $Y = 36$ and give an interpretation of these results.

Exercise 4.4*

1. Use the chain rule to differentiate

    (a) $y = (2x + 1)^{10}$ **(b)** $y = (x^2 + 3x - 5)^3$ **(c)** $y = \dfrac{1}{7x - 3}$

    (d) $y = \dfrac{1}{x^2 + 1}$ **(e)** $y = \sqrt{(8x - 1)}$ **(f)** $y = \dfrac{1}{\sqrt[3]{(6x - 5)}}$

2. Use the product rule to differentiate

    (a) $y = x^2(x + 5)^3$ **(b)** $y = x^5(4x + 5)^2$ **(c)** $y = x\sqrt[4]{(x + 1)}$

3. Use the quotient rule to differentiate

    (a) $y = \dfrac{x^2}{x + 4}$ **(b)** $y = \dfrac{2x - 1}{x + 1}$ **(c)** $y = \dfrac{x^3}{\sqrt{(x - 1)}}$

4. Differentiate

    (a) $y = x(x - 3)^4$ **(b)** $y = x\sqrt{(2x - 3)}$ **(c)** $y = \dfrac{x^3}{(3x + 5)^2}$ **(d)** $y = \dfrac{x}{x^2 + 1}$

    (e) $y = \dfrac{ax + b}{cx + d}$ **(f)** $y = (ax + b)^m(cx + d)^n$ **(g)** $y = x(x + 2)^2(x + 3)^3$

5. Find an expression, simplified as far as possible, for the second-order derivative of the function, $y = \dfrac{x}{2x + 1}$.

6. Find expressions for marginal revenue in the case when the demand function is given by

    (a) $P = \sqrt{(100 - 2Q)}$ **(b)** $P = \dfrac{100}{\sqrt{2 + Q}}$

7. Determine the marginal propensity to consume for the consumption function

    $$C = \frac{650 + 2Y^2}{9 + Y}$$

    when $Y = 21$, correct to 3 decimal places.

    Deduce the corresponding value of the marginal propensity to save and comment on the implications of these results.

8. If the total cost function is given by

    $$TC = \frac{2Q^2 + 10Q}{Q + 3}$$

    show that the marginal cost function is

    $$MC = 2 + \frac{12}{(Q + 3)^2}$$

    Hence comment on the behaviour of MC as Q increases.

9. If the demand function of a good is $P = a - \sqrt{bQ + c}$ show that the marginal revenue function is

    $$MR = a - \frac{3bQ + 2c}{2\sqrt{bQ + c}}$$

SECTION 4.5
Elasticity

Objectives

At the end of this section you should be able to:

- Calculate price elasticity averaged along an arc.
- Calculate price elasticity evaluated at a point.
- Decide whether supply and demand are inelastic, unit elastic or elastic.
- Understand the relationship between price elasticity of demand and revenue.
- Determine the price elasticity for general linear demand functions.

One important problem in business is to determine the effect on revenue of a change in the price of a good. Let us suppose that a firm's demand curve is downward-sloping. If the firm lowers the price then it will receive less for each item, but the number of items sold increases. The formula for total revenue, TR, is

$$TR = PQ$$

and it is not immediately obvious what the net effect on TR will be as P decreases and Q increases. The crucial factor here is not the absolute changes in P and Q but rather the proportional or percentage changes. Intuitively, we expect that if the percentage rise in Q is greater than the percentage fall in P then the firm experiences an increase in revenue. Under these circumstances we say that demand is **elastic**, since the demand is relatively sensitive to changes in price. Similarly, demand is said to be **inelastic** if demand is relatively insensitive to price changes. In this case, the percentage change in quantity is less than the percentage change in price. A firm can then increase revenue by raising the price of the good. Although demand falls as a result, the increase in price more than compensates for the reduced volume of sales and revenue rises. Of course, it could happen that the percentage changes in price and quantity are equal, leaving revenue unchanged. We use the term **unit elastic** to describe this situation.

We quantify the responsiveness of demand to price change by defining the **price elasticity of demand** to be

$$E = \frac{\text{percentage change in demand}}{\text{percentage change in price}}$$

Notice that because the demand curve slopes downwards, a positive change in price leads to a negative change in quantity and vice versa. Consequently, the value of E is always negative. It is usual for economists to ignore the negative sign and consider just the magnitude of elasticity. If this positive value is denoted by $|E|$ then the previous classification of demand functions can be restated more succinctly as:

Demand is said to be

- inelastic if $|E| < 1$
- unit elastic if $|E| = 1$
- elastic if $|E| > 1$

As usual, we denote the changes in P and Q by ΔP and ΔQ respectively, and seek a formula for E in terms of these symbols. To motivate this, suppose that the price of a good is $12 and that it rises to $18. A moment's thought should convince you that the percentage change in price is then 50%. You can probably work this out in your head without thinking too hard. However, it is worthwhile identifying the mathematical process involved. To obtain this figure we first express the change

$$18 - 12 = 6$$

as a fraction of the original to get

$$\frac{6}{12} = 0.5$$

and then multiply by 100 to express it as a percentage. This simple example gives us a clue as to how we might find a formula for E. In general, the percentage change in price is

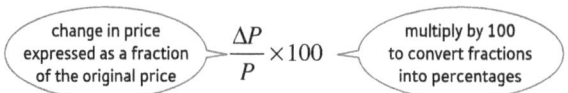

$$\text{change in price expressed as a fraction of the original price} \quad \frac{\Delta P}{P} \times 100 \quad \text{multiply by 100 to convert fractions into percentages}$$

Similarly, the percentage change in quantity is

$$\frac{\Delta Q}{Q} \times 100$$

Hence

$$E = \left(\frac{\Delta Q}{Q} \times 100 \right) \div \left(\frac{\Delta P}{P} \times 100 \right)$$

Now, when we divide two fractions we turn the denominator upside down and multiply, so

$$E = \left(\frac{\Delta Q}{Q} \times \cancel{100} \right) \times \left(\frac{P}{\cancel{100} \times \Delta P} \right)$$

$$= \frac{P}{Q} \times \frac{\Delta Q}{\Delta P}$$

A typical demand curve is illustrated in Figure 4.17, in which a price fall from P_1 to P_2 causes an increase in demand from Q_1 to Q_2.

To be specific, let us suppose that the demand function is given by

$$P = 200 - Q^2$$

with $P_1 = 136$ and $P_2 = 119$.

The corresponding values of Q_1 and Q_2 are obtained from the demand equation

$$P = 200 - Q^2$$

by substituting $P = 136$ and 119 respectively and solving for Q. For example, if $P = 136$ then

$$136 = 200 - Q^2$$

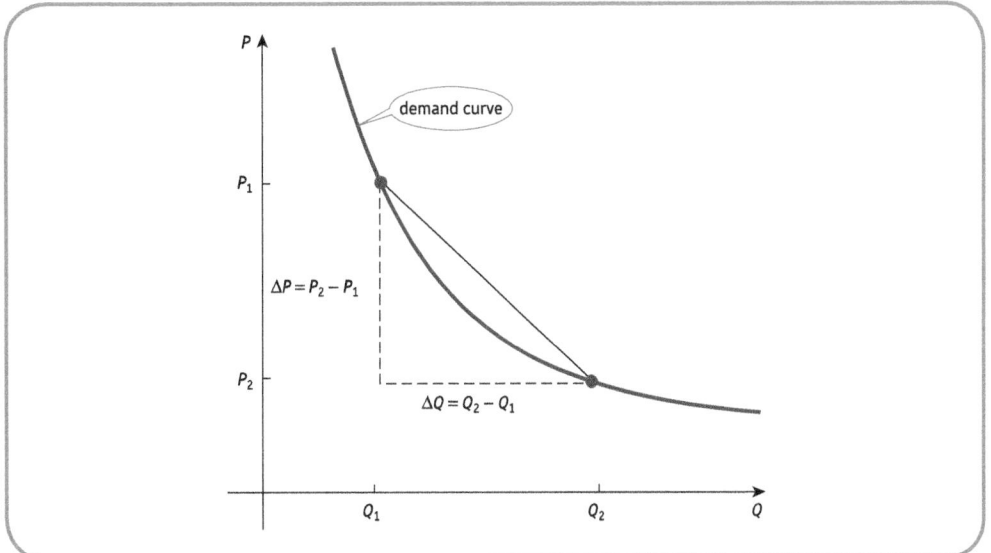

Figure 4.17

which rearranges to give

$$Q^2 = 200 - 136 = 64$$

This has solution $Q = \pm 8$ and, since we can obviously ignore the negative quantity, we have $Q_1 = 8$. Similarly, setting $P = 119$ gives $Q_2 = 9$. The elasticity formula is

$$E = \frac{P}{Q} \times \frac{\Delta Q}{\Delta P}$$

and the values of ΔP and ΔQ are easily worked out to be

$$\Delta P = 119 - 136 = -17$$

$$\Delta Q = 9 - 8 = 1$$

However, it is not at all clear what to take for P and Q. Do we take P to be 136 or 119? Clearly we are going to get two different answers depending on our choice. A sensible compromise is to use their average and take

$$P = \frac{1}{2}(136 + 119) = 127.5$$

Similarly, averaging the Q values gives

$$Q = \frac{1}{2}(8 + 9) = 8.5$$

Hence

$$E = \frac{127.5}{8.5} \times \left(\frac{1}{-17} \right) = -0.88$$

This value is an estimate of elasticity averaged over a section of the demand curve between (Q_1, P_1) and (Q_2, P_2). For this reason it is called **arc elasticity** and is obtained by replacing P by $\frac{1}{2}(P_1 + P_2)$ and Q by $\frac{1}{2}(Q_1 + Q_2)$ in the general formula.

Practice Problem

1. Given the demand function

    $$P = 1000 - 2Q$$

    calculate the arc elasticity as P falls from 210 to 200.

A disappointing feature of this approach is the need to compromise and calculate the elasticity averaged along an arc rather than calculate the exact value at a point. A formula for the latter can easily be deduced from

$$E = \frac{P}{Q} \times \frac{\Delta Q}{\Delta P}$$

by considering the limit as ΔQ and ΔP tend to zero in Figure 4.17. All that happens is that the arc shrinks to a point and the ratio $\Delta Q/\Delta P$ tends to dQ/dP. The price elasticity at a point (**point elasticity**) may therefore be found from

$$E = \frac{P}{Q} \times \frac{dQ}{dP}$$

Example

Given the demand function

$$P = 50 - 2Q$$

find the elasticity when the price is 30. Is demand inelastic, unit elastic or elastic at this price?

Solution

To find dQ/dP we need to differentiate Q with respect to P. However, we are actually given a formula for P in terms of Q, so we need to transpose

$$P = 50 - 2Q$$

for Q. Adding $2Q$ to both sides gives

$$P + 2Q = 50$$

and if we subtract P then

$$2Q = 50 - P$$

Finally, dividing through by 2 gives

$$Q = 25 - \tfrac{1}{2}P$$

Hence

$$\frac{dQ}{dP} = -\tfrac{1}{2}$$

We are given that $P = 30$ so, at this price, demand is

$$Q = 25 - \tfrac{1}{2}(30) = 10$$

These values can now be substituted into

$$E = \frac{P}{Q} \times \frac{dQ}{dP}$$

to get

$$E = \frac{30}{10} \times \left(-\frac{1}{2}\right) = -1.5$$

Moreover, since $|1.5| > 1$, demand is elastic at this price.

Practice Problem

2. Given the demand function

$$P = 100 - Q$$

calculate the magnitude of the price elasticity of demand when the price is

(a) 10   **(b)** 50   **(c)** 90

Is the demand inelastic, unit elastic or elastic at these prices?

It is quite common in economics to be given the demand function in the form

$$P = f(Q)$$

where P is a function of Q. In order to evaluate elasticity it is necessary to find

$$\frac{dQ}{dP}$$

which assumes that Q is actually given as a function of P. Consequently, we may have to transpose the demand equation and find an expression for Q in terms of P before we perform the differentiation. This was the approach taken in the previous example. Unfortunately, if $f(Q)$ is a complicated expression, it may be difficult, if not impossible, to carry out the initial rearrangement to extract Q. An alternative approach is based on the fact that

$$\frac{dQ}{dP} = \frac{1}{dP/dQ}$$

A proof of this can be obtained via the chain rule, although we omit the details. This result shows that we can find dQ/dP by just differentiating the original demand function to get dP/dQ and reciprocating.

Example

Given the demand function

$$P = -Q^2 - 4Q + 96$$

find the price elasticity of demand when $P = 51$. If this price rises by 2%, calculate the corresponding percentage change in demand.

Solution

We are given that $P = 51$, so to find the corresponding demand we need to solve the quadratic equation

$$-Q^2 - 4Q + 96 = 51$$

that is,

$$-Q^2 - 4Q + 45 = 0$$

To do this we use the standard formula

$$\frac{-b \pm \sqrt{b^2 - 4ac}}{2a}$$

discussed in Section 2.1, which gives

$$Q = \frac{-(-4) \pm \sqrt{((-4)^2 - 4(-1)(45))}}{2(-1)}$$

$$= \frac{4 \pm \sqrt{196}}{-2}$$

$$= \frac{4 \pm 14}{-2}$$

The two solutions are -9 and 5. As usual, the negative value can be ignored, since it does not make sense to have a negative quantity, so $Q = 5$.

To find the value of E we also need to calculate

$$\frac{dQ}{dP}$$

from the demand equation, $P = -Q^2 - 4Q + 96$. It is not at all easy to transpose this for Q. Indeed, we would have to use the formula for solving a quadratic, as before, replacing the number 51 with the letter P. Unfortunately this expression involves square roots and the subsequent differentiation is quite messy. (You might like to have a go at this yourself!) However, it is easy to differentiate the given expression with respect to Q to get

$$\frac{dP}{dQ} = -2Q - 4$$

and so

$$\frac{dQ}{dP} = \frac{1}{dP/dQ} = \frac{1}{-2Q - 4}$$

Finally, putting $Q = 5$ gives

$$\frac{dQ}{dP} = -\frac{1}{14}$$

The price elasticity of demand is given by

$$E = \frac{P}{Q} \times \frac{dQ}{dP}$$

and if we substitute $P = 51$, $Q = 5$ and $dQ/dP = -1/14$ we get

$$E = \frac{51}{5} \times \left(-\frac{1}{14}\right) = -0.73$$

To discover the effect on Q due to a 2% rise in P we return to the original definition

$$E = \frac{\text{percentage change in demand}}{\text{percentage change in price}}$$

We know that $E = -0.73$ and that the percentage change in price is 2%, so

$$-0.73 = \frac{\text{percentage change in demand}}{2\%}$$

which shows that demand changes by

$$-0.73 \times 2\% = -1.46\%$$

A 2% rise in price therefore leads to a fall in demand of 1.46%.

Practice Problem

3. Given the demand equation

   $$P = -Q^2 - 10Q + 150$$

   find the price elasticity of demand when $Q = 4$. Estimate the percentage change in price needed to increase demand by 10%.

The **price elasticity of supply** is defined in an analogous way to that of demand. We define

$$E = \frac{\text{percentage change in supply}}{\text{percentage change in price}}$$

An increase in price leads to an increase in supply, so E is positive.

Example

Given the supply function

$$P = 10 + \sqrt{Q}$$

find the price elasticity of supply

(a) averaged along an arc between $Q = 100$ and $Q = 105$

(b) at the point $Q = 100$.

Solution

(a) We are given that

$$Q_1 = 100, \, Q_2 = 105$$

so that

$$P_1 = 10 + \sqrt{100} = 20 \text{ and } P_2 = 10 + \sqrt{105} = 20.247$$

Hence

$$\Delta P = 20.247 - 20 = 0.247, \qquad \Delta Q = 105 - 100 = 5$$

$$P = \frac{1}{2}(20 + 20.247) = 20.123, \qquad Q = \frac{1}{2}(100 + 105) = 102.5$$

The formula for arc elasticity gives

$$E = \frac{P}{Q} \times \frac{\Delta Q}{\Delta P} = \frac{20.123}{102.5} \times \frac{5}{0.247} = 3.97$$

(b) To evaluate the elasticity at the point $Q = 100$, we need to find the derivative, $\dfrac{dQ}{dP}$. The supply equation

$$P = 10 + Q^{1/2}$$

differentiates to give

$$\frac{dP}{dQ} = \frac{1}{2}Q^{-1/2} = \frac{1}{2\sqrt{Q}}$$

so that

$$\frac{dQ}{dP} = 2\sqrt{Q}$$

At the point $Q = 100$, we get

$$\frac{dQ}{dP} = 2\sqrt{100} = 20$$

The formula for point elasticity gives

$$E = \frac{P}{Q} \times \frac{dQ}{dP} = \frac{20}{100} \times 20 = 4$$

Notice that, as expected, the answers to parts (a) and (b) are nearly the same.

Practice Problem

4. If the supply equation is

$$Q = 150 + 5P + 0.1P^2$$

calculate the price elasticity of supply

(a) averaged along an arc between $P = 9$ and $P = 11$

(b) at the point $P = 10$.

Advice

The concept of elasticity can be applied to more general functions and we consider some of these in the next chapter. For the moment we investigate the theoretical properties of demand elasticity. The following material is more difficult to understand than the foregoing, so you may prefer just to concentrate on the conclusions and skip the intermediate derivations.

We begin by analysing the relationship between elasticity and marginal revenue. Marginal revenue, MR, is given by

$$MR = \frac{d(TR)}{dQ}$$

Now TR is equal to the product PQ, so we can apply the product rule to differentiate it. If

$$u = P \quad \text{and} \quad v = Q$$

then

$$\frac{du}{dQ} = \frac{dP}{dQ} \text{ and } \frac{dv}{dQ} = \frac{dQ}{dQ} = 1$$

By the product rule

$$MR = u\frac{dv}{dQ} + v\frac{du}{dQ}$$

$$= P + Q \times \frac{dP}{dQ}$$

$$= P\left(1 + \frac{Q}{P} \times \frac{dP}{dQ}\right)$$

check this by multiplying out the brackets

Now

$$\frac{P}{Q} \times \frac{dQ}{dP} = E$$

so

$$\frac{Q}{P} \times \frac{dP}{dQ} = \frac{1}{E}$$

turn both sides upside down

This can be substituted into the expression for MR to get

$$MR = P\left(1 + \frac{1}{E}\right)$$

The connection between marginal revenue and demand elasticity is now complete, and this formula can be used to justify the intuitive argument that we gave at the beginning of this section concerning revenue and elasticity. Observe that if $-1 < E < 0$ then $1/E < -1$, so MR is negative for any value of P. It follows that the revenue function is decreasing in regions where demand is inelastic, because MR determines the slope of the revenue curve. Similarly, if $E < -1$ then $1/E > -1$, so MR is positive for any price, P, and the revenue curve is upwards. In other words, the revenue function is increasing in regions where demand is elastic. Finally, if $E = -1$ then MR is 0, and so the slope of the revenue curve is horizontal at points where demand is unit elastic.

Throughout this section we have taken specific functions and evaluated the elasticity at particular points. It is more instructive to consider general functions and to deduce general expressions for elasticity. Consider the standard linear downward-sloping demand function

$$P = aQ + b$$

when $a < 0$ and $b > 0$. As noted in Section 4.3, this typifies the demand function faced by a monopolist. To transpose this equation for Q, we subtract b from both sides to get

$$aQ = P - b$$

and then divide through by a to get

$$Q = \frac{1}{a}(P - b)$$

Hence

$$\frac{dQ}{dP} = \frac{1}{a}$$

The formula for elasticity of demand is

$$E = \frac{P}{Q} \times \frac{dQ}{dP}$$

so replacing Q by $(1/a)(P - b)$ and dQ/dP by $1/a$ gives

$$E = \frac{P}{(1/a)(P-b)} \times \frac{1}{a}$$

$$= \frac{P}{P - b}$$

Notice that this formula involves P and b but not a. Elasticity is therefore independent of the slope of linear demand curves. In particular, this shows that, corresponding to any price P, the elasticities of the two demand functions sketched in Figure 4.18 are identical. This is perhaps a rather surprising result. We might have expected demand to be more elastic at point A than at point B, since A is on the steeper curve. However, the mathematics shows that this is not the case. (Can you explain, in economic terms, why this is so?)

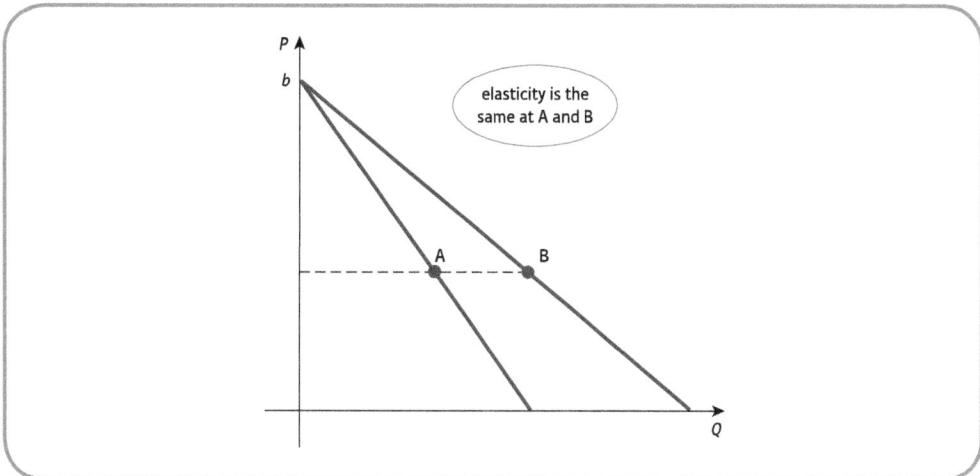

Figure 4.18

Another interesting feature of the result

$$E = \frac{P}{P - b}$$

is the fact that b occurs in the denominator of this fraction, so that corresponding to any price, P, the larger the value of the intercept, b, the smaller the magnitude of the elasticity. In Figure 4.19, the magnitude of the elasticity at C is smaller than that at D because C lies on the curve with the larger intercept.

The dependence of E on P is also worthy of note. It shows that elasticity varies along a linear demand curve. This is illustrated in Figure 4.20. At the left-hand end, $P = b$, so

$$E = \frac{b}{b - b} = \frac{b}{0} = \infty \quad \text{(read 'infinity')}$$

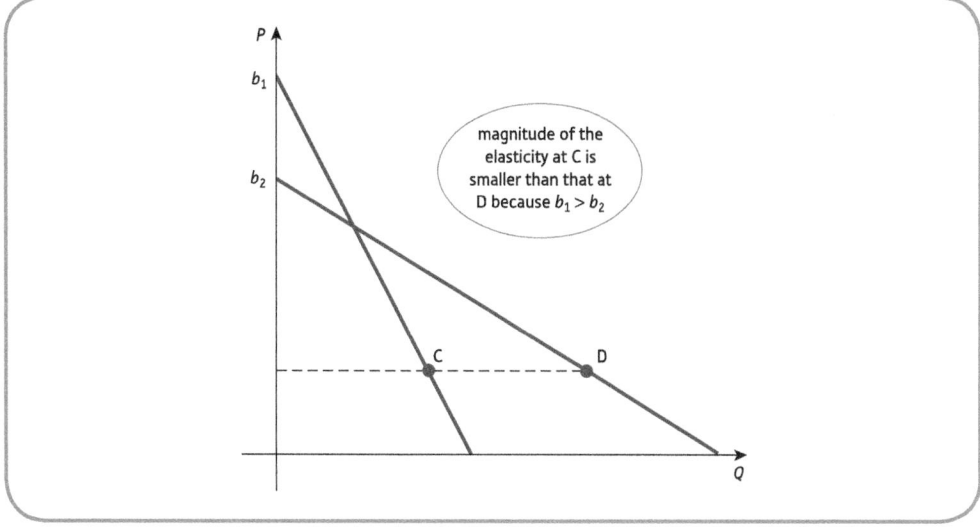

Figure 4.19

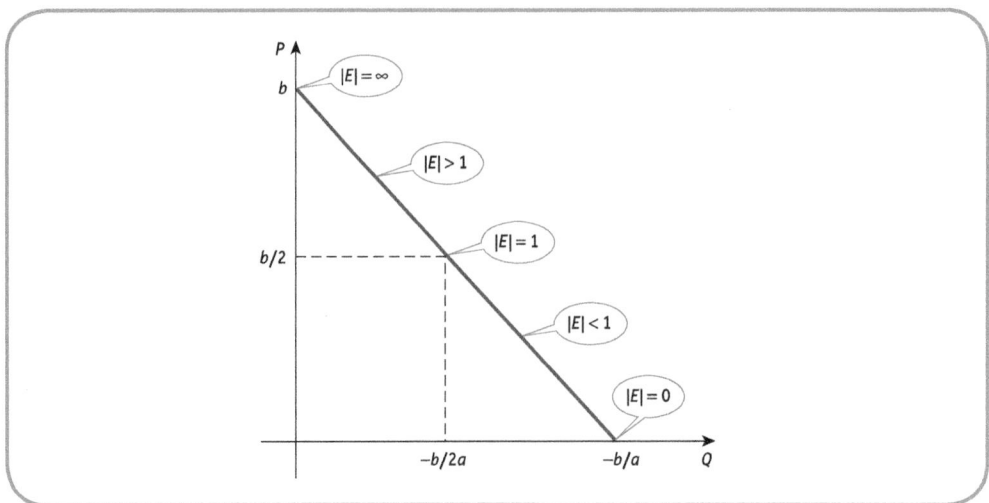

Figure 4.20

At the right-hand end, $P = 0$, so

$$E = \frac{0}{0 - b} = \frac{0}{-b} = 0$$

As you move down the demand curve, the elasticity decreases from ∞ to 0, taking all possible values. Demand is unit elastic when $E = -1$ and the price at which this occurs can be found by solving

$$\frac{P}{P - b} = -1 \quad \text{for} \quad P$$

$$\quad P = b - P \quad \text{(multiply both sides by } P - b)$$

$$\quad 2P = b \quad \quad \text{(add } P \text{ to both sides)}$$

$$\quad P = \frac{b}{2} \quad \quad \text{(divide both sides by 2)}$$

The corresponding quantity can be found by substituting $P = b/2$ into the transposed demand equation to get

$$Q = \frac{1}{a}\left(\frac{b}{2} - b\right) = -\frac{b}{2a}$$

Demand is unit elastic exactly halfway along the demand curve. To the left of this point $|E| > 1$ and demand is elastic, whereas to the right $|E| < 1$ and demand is inelastic.

In our discussion of general demand functions, we have concentrated on those which are represented by straight lines since these are commonly used in simple economic models. There are other possibilities and Question 4 in Exercise 4.5* investigates a class of functions that have constant elasticity.

Key Terms

Arc elasticity   Elasticity measured between two points on a curve.

Elastic demand   Where the percentage change in demand is more than the corresponding percentage change in price: $|E| > 1$.

Inelastic demand   Where the percentage change in demand is less than the corresponding percentage change in price: $|E| < 1$.

Point elasticity   Elasticity measured at a particular point on a curve, e.g. for a supply curve,
$E = \dfrac{P}{Q} \times \dfrac{dQ}{dP}$.

Price elasticity of demand   A measure of the responsiveness of the change in demand due to a change in price: (percentage change in demand) ÷ (percentage change in price).

Price elasticity of supply   A measure of the responsiveness of the change in supply due to a change in price: (percentage change in supply) ÷ (percentage change in price).

Unit elasticity of demand   Where the percentage change in demand is the same as the percentage change in price: $|E| = 1$.

Exercise 4.5

1. Given the demand function

    $$P = 500 - 4Q^2$$

    calculate the price elasticity of demand averaged along an arc joining $Q = 8$ and $Q = 10$.

2. Find the price elasticity of demand at the point $Q = 9$ for the demand function

    $$P = 500 - 4Q^2$$

    and compare your answer with that of Question 1.

3. Find the price elasticity of demand at $P = 6$ for each of the following demand functions:

    (a) $P = 30 - 2Q$

    (b) $P = 30 - 12Q$

    (c) $P = \sqrt{(100 - 2Q)}$

4. **(a)** If an airline increases prices for business class flights by 8%, demand falls by about 2.5%. Estimate the elasticity of demand. Is demand elastic, inelastic or unit elastic?

    (b) Explain whether you would expect a similar result to hold for economy class flights.

5. The demand function of a good is given by

    $$Q = \dfrac{1000}{P^2}$$

    (a) Calculate the price elasticity of demand at $P = 5$ and hence estimate the percentage change in demand when P increases by 2%.

    (b) Comment on the accuracy of your estimate in part (a) by calculating the exact percentage change in demand when P increases from 5 to 5.1.

6. (a) Find the elasticity of demand in terms of Q for the demand function, $P = 20 - 0.05Q$.

   (b) For what value of Q is demand unit elastic?

   (c) Find an expression for MR and verify that $MR = 0$ when demand is unit elastic.

7. Consider the supply equation

   $$Q = 4 + 0.1P^2$$

   (a) Write down an expression for dQ/dP.

   (b) Show that the supply equation can be rearranged as

   $$P = \sqrt{(10Q - 40)}$$

   Differentiate this to find an expression for dP/dQ.

   (c) Use your answers to parts (a) and (b) to verify that

   $$\frac{dQ}{dP} = \frac{1}{dP/dQ}$$

   (d) Calculate the elasticity of supply at the point $Q = 14$.

8. If the supply equation is

   $$Q = 7 + 0.1P + 0.004P^2$$

   find the price elasticity of supply if the current price is 80.

   (a) Is supply elastic, inelastic or unit elastic at this price?

   (b) Estimate the percentage change in supply if the price rises by 5%.

Exercise 4.5*

1. Find the elasticity for the demand function

   $$Q = 80 - 2P - 0.5P^2$$

   averaged along an arc joining $Q = 32$ to $Q = 50$. Give your answer to two decimal places.

2. Consider the supply equation

   $$P = 7 + 2Q^2$$

   By evaluating the price elasticity of supply at the point $P = 105$, estimate the percentage increase in supply when the price rises by 7%.

3. If the demand equation is

   $$Q + 4P = 60$$

   find a general expression for the price elasticity of demand in terms of P. For what value of P is demand unit elastic?

4. Show that the price elasticity of demand is constant for the demand functions

   $$P = \frac{A}{Q^n}$$

   where A and n are positive constants.

5. Find a general expression for the point elasticity of supply for the function

$$Q = aP + b \ (a > 0)$$

Deduce that the supply function is

(a) unit elastic when $b = 0$

(b) inelastic when $b > 0$.

Give a brief geometrical interpretation of these results.

6. A supply function is given by

$$Q = 40 + 0.1P^2$$

(1) Find the price elasticity of supply averaged along an arc between $P = 11$ and $P = 13$. Give your answer correct to 3 decimal places.

(2) Find an expression for price elasticity of supply at a general point, P.

Hence:

(a) Estimate the percentage change in supply when the price increases by 5% from its current level of 17. Give your answer correct to 1 decimal place.

(b) Find the price at which supply is unit elastic.

7. (a) Show that the elasticity of the supply function

$$P = aQ + b$$

is given by

$$E = \frac{P}{P - b}$$

(b) Consider the two supply functions

$$P = 2Q + 5 \text{ and } P = aQ + b$$

The quantity supplied is the same for both functions when $P = 10$, and at this point, the price elasticity of supply for the second function is five times larger than that for the first function. Find the values of a and b.

8. (a) If E denotes the elasticity of a general supply function, $Q = f(P)$, show that the elasticity of:

(i) $Q = [f(P)]^n$ is nE **(ii)** $Q = \lambda f(P)$ is E **(iii)** $Q = \lambda + f(P)$ is $\dfrac{f(P)E}{\lambda + f(P)}$

where n and λ are positive constants.

(b) Show that the elasticity of the supply function $Q = P$ is 1 and use the results of part (a) to write down the elasticity of

(i) $Q = P^3$ **(ii)** $Q = 10P\sqrt{P}$ **(iii)** $Q = 5\sqrt{P} - 2$

SECTION 4.6
Optimisation of economic functions

Objectives

At the end of this section you should be able to:

- Use the first-order derivative to find the stationary points of a function.
- Use the second-order derivative to classify the stationary points of a function.
- Find the maximum and minimum points of an economic function.
- Use stationary points to sketch graphs of economic functions.

In Section 2.1 a simple three-step strategy was described for sketching graphs of quadratic functions of the form

$$f(x) = ax^2 + bx + c$$

The basic idea is to solve the corresponding equation

$$ax^2 + bx + c = 0$$

to find where the graph crosses the x axis. Provided that the quadratic equation has at least one solution, it is then possible to deduce the coordinates of the maximum or minimum point of the parabola. For example, if there are two solutions, then by symmetry the graph turns round at the point exactly halfway between these solutions. Unfortunately, if the quadratic equation has no solution then only a limited sketch can be obtained using this approach.

In this section we show how the techniques of calculus can be used to find the coordinates of the turning point of a parabola. The beauty of this approach is that it can be used to locate the maximum and minimum points of any economic function, not just those represented by quadratics. Look at the graph in Figure 4.21. Points B, C, D, E, F and G are referred to as the **stationary points** (sometimes called **critical points**, **turning points** or **extrema**) of the function. At a stationary point the tangent to the graph is horizontal and so has zero slope.

Consequently, at a stationary point of a function $f(x)$,

$$f'(x) = 0$$

The reason for using the word 'stationary' is historical. Calculus was originally used by astronomers to predict planetary motion. If a graph of the distance travelled by an object is sketched against time then the speed of the object is given by the slope, since this represents the rate of change of distance with respect to time. It follows that if the graph is horizontal at some point then the speed is zero and the object is instantaneously at rest: that is, stationary.

Stationary points are classified into one of three types: local maxima, local minima and stationary points of inflection.

At a **local maximum** (sometimes called a relative maximum) the graph falls away on both sides. Points B and E are the local maxima for the function sketched in Figure 4.21.

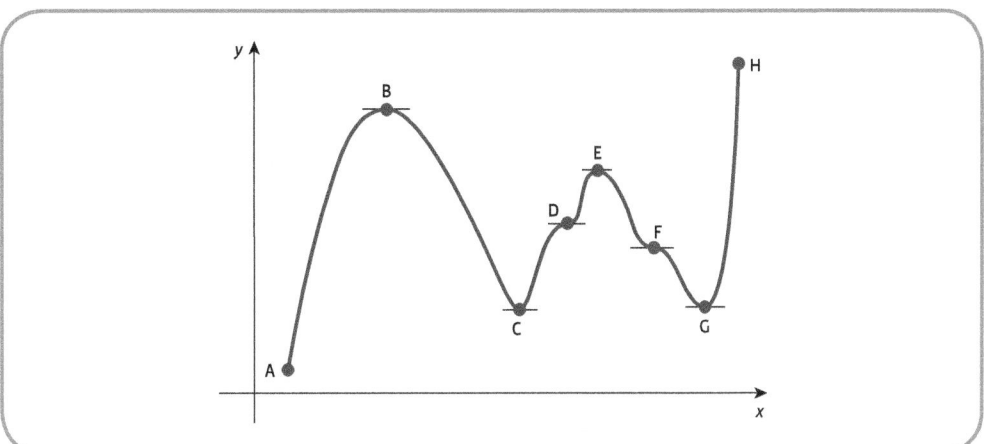

Figure 4.21

The word 'local' is used to highlight the fact that, although these are the maximum points relative to their locality or neighbourhood, they may not be the overall or global maximum. In Figure 4.21 the highest point on the graph actually occurs at the right-hand end, H, which is not a stationary point, since the slope is not zero at H.

At a **local minimum** (sometimes called a relative minimum) the graph rises on both sides. Points C and G are the local minima in Figure 4.21. Again, it is not necessary for the global minimum to be one of the local minima. In Figure 4.21 the lowest point on the graph occurs at the left-hand end, A, which is not a stationary point.

At a **stationary point of inflection** the graph rises on one side and falls on the other. The stationary points of inflection in Figure 4.21 are labelled D and F. These points are of little value in economics, although they do sometimes assist in sketching graphs of economic functions. Maxima and minima, on the other hand, are important. The calculation of the maximum points of the revenue and profit functions is clearly worthwhile. Likewise, it is useful to be able to find the minimum points of average cost functions.

For most examples in economics, the local maximum and minimum points coincide with the global maximum and minimum. For this reason we shall drop the word 'local' when describing stationary points. However, it should always be borne in mind that the global maximum and minimum could actually be attained at an end point and this possibility may need to be checked. This can be done by comparing the function values at the end points with those of the stationary points and then deciding which of them gives rise to the largest or smallest values.

Two obvious questions remain. How do we find the stationary points of any given function and how do we classify them? The first question is easily answered. As we mentioned earlier, stationary points satisfy the equation

$$f'(x) = 0$$

so all we need do is to differentiate the function, to equate to zero and to solve the resulting algebraic equation. The classification is equally straightforward. It can be shown that if a function has a stationary point at $x = a$ then

- if $f''(a) > 0$ then $f(x)$ has a minimum at $x = a$
- if $f''(a) < 0$ then $f(x)$ has a maximum at $x = a$.

Therefore, all we need do is to differentiate the function a second time and to evaluate this second-order derivative at each point. A point is a minimum if this value is positive and a maximum if this value is negative. These facts are consistent with our interpretation of the second-order derivative in Section 4.2. If $f''(a) > 0$ the graph bends upwards at $x = a$ (points C and G in Figure 4.21). If $f''(a) < 0$ the graph bends downwards at $x = a$ (points B and E in Figure 4.21). There is, of course, a third possibility, namely $f''(a) = 0$. Sadly, when this happens it provides no information whatsoever about the stationary point. The point $x = a$ could be a maximum, minimum or inflection. This situation is illustrated in Question 2 in Exercise 4.6* at the end of this section.

Advice

If you are unlucky enough to encounter this case, you can always classify the point by tabulating the function values in the vicinity and use these to produce a local sketch.

To summarise, the method for finding and classifying stationary points of a function, $f(x)$, is as follows:

Step 1

Solve the equation $f'(x) = 0$ to find the stationary points, $x = a$.

Step 2

If

- $f''(a) > 0$ then the function has a minimum at $x = a$
- $f''(a) < 0$ then the function has a maximum at $x = a$
- $f''(a) = 0$ then the point cannot be classified using the available information.

Example

Find and classify the stationary points of the following functions. Hence sketch their graphs.

(a) $f(x) = x^2 - 4x + 5$ **(b)** $f(x) = 2x^3 + 3x^2 - 12x + 4$

Solution

(a) In order to use steps 1 and 2 we need to find the first- and second-order derivatives of the function

$$f(x) = x^2 - 4x + 5$$

Differentiating once gives

$$f'(x) = 2x - 4$$

and differentiating a second time gives

$$f''(x) = 2$$

Step 1

The stationary points are the solutions of the equation

$$f'(x) = 0$$

so we need to solve

$$2x - 4 = 0$$

This is a linear equation so has just one solution. Adding 4 to both sides gives

$$2x = 4$$

and dividing through by 2 shows that the stationary point occurs at

$$x = 2$$

Step 2

To classify this point we need to evaluate

$$f''(2)$$

In this case

$$f''(x) = 2$$

for all values of x, so in particular

$$f''(2) = 2$$

This number is positive, so the function has a minimum at $x = 2$.

We have shown that the minimum point occurs at $x = 2$. The corresponding value of y is easily found by substituting this number into the function to get

$$y = (2)^2 - 4(2) + 5 = 1$$

so the minimum point has coordinates $(2, 1)$. A graph of $f(x)$ is shown in Figure 4.22.

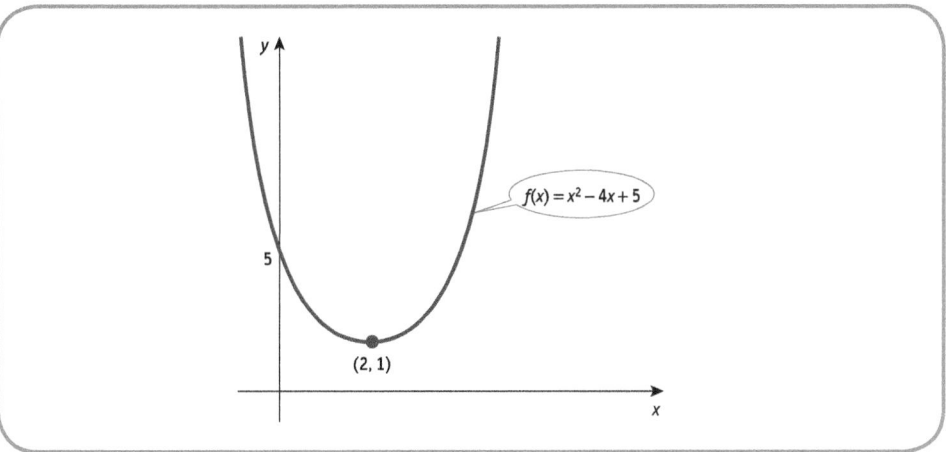

Figure 4.22

(b) In order to use steps 1 and 2 we need to find the first- and second-order derivatives of the function

$$f(x) = 2x^3 + 3x^2 - 12x + 4$$

Differentiating once gives

$$f'(x) = 6x^2 + 6x - 12$$

and differentiating a second time gives

$$f''(x) = 12x + 6$$

Step 1

The stationary points are the solutions of the equation

$$f'(x) = 0$$

so we need to solve

$$6x^2 + 6x - 12 = 0$$

This is a quadratic equation and so can be solved using 'the formula'. However, before doing so, it is a good idea to divide both sides by 6 to avoid large numbers. The resulting equation

$$x^2 + x - 2 = 0$$

has solution

$$x = \frac{-1 \pm \sqrt{(1^2 - 4(1)(-2))}}{2(1)} = \frac{-1 \pm \sqrt{9}}{2} = \frac{-1 \pm 3}{2} = -2, 1$$

In general, whenever $f(x)$ is a cubic function the stationary points are the solutions of a quadratic equation, $f'(x) = 0$. Moreover, we know from Section 2.1 that such an equation can have two, one or no solutions. It follows that a cubic equation can have two, one or no stationary points. In this particular example we have seen that there are two stationary points, at $x = -2$ and $x = 1$.

Step 2

To classify these points we need to evaluate $f''(-2)$ and $f''(1)$. Now

$$f''(-2) = 12(-2) + 6 = -18$$

This is negative, so there is a maximum at $x = -2$. When $x = -2$,

$$y = 2(-2)^3 + 3(-2)^2 - 12(-2) + 4 = 24$$

so the maximum point has coordinates $(-2, 24)$. Now

$$f''(1) = 12(1) + 6 = 18$$

This is positive, so there is a minimum at $x = 1$. When $x = 1$,

$$y = 2(1)^3 + 3(1)^2 - 12(1) + 4 = -3$$

so the minimum point has coordinates $(1, -3)$.

This information enables a partial sketch to be drawn as shown in Figure 4.23. Before we can be confident about the complete picture it is useful to plot a few more points such as those below:

x	−10	0	10
y	−1816	4	2184

This table indicates that when x is positive the graph falls steeply downwards from a great height. Similarly, when x is negative the graph quickly disappears off the bottom of the page. The curve cannot wiggle and turn round except at the two stationary points already plotted (otherwise it would have more stationary points, which we know is not the case). We now have enough information to join up the pieces and so sketch a complete picture as shown in Figure 4.24.

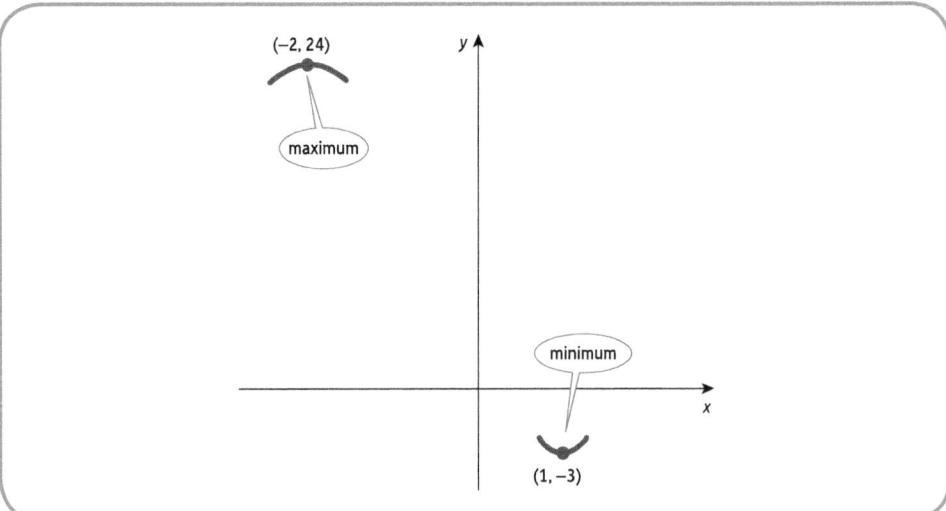

Figure 4.23

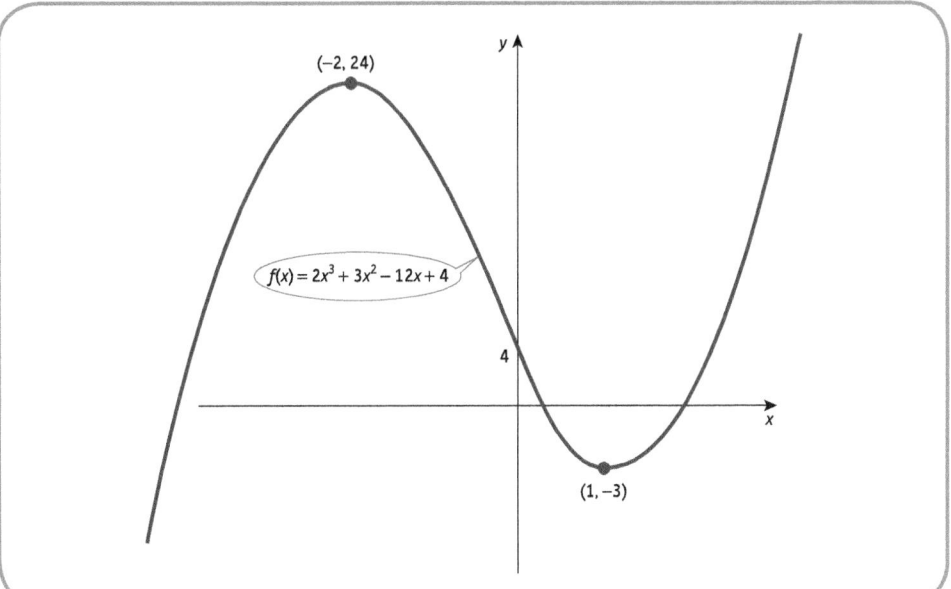

Figure 4.24

In an ideal world it would be nice to calculate the three points at which the graph crosses the x axis. These are the solutions of

$$2x^3 + 3x^2 - 12x + 4 = 0$$

There is a formula for solving cubic equations, just as there is for quadratic equations, but it is extremely complicated and is beyond the scope of this book.

Practice Problem

1. Find and classify the stationary points of the following functions. Hence sketch their graphs.

   (a) $y = 3x^2 + 12x - 35$ (b) $y = -2x^3 + 15x^2 - 36x + 27$

The task of finding the maximum and minimum values of a function is referred to as **optimisation**. This is an important topic in mathematical economics. It provides a rich source of examination questions and we devote the remaining part of this section and the whole of the next to applications of it. In this section we demonstrate the use of stationary points by working through four 'examination-type' problems in detail. These problems involve the optimisation of specific revenue, cost, profit and production functions. They are not intended to exhaust all possibilities, although they are fairly typical. The next section describes how the mathematics of optimisation can be used to derive general theoretical results.

Example

A firm's short-run production function is given by

$$Q = 6L^2 - 0.2L^3$$

where L denotes the number of workers.

(a) Find the size of the workforce that maximises output and hence sketch a graph of this production function.

(b) Find the size of the workforce that maximises the average product of labour. Calculate MP_L and AP_L at this value of L. What do you observe?

Solution

(a) In the first part of this example we want to find the value of L which maximises

$$Q = 6L^2 - 0.2L^3$$

Step 1

At a stationary point

$$\frac{dQ}{dL} = 12L - 0.6L^2 = 0$$

This is a quadratic equation and so we could use 'the formula' to find L. However, this is not really necessary in this case because both terms have a common factor of L and the equation may be written as

$$L(12 - 0.6L) = 0$$

It follows that either

$$L = 0 \text{ or } 12 - 0.6L = 0$$

that is, the equation has solutions

$$L = 0 \text{ and } L = 12/0.6 = 20$$

Step 2

It is obvious on economic grounds that $L = 0$ is a minimum and presumably $L = 20$ is the maximum. We can, of course, check this by differentiating a second time to get

$$\frac{d^2 Q}{dL^2} = 12 - 1.2L$$

When $L = 0$,

$$\frac{d^2 Q}{dL^2} = 12 > 0$$

which confirms that $L = 0$ is a minimum. The corresponding output is given by

$$Q = 6(0)^2 - 0.2(0)^3 = 0$$

as expected. When $L = 20$,

$$\frac{d^2 Q}{dL^2} = -12 < 0$$

which confirms that $L = 20$ is a maximum.

The firm should therefore employ 20 workers to achieve a maximum output

$$Q = 6(20)^2 - 0.2(20)^3 = 800$$

We have shown that the minimum point on the graph has coordinates $(0, 0)$ and the maximum point has coordinates $(20, 800)$. There are no further turning points, so the graph of the production function has the shape sketched in Figure 4.25.

It is possible to find the precise values of L at which the graph crosses the horizontal axis. The production function is given by

$$Q = 6L^2 - 0.2L^3$$

so we need to solve

$$6L^2 - 0.2L^3 = 0$$

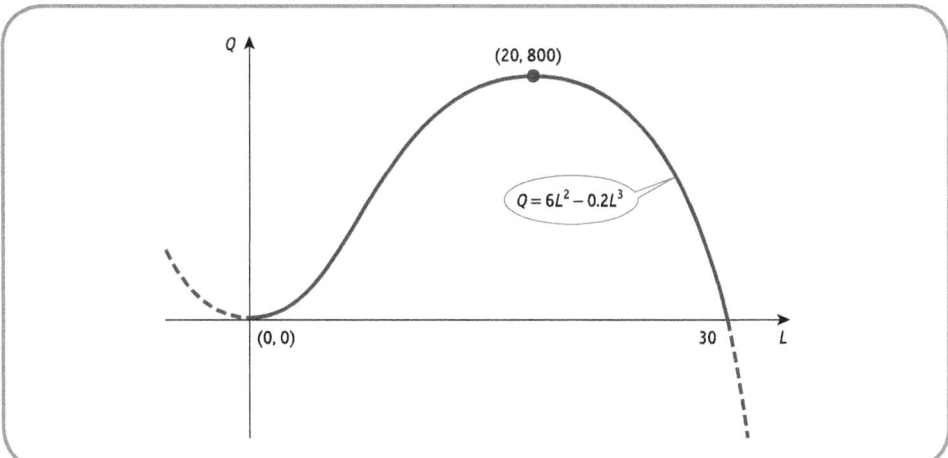

Figure 4.25

We can take out a factor of L^2 to get

$$L^2(6 - 0.2L) = 0$$

Hence, either

$$L^2 = 0 \text{ or } 6 - 0.2L = 0$$

The first of these merely confirms the fact that the curve passes through the origin, whereas the second shows that the curve intersects the L axis at $L = 6/0.2 = 30$.

(b) In the second part of this example we want to find the value of L which maximises the average product of labour. This is a concept that we have not met before in this text, although it is not difficult to guess how it might be defined.

The **average product of labour**, AP_L, is taken to be total output divided by labour, so that in symbols

$$AP_L = \frac{Q}{L}$$

This is sometimes called **labour productivity**, since it measures the average output per worker.

In this example,

$$AP_L = \frac{6L^2 - 0.2L^3}{L} = 6L - 0.2L^2$$

Step 1

At a stationary point

$$\frac{d(AP_L)}{dL} = 0$$

so

$$6 - 0.4L = 0$$

which has solution $L = 6/0.4 = 15$.

Step 2

To classify this stationary point we differentiate a second time to get

$$\frac{d(AP_L)}{dL} = -0.4 < 0$$

which shows that it is a maximum.

The labour productivity is therefore greatest when the firm employs 15 workers. In fact, the corresponding labour productivity, AP_L, is

$$6(15) - 0.2(15)^2 = 45$$

In other words, the largest number of goods produced per worker is 45.

Finally, we are invited to calculate the value of MP_L at this point. To find an expression for MP_L we need to differentiate Q with respect to L to get

$$MP_L = 12L - 0.6L^2$$

When $L = 15$,

$$MP_L = 12(15) - 0.6(15)^2 = 45$$

We observe that at $L = 15$ the values of MP_L and AP_L are equal.

In this particular example we discovered that at the point of maximum average product of labour

marginal product of labour $=$ average product of labour

There is nothing special about this example and in the next section we show that this result holds for any production function.

Practice Problem

2. A firm's short-run production function is given by

$$Q = 300L^2 - L^4$$

where L denotes the number of workers. Find the size of the workforce that maximises the average product of labour and verify that at this value of L

$$MP_L = AP_L$$

Example

The demand equation of a good is

$$P + Q = 30$$

and the total cost function is

$$TC = \tfrac{1}{2}Q^2 + 6Q + 7$$

(a) Find the level of output that maximises total revenue.

(b) Find the level of output that maximises profit. Calculate MR and MC at this value of Q. What do you observe?

Solution

(a) In the first part of this example we want to find the value of Q which maximises total revenue. To do this we use the given demand equation to find an expression for TR and then apply the theory of stationary points in the usual way.

The total revenue is defined by

$$TR = PQ$$

We seek the value of Q which maximises TR, so we express TR in terms of the variable Q only. The demand equation

$$P + Q = 30$$

can be rearranged to get

$$P = 30 - Q$$

Hence

$$\begin{aligned} TR &= (30 - Q)Q \\ &= 30Q - Q^2 \end{aligned}$$

Step 1

At a stationary point

$$\frac{d(TR)}{dQ} = 0$$

so

$$30 - 2Q = 0$$

which has solution $Q = 30/2 = 15$.

Step 2

To classify this point we differentiate a second time to get

$$\frac{d^2(TR)}{dQ^2} = -2$$

This is negative, so TR has a maximum at $Q = 15$.

(b) In the second part of this example we want to find the value of Q which maximises profit. To do this we begin by determining an expression for profit in terms of Q. Once this has been done, it is then a simple matter to work out the first- and second-order derivatives and so to find and classify the stationary points of the profit function.

The profit function is defined by

$$\pi = TR - TC$$

From part (a)

$$TR = 30Q - Q^2$$

We are given the total cost function

$$TC = \tfrac{1}{2}Q^2 + 6Q + 7$$

Hence

$$\pi = (30Q - Q^2) - (\tfrac{1}{2}Q^2 + 6Q + 7)$$
$$= 30Q - Q^2 - \tfrac{1}{2}Q^2 - 6Q - 7$$
$$= -\tfrac{3}{2}Q^2 + 24Q - 7$$

Step 1

At a stationary point

$$\frac{d\pi}{dQ} = 0$$

so

$$-3Q + 24 = 0$$

which has solution $Q = 24/3 = 8$.

Step 2

To classify this point we differentiate a second time to get

$$\frac{d^2\pi}{dQ^2} = -3$$

This is negative, so π has a maximum at $Q = 8$. In fact, the corresponding maximum profit is

$$\pi = -{}^3/_2(8)^2 + 24(8) - 7 = 89$$

Finally, we are invited to calculate the marginal revenue and marginal cost at this particular value of Q. To find expressions for MR and MC we need only differentiate TR and TC, respectively. If

$$TR = 30Q - Q^2$$

then

$$MR = \frac{d(TR)}{dQ}$$

$$= 30 - 2Q$$

so when $Q = 8$

$$MR = 30 - 2(8) = 14$$

If

$$TC = {}^1/_2Q^2 + 6Q + 7$$

then

$$MC = \frac{d(TC)}{dQ}$$

$$= Q + 6$$

so when $Q = 8$

$$MC = 8 + 6 = 14$$

We observe that at $Q = 8$, the values of MR and MC are equal.

In this particular example we discovered that at the point of maximum profit,

marginal revenue = marginal cost

There is nothing special about this example and in the next section we show that this result holds for any profit function.

Practice Problem

3. The demand equation of a good is given by

$$P + 2Q = 20$$

and the total cost function is

$$Q^3 - 8Q^2 + 20Q + 2$$

(a) Find the level of output that maximises total revenue.

(b) Find the maximum profit and the value of Q at which it is achieved. Verify that, at this value of Q, MR = MC.

Example

The cost of building an office block, x floors high, is made up of three components:

(1) $10 million for the land

(2) $\$^1/_4$ million per floor

(3) specialised costs of $\$10\,000x$ per floor.

How many floors should the block contain if the average cost per floor is to be minimised?

Solution

The $10 million for the land is a fixed cost because it is independent of the number of floors. Each floor costs $\$^1/_4$ million, so if the building has x floors altogether then the cost will be $250\,000x$.

In addition there are specialised costs of $10\,000x$ per floor, so if there are x floors this will be

$$(10\,000x)x = 10\,000x^2$$

Notice the square term here, which means that the specialised costs rise dramatically with increasing x. This is to be expected, since a tall building requires a more complicated design. It may also be necessary to use more expensive materials.

The total cost, TC, is the sum of the three components: that is,

$$\text{TC} = 10\,000\,000 + 250\,000x + 10\,000x^2$$

The average cost per floor, AC, is found by dividing the total cost by the number of floors: that is,

$$\text{AC} = \frac{\text{TC}}{x} = \frac{10\,000\,000 + 250\,000x + 10\,000x^2}{x}$$

$$= \frac{10\,000\,000}{x} + 250\,000 + 10\,000x$$

$$= 10\,000\,000x^{-1} + 250\,000 + 10\,000x$$

Step 1

At a stationary point

$$\frac{d(\text{AC})}{dx} = 0$$

In this case

$$\frac{d(\text{AC})}{dx} = -10\,000\,000x^{-2} + 10\,000 = \frac{-10\,000\,000}{x^2} + 10\,000$$

so we need to solve

$$10\,000 = \frac{10\,000\,000}{x^2} \quad \text{or equivalently } 10\,000x^2 = 10\,000\,000$$

Hence

$$x^2 = \frac{10\,000\,000}{10\,000} = 1000$$

This has solution

$$x = \pm\sqrt{1000} = \pm 31.6$$

We can obviously ignore the negative value because it does not make sense to build an office block with a negative number of floors, so we can deduce that $x = 31.6$.

Step 2

To confirm that this is a minimum we need to differentiate a second time. Now

$$\frac{d(AC)}{dx} = -10\,000\,000x^{-2} + 10\,000$$

so

$$\frac{d^2(AC)}{dx^2} = -2(-10\,000\,000)x^{-3} = \frac{20\,000\,000}{x^3}$$

When $x = 31.6$ we see that

$$\frac{d^2(AC)}{dx^2} = \frac{20\,000\,000}{(31.6)^3} = 633.8$$

It follows that $x = 31.6$ is indeed a minimum because the second-order derivative is a positive number.

At this stage it is tempting to state that the answer is 31.6. This is mathematically correct but is a physical impossibility since x must be a whole number. To decide whether to take x to be 31 or 32 we simply evaluate AC for these two values of x and choose the one that produces the lower average cost.

When $x = 31$,

$$AC = \frac{10\,000\,000}{31} + 250\,000 + 10\,000(31) = \$882\,581$$

When $x = 32$,

$$AC = \frac{10\,000\,000}{32} + 250\,000 + 10\,000(32) = \$882\,500$$

Therefore an office block 32 floors high produces the lowest average cost per floor.

Practice Problem

4. The total cost function of a good is given by

   $$TC = Q^2 + 3Q + 36$$

   Calculate the level of output that minimises average cost. Find AC and MC at this value of Q. What do you observe?

Example

The supply and demand equations of a good are given by

$$P = Q_S + 8$$

and

$$P = -3Q_D + 80$$

respectively.

The government decides to impose a tax, t, per unit. Find the value of t which maximises the government's total tax revenue on the assumption that equilibrium conditions prevail in the market.

Solution

The idea of taxation was first introduced in Chapter 1. In Section 1.5 the equilibrium price and quantity were calculated from a given value of t. In this example t is unknown but the analysis is exactly the same. All we need to do is to carry the letter t through the usual calculations and then to choose t at the end so as to maximise the total tax revenue.

To take account of the tax we replace P by $P - t$ in the supply equation. This is because the price that the supplier actually receives is the price, P, that the consumer pays less the tax, t, deducted by the government. The new supply equation is then

$$P - t = Q_S + 8$$

so that

$$P = Q_S + 8 + t$$

In equilibrium

$$Q_S = Q_D$$

If this common value is denoted by Q then the supply and demand equations become

$$P = Q + 8 + t$$
$$P = -3Q + 80$$

Hence

$$Q + 8 + t = -3Q + 80$$

since both sides are equal to P. This can be rearranged to give

$$\begin{aligned} Q &= -3Q + 72 - t & &\text{(subtract } 8 + t \text{ from both sides)} \\ 4Q &= 72 - t & &\text{(add } 3Q \text{ to both sides)} \\ Q &= 18 - {}^{1}/_{4}t & &\text{(divide both sides by 4)} \end{aligned}$$

Now, if the number of goods sold is Q and the government raises t per good then the total tax revenue, T, is given by

$$\begin{aligned} T &= tQ \\ &= t(18 - {}^{1}/_{4}t) \\ &= 18t - {}^{1}/_{4}t^2 \end{aligned}$$

This then is the expression that we wish to maximise.

Step 1

At a stationary point

$$\frac{dT}{dt} = 0$$

so

$$18 - \frac{1}{2}t = 0$$

which has solution

$$t = 36$$

Step 2

To classify this point we differentiate a second time to get

$$\frac{d^2T}{dt^2} = -\frac{1}{2} < 0$$

which confirms that it is a maximum.

Hence the government should impose a tax of \$36 on each good.

Practice Problem

5. The supply and demand equations of a good are given by

$$P = {}^{1}\!/_{2}Q_{S} + 25$$

and

$$P = -2Q_{D} + 50$$

respectively.

The government decides to impose a tax, t, per unit. Find the value of t which maximises the government's total tax revenue on the assumption that equilibrium conditions prevail in the market.

In theory a spreadsheet such as Excel could be used to solve optimisation problems, although it cannot handle the associated mathematics. The preferred method is to use a symbolic computation system such as Maple, Matlab, Mathcad or Derive which can not only sketch the graphs of functions but also differentiate and solve equations. Consequently it is possible to obtain the exact solution using one of these packages.

Key Terms

Average product of labour (labour productivity)   Output per worker: $AP_L = Q/L$.

Maximum (local) point   A point on a curve which has the highest function value in comparison with other values in its neighbourhood; at such a point the first-order derivative is zero and the second-order derivative is either zero or negative.

Minimum (local) point   A point on a curve which has the lowest function value in comparison with other values in its neighbourhood; at such a point the first-order derivative is zero and the second-order derivative is either zero or positive.

Optimisation   The determination of the optimal (usually stationary) points of a function.

Stationary point of inflection   A stationary point that is neither a maximum nor a minimum; at such a point both the first- and second-order derivatives are zero.

Stationary points (critical points, turning points, extrema)   Points on a graph at which the tangent is horizontal; at a stationary point the first-order derivative is zero.

Exercise 4.6

1. Find and classify the stationary points of the following functions. Hence give a rough sketch of their graphs.

    (a) $y = -x^2 + x + 1$ (b) $y = x^2 - 4x + 4$ (c) $y = x^2 - 20x + 105$ (d) $y = -x^3 + 3x$

2. If the demand equation of a good is

    $$P = 40 - 2Q$$

    find the level of output that maximises total revenue.

3. A firm's short-run production function is given by

    $$Q = 30L^2 - 0.5L^3$$

    Find the value of L which maximises AP_L and verify that $MP_L = AP_L$ at this point.

4. If the fixed costs are 13 and the variable costs are $Q + 2$ per unit, show that the average cost function is

    $$AC = \frac{13}{Q} + Q + 2$$

    (a) Calculate the values of AC when $Q = 1, 2, 3, \ldots, 6$. Plot these points on graph paper and hence produce an accurate graph of AC against Q.

    (b) Use your graph to estimate the minimum average cost.

    (c) Use differentiation to confirm your estimate obtained in part (b).

5. The demand and total cost functions of a good are

    $$4P + Q - 16 = 0$$

    and

    $$TC = 4 + 2Q - \frac{3Q^2}{10} + \frac{Q^3}{20}$$

    respectively.

(a) Find expressions for TR, π, MR and MC in terms of Q.

(b) Solve the equation

$$\frac{d\pi}{dQ} = 0$$

and hence determine the value of Q which maximises profit.

(c) Verify that, at the point of maximum profit, MR = MC.

6. The supply and demand equations of a good are given by

$$3P - Q_S = 3$$

and

$$2P + Q_D = 14$$

respectively.

    The government decides to impose a tax, t, per unit. Find the value of t which maximises the government's total tax revenue on the assumption that equilibrium conditions prevail in the market.

7. A manufacturer has fixed costs of \$200 each week, and the variable costs per unit can be expressed by the function, VC = $2Q - 36$.

(a) Find an expression for the total cost function and deduce that the average cost function is given by

$$AC = \frac{200}{Q} + 2Q - 36$$

(b) Find the stationary point of this function and show that this is a minimum.

(c) Verify that, at this stationary point, average cost is the same as marginal cost.

8. A firm's short-run production function is given by

$$Q = 3\sqrt{L}$$

where L is the number of units of labour.

    If the price per unit sold is \$50 and the price per unit of labour is \$10, find the value of L needed to maximise profits. You may assume that the firm sells all that it produces and you can ignore all other costs.

9. The average cost per person of hiring a tour guide on a week's river cruise for a maximum party size of 30 people is given by

$$AC = 3Q^2 - 192Q + 3500 \qquad (0 < Q \le 30)$$

Find the minimum average cost for the trip.

10. An electronic components firm launches a new product on 1st January. During the following year a rough estimate of the number of orders, S, received t days after the launch is given by

$$S = t^2 - 0.002t^3$$

What is the maximum number of orders received on any one day of the year?

Exercise 4.6*

1. A firm's demand function is

   $$P = 60 - 0.5Q$$

   If fixed costs are 10 and variable costs are $Q + 3$ per unit, find the maximum profit.

2. Show that all of the following functions have a stationary point at $x = 0$. Verify in each case that $f''(0) = 0$. Classify these points by producing a rough sketch of each function.

   (a) $f(x) = x^3$ **(b)** $f(x) = x^4$ **(c)** $f(x) = -x^6$

3. If fixed costs are 15 and the variable costs are $2Q$ per unit, write down expressions for TC, AC and MC. Find the value of Q which minimises AC and verify that AC = MC at this point.

4. Daily sales, S, of a new product for the first two weeks after the launch is modelled by

   $$S = t^3 - 24t^2 + 180t + 60 \qquad (0 \le t \le 13)$$

   where t is the number of days.

   (a) Find and classify the stationary points of this function.

   (b) Sketch a graph of S against t on the interval $0 \le t \le 13$.

   (c) Find the maximum and minimum daily sales during the period between $t = 5$ and $t = 9$.

5. If the demand function of a good is

   $$P = \sqrt{(1000 - 4Q)}$$

   find the value of Q which maximises total revenue.

6. A firm's total cost and demand functions are given by

   $$TC = Q^2 + 50Q + 10 \text{ and } P = 200 - 4Q$$

   respectively.

   (a) Find the level of output needed to maximise the firm's profit.

   (b) The government imposes a tax of $\$t$ per good. If the firm adds this tax to its costs and continues to maximise profit, show that the price of the good increases by two-fifths of the tax, irrespective of the value of t.

7. Given that the cubic function, $f(x) = x^3 + ax^2 + bx + c$ has a stationary point at $(2, 5)$, and that it passes through $(1, 3)$, find the values of a, b and c.

8. The total revenue function of a good is given by:

   $$TR = 0.2Q^3 \text{ on } 0 \le Q \le 5$$

   $$TR = -4Q^2 + 55Q - 150 \text{ on } 5 \le Q \le 10$$

   (a) Sketch a graph of TR against Q on the interval $0 \le Q \le 10$.

   (b) Find the maximum revenue and the value of Q at which it is achieved.

   (c) For what value of Q is the marginal revenue a maximum?

SECTION 4.7

Further optimisation of economic functions

The previous section demonstrated how mathematics can be used to optimise particular economic functions. Those examples suggested two important results:

1. If a firm maximises profit then MR = MC.

2. If a firm maximises average product of labour then $AP_L = MP_L$.

Although these results were found to hold for all of the examples considered in Section 4.6, it does not necessarily follow that the results are always true. The aim of this section is to prove these assertions without reference to specific functions and hence to demonstrate their generality.

Advice

You may prefer to skip these proofs at a first reading and just concentrate on the worked example (and Practice Problem 2 and Question 3 in Exercise 4.7*) on price discrimination.

Justification of the first result turns out to be really quite easy. Profit, π, is defined to be the difference between total revenue, TR, and total cost, TC: that is,

$$\pi = TR - TC$$

To find the stationary points of π we differentiate with respect to Q and equate to zero: that is,

$$\frac{d\pi}{dQ} = \frac{d(TR)}{dQ} - \frac{(TC)}{dQ} = 0$$

where we have used the difference rule to differentiate the right-hand side. In Section 4.3 we defined

$$\text{MR} = \frac{d(\text{TR})}{dQ} \text{ and } \text{MC} = \frac{d(\text{TR})}{dQ}$$

so the previous equation is equivalent to

$$\text{MR} - \text{MC} = 0$$

and so MR = MC as required.

The stationary points of the profit function can therefore be found by sketching the MR and MC curves on the same diagram and inspecting the points of intersection. Figure 4.26 shows typical marginal revenue and marginal cost curves. The result

$$\text{MR} = \text{MC}$$

holds for any stationary point. Consequently, if this equation has more than one solution then we need some further information before we can decide on the profit-maximising level of output. In Figure 4.26 there are two points of intersection, Q_1 and Q_2, and it turns out (as you discovered in Practice Problem 3 and Question 5 of Exercise 4.6 in the previous section) that one of these is a maximum while the other is a minimum. Obviously, in any actual example, we can classify these points by evaluating second-order derivatives. However, it would be nice to make this decision just by inspecting the graphs of marginal revenue and marginal cost. To see how this can be done let us return to the equation

$$\frac{d\pi}{dQ} = \text{MR} - \text{MC}$$

and differentiate again with respect to Q to get

$$\frac{d^2\pi}{dQ^2} = \frac{d(\text{MR})}{dQ} - \frac{d(\text{MC})}{dQ}$$

Now if $d^2\pi/dQ^2 < 0$ then the profit is a maximum. This will be so when

$$\frac{d(\text{MR})}{dQ} < \frac{d(\text{MC})}{dQ}$$

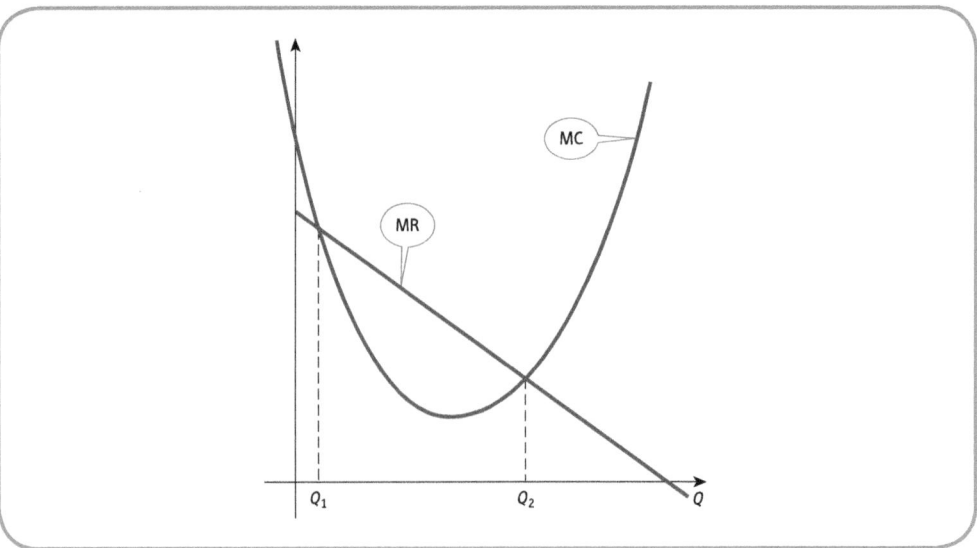

Figure 4.26

that is, when the slope of the marginal revenue curve is less than the slope of the marginal cost curve.

Looking at Figure 4.26, we deduce that this criterion is true at Q_2, so this must be the desired level of output needed to maximise profit. Note also from Figure 4.26 that the statement 'the slope of the marginal revenue curve is less than the slope of the marginal cost curve' is equivalent to saying that 'the marginal cost curve cuts the marginal revenue curve from below'. It is this latter form that is often quoted in economics textbooks. A similar argument shows that, at a minimum point, the marginal cost curve cuts the marginal revenue curve from above and so we can deduce that profit is a minimum at Q_1 in Figure 4.26. In practice, the task of sketching the graphs of MR and MC and reading off the coordinates of the points of intersection is not an attractive one, particularly if MR and MC are complicated functions. However, it might turn out that MR and MC are both linear, in which case a graphical approach is feasible.

Practice Problem

1. A monopolist's demand function is

$$P = 25 - 0.5Q$$

The fixed costs of production are 7 and the variable costs are $Q + 1$ per unit.

(a) Show that

$$TR = 25Q - 0.5Q^2 \text{ and } TC = Q^2 + Q + 7$$

and deduce the corresponding expressions for MR and MC.

(b) Sketch the graphs of MR and MC on the same diagram and hence find the value of Q which maximises profit.

Quite often a firm identifies more than one market in which it wishes to sell its goods. For example, a firm might decide to export goods to several countries and demand conditions are likely to be different in each one. The firm may be able to take advantage of this and increase overall profit by charging different prices in each country. The theoretical result 'marginal revenue equals marginal cost' can be applied in each market separately to find the optimal pricing policy.

Example

A firm is allowed to charge different prices for its domestic and industrial customers. If P_1 and Q_1 denote the price and demand for the domestic market then the demand equation is

$$P_1 + Q_1 = 500$$

If P_2 and Q_2 denote the price and demand for the industrial market then the demand equation is

$$2P_2 + 3Q_2 = 720$$

The total cost function is

$$TC = 50\ 000 + 20Q$$

where $Q = Q_1 + Q_2$. Determine the prices (in dollars) that the firm should charge to maximise profits:

(a) with price discrimination

(b) without price discrimination.

Compare the profits obtained in parts (a) and (b).

Solution

(a) The important thing to notice is that the total cost function is independent of the market and so marginal costs are the same in each case. In fact, since

$$TC = 50\,000 + 20Q$$

we have MC = 20. All we have to do to maximise profits is to find an expression for the marginal revenue for each market and to equate this to the constant value of marginal cost.

Domestic market

The demand equation

$$P_1 + Q_1 = 500$$

rearranges to give

$$P_1 = 500 - Q_1$$

so the total revenue function for this market is

$$TR_1 = (500 - Q_1)Q_1 = 500Q_1 - Q_1^2$$

Hence

$$MR_1 = \frac{d(TR_1)}{dQ_1} = 500 - 2Q_1$$

For maximum profit

$$MR_1 = MC$$

so

$$500 - 2Q_1 = 20$$

which has solution $Q_1 = 240$. The corresponding price is found by substituting this value into the demand equation to get

$$P_1 = 500 - 240 = \$260$$

To maximise profit the firm should charge its domestic customers $260 per good.

Industrial market

The demand equation

$$2P_2 + 3Q_2 = 720$$

rearranges to give

$$P_2 = 360 - {}^3\!/_2Q_2$$

so the total revenue function for this market is

$$TR_2 = (360 - {}^3\!/_2Q_2)Q_2 = 360Q - {}^3\!/_2Q_2^2$$

Hence

$$\text{MR}_2 = \frac{d(\text{TR}_2)}{dQ_2} = 360 - 3Q_2$$

For maximum profit

$$\text{MR}_2 = \text{MC}$$

so

$$360 - 3Q_2 = 20$$

which has solution $Q_2 = 340/3$. The corresponding price is obtained by substituting this value into the demand equation to get

$$P_2 = 360 - \frac{3}{2}\left(\frac{340}{3}\right) = \$190$$

To maximise profits the firm should charge its industrial customers \$190 per good, which is lower than the price charged to its domestic customers.

(b) If there is no price discrimination then $P_1 = P_2 = P$, say, and the demand functions for the domestic and industrial markets become

$$P + Q_1 = 500$$

and

$$2P + 3Q_2 = 720$$

respectively. We can use these to deduce a single demand equation for the combined market. We need to relate the price, P, of each good to the total demand, $Q = Q_1 + Q_2$.

This can be done by rearranging the given demand equations for Q_1 and Q_2 and then adding. For the domestic market

$$Q_1 = 500 - P$$

and for the industrial market

$$Q_2 = 240 - {}^2\!/_3 P$$

Hence

$$Q = Q_1 + Q_2 = 740 - {}^5\!/_3 P$$

The demand equation for the combined market is therefore

$$Q + {}^5\!/_3 P = 740$$

The usual procedure for profit maximisation can now be applied. This demand equation rearranges to give

$$P = 444 - {}^3\!/_5 Q$$

enabling the total revenue function to be written down as

$$\text{TR} = \left(444 - \frac{3}{5}Q\right)Q = 444Q - \frac{3Q^2}{5}$$

Hence

$$MR = \frac{d(TR)}{dQ} = 444 - \frac{6}{5}Q$$

For maximum profit

$$MR = MC$$

so

$$444 - \frac{6}{5}Q = 20$$

which has solution $Q = 1060/3$. The corresponding price is found by substituting this value into the demand equation to get

$$P = 444 - \frac{3}{5}\left(\frac{1060}{3}\right) = \$232$$

To maximise profit without discrimination the firm needs to charge a uniform price of \$232 for each good. Notice that this price lies between the prices charged to its domestic and industrial customers with discrimination.

To evaluate the profit under each policy we need to work out the total revenue and subtract the total cost. In part (a) the firm sells 240 goods at \$260 each in the domestic market and sells 340/3 goods at \$190 each in the industrial market, so the total revenue received is

$$240 \times 260 + \frac{340}{3} \times 190 = \$83\,933.33$$

The total number of goods produced is

$$240 + \frac{340}{3} = \frac{1060}{3}$$

so the total cost is

$$50\,000 + 20 \times \frac{1060}{3} = \$57\,066.67$$

Therefore the profit with price discrimination is

$$83\,933.33 - 57\,066.67 = \$26\,866.67$$

In part (b) the firm sells 1060/3 goods at \$232 each, so total revenue is

$$\frac{1060}{3} \times 232 = \$81\,973.33$$

Now the total number of goods produced under both pricing policies is the same: that is, 1060/3. Consequently, the total cost of production in part (b) must be the same as part (a): that is,

$$TC = \$57\,066.67$$

The profit without price discrimination is

$$81\,973.33 - 57\,066.67 = \$24\,906.66$$

As expected, the profits are higher with discrimination than without.

Practice Problem

2. A firm has the possibility of charging different prices in its domestic and foreign markets. The corresponding demand equations are given by

$$Q_1 = 300 - P_1$$
$$Q_2 = 400 - 2P_2$$

The total cost function is

$$TC = 5000 + 100Q$$

where $Q = Q_1 + Q_2$.

Determine the prices (in dollars) that the firm should charge to maximise profits

(a) with price discrimination

(b) without price discrimination.

Compare the profits obtained in parts (a) and (b).

In the previous example and in Practice Problem 2 we assumed that the marginal costs were the same in each market. The level of output that maximises profit with price discrimination was found by equating marginal revenue to this common value of marginal cost. It follows that the marginal revenue must be the same in each market. In symbols

$$MR_1 = MC \text{ and } MR_2 = MC$$

so

$$MR_1 = MR_2$$

This fact is obvious on economic grounds. If it were not true then the firm's policy would be to increase sales in the market where marginal revenue is higher and to decrease sales by the same amount in the market where the marginal revenue is lower. The effect would be to increase revenue while keeping costs fixed, thereby raising profit. This property leads to an interesting result connecting price, P, with elasticity of demand, E. In Section 4.5 we derived the formula

$$MR = P\left(1 + \frac{1}{E}\right)$$

If we let the price elasticity of demand in two markets be denoted by E_1 and E_2 corresponding to prices P_1 and P_2 then the equation

$$MR_1 = MR_2$$

becomes

$$P_1\left(1 + \frac{1}{E_1}\right) = P_2\left(1 + \frac{1}{E_2}\right)$$

This equation holds whenever a firm chooses its prices P_1 and P_2 to maximise profits in each market. Note that if $|E_1| < |E_2|$ then this equation can only be true if $P_1 > P_2$. In other words, the firm charges the higher price in the market where the magnitude of the elasticity of demand is lower.

Practice Problem

3. Calculate the price elasticity of demand at the point of maximum profit for each of the demand functions given in Practice Problem 2 with price discrimination. Verify that the firm charges the higher price in the market with the lower value of $|E|$.

The previous discussion concentrated on profit. We now turn our attention to average product of labour and prove result (2) stated at the beginning of this section. This concept is defined by

$$\mathrm{AP}_L = \frac{Q}{L}$$

where Q is output and L is labour. The maximisation of AP_L is a little more complicated than before, since it is necessary to use the quotient rule to differentiate this function. In the notation of Section 4.4 we write

$$u = Q \quad \text{and} \quad v = L$$

so

$$\frac{du}{dL} = \frac{dQ}{dL} = \mathrm{MP}_L \quad \text{and} \quad \frac{dv}{dL} = \frac{dL}{dL} = 1$$

where we have used the fact that the derivative of output with respect to labour is the marginal product of labour.

The quotient rule gives

$$\frac{d(\mathrm{AP}_L)}{dL} = \frac{v\, du/dL - u\, dv/dL}{v^2}$$

$$= \frac{L(\mathrm{MP}_L) - Q(1)}{L^2}$$

$$= \frac{\mathrm{MP}_L - Q/L}{L} \qquad \text{divide top and bottom by } L$$

$$= \frac{\mathrm{MP}_L - \mathrm{AP}_L}{L} \qquad \text{by definition, } \mathrm{AP}_L = \frac{Q}{L}$$

At a stationary point

$$\frac{d(\mathrm{AP}_L)}{dL} = 0$$

Hence

$$\mathrm{MP}_L = \mathrm{AP}_L$$

as required.

This analysis shows that, at a stationary point of the average product of labour function, the marginal product of labour equals the average product of labour. The above argument provides a formal proof that this result is true for any average product of labour function. Figure 4.27

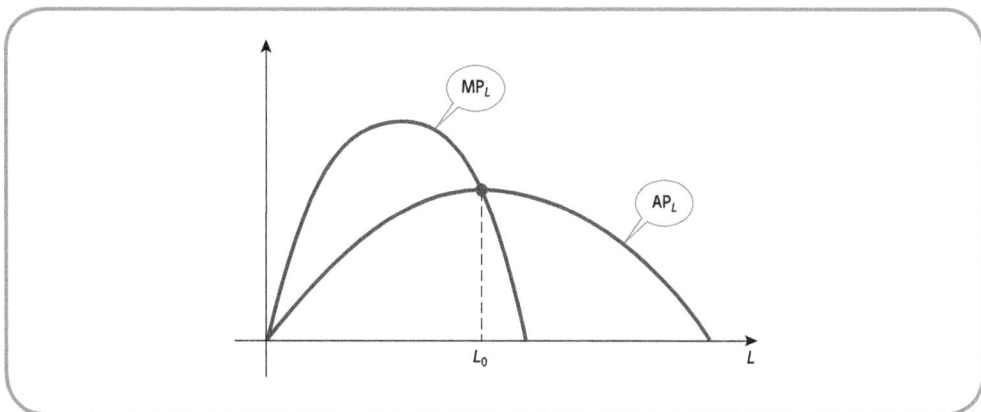

Figure 4.27

shows typical average and marginal product functions. Note that the two curves intersect at the peak of the AP_L curve. To the left of this point the AP_L function is increasing, so that

$$\frac{d(AP_L)}{dL} > 0$$

Now we have just seen that

$$\frac{d(AP_L)}{dL} = \frac{MP_L - AP_L}{L}$$

so we deduce that, to the left of the maximum, $MP_L > AP_L$. In other words, in this region the graph of marginal product of labour lies above that of average product of labour. Similarly, to the right of the maximum, AP_L is decreasing, so that

$$\frac{d(AP_L)}{dL} < 0$$

and hence $MP_L < AP_L$. The graph of marginal product of labour therefore lies below that of average product of labour in this region.

We deduce that if the stationary point is a maximum then the MP_L curve cuts the AP_L curve from above. A similar argument can be used for any average function. The particular case of the average cost function is investigated in Question 8 in Exercise 4.7*.

We conclude this section by investigating a simple model of inventory control in business. Most firms need to buy and store goods during the year. A furniture manufacturer has to obtain wood and other raw materials to make its goods, and a grocery store needs to have a regular supply of frozen food to store in its freezers. Management needs to make decisions about when to order more stock and the size of each order. Let us suppose that the annual demand is D items and that the firm orders Q of these at regular intervals during the year. For example if the demand is 12 000 the firm might place an order for 1000 items each month. Alternatively the firm could increase the order size to 3000 items and thereby reduce the number of orders to just 12 000/3000 = 4 times a year. In general, orders are made D/Q times a year.

There are many costs incurred in inventory control (including opportunity costs) but we shall consider just two: ordering costs and holding costs. We consider each of these in turn.

There will always be a cost of raising an order which includes a fixed administrative charge, delivery charge and the cost of setting up a production run. If the cost of placing each order is $R then the total cost is found by multiplying R by the number of orders, D/Q so

$$\text{total annual order cost} = \frac{DR}{Q}$$

The other major cost incurred is the stockholding cost. This includes the cost of storage, insurance and interest lost on the capital used to buy these goods waiting to be sold. In the simplest model we will assume that the level of stock falls at a constant rate throughout the year and that the firm waits until the stock levels are zero before re-ordering. If we further assume that the stock is replenished instantly then the variation of stock levels during the course of a year would be modelled by the pattern shown in Figure 4.28. In practice this may not occur. There are likely to be seasonal variations in demand so the gradients of each section of the graph may vary from one cycle to the next and demand may not even be linear. Also it is not good practice to wait until shelves are empty before reordering stock and, since goods do not arrive instantly, firms build in a lead time to allow for this. However, as a first model of the real situation we will assume that stock levels follow the pattern shown in Figure 4.28.

In each period the average number of items stored is Q/2, and, since this pattern is replicated throughout the year, the average number of items held in store each year is Q/2. If it costs $H to store one item for one year then the total annual holding cost is

$$H \times \frac{Q}{2} = \frac{HQ}{2}$$

If C denotes the total cost per annum then we can add the order and holding costs to deduce that

$$C = \frac{DR}{Q} + \frac{HQ}{2}$$

Figure 4.29 shows a graph of order cost, holding cost and total cost plotted against Q. As expected, to cut down on the order costs it is best to make Q as large as possible so that you don't have to incur the overheads for ordering the goods. On the other hand, to minimise holding costs you want to make Q as small as possible. These conflicting interests lead to an overall single minimum as shown by the graph of C in Figure 4.29.

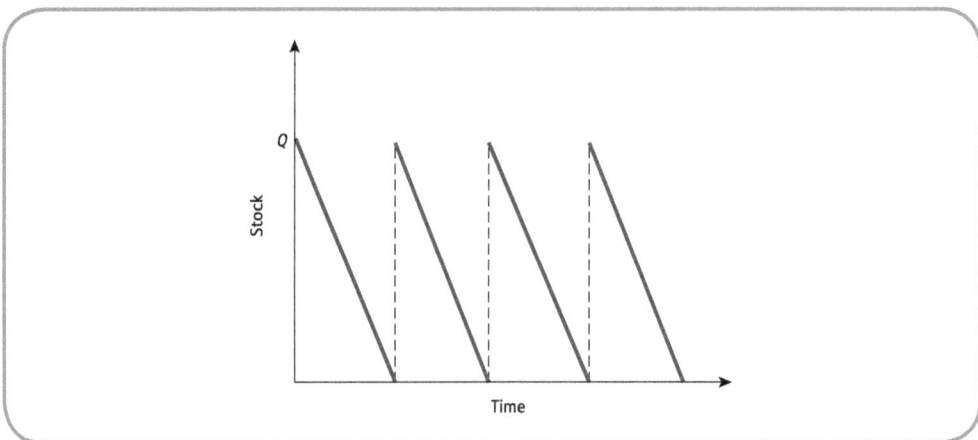

Figure 4.28

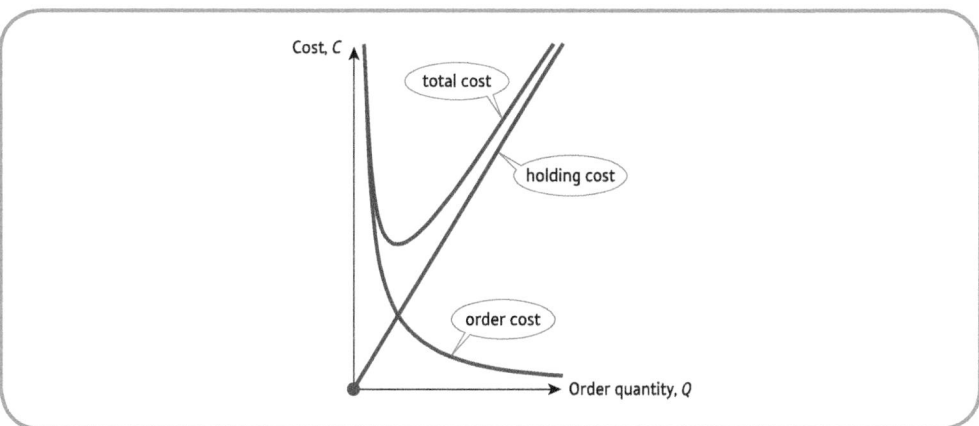

Figure 4.29

At a stationary point, $\dfrac{dC}{dQ} = 0$ so we need to differentiate

$$C = (DR)Q^{-1} + \frac{HQ}{2}$$

with respect to Q. The remaining letters, D, R and H are all constants so

$$\frac{dC}{dQ} = -(DR)Q^{-2} + \frac{H}{2} = \frac{-DR}{Q^2} + \frac{H}{2}$$

The stationary point can be found by solving

$$\frac{H}{2} = \frac{DR}{Q^2}$$

for Q:

$$Q^2 = \frac{2DR}{H}$$

so

$$Q = \sqrt{\frac{2DR}{H}}$$

This value of Q is called the **economic order quantity** (EOQ). It provides a formula for the optimal order size in terms of annual demand, D, cost of placing each order, R and annual cost of holding an item in stock, H. If the order exceeds EOQ then you order less frequently and, although the ordering costs decrease, the holding costs rise more than this. On the other hand, if the order is below the EOQ then you order more frequently and, although the holding costs decrease, this is offset by higher ordering costs. The graph shown in Figure 4.29 shows clearly that this stationary point is a minimum but it is possible to show this by investigating the sign of the second-order derivative, d^2C/dQ^2 (see Question 5 in Exercise 4.7*).

> ### Key Term
>
> **Economic order quantity**   The quantity of a product that should be ordered so as to minimise the total cost that includes ordering costs and holding costs.

Exercise 4.7*

1. A firm's demand function is

   $$P = aQ + b \; (a < 0, b > 0)$$

   Fixed costs are c and variable costs per unit are d.

   (a) Write down general expressions for TR and TC.

   (b) By differentiating the expressions in part (a), deduce MR and MC.

   (c) Use your answers to (b) to show that profit, π, is maximised when

   $$Q = \frac{d - b}{2a}$$

2. **(a)** In Section 4.5 the following relationship between marginal revenue, MR, and price elasticity of demand, E, was derived:

   $$\mathrm{MR} = P\left(1 + \frac{1}{E}\right)$$

   Use this result to show that at the point of maximum total revenue, $E = -1$.

   (b) Verify the result of part (a) for the demand function

   $$2P + 3Q = 60$$

3. The demand functions for a firm's domestic and foreign markets are

   $$P_1 = 50 - 5Q_1$$
   $$P_2 = 30 - 4Q_2$$

   and the total cost function is

   $$\mathrm{TC} = 10 + 10Q$$

   where $Q = Q_1 + Q_2$. Determine the prices needed to maximise profit

   (a) with price discrimination

   (b) without price discrimination.

   Compare the profits obtained in parts (a) and (b).

4. Show that if the marginal cost curve cuts the marginal revenue curve from above then profit is a minimum.

5. **(a)** Find an expression for the second-order derivative, $\mathrm{d}^2C/\mathrm{d}Q^2$, of the cost function

   $$C = \frac{DR}{Q} + \frac{HQ}{2}$$

   and hence show that the economic order quantity, $Q = \sqrt{\dfrac{2DR}{H}}$, is a minimum point.

   (b) Obtain a simplified expression for the minimum cost.

6. **(a)** The annual demand of a good is 2000 units, the fixed cost of placing an order is $40 and the annual cost of storing an item is $100. Assuming that the same order is placed at regular intervals throughout the year, and that the firm waits for stock levels to reduce to zero before ordering new stock, work out how many items should be ordered each time to minimise total costs. What is the minimum total cost?

   (b) Repeat part (a) if the annual cost of storage costs falls to $64.

   (c) Repeat part (a) if the fixed cost of placing an order rises to $160.

   (d) What effect do changes in order costs and holding costs have on the minimum total cost?

7. If the total cost function $TC = aQ^2 + bQ + c$, write down an expression for the average cost function, AC. Show that AC is a minimum when $Q = \sqrt{\dfrac{c}{a}}$ and find the corresponding value of AC.

8. **(a)** Show that, at a stationary point of an average cost function, average cost equals marginal cost.

   (b) Show that if the marginal cost curve cuts the average cost curve from below then average cost is a minimum.

9. In a competitive market the equilibrium price, P, and quantity, Q, are found by setting $Q_S = Q_D = Q$ in the supply and demand equations

$$P = aQ_S + b \ (a > 0, b > 0)$$
$$P = -cQ_D + d \ (c > 0, d > 0)$$

If the government levies an excise tax, t, per unit, show that

$$Q = \frac{d - b - t}{a + c}$$

Deduce that the government's tax revenue, $T = tQ$, is maximised by taking

$$t = \frac{d - b}{2}$$

SECTION 4.8

The derivative of the exponential and natural logarithm functions

Objectives

At the end of this section you should be able to:

- Differentiate the exponential function.
- Differentiate the natural logarithm function.
- Use the chain, product and quotient rules to differentiate combinations of these functions.
- Appreciate the use of the exponential function in economic modelling.

In this section we investigate the derived functions associated with the exponential and natural logarithm functions, e^x and $\ln x$. The approach that we adopt is similar to that used in Section 4.1. The derivative of a function determines the slope of the graph of a function. Consequently, to discover how to differentiate an unfamiliar function we first produce an accurate sketch and then measure the slopes of the tangents at selected points.

Advice

The functions, e^x and $\ln x$ were first introduced in Section 2.4. You might find it useful to remind yourself how these functions are defined before working through the rest of the current section.

Figure 4.30 shows a sketch of the exponential function, e^x, based on the table of values:

x	−2.0	−1.5	−1.0	−0.5	0.0	0.5	1.0	1.5
$f(x)$	0.14	0.22	0.37	0.61	1.00	1.65	2.72	4.48

From the graph we see that the slopes of the tangents at $x = -1$, $x = 0$ and $x = 1$ are

$$f'(-1) = \frac{0.20}{0.50} = 0.4$$

$$f'(0) = \frac{0.50}{0.50} = 1.0$$

$$f'(1) = \frac{1.35}{0.50} = 2.7$$

These results are obtained by measurement and so are quoted to only 1 decimal place. We cannot really expect to achieve any greater accuracy using this approach.

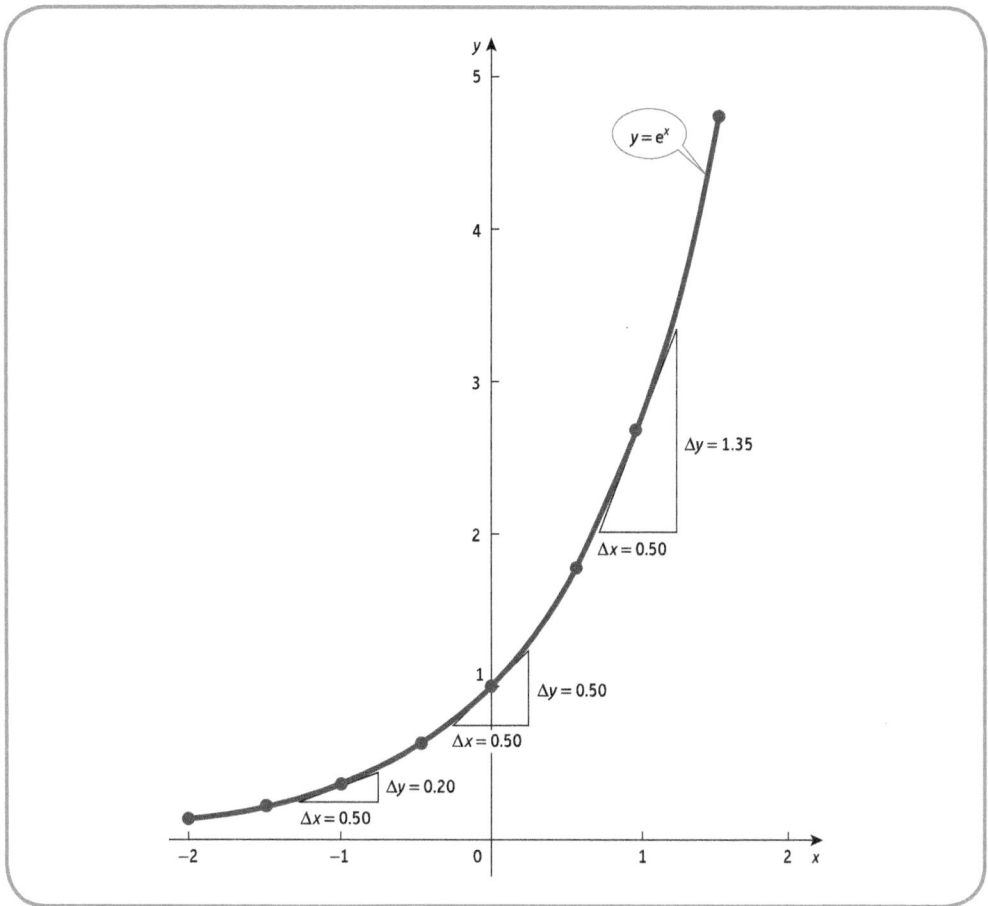

Figure 4.30

The values of x, $f(x)$ and $f'(x)$ are summarised in the following table. The values of $f(x)$ are rounded to 1 decimal place in order to compare with the graphical estimates of $f'(x)$.

x	-1	0	1
$f(x)$	0.4	1.0	2.7
$f'(x)$	0.4	1.0	2.7

Notice that the values of $f(x)$ and $f'(x)$ are identical to within the accuracy quoted.

These results suggest that the slope of the graph at each point is the same as the function value at that point: that is, e^x differentiates to itself. Symbolically,

if $f(x) = e^x$ then $f'(x) = e^x$

or, equivalently,

if $y = e^x$ then $\dfrac{dy}{dx} = e^x$

Practice Problem

1. Use your calculator to complete the following table of function values and hence sketch an accurate graph of $f(x) = \ln x$:

x	0.50	1.00	1.50	2.00	2.50	3.00	3.50	4.00
$f(x)$			0.41				1.25	

Draw the tangents to the graph at $x = 1$, 2 and 3. Hence estimate the values of $f'(1)$, $f'(2)$ and $f'(3)$. Suggest a general formula for the derived function $f'(x)$.

[Hint: for the last part you may find it helpful to rewrite your estimates of $f'(x)$ as simple fractions.]

In fact, it is possible to prove that, for any value of the constant m,

$$\text{if}\quad y = e^{mx} \quad \text{then} \quad \frac{dy}{dx} = me^{mx}$$

and

$$\text{if}\quad y = \ln mx \quad \text{then} \quad \frac{dy}{dx} = \frac{1}{x}$$

In particular, we see by setting $m = 1$ that

e^x differentiates to e^x

and that

$\ln x$ differentiates to $\dfrac{1}{x}$

which agree with our practical investigations.

Example

Differentiate

(a) $y = e^{2x}$

(b) $y = e^{-7x}$

(c) $y = \ln 5x \ (x > 0)$

(d) $y = \ln 559x \ (x > 0)$

Solution

(a) Setting $m = 2$ in the general formula shows that

$$\text{if}\quad y = e^{2x} \quad \text{then} \quad \frac{dy}{dx} = 2e^{2x}$$

Notice that when exponential functions are differentiated the power itself does not change. All that happens is that the coefficient of x comes down to the front.

(b) Setting $m = -7$ in the general formula shows that

$$\text{if} \quad y = e^{-7x} \quad \text{then} \quad \frac{dy}{dx} = -7e^{-7x}$$

(c) Setting $m = 5$ in the general formula shows that

$$\text{if} \quad y = \ln 5x \quad \text{then} \quad \frac{dy}{dx} = \frac{1}{x}$$

Notice the restriction $x > 0$ stated in the question. This is needed to ensure that we do not attempt to take the logarithm of a negative number, which is impossible.

(d) Setting $m = 559$ in the general formula shows that

$$\text{if} \quad y = \ln 559x \quad \text{then} \quad \frac{dy}{dx} = \frac{1}{x}$$

Notice that we get the same answer as part (c). The derivative of the natural logarithm function does not depend on the coefficient of x. This fact may seem rather strange but it is easily accounted for. The first rule of logarithms shows that $\ln 559x$ is the same as

$\ln 559 + \ln x$

The first term is merely a constant, so differentiates to zero, and the second term differentiates to $1/x$.

Practice Problem

2. Differentiate

(a) $y = e^{3x}$ **(b)** $y = e^{-x}$ **(c)** $y = \ln 3x \ (x > 0)$ **(d)** $y = \ln 51\,234x \ (x > 0)$

The chain rule can be used to explain what happens to the m when differentiating e^{mx}. The outer function is the exponential, which differentiates to itself, and the inner function is mx, which differentiates to m. Hence, by the chain rule,

$$\text{if} \quad y = e^{mx} \quad \text{then} \quad \frac{dy}{dx} = e^{mx} \times m = me^{mx}$$

Similarly, noting that the natural logarithm function differentiates to the reciprocal function,

$$\text{if} \quad y = \ln mx \quad \text{then} \quad \frac{dy}{dx} = \frac{1}{mx} \times m = \frac{1}{x}$$

The chain, product and quotient rules can be used to differentiate more complicated functions involving e^x and $\ln x$.

Example

Differentiate

(a) $y = x^3 e^{2x}$ **(b)** $y = \ln(x^2 + 2x + 1)$ **(c)** $y = \dfrac{e^{3x}}{x^2 + 2}$

Solution

(a) The function $x^3 e^{2x}$ involves the product of two simpler functions, x^3 and e^{2x}, so we need to use the product rule to differentiate it. Putting

$$u = x^3 \quad \text{and} \quad v = e^{2x}$$

gives

$$\frac{du}{dx} = 3x^2 \quad \text{and} \quad \frac{dv}{dx} = 2e^{2x}$$

By the product rule

$$\frac{dy}{dx} = u\frac{dv}{dx} + v\frac{du}{dx} = x^3\left[2e^{2x}\right] + e^{2x}\left[3x^2\right] = 2x^3 e^{2x} + 3x^2 e^{2x}$$

There is a common factor of $x^2 e^{2x}$, which goes into the first term $2x$ times and into the second term 3 times. Hence

$$\frac{dy}{dx} = x^2 e^{2x}(2x + 3)$$

(b) The expression $\ln(x^2 + 2x + 1)$ can be regarded as a function of a function, so we can use the chain rule to differentiate it. We first differentiate the outer log function to get

$$\frac{1}{x^2 + 2x + 1}$$

and then multiply by the derivative of the inner function, $x^2 + 2x + 1$, which is $2x + 2$. Hence

$$\frac{dy}{dx} = \frac{2x + 2}{x^2 + 2x + 1}$$

(c) The function

$$\frac{e^{3x}}{x^2 + 2}$$

is the quotient of the simpler functions

$$u = e^{3x} \quad \text{and} \quad v = x^2 + 2$$

for which

$$\frac{du}{dx} = 3e^{3x} \quad \text{and} \quad \frac{dv}{dx} = 2x$$

By the quotient rule

$$\frac{dy}{dx} = \frac{v\dfrac{du}{dx} - u\dfrac{dv}{dx}}{v^2} = \frac{(x^2 + 2)(3e^{3x}) - e^{3x}(2x)}{(x^2 + 2)^2} = \frac{e^{3x}[3(x^2 + 2) - 2x]}{(x^2 + 2)^2} = \frac{e^{3x}(3x^2 - 2x + 6)}{(x^2 + 2)^2}$$

Differentiation **341**

Practice Problem

3. Differentiate

   (a) $y = x^4 \ln x$

   (b) $y = e^{x^2}$

   (c) $y = \dfrac{\ln x}{x + 2}$

Advice

If you ever need to differentiate a function of the form:

$$\ln \text{ (an inner function involving products, quotients or powers of } x)$$

then it is usually quicker to use the rules of logs to expand the expression before you begin. The three rules are

Rule 1	$\ln(x \times y) = \ln x + \ln y$
Rule 2	$\ln(x \div y) = \ln x - \ln y$
Rule 3	$\ln x^m = m \ln x$

The following example shows how to apply this 'trick' in practice.

Example

Differentiate

(a) $y = \ln(x(x + 1)^4)$ (b) $y = \ln\left(\dfrac{x}{\sqrt{(x + 5)}}\right)$

Solution

(a) From rule 1

$$\ln(x(x + 1)^4) = \ln x + \ln(x + 1)^4$$

which can be simplified further using rule 3 to give

$$y = \ln x + 4 \ln(x + 1)$$

Differentiation of this new expression is simple. We see immediately that

$$\frac{dy}{dx} = \frac{1}{x} + \frac{4}{x + 1}$$

If desired the final answer can be put over a common denominator

$$\frac{1}{x} + \frac{4}{x + 1} = \frac{(x + 1) + 4x}{x(x + 1)} = \frac{5x + 1}{x(x + 1)}$$

(b) The quickest way to differentiate

$$y = \ln\left(\frac{x}{\sqrt{(x+5)}}\right)$$

is to expand first to get

$$y = \ln x - \ln(x+5)^{1/2} \quad \text{(rule 2)}$$

$$= \ln x - \frac{1}{2}\ln(x+5) \quad \text{(rule 3)}$$

Again this expression is easy to differentiate:

$$\frac{dy}{dx} = \frac{1}{x} - \frac{1}{2(x+5)}$$

If desired, this can be written as a single fraction:

$$\frac{1}{x} - \frac{1}{2(x+5)} = \frac{2(x+5)-x}{2x(x+5)} = \frac{x+10}{2x(x+5)}$$

Practice Problem

4. Differentiate the following functions by first expanding each expression using the rules of logs:

   (a) $y = \ln(x^3(x+2)^4)$ **(b)** $y = \ln\left(\frac{x^2}{2x+3}\right)$

Exponential and natural logarithm functions provide good mathematical models in many areas of economics and we conclude this chapter with some illustrative examples.

Example

A firm's short-run production function is given by

$$Q = L^2 e^{-0.01L}$$

Find the value of L that maximises the average product of labour.

Solution

The average product of labour is given by

$$AP_L = \frac{Q}{L} = \frac{L^2 e^{-0.01L}}{L} = L e^{-0.01L}$$

To maximise this function we adopt the strategy described in Section 4.6.

Step 1

At a stationary point

$$\frac{d(AP_L)}{dL} = 0$$

To differentiate $Le^{-0.01L}$, we use the product rule. If

$$u = L \quad \text{and} \quad v = e^{-0.01L}$$

then

$$\frac{du}{dL} = 1 \quad \text{and} \quad \frac{dv}{dL} = -0.01e^{-0.01L}$$

e^{mx} differentiates to me^{mx}

By the product rule

$$\frac{d(AP_L)}{dL} = u\frac{dv}{dL} + v\frac{du}{dL} = L(-0.01e^{-0.01L}) + e^{-0.01L} = (1 - 0.01L)e^{-0.01L}$$

We know that a negative exponential is never equal to zero. (Although $e^{-0.01L}$ gets ever closer to zero as L increases, it never actually reaches it for finite values of L.) Hence the only way that

$$(1 - 0.01L)e^{-0.01L}$$

can equal zero is when

$$1 - 0.01L = 0$$

which has solution $L = 100$.

Step 2

To show that this is a maximum we need to differentiate a second time. To do this we apply the product rule to

$$(1 - 0.01L)e^{-0.01L}$$

taking

$$u = 1 - 0.01L \quad \text{and} \quad v = e^{-0.01L}$$

for which

$$\frac{du}{dL} = -0.01 \quad \text{and} \quad \frac{dv}{dL} = -0.01e^{-0.01L}$$

Hence

$$\frac{d^2(AP_L)}{dL^2} = u\frac{dv}{dL} + v\frac{du}{dL} = (1 - 0.01L)(-0.01e^{-0.01L}) + e^{-0.01L}(-0.01) = (-0.02 + 0.0001L)e^{-0.01L}$$

Finally, putting $L = 100$ into this gives

$$\frac{d^2(AP_L)}{dL^2} = -0.0037$$

The fact that this is negative shows that the stationary point, $L = 100$, is indeed a maximum.

Practice Problem

5. The demand function of a good is given by

    $$Q = 1000e^{-0.2P}$$

    If fixed costs are 100 and the variable costs are 2 per unit, show that the profit function is given by

    $$\pi = 1000Pe^{-0.2P} - 2000e^{-0.2P} - 100$$

    Find the price needed to maximise profit.

Example

A firm estimates that the total revenue received from the sale of Q goods is given by

$$TR = \ln(1 + 1000Q^2)$$

Calculate the marginal revenue when $Q = 10$.

Solution

The marginal revenue function is obtained by differentiating the total revenue function. To differentiate $\ln(1 + 1000Q^2)$ we use the chain rule. We first differentiate the outer log function to get

$$\frac{1}{1 + 1000Q^2}$$

natural logs differentiate to reciprocals

and then multiply by the derivative of the inner function, $1 + 1000Q^2$, to get $2000Q$. Hence

$$MR = \frac{d(TR)}{dQ} = \frac{2000Q}{1 + 1000Q^2}$$

At $Q = 10$,

$$MR = \frac{2000(10)}{1 + 1000(10)^2} = 0.2$$

Practice Problem

6. If the demand equation is

    $$P = 200 - 40 \ln(Q + 1)$$

    calculate the price elasticity of demand when $Q = 20$.

Exercise 4.8

1. Write down the derivative of

   (a) $y = e^{6x}$ **(b)** $y = e^{-342x}$ **(c)** $y = 2e^{-x} + 4e^x$ **(d)** $y = 10e^{4x} - 2x^2 + 7$

2. If \$4000 is saved in an account offering a return of 4% compounded continuously the future value, S, after t years is given by

   $$S = 4000e^{0.04t}$$

   (1) Calculate the value of S when

       (a) $t = 5$ **(b)** $t = 5.01$

       and hence estimate the rate of growth at $t = 5$. Round your answers to 2 decimal places.

   (2) Write down an expression for $\dfrac{dS}{dt}$ and hence find the exact value of the rate of growth after 5 years.

3. Write down the derivative of

   (a) $y = \ln(3x)$ $(x > 0)$ **(b)** $y = \ln(-13x)$ $(x < 0)$

4. Use the chain rule to differentiate

   (a) $y = e^{x^3}$ **(b)** $y = \ln(x^4 + 3x^2)$

5. Use the product rule to differentiate

   (a) $y = x^4 e^{2x}$ **(b)** $y = x \ln x$

6. Use the quotient rule to differentiate

   (a) $y = \dfrac{e^{4x}}{x^2 + 2}$ **(b)** $y = \dfrac{e^x}{\ln x}$

7. Find and classify the stationary points of

   (a) $y = xe^{-x}$ **(b)** $y = \ln x - x$

   Hence sketch their graphs.

8. Since the beginning of the year, weekly sales of a luxury good are found to have decreased exponentially. After t weeks sales can be modelled by $3000e^{-0.02t}$.

   (a) Work out the weekly sales when $t = 12$ and $t = 13$ and hence find the decrease in sales during this time.

   (b) Use differentiation to work out the rate of decrease in sales after 12 weeks and compare this with your answer to part (a).

9. Find the output needed to maximise profit given that the total cost and total revenue functions are

   $$\text{TC} = 2Q \quad \text{and} \quad \text{TR} = 100\ln(Q + 1)$$

   respectively.

10. If a firm's production function is given by

   $$Q = 700Le^{-0.02L}$$

   find the value of L that maximises output.

11. The demand function of a good is given by

$$P = 100e^{-0.1Q}$$

Show that demand is unit elastic when $Q = 10$.

Exercise 4.8*

1. Differentiate:

(a) $y = e^{2x} - 3e^{-4x}$ (b) xe^{4x} (c) $\dfrac{e^{-x}}{x^2}$ (d) $x^m \ln x$ (e) $x(\ln x - 1)$

(f) $\dfrac{x^n}{\ln x}$ (g) $\dfrac{e^{mx}}{(ax+b)^n}$ (h) $\dfrac{e^{ax}}{(\ln bx)^n}$ (i) $\dfrac{e^x - 1}{e^x + 1}$

2. Use the rules of logarithms to expand each of the following functions. Hence find their derivatives.

(a) $y = \ln\left(\dfrac{x}{x+1}\right)$ (b) $y = \ln(x\sqrt{(3x-1)})$ (c) $y = \ln\sqrt{\dfrac{x+1}{x-1}}$

3. The growth rate of an economic variable, y, is defined to be $\dfrac{dy}{dt} \div y$.

(a) Use this definition to find the growth rate of the variable, $y = Ae^{kt}$.

(b) The gross domestic product, GDP, and the size of the population, N, of a country grow exponentially, so that after t years, $GDP = Ae^{at}$ and $N = Be^{bt}$.

(i) State the growth rates for GDP and N.

(ii) Show that the GDP per capita also grows exponentially and write down its growth rate.

4. Differentiate the following functions with respect to x, simplifying your answers as far as possible:

(a) $y = x^4 e^{-2x^2}$ (b) $y = \ln\left(\dfrac{3}{(x+1)^2}\right)$

5. Find and classify the stationary points of

(a) $y = xe^{ax}$ (b) $y = \ln(ax^2 + bx)$

where $a < 0$.

6. (a) Use the quotient rule to show that the derivative of the function

$$y = \dfrac{2x+1}{\sqrt{4x+3}}$$

is given by

$$\dfrac{4(x+1)}{(4x+3)\sqrt{4x+3}}$$

(b) Use the chain rule to differentiate the function

$$y = \ln\left(\frac{2x+1}{\sqrt{4x+3}}\right)$$

(c) Confirm that your answer to part (b) is correct by first expanding

$$\ln\left(\frac{2x+1}{\sqrt{4x+3}}\right)$$

using the rules of logs and then differentiating.

7. A firm's short-run production function is given by

$$Q = L^3 e^{-0.02L}$$

Find the value of L that maximises the average product of labour.

8. Find an expression for the price elasticity of demand for the demand curve

$$P = 500 - 75 \ln(2Q + 1)$$

9. Find an expression for the marginal revenue for each of the following demand curves:

(a) $P = \dfrac{e^{Q^2}}{Q^2}$ (b) $P = \ln\left(\dfrac{2Q}{3Q+1}\right)$

10. The demand function of a good is given by $Q = 4000e^{-0.01P}$

(a) Find an expression, in terms of P, for the elasticity of demand and hence determine the range of values of P when the demand is inelastic.

(b) Find the price which maximises total revenue.

11. If the total cost function is given by $TC = 20\sqrt{Q}e^{Q/4}$ find the value of Q which minimises average cost.

12. The logistic model of growth takes the general form,

$$y = \frac{k}{1 + be^{-at}}$$

where k, a and b are positive constants.

(a) Find an expression for dy/dt and deduce that the gradient is positive.

(b) Find an expression for d^2y/dt^2 and deduce that the graph is convex when $t < (\ln b)/a$ and concave when $t > (\ln b)/a$.

(c) State the coordinates of the point where the graph intercepts the y axis and describe the behaviour of the graph as $t \to \infty$.

(d) Sketch a graph of this logistic function.

13. An art collector owns a painting which is currently valued at $2 million. After t years it is expected that the painting will be worth V million dollars where $V = 2e^{\sqrt{t}}$.

(a) If the interest rate is 10% compounded continuously show that after t years the present value of the painting is given by $PV = 2e^{\sqrt{t}-0.1t}$.

(b) The collector decides to sell the painting after T years where T is chosen to maximise PV. Work out the value of T.

Formal mathematics

In more advanced books on mathematics the derivative is defined via the concept of a limit and is usually written in symbols as

$$\frac{dy}{dx} = \lim_{\Delta \to \infty} \frac{\Delta y}{\Delta x}$$

Look at Figure 4.31. Points A and B both lie on the curve $y = f(x)$ and their x and y coordinates differ by Δx and Δy respectively. A line AB which joins two points on the curve is known as a chord and it has slope $\Delta y / \Delta x$.

Now look at Figure 4.32, which shows a variety of chords, AB_1, AB_2, AB_3, ..., corresponding to smaller and smaller 'widths' Δx. As the right-hand end points, B_1, B_2, B_3, ..., get closer to A, the 'width', Δx, tends to zero. More significantly, the slope of the chord gets closer to that of the tangent at A. We describe this by saying that in the limit, as Δx tends to zero, the slope of the chord, $\Delta y / \Delta x$, is equal to that of the tangent. This limit is written

$$\lim_{\Delta x \to 0} \frac{\Delta y}{\Delta x}$$

We deduce that the formal definition

$$\frac{dy}{dx} = \lim_{\Delta \to \infty} \frac{\Delta y}{\Delta x}$$

coincides with the idea that dy/dx represents the slope of the tangent, which is the approach adopted in this book.

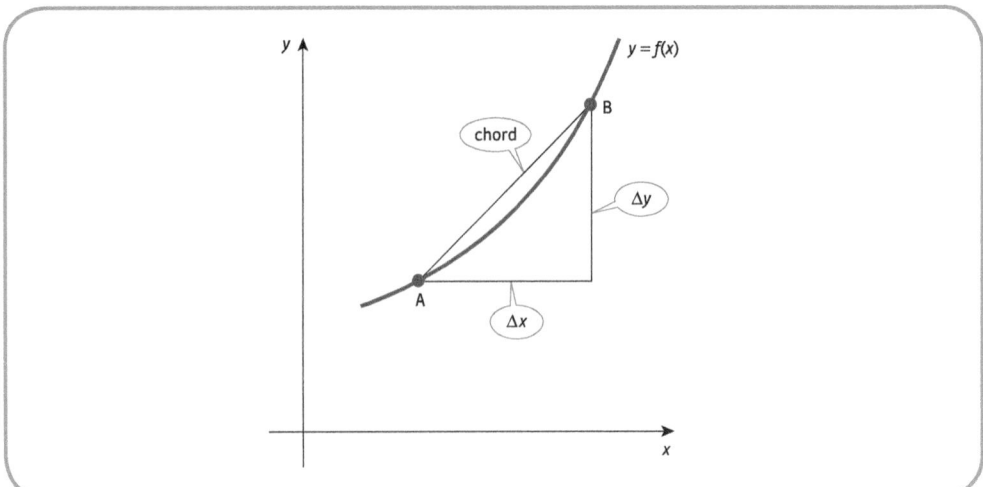

Figure 4.31

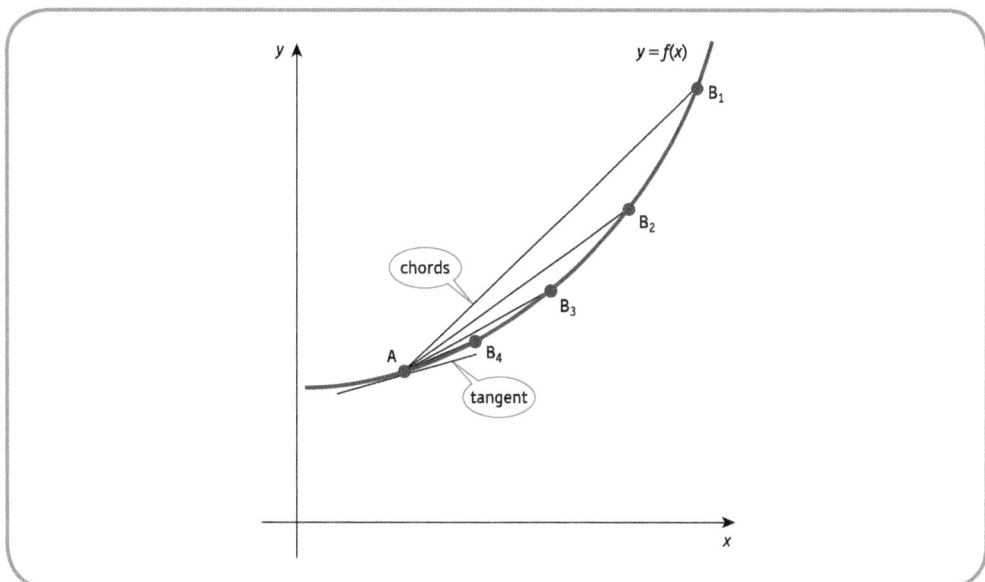

Figure 4.32

Throughout this chapter we have assumed that all functions can be differentiated. The function must at least be continuous at a point before we can even think about trying to draw a tangent at any point. For the function sketched in Figure 4.33 tangents could be drawn at every point on the graph except at $x = 2$ where the graph is discontinuous. We say that this function is not differentiable at $x = 2$.

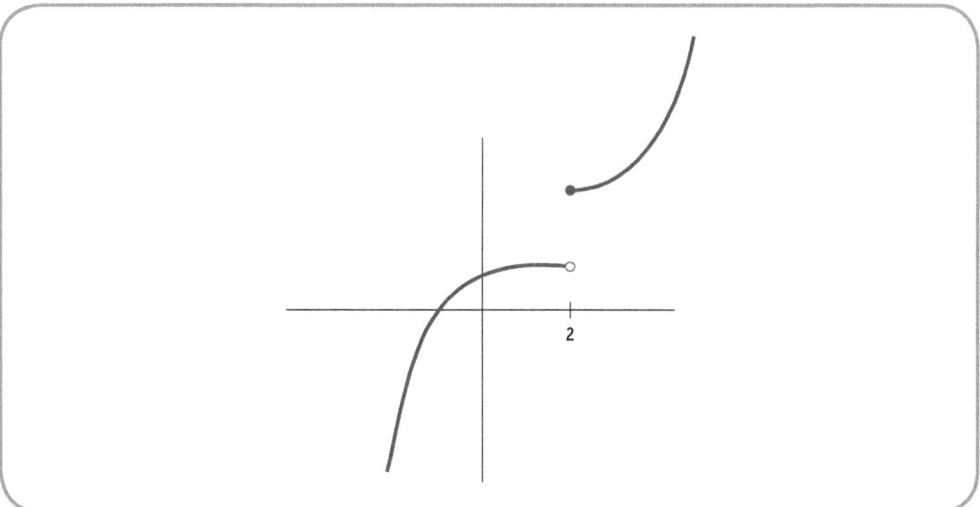

Figure 4.33

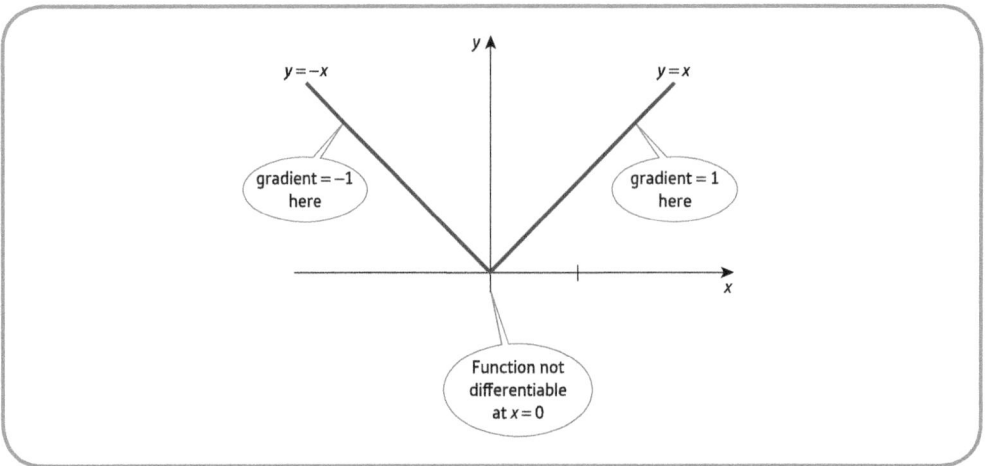

Figure 4.34

Even if a function is continuous everywhere, it still might not be possible to draw a tangent unless the curve is smooth. A classic example of such a function is the modulus function, $f(x) = |x|$ which is defined as

$$|x| = \begin{cases} -x, & \text{if } x < 0 \\ x, & \text{if } x \geq 0 \end{cases}$$

The graph of the modulus function is sketched in Figure 4.34 and has a sharp corner at $x = 0$, making it impossible to draw a tangent there.

To the left of the origin the graph has a constant slope of −1 and to the right of the origin the graph has a constant slope of +1. However, at $x = 0$ we cannot draw a tangent so the modulus function is differentiable at all values of x except for $x = 0$. This can also be seen from the definition,

$$f'(x) = \lim_{\Delta x \to 0} \frac{\Delta y}{\Delta x}$$

As $\Delta x \to 0$ through positive values (i.e. from the right) the limit is +1 whereas as $\Delta x \to 0$ through negative values (i.e. from the left) the limit is −1. The limits can both be found but it is the fact that they are different values that prevents us from finding the derivative at $x = 0$.

1 Descriptive statistics

Contents

→

Contents
continued

Learning
outcomes

By the end of this chapter you should be able to:

- recognise different types of data and use appropriate methods to summarise and analyse them;

- use graphical techniques to provide a visual summary of one or more data series;

- use numerical techniques (such as an average) to summarise data series;

- recognise the strengths and limitations of such methods;

- recognise the usefulness of data transformations to gain additional insight into a set of data.

Complete your diagnostic test for Chapter 1 now to create your personal study plan. Exercises with an icon ⑦ are also available for practice in MathXL with additional supporting resources.

Introduction

The aim of descriptive statistical methods is simple: to present information in a clear, concise and accurate manner. The difficulty in analysing many phenomena, be they economic, social or otherwise, is that there is simply too much information for the mind to assimilate. The task of descriptive methods is therefore to summarise all this information and draw out the main features, without distorting the picture.

Consider, for example, the problem of presenting information about the wealth of British citizens (which follows later in this chapter). There are about 17 million adults for whom data are available: to present the data in raw form (i.e. the wealth holdings of each and every person) would be neither useful nor informative (it would take about 30 000 pages of a book, for example). It would be more useful to have much less information, but information that was still representative of the original data. In doing this, much of the original information would be deliberately lost; in fact, descriptive statistics might be described as the art of constructively throwing away much of the data!

There are many ways of summarising data and there are few hard and fast rules about how you should proceed. Newspapers and magazines often provide innovative (although not always successful) ways of presenting data. There are, however, a number of techniques that are tried and tested, and these are the subject of this chapter. These are successful because: (a) they tell us something useful about the underlying data; and (b) they are reasonably familiar to many people, so we can all talk in a common language. For example, the average tells us about the location of the data and is a familiar concept to most people. For example, my son talks of his day at school being 'average'.

The appropriate method of analysing the data will depend on a number of factors: the type of data under consideration; the sophistication of the audience; and the 'message' that it is intended to convey. One would use different methods to persuade academics of the validity of one's theory about inflation than one would use to persuade consumers that Brand X powder washes whiter than Brand Y. To illustrate the use of the various methods, three different topics are covered in this chapter. First we look at the relationship between educational attainment and employment prospects. Do higher qualifications improve your employment chances? The data come from people surveyed in 2004/5, so we have a sample of cross-section data giving a picture of the situation at one point in time. We look at the distribution of educational attainments amongst those surveyed, as well as the relationship to employment outcomes. In this example we simply count the numbers of people in different categories (e.g. the number of people with a degree qualification who are employed).

Second, we examine the distribution of wealth in the UK in 2003. The data are again cross-section, but this time we can use more sophisticated methods since wealth is measured on a ratio scale. Someone with £200 000 of wealth is twice as wealthy as someone with £100 000 for example, and there is a meaning to this ratio. In the case of education, one cannot say with any precision that one person is twice as educated as another (hence the perennial debate about educational standards). The educational categories may be ordered (so one person can be more educated than another, although even that may be ambiguous) but we cannot measure the 'distance' between them. We refer to this as education being measured on an ordinal scale. In contrast, there is not an obvious natural ordering to the three employment categories (employed, unemployed, inactive), so this is measured on a nominal scale.

Third, we look at national spending on investment over the period 1973 to 2005. This is time series data, as we have a number of observations on the variable measured at different points in time. Here it is important to take account of the time dimension of the data: things would look different if the observations were in the order 1973, 1983, 1977, . . . rather than in correct time order.

We also look at the relationship between two variables – investment and output – over that period of time and find appropriate methods of presenting it.

In all three cases we make use of both graphical and numerical methods of summarising the data. Although there are some differences between the methods used in the three cases these are not watertight compartments: the methods used in one case might also be suitable in another, perhaps with slight modification. Part of the skill of the statistician is to know which methods of analysis and presentation are best suited to each particular problem.

Summarising data using graphical techniques

Education and employment, or, after all this, will you get a job?

We begin by looking at a question which should be of interest to you: how does education affect your chances of getting a job? It is now clear that education improves one's life chances in various ways, one of the possible benefits being that it reduces the chances of being out of work. But by how much does it reduce those chances? We shall use a variety of graphical techniques to explore the question.

The raw data for this investigation come from the *Education and Training Statistics for the U.K.* 2006.[1] Some of these data are presented in Table 1.1 and show the numbers of people by employment status (either in work, unemployed, or inactive, i.e. not seeking work) and by educational qualification (higher education, A-levels, other qualification or no qualification). The table gives a cross-tabulation of employment status by educational qualification and is simply a count (the frequency) of the number of people falling into each of the 12 cells of the table. For example, there were 8 541 000 people in work who had experience of higher education. This is part of a total of just over 36 million people of working age. Note that the numbers in the table are in thousands, for the sake of clarity.

Table 1.1 **Economic status and educational qualifications, 2006** *(numbers in 000s)*

	Higher education	A levels	Other qualification	No qualification	Total
In work	8541	5501	10 702	2260	27 004
Unemployed	232	247	758	309	1546
Inactive	1024	1418	3150	2284	7876
Total	9797	7166	14 610	4853	36 426

---

[1] This is now an internet-only publication, available at http://www.dcsf.gov.uk/rsgateway/DB/VOL/v000696/Vweb03-2006V1.pdf.

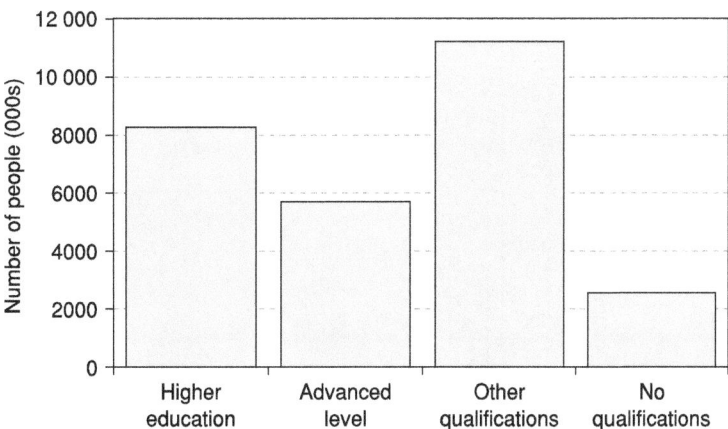

Figure 1.1
Educational qualifications of people in work in the UK, 2006

Note: The height of each bar is determined by the associated frequency. The first bar is 8541 units high, the second is 5501 units high and so on. The ordering of the bars could be reversed ('no qualifications' becoming the first category) without altering the message.

The bar chart

The first graphical technique we shall use is the bar chart and this is shown in Figure 1.1. This summarises the educational qualifications of those in work, i.e. the data in the first row of the table. The four educational categories are arranged along the horizontal (*x*) axis, while the frequencies are measured on the vertical (*y*) axis. The height of each bar represents the numbers in work for that category.

The biggest group is seen to be those with 'other qualifications', although this is now not much bigger than the 'higher education' category (the numbers entering higher education have been increasing substantially in the UK over time, although this is not evident in this chart, which uses cross-section data). The 'no qualifications' category is the smallest, although it does make up a substantial fraction of those in work.

It would be interesting to compare this distribution with those for the unemployed and inactive. This is done in Figure 1.2, which adds bars for these other two categories. This multiple bar chart shows that, as for the 'in work' category, among the inactive and unemployed, the largest group consists of those with 'other' qualifications (which are typically vocational qualifications). These findings simply reflect the fact that 'other qualifications' is the largest category. We can also begin to see whether more education increases your chance of having a job. For example, compare the height of the 'in work' bar to the 'inactive' bar. It is relatively much higher for those with higher education than for those with no qualifications. In other words, the likelihood of being inactive rather than employed is lower for graduates. However, we are having to make judgements about the relative heights of different bars simply by eye, and it is easy to make a mistake. It would be better if we could draw charts that would better highlight the differences. Figure 1.3 shows an alternative method of presentation: the stacked bar chart. In this case the bars are stacked one on top of another instead of being placed side by side. This is perhaps slightly better

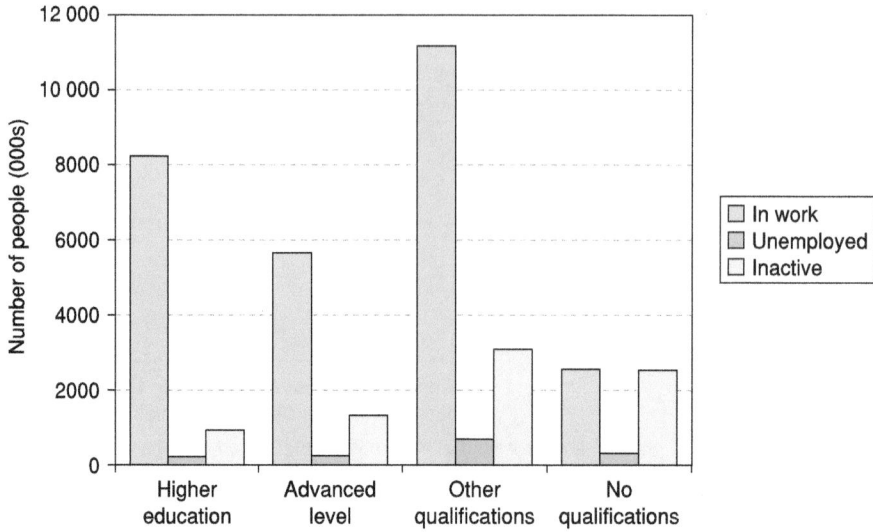

Figure 1.2
Educational qualifications by employment category

Note: The bars for the unemployed and inactive categories are constructed in the same way as for those in work: the height of the bar is determined by the frequency.

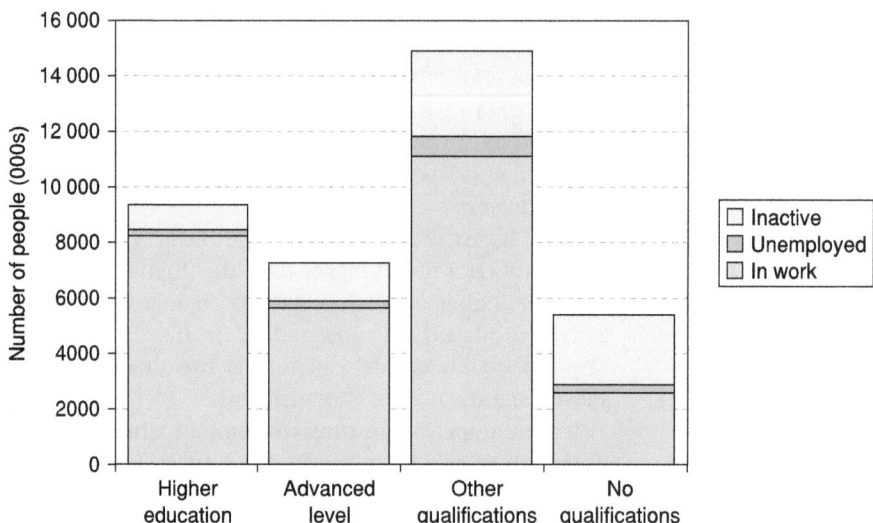

Figure 1.3
Stacked bar chart of educational qualifications and employment status

Note: The overall height of each bar is determined by the sum of the frequencies of the category, given in the final row of Table 1.1.

and the different overall sizes of the categories is clearly brought out. However, we are still having to make tricky visual judgements about proportions.

A clearer picture emerges if the data are transformed to (column) percentages, i.e. the columns are expressed as percentages of the column totals (e.g. the *proportion* of graduates are in work, rather than the number). This makes it easier directly to compare the different educational categories. These figures are shown in Table 1.2.

Having done this, it is easier to make a direct comparison of the different education categories (columns). This is shown in Figure 1.4, where all the bars

Table 1.2 **Economic status and educational qualifications: column percentages**

	Higher education	A levels	Other qualification	No qualification	All
In work	87%	77%	73%	47%	74%
Unemployed	2%	3%	5%	6%	4%
Inactive	10%	20%	22%	47%	22%
Totals	99%	100%	100%	100%	100%

Note: The column percentages are obtained by dividing each frequency by the column total. For example, 87% is 8541 divided by 9797; 77% is 5501 divided by 7166, and so on. Columns may not sum to 100% due to rounding.

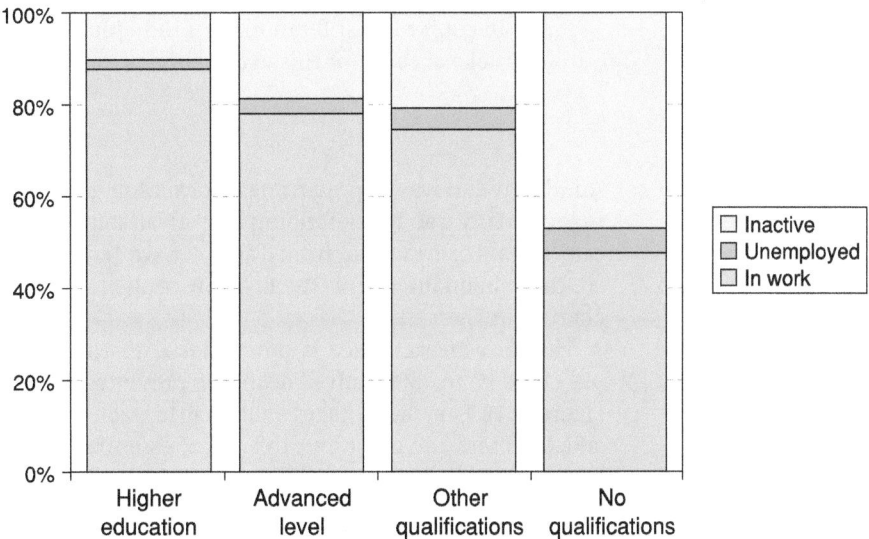

Figure 1.4
Percentages in each employment category, by educational qualification

are of the same height (representing 100%) and the components of each bar now show the *proportions* of people in each educational category either in work, unemployed or inactive.

It is now clear how economic status differs according to education and the result is quite dramatic. In particular:

● The probability of unemployment increases rapidly with lower educational attainment (this interprets proportions as probabilities, i.e. if 10% are out of work then the probability that a person picked at random is unemployed is 10%).
● The biggest difference is between the no qualifications category and the other three, which have relatively smaller differences between them. In particular, A-levels and other qualifications show a similar pattern.

Notice that we have looked at the data in different ways, drawing different charts for the purpose. You need to consider which type of chart of most suitable for the data you have and the questions you want to ask. There is no one graph that is ideal for all circumstances.

Can we safely conclude therefore that the probability of your being un-employed is significantly reduced by education? Could we go further and argue that the route to lower unemployment generally is through investment in education? The answer *may* be 'yes' to both questions, but we have not proved it. Two important considerations are as follows:

● Innate ability has been ignored. Those with higher ability are more likely to be employed *and* are more likely to receive more education. Ideally we would like to compare individuals of similar ability but with different amounts of education.

● Even if additional education does reduce a person's probability of becoming unemployed, this may be at the expense of someone else, who loses their job to the more educated individual. In other words, additional education does not reduce total unemployment but only shifts it around among the labour force. Of course it is still rational for individuals to invest in education if they do not take account of this externality.

The pie chart

Another useful way of presenting information graphically is the pie chart, which is particularly good at describing how a variable is distributed between different categories. For example, from Table 1.1 we have the distribution of people by educational qualification (the first row of the table). This can be shown in a pie chart as in Figure 1.5.

The area of each slice is proportional to the respective frequency and the pie chart is an alternative means of presentation to the bar chart shown in Figure 1.1. The percentages falling into each education category have been added around the chart, but this is not essential. For presentational purposes it is best not to have too many slices in the chart: beyond about six the chart tends to look crowded. It might be worth amalgamating less important categories to make a chart look clearer.

The chart reveals that 40% of those employed fall into the 'other qualification' category, and that just 8% have no qualifications. This may be

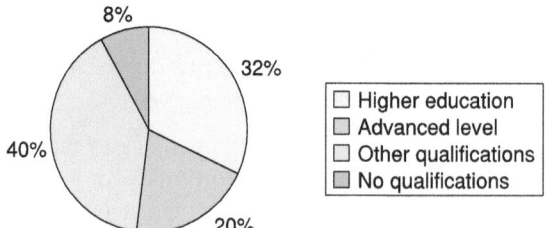

Note: If you have to draw a pie chart by hand, the angle of each slice can be calculated as follows:

$$angle = \frac{frequency}{total\ frequency} \times 360.$$

Figure 1.5
Educational qualifications of those in work

The angle of the first slice, for example, is

$$\frac{8541}{27\ 004} \times 360 = 113.9°.$$

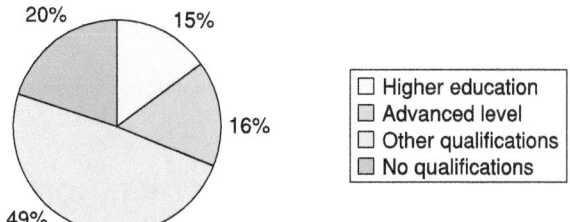

Figure 1.6
Educational
qualifications of the
unemployed

contrasted with Figure 1.6, which shows a similar chart for the unemployed (the second row of Table 1.1).

The 'other qualification' category is a little larger in this case, but the 'no qualification' group now accounts for 20% of the unemployed, a big increase. Further, the proportion with a degree approximately halves from 32% to 15%.

Producing charts using Microsoft Excel

Most of the charts in this book were produced using Excel's charting facility. Without wishing to dictate a precise style, you should aim for a similar, uncluttered look. Some tips you might find useful are:

- Make the grid lines dashed in a light grey colour (they are not actually part of the chart, hence should be discreet) or eliminate altogether.
- Get rid of the background fill (grey by default, alter to 'No fill'). It does not look great when printed.
- On the x-axis, make the labels horizontal or vertical, not slanted – it is then difficult to see which point they refer to. If they are slanted, double click on the x-axis then click the alignment tab.
- Colour charts look great on-screen but unclear if printed in black and white. Change the style type of the lines or markers (e.g. make some dashed) to distinguish them on paper.
- Both axes start at zero by default. If all your observations are large numbers this may result in the data points being crowded into one corner of the graph. Alter the scale on the axes to fix this: set the minimum value on the axis to be slightly less than the minimum observation.

Otherwise, Excel's default options will usually give a good result.

Exercise 1.1

The following table shows the total numbers (in millions) of tourists visiting each country and the numbers of English tourists visiting each country:

	France	Germany	Italy	Spain
All tourists	12.4	3.2	7.5	9.8
English tourists	2.7	0.2	1.0	3.6

(a) Draw a bar chart showing the total numbers visiting each country.

(b) Draw a stacked bar chart, which shows English and non-English tourists making up the total visitors to each country.

(c) Draw a pie chart showing the distribution of all tourists between the four destination countries.

(d) Do the same for English tourists and compare results.

Looking at cross-section data: wealth in the UK in 2003

Frequency tables and histograms

We now move on to examine data in a different form. The data on employment and education consisted simply of frequencies, where a characteristic (such as higher education) was either present or absent for a particular individual. We now look at the distribution of wealth – a variable that can be measured on a ratio scale so that a different value is associated with each individual. For example, one person might have £1000 of wealth, another might have £1 million. Different presentational techniques will be used to analyse this type of data. We use these techniques to investigate questions such as how much wealth does the average person have and whether wealth is evenly distributed or not.

The data are given in Table 1.3, which shows the distribution of wealth in the UK for the year 2003 (the latest available at the time of writing), available at http://www.hmrc.gov.uk/stats/personal_wealth/menu.htm. This is an example of a frequency table. Wealth is difficult to define and to measure; the data shown here refer to *marketable* wealth (i.e. items such as the right to a pension, which cannot be sold, are excluded) and are estimates for the population (of adults) as a whole based on taxation data.

Wealth is divided into 14 class intervals: £0 up to (but not including) £10 000; £10 000 up to £24 999, etc., and the number (or frequency) of

Table 1.3 The distribution of wealth, UK, 2003

Class interval (£)	Numbers (thousands)
0–9999	2448
10 000–24 999	1823
25 000–39 999	1375
40 000–49 999	480
50 000–59 999	665
60 000–79 999	1315
80 000–99 999	1640
100 000–149 999	2151
150 000–199 000	2215
200 000–299 000	1856
300 000–499 999	1057
500 000–999 999	439
1 000 000–1 999 999	122
2 000 000 or more	50
Total	17 636

Note: It would be impossible to show the wealth of all 18 million individuals, so it has been summarised in this frequency table.

individuals within each class interval is shown. Note that the widths of the intervals (the class widths) vary up the wealth scale: the first is £10 000, the second £15 000 (= 25 000 − 10 000); the third £15 000 also and so on. This will prove an important factor when it comes to graphical presentation of the data.

This table has been constructed from the original 17 636 000 observations on individuals' wealth, so it is already a summary of the original data (note that all the frequencies have been expressed in thousands in the table) and much of the original information is lost. The first decision to make if one had to draw up such a frequency table from the raw data is how many class intervals to have, and how wide they should be. It simplifies matters if they are all of the same width but in this case it is not feasible: if 10 000 were chosen as the standard width there would be many intervals between 500 000 and 1 000 000 (50 of them in fact), most of which would have a zero or very low frequency. If 100 000 were the standard width, there would be only a few intervals and the first (0–100 000) would contain 9746 observations (55% of all observations), so almost all the interesting detail would be lost. A compromise between these extremes has to be found.

A useful rule of thumb is that the number of class intervals should equal the square root of the total frequency, subject to a maximum of about 12 intervals. Thus, for example, a total of 25 observations should be allocated to five intervals; 100 observations should be grouped into 10 intervals; and 17 636 should be grouped into about 12 (14 are used here). The class widths should be equal in so far as this is feasible, but should increase when the frequencies become very small.

To present these data graphically one could draw a bar chart as in the case of education above, and this is presented in Figure 1.7. Before reading on, spend some time looking at it and ask yourself what is wrong with it.

The answer is that the figure gives a completely misleading picture of the data! (Incidentally, this is the picture that you will get using a spreadsheet computer program, as I have done here. All the standard packages appear to do this, so beware. One wonders how many decisions have been influenced by data presented in this incorrect manner.)

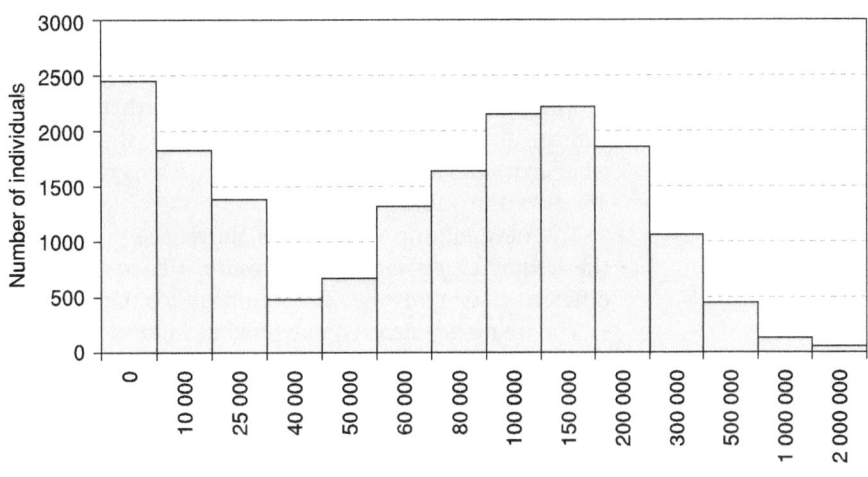

Figure 1.7
Bar chart of the distribution of wealth in the UK, 2003

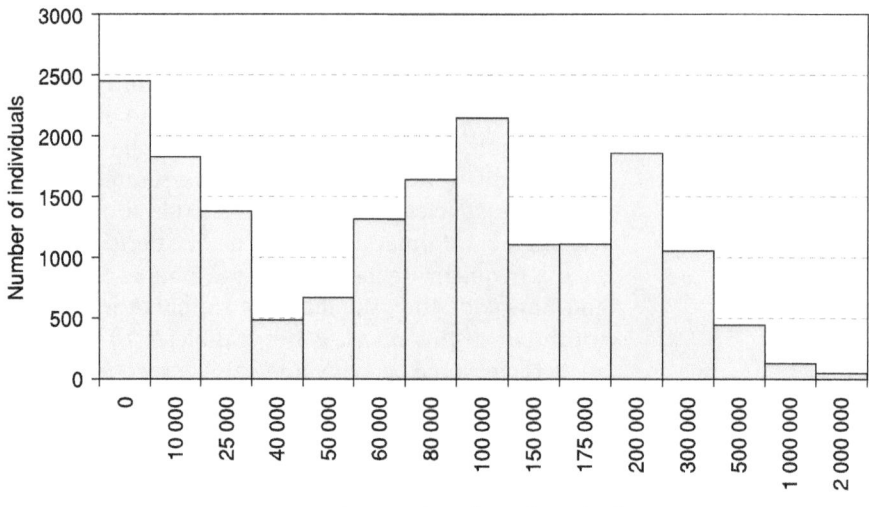

Figure 1.8
The wealth distribution
with alternative class
intervals

Why is the figure wrong? Consider the following argument. The diagram appears to show that there are few individuals around £40 000 to £60 000 (the frequency is at a low of 480 (thousand)) but many around £150 000. But this is just the result of the difference in the class width at these points (10 000 at £40 000 and 50 000 at £150 000). Suppose that we divide up the £150 000–£200 000 class into two: £150 000 to £175 000 and £175 000 to £200 000. We divide the frequency of 2215 equally between the two (this is an arbitrary decision but illustrates the point). The graph now looks like Figure 1.8.

Comparing Figures 1.7 and 1.8 reveals a difference: the hump around £150 000 has now disappeared, replaced by a small crater. But this is disturbing – it means that the shape of the distribution can be altered simply by altering the class widths. If so, how can we rely upon visual inspection of the distribution? What does the 'real' distribution look like? A better method would make the shape of the distribution independent of how the class intervals are arranged. This can be done by drawing a histogram.

The histogram

A histogram is similar to a bar chart except that it corrects for differences in class widths. If all the class widths are identical, then there is no difference between a bar chart and a histogram. The calculations required to produce the histogram are shown in Table 1.4.

The new column in the table shows the frequency density, which measures the frequency *per unit of class width*. Hence it allows a direct comparison of different class intervals, i.e. accounting for the difference in class widths.

The frequency density is defined as follows

$$\text{frequency density} = \frac{\text{frequency}}{\text{class width}} \tag{1.1}$$

Using this formula corrects the figures for differing class widths. Thus 0.2448 = 2448/10 000 is the first frequency density, 0.1215 = 1823/15 000 is the second,

Table 1.4 Calculation of frequency densities

Range	Number or frequency	Class width	Frequency density
0–	2448	10 000	0.2448
10 000–	1823	15 000	0.1215
25 000–	1375	15 000	0.0917
40 000–	480	10 000	0.0480
50 000–	665	10 000	0.0665
60 000–	1315	20 000	0.0658
80 000–	1640	20 000	0.0820
100 000–	2151	50 000	0.0430
150 000–	2215	50 000	0.0443
200 000–	3524	3 800 000	0.0009

Note: As an alternative to the frequency density, one could calculate the frequency per 'standard' class width, with the standard width chosen to be 10 000 (the narrowest class). The values in column 4 would then be 2448; 1215.3 (= 1823 ÷ 1.5); 916.7; etc. This would lead to the same shape of histogram as using the frequency density.

etc. Above £200 000 the class widths are very large and the frequencies small (too small to be visible on the histogram), so these classes have been combined.

The width of the final interval is unknown, so has to be estimated in order to calculate the frequency density. It is likely to be extremely wide since the wealthiest person may well have assets valued at several £m (or even £bn); the value we assume will affect the calculation of the frequency density and therefore of the shape of the histogram. Fortunately it is in the tail of the distribution and only affects a small number of observations. Here we assume (arbitrarily) a width of £3.8m to be a 'reasonable' figure, giving an upper class boundary of £4m.

The frequency density is then plotted on the vertical axis against wealth on the horizontal axis to give the histogram. One further point needs to be made: the scale on the wealth axis should be linear as far as possible, e.g. £50 000 should be twice as far from the origin as £25 000. However, it is difficult to fit all the values onto the horizontal axis without squeezing the graph excessively at lower levels of wealth, where most observations are located. Therefore the classes above £100 000 have been squeezed and the reader's attention is drawn to this. The result is shown in Figure 1.9.

The effect of taking frequency densities is to make the *area* of each block in the histogram represent the frequency, rather than the height, which now shows the density. This has the effect of giving an accurate picture of the shape of the distribution.

Having done all this, what does the histogram show?

- The histogram is heavily skewed to the right (i.e. the long tail is to the right).
- The modal class interval is £0–£10 000 (i.e. has the greatest density: no other £10 000 interval has more individuals in it).
- A little under half of all people (45.9% in fact) have less than £80 000 of marketable wealth.
- About 20% of people have more than £200 000 of wealth.[2]

---

[2] Due to the compressing of some class widths, it is difficult to see this accurately on the histogram. There are limitations to graphical presentation.

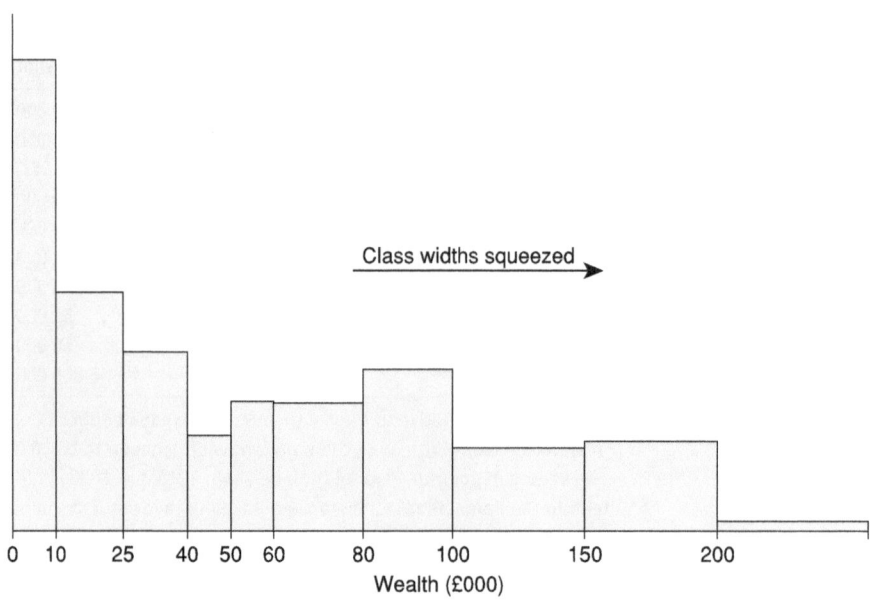

Figure 1.9
Histogram of the distribution of wealth in the UK, 2003

Note: A frequency polygon would be the result if, instead of drawing blocks for the histogram, lines were drawn connecting the centres of the top of each block. The diagram is better drawn with blocks, in general.

The figure shows quite a high degree of inequality in the wealth distribution. Whether this is acceptable or even desirable is a value judgement. It should be noted that part of the inequality is due to differences in age: younger people have not yet had enough time to acquire much wealth and therefore appear worse off, although in life-time terms this may not be the case. To obtain a better picture of the distribution of wealth would require some analysis of the acquisition of wealth over the life-cycle (or comparing individuals of a similar age). In fact, correcting for age differences does not make a big difference to the pattern of wealth distribution (on this point and on inequality in wealth in general, see Atkinson (1983), Chapters 7 and 8).

Relative frequency and cumulative frequency distributions

An alternative way of illustrating the wealth distribution uses the relative and cumulative frequencies of the data. The relative frequencies show the *proportion* of observations that fall into each class interval, so, for example, 2.72% of individuals have wealth holdings between £40 000 and £50 000 (480 000 out of 17 636 000 individuals). Relative frequencies are shown in the third column of Table 1.5, using the following formula[3]

$$Relative\ frequency = \frac{frequency}{sum\ of\ frequencies} = \frac{f}{\Sigma f} \tag{1.2}$$

---

[3] If you are unfamiliar with the Σ notation then read Appendix 1A to this chapter before continuing.

Table 1.5 Calculation of relative and cumulative frequencies

Range	Frequency	Relative frequency (%)	Cumulative frequency
0–	2448	13.9	2448
10 000–	1823	10.3	4271
25 000–	1375	7.8	5646
40 000–	480	2.7	6126
50 000–	665	3.8	6791
60 000–	1315	7.5	8106
80 000–	1640	9.3	9746
100 000–	2151	12.2	11 897
150 000–	2215	12.6	14 112
200 000–	1856	10.5	15 968
300 000–	1057	6.0	17 025
500 000–	439	2.5	17 464
1 000 000–	122	0.7	17 586
2 000 000–	50	0.3	17 636
Total	17 636	100.00	

Note: Relative frequencies are calculated in the same way as the column percentages in Table 1.2. Thus for example, 13.9% is 2448 divided by 17 636. Cumulative frequencies are obtained by cumulating, or successively adding, the frequencies. For example, 4271 is 2448 + 1823, 5646 is 4271 + 1375, etc.

The AIDS epidemic

To show how descriptive statistics can be helpful in presenting information we show below the 'population pyramid' for Botswana (one of the countries most seriously affected by AIDS), projected for the year 2020. This is essentially two bar charts (one for men, one for women) laid on their sides, showing the frequencies in each age category (rather than wealth categories). The inner pyramid (in the darker colour) shows the projected population given the existence of AIDS; the outer pyramid assumes no deaths from AIDS.

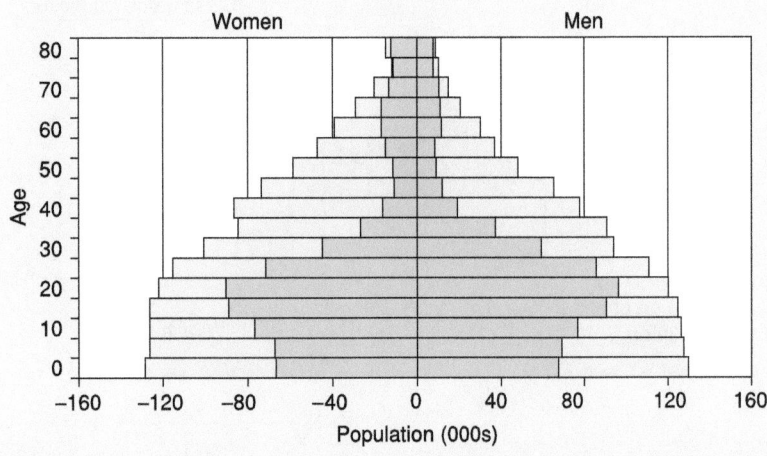

Original source of data: US Census Bureau, *World Population Profile 2000*. Graph adapted from the UNAIDS web site at http://www.unaids.org/epidemic_update/report/Epi_report.htm#thepopulation.

> One can immediately see the huge effect of AIDS, especially on the 40–60 age group (currently aged 20–40), for both men and women. These people would normally be in the most productive phase of their lives but, with AIDS, the country will suffer enormously with many old and young people dependent on a small working population. The severity of the future problems is brought out vividly in this simple graphic, based on the bar chart.

The sum of the relative frequencies has to be 100% and this acts as a check on the calculations.

The cumulative frequencies, shown in the fourth column, are obtained by cumulating (successively adding) the frequencies. The cumulative frequencies show the total number of individuals with wealth *up to* a given amount; for example, about 10 million people have less than £100 000 of wealth.

Both relative and cumulative frequency distributions can be drawn, in a similar way to the histogram. In fact, the relative frequency distribution has exactly the same shape as the frequency distribution. This is shown in Figure 1.10. This time we have written the relative frequencies above the appropriate column, although this is not essential.

The cumulative frequency distribution is shown in Figure 1.11, where the blocks increase in height as wealth increases. The simplest way to draw this is to cumulate the frequency densities (shown in the final column of Table 1.4) and to use these values as the *y*-axis coordinates.

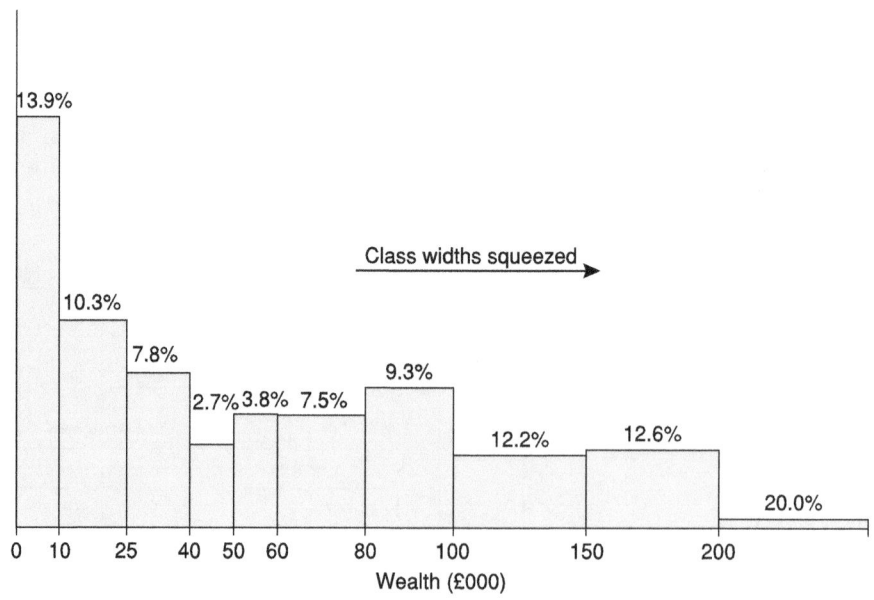

Figure 1.10
The relative density frequency distribution of wealth in the UK, 2003

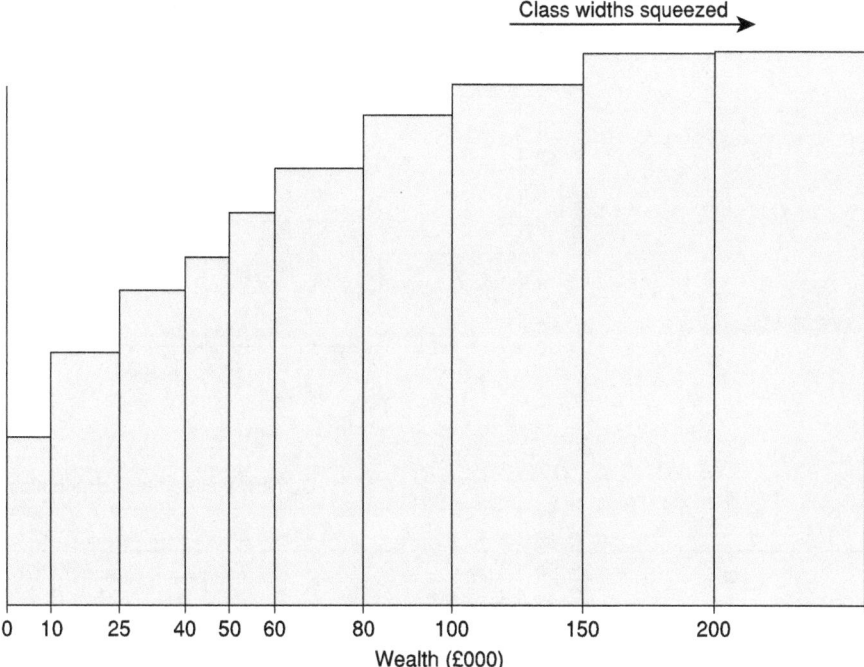

Class widths squeezed

Wealth (£000)

0 10 25 40 50 60 80 100 150 200

Figure 1.11
The cumulative
frequency distribution of
wealth in the UK, 2003

Note: The *y*-axis coordinates are obtained by cumulating the frequency densities in Table 1.4
above. For example, the first two *y* coordinates are 0.2448, 0.3663.

There is a mass of detail in the sections above, so this worked example
is intended to focus on the essential calculations required to produce the
summary graphs. Simple artificial data are deliberately used to avoid the
distraction of a lengthy interpretation of the results and their meaning. The
data on the variable X and its frequencies f are shown in the following table,
with the calculations required:

X	Frequency, f	Relative frequency	Cumulative frequency, F
10	6	0.17	6
11	8	0.23	14
12	15	0.43	29
13	5	0.14	34
14	1	0.03	35
Total	35	1.00	

Notes:
The X values are unique but could be considered the mid-point of a range, as earlier.
The relative frequencies are calculated as $0.17 = 6/35$, $0.23 = 8/35$, etc.
The cumulative frequencies are calculated as $14 = 6 + 8$, $29 = 6 + 8 + 15$, etc.
The symbol F usually denotes the cumulative frequency in statistical work.

→

The resulting bar chart and cumulative frequency distribution are:

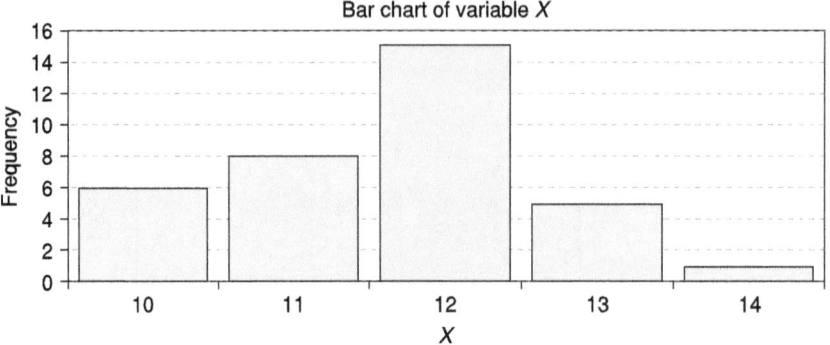

and

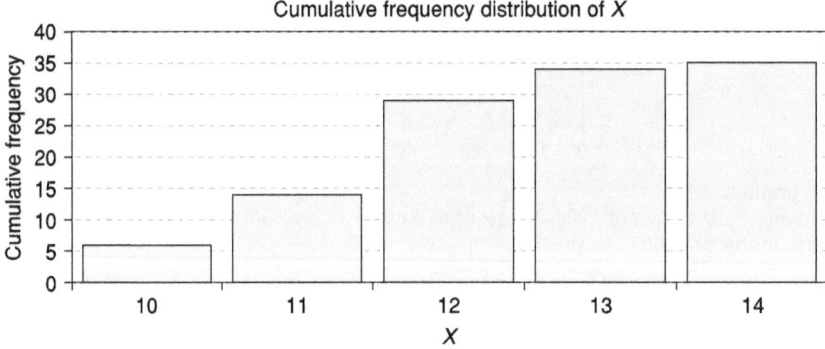

Exercise 1.2   Given the following data:

Range	Frequency
0–10	20
11–30	40
31–60	30
60–100	20

(a) Draw both a bar chart and a histogram of the data and compare them.

(b) Calculate cumulative frequencies and draw a cumulative frequency diagram.

Summarising data using numerical techniques

Graphical methods are an excellent means of obtaining a quick overview of the data, but they are not particularly precise, nor do they lend themselves to further analysis. For this we must turn to numerical measures such as the average. There are a number of different ways in which we may describe a distribution such as that for wealth. If we think of trying to describe the histogram, it is useful to have:

- A measure of location giving an idea of whether people own a lot of wealth or a little. An example is the average, which gives some idea of where the distribution is located along the x-axis. In fact, we will encounter three different measures of the 'average':
  - the mean;
  - the median;
  - the mode.
- A measure of dispersion showing how wealth is dispersed around (usually) the average, whether it is concentrated close to the average or is generally far away from it. An example here is the standard deviation.
- A measure of skewness showing how symmetric or not the distribution is, i.e. whether the left half of the distribution is a mirror image of the right half or not. This is obviously not the case for the wealth distribution.

We consider each type of measure in turn.

Measures of location: the mean

The arithmetic mean, commonly called the average, is the most familiar measure of location, and is obtained simply by adding all the observations and dividing by the number of observations. If we denote the wealth of the ith household by x_i (so that the index i runs from 1 to N, where N is the number of observations; as an example, x_3 would be the wealth of the third household) then the mean is given by the following formula

$$\mu = \frac{\sum_{i=1}^{i=N} x_i}{N} \tag{1.3}$$

where μ (the Greek letter mu, pronounced 'myu'[4]) denotes the mean and $\sum_{i=1}^{i=N} x_i$

(read 'sigma x i, from $i = 1$ to N', Σ being the Greek capital letter sigma) means the sum of the x values. We may simplify this to

$$\mu = \frac{\sum x}{N} \tag{1.4}$$

when it is obvious which x values are being summed (usually all the available observations). This latter form is more easily readable and we will generally use this.

> ### Worked example 1.2
>
> We will find the mean of the values 17, 25, 28, 20, 35. The total of these five numbers is 125, so we have $N = 5$ and $\sum x = 125$. Therefore the mean is
>
> $$\mu = \frac{\sum x}{N} = \frac{125}{5} = 25$$

Formula (1.3) can only be used when all the individual x values are known. The frequency table for wealth does not show all 17 million observations, however,

---

[4] Well, mathematicians pronounce it like this, but modern Greeks do not. For them it is 'mi'.

but only the range of values for each class interval and the associated frequency. In this case of grouped data the following equivalent formula may be used

$$\mu = \frac{\sum\limits_{i=1}^{i=C} f_i x_i}{\sum\limits_{i=1}^{i=C} f_i} \qquad (1.5)$$

or, more simply

$$\mu = \frac{\sum fx}{\sum f} \qquad (1.6)$$

In this formula

- x denotes the mid-point of each class interval, since the individual x values are unknown. The mid-point is used as the representative x value for each class. In the first class interval, for example, we do not know precisely where each of the 2448 observations lies. Hence we *assume* they all lie at the mid-point, £5000. This will cause a slight inaccuracy – because the distribution is so skewed, there are more households below the mid-point than above it in every class interval except, perhaps, the first. We ignore this problem here, and it is less of a problem for most distributions which are less skewed than this one.
- The summation runs from 1 to C, the number of class intervals, or distinct x values. f times x gives the total wealth in each class interval. If we sum over the 14 class intervals we obtain the total wealth of all individuals.
- $\sum f_i = N$ gives the total number of observations, the sum of the individual frequencies. The calculation of the mean, μ, for the wealth data is shown in Table 1.6.

Table 1.6 **The calculation of average wealth**

Range	x	f	fx
0–	5.0	2448	12 240
10 000–	17.5	1823	31 902
25 000–	32.5	1375	44 687
40 000–	45.0	480	21 600
50 000–	55.0	665	36 575
60 000–	70.0	1315	92 050
80 000–	90.0	1640	147 600
100 000–	125.0	2151	268 875
150 000–	175.0	2215	387 625
200 000–	250.0	1856	464 000
300 000–	400.0	1057	422 800
500 000–	750.0	439	329 250
1 000 000–	1500.0	122	183 000
2 000 000–	3000.0	50	150 000
Total		17 636	2 592 205

Note: The *fx* column gives the product of the values in the *f* and *x* columns (so, for example, 5.0 × 2448 = 12 240, which is the total wealth held by those in the first class interval). The sum of the *fx* values gives total wealth.

From this we obtain

$$\mu = \frac{2\ 592\ 205}{17\ 636} = 146.984$$

Note that the x values are expressed in £000, so we must remember that the mean will also be in £000; the average wealth holding is therefore £146 984. Note that the frequencies have also been divided by 1000, but this has no effect upon the calculation of the mean since f appears in both numerator and denominator of the formula for the mean.

The mean tells us that if the total wealth were divided up equally between all individuals, each would have £146 984. This value may seem surprising, since the histogram clearly shows most people have wealth below this point (approximately 65% of individuals are below the mean, in fact). The mean does not seem to be typical of the wealth that most people have. The reason the mean has such a high value is that there are some individuals whose wealth is way above the figure of £146 984 – up into the £millions, in fact. The mean is the 'balancing point' of the distribution – if the histogram were a physical model, it would balance on a fulcrum placed at 146 984. The few very high wealth levels exert a lot of leverage and counter-balance the more numerous individuals below the mean.

> ### Worked example 1.3
>
> Suppose we have 10 families with a single television in their homes, 12 families with two televisions each and 3 families with three. You can probably work out in your head that there are 43 televisions in total (10 + 24 + 9) owned by the 25 families (10 + 12 + 3). The average number of televisions per family is therefore 43/25 = 1.72.
>
> Setting this out formally, we have (as for the wealth distribution, but simpler):
>
> | x | f | fx |
> |---|---|---|
> | 1 | 10 | 10 |
> | 2 | 12 | 24 |
> | 3 | 3 | 9 |
> | Totals | 25 | 43 |
>
> This gives our resulting mean as 1.72. Note that our data are discrete values in this case and we have the actual values, not a broad class interval.

The mean as the expected value

We also refer to the mean as the expected value of x and write

$$E(x) = \mu = 146\ 984 \tag{1.7}$$

$E(x)$ is read 'E of x' or 'the expected value of x'. The mean is the expected value in the sense that, if we selected a household at random from the population we would 'expect', its wealth to be £146 984. It is important to note that this is a *statistical* expectation, rather than the everyday use of the term. Most of the random individuals we encounter have wealth substantially below this value. Most people might therefore 'expect' a lower value because that is their everyday experience; but statisticians are different, they always expect the mean value.

The expected value notation is particularly useful in keeping track of the effects upon the mean of certain data transformations (e.g. dividing wealth by 1000 also divides the mean by 1000); Appendix 1B provides a detailed explanation. Use is also made of the E operator in inferential statistics, to describe the properties of estimators (see Chapter 4).

The sample mean and the population mean

Very often we have only a sample of data (as in the worked example above), and it is important to distinguish this case from the one where we have all the possible observations. For this reason, the sample mean is given by

$$\bar{x} = \frac{\sum x}{n} \text{ or } \bar{x} = \frac{\sum fx}{\sum f} \text{ for grouped data} \tag{1.8}$$

Note the distinctions between μ (the population mean) and $\bar{x}$ (the sample mean), and between N (the size of the population) and n (the sample size). Otherwise, the calculations are identical. It is a convention to use Greek letters, such as μ, to refer to the population and Roman letters, such as $\bar{x}$, to refer to a sample.

The weighted average

Sometimes observations have to be given different weightings in calculating the average, as the following example. Consider the problem of calculating the average spending per pupil by an education authority. Some figures for spending on primary (ages 5 to 11), secondary (11 to 16) and post-16 pupils are given in Table 1.7.

Clearly, significantly more is spent on secondary and post-16 pupils (a general pattern throughout England and most other countries) and the overall average should lie somewhere between 1750 and 3820. However, taking a simple average of these values would give the wrong answer, because there are different numbers of children in the three age ranges. The numbers and proportions of children in each age group are given in Table 1.8.

Table 1.7 **Cost per pupil in different types of school (£ p.a.)**

	Primary	Secondary	Post-16
Unit cost	1750	3100	3820

Table 1.8 **Numbers and proportions of pupils in each age range**

	Primary	Secondary	Post-16	Total
Numbers	8000	7000	3000	18 000
Proportion	44%	39%	17%	

As there are relatively more primary school children than secondary, and relatively fewer post-16 pupils, the primary unit cost should be given greatest weight in the averaging process and the post-16 unit cost the least. The weighted average is obtained by multiplying each unit cost figure by the proportion of children in each category and summing. The weighted average is therefore

$$0.44 \times 1750 + 0.39 \times 3100 + 0.17 \times 3820 = 2628 \qquad (1.9)$$

The weighted average gives an answer closer to the primary unit cost than does the simple average of the three figures (2890 in this case), which would be misleading. The formula for the weighted average is

$$\bar{x}_w = \sum_i w_i x_i \qquad (1.10)$$

where w represents the weights, *which must sum to one*, i.e.

$$\sum_i w_i = 1 \qquad (1.11)$$

and x represents the unit cost figures.

Notice that what we have done is equivalent to multiplying each unit cost by its frequency (8000, etc.) and then dividing the sum by the grand total of 18 000. This is the same as the procedure we used for the wealth calculation. The difference with weights is that we first divide 8000 by 18 000 (and 7000 by 18 000, etc.) to obtain the weights, which must then sum to one, and use these weights in formula (1.10).

Calculating your degree result

If you are a university student your final degree result will probably be calculated as a weighted average of your marks on the individual courses. The weights may be based on the credits associated with each course or on some other factors. For example, in my university the average mark for a year is a weighted average of the marks on each course, the weights being the credit values of each course.

The grand mean G, on which classification is based, is then a weighted average of the averages for the different years, as follows

$$G = \frac{0 \times Year\ 1 + 40 \times Year\ 2 + 60 \times Year\ 3}{100}$$

i.e. the year 3 mark has a weight of 60%, year 2 is weighted 40% and the first year is not counted at all.

For students taking a year abroad the formula is slightly different

$$G = \frac{0 \times Year\ 1 + 40 \times Year\ 2 + 25 \times Yabroad + 60 \times Year\ 3}{125}$$

Note that, to accommodate the year abroad mark, the weights on years 2 and 3 are reduced (to 40/125 = 32% and 60/125 = 48% respectively).

The median

Returning to the study of wealth, the unrepresentative result for the mean suggests that we may prefer a measure of location which is not so strongly affected by outliers (extreme observations) and skewness.

The median is a measure of location which is more robust to such extreme values; it may be defined by the following procedure. Imagine everyone in a line from poorest to wealthiest. Go to the individual located halfway along the line. Ask what their wealth is. Their answer is the median. The median is clearly unaffected by extreme values, unlike the mean: if the wealth of the richest person were doubled (with no reduction in anyone else's wealth) there would be no effect upon the median. The calculation of the median is not so straightforward as for the mean, especially for grouped data. The following worked example shows how to calculate the median for ungrouped data.

Worked example 1.4 **The median**

Calculate the median of the following values: 45, 12, 33, 80, 77.

First we put them into ascending order: 12, 33, 45, 77, 80.

It is then easy to see that the middle value is 45. This is the median. Note that if the value of the largest observation changes to, say, 150, the value of the median is unchanged. This is not the case for the mean, which would change from 49.4 to 63.4.

If there is an even number of observations, then there is no middle observation. The solution is to take the average of the two middle observations. For example:

Find the median of 12, 33, 45, 63, 77, 80.

Note the new observation, 63, making six observations. The median value is halfway between the third and fourth observations, i.e. (45 + 63)/2 = 54.

For grouped data there are two stages to the calculation: first we must first identify the class interval which contains the median person, then we must calculate where in the interval that person lies.

(1) To find the appropriate class interval: since there are 17 636 000 observations, we need the wealth of the person who is 8 818 000 in rank order. The table of cumulative frequencies (see Table 1.5 above) is the most suitable for this. There are 8 106 000 individuals with wealth of less than £80 000 and 9 746 000 with wealth of less than £100 000. The middle person therefore falls into the £80 000–100 000 class. Furthermore, given that 8 818 000 falls roughly half way between 8 106 000 and 9 746 000 it follows that the median is close to the middle of the class interval. We now go on to make this statement more precise.

(2) To find the position in the class interval, we can now use formula (1.12)

$$median = x_L + (x_U - x_L)\left\{\frac{\frac{N+1}{2} - F}{f}\right\} \tag{1.12}$$

where

x_L = the lower limit of the class interval containing the median

x_U = the upper limit of this class interval

N = the number of observations (using $N + 1$ rather than N in the formula is only important when N is relatively small)

F = the cumulative frequency of the class intervals up to (but not including) the one containing the median

f = the frequency for the class interval containing the median.

For the wealth distribution we have

$$median = 80\,000 + (100\,000 - 80\,000)\left\{\frac{\dfrac{17\,636\,000}{2} - 8\,106\,000}{1\,640\,000}\right\} = £90\,829$$

This alternative measure of location gives a very different impression: it is less than two-thirds of the mean. Nevertheless, it is equally valid despite having a different meaning. It demonstrates that the person 'in the middle' has wealth of £90 829 and in this sense is typical of the UK population. Before going on to compare these measures further we examine a third: the mode.

Generalising the median – quantiles

The idea of the median as the middle of the distribution can be extended: quartiles divide the distribution into four equal parts, quintiles into five, deciles into 10, and finally percentiles divide the distribution into 100 equal parts. Generically they are known as quantiles. We shall illustrate the idea by examining deciles (quartiles are covered below).

The first decile occurs one-tenth of the way along the line of people ranked from poorest to wealthiest. This means we require the wealth of the person ranked 1 763 600 (= $N/10$) in the distribution. From the table of cumulative frequencies, this person lies in the first class interval. Adapting formula (1.12), we obtain

$$first\ decile = 0 + (10\,000 - 0) \times \left\{\frac{1\,763\,600 - 0}{2\,448\,000}\right\} = £7203$$

Thus we estimate that any household with less than £7203 of wealth falls into the bottom 10% of the wealth distribution. In a similar fashion, the ninth decile can be found by calculating the wealth of the household ranked 15 872 400 (= $N \times 9/10$) in the distribution.

 The mode

The mode is defined as that level of wealth which occurs with the greatest frequency, in other words the value that occurs most often. It is most useful and easiest to calculate when one has all the data and there are relatively few distinct observations. This is the case in the simple example below.

Suppose we have the following data on sales of dresses by a shop, according to size

Size	Sales
8	7
10	25
12	36
14	11
16	3
18	1

The modal size is 12. There are more women buying dresses of this size than any other. This may be the most useful form of average as far as the shop is concerned. Although it needs to stock a range of sizes, it knows it needs to order more dresses in size 12 than in any other size. The mean would not be so helpful in this case (it is $\bar{x} = 11.7$) as it is not an actual dress size.

In the case of grouped data matters are more complicated. It is the modal class interval which is required, once the intervals have been corrected for width (otherwise a wider class interval is unfairly compared with a narrower one). For this, we can again make use of the frequency densities. From Table 1.4 it can be seen that it is the first interval, from £0 to £10 000, which has the highest frequency density. It is 'typical' of the distribution because it is the one which occurs most often (using the frequency densities, *not* frequencies). The wealth distribution is most concentrated at this level and more people are like this in terms of wealth than anything else. Once again it is notable how different it is from both the median and the mean.

The three measures of location give different messages because of the skewness of the distribution: if it were symmetric they would all give approximately the same answer. Here we have a rather extreme case of skewness, but it does serve to illustrate how the different measures of location compare. When the distribution is skewed to the right, as here, they will be in the order mode, median, mean; if skewed to the left the ordering is reversed. If the distribution has more than one peak then this rule for orderings may not apply.

Which of the measures is 'correct' or most useful? In this particular case the mean is not very useful: it is heavily influenced by extreme values. The median is therefore often used when discussing wealth (and income) distributions. Where inequality is even more pronounced, as in some less developed countries, then the mean is even less informative. The mode is also quite useful in telling us about a large section of the population, although it can be sensitive to how the class intervals are arranged. If the data were arranged such that there was a class interval of £5000 to £15 000, then this might well be the modal class, conveying a slightly different impression.

The three different measures of location are marked on the histogram in Figure 1.12. This brings out the substantial difference between the measures for a skewed distribution such as for wealth.

Exercise 1.3

?

(a) For the data in Exercise 2, calculate the mean, median and mode of the data.

(b) Mark these values on the histogram you drew for Exercise 2.

Measures of dispersion

Two different distributions (e.g. wealth in two different countries) might have the same mean yet look very different, as shown in Figure 1.13 (the distributions have been drawn using smooth curves rather than bars to improve clarity). In one country everyone might have a similar level of wealth (curve B). In another, although the average is the same there might be extremes of great wealth and poverty (curve A). A measure of dispersion is a number which allows us to distinguish between these two situations.

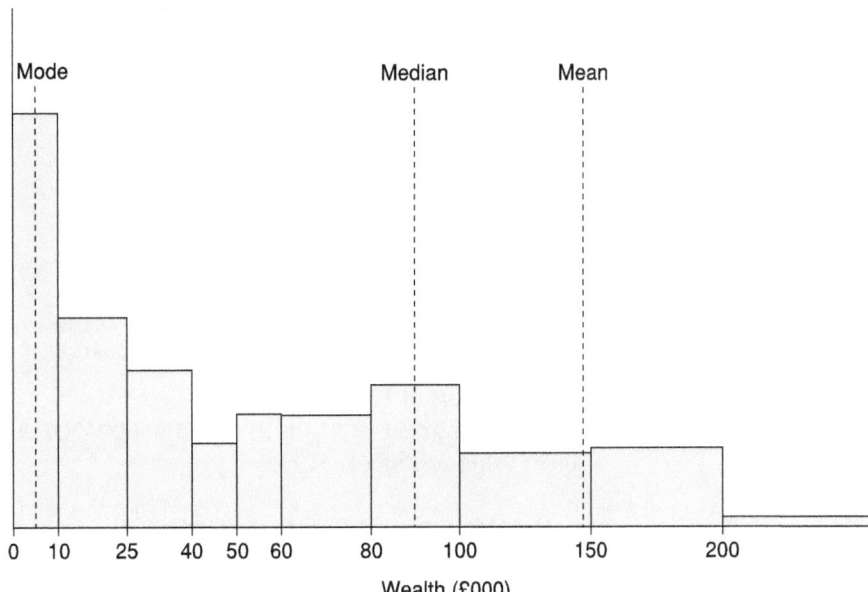

Figure 1.12
The histogram with
mean, median and mode
marked

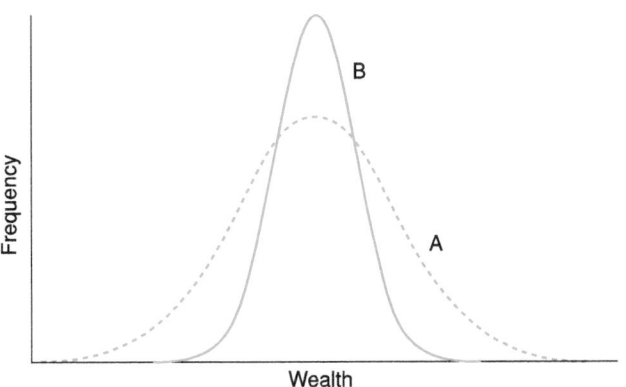

Figure 1.13
Two distributions with
different degrees of
dispersion

Note: Distribution A has a greater degree of dispersion than B, where everyone has a similar
level of wealth.

The simplest measure of dispersion is the range, which is the difference
between the smallest and largest observations. It is impossible to calculate
accurately from the table of wealth holdings since the largest observation is not
available. In any case, it is not a very useful figure since it relies on two extreme
values and ignores the rest of the distribution. In simpler cases it might be
more informative. For example, in an exam the marks may range from a low of
28% to a high of 74%. In this case the range is 74 – 28 = 46 and this tells us
something useful.

An improvement is the inter-quartile range (IQR), which is the difference
between the first and third quartiles. It therefore defines the limits of wealth
of the middle half of the distribution and ignores the very extremes of the

distribution. To calculate the first quartile (which we label Q_1) we have to go one-quarter of the way along the line of wealth holders (ranked from poorest to wealthiest) and ask the person in that position what their wealth is. Their answer is the first quartile. The calculation is as follows:

- one-quarter of 17 636 is 4409;
- the person ranked 4409 is in the £25 000–40 000 class;
- adapting formula (1.12)

$$Q_1 = 25\ 000 + (40\ 000 - 25\ 000) \left\{ \frac{4409 - 4271}{1375} \right\} = 26\ 505.5 \qquad (1.13)$$

The third quartile is calculated in similar fashion:

- three-quarters of 17 636 is 13 227;
- the person ranked 13 227 is in the £150 000–200 000 class;
- again using formula (1.12)

$$Q_3 = 150\ 000 + (200\ 000 - 150\ 000) \left\{ \frac{13\ 227 - 11\ 897}{2215} \right\} = 180\ 022.6$$

and therefore the inter-quartile range is $Q_3 - Q_1 = 180\ 022 - 26\ 505 = 153\ 517$. This might be reasonably rounded to £150 000 given the approximations in our calculation, and is a much more memorable figure.

This gives one summary measure of the dispersion of the distribution: the higher the value the more spread-out is the distribution. Two different wealth distributions might be compared according to their inter-quartile ranges therefore, with the country having the larger figure exhibiting greater inequality. Note that the figures would have to be expressed in a common unit of currency for this comparison to be valid.

Worked example 1.5 **The range and inter-quartile range**

Suppose 110 children take a test, with the following results:

Mark, X	Frequency, f	Cumulative frequency, F
13	5	5
14	13	18
15	29	47
16	33	80
17	17	97
18	8	105
19	4	109
20	1	110
Total	110	

The range is simply $20 - 13 = 7$. The inter-quartile range requires calculation of the quartiles. Q_1 is given by the value of the 27.5th observation ($= 110/4$), which is 15. Q_3 is the value of the 82.5th observation ($= 110 \times 0.75$) which is 17. The IQR is therefore $17 - 15 = 2$ marks. Half the students achieve marks within this range.

Notice that a slight change in the data (three more students getting 16 rather than 17 marks) would alter the IQR to 1 mark (16–15). The result should be treated with some caution therefore. This is a common problem when there are few distinct values of the variable (eight in this example). It is often worth considering whether a few small changes to the data could alter the calculation considerably. In such a case, the original result might not be very robust.

The variance

A more useful measure of dispersion is the variance, which makes use of all of the information available, rather than trimming the extremes of the distribution. The variance is denoted by the symbol σ^2. σ is the Greek lower-case letter sigma, so σ^2 is read 'sigma squared'. It has a completely different meaning from Σ (capital sigma) used before. Its formula is

$$\sigma^2 = \frac{\Sigma(x - \mu)^2}{N} \qquad (1.14)$$

In this formula, $x - \mu$ measures the distance from each observation to the mean. Squaring these makes all the deviations positive, whether above or below the mean. We then take the average of all the squared deviations from the mean. A more dispersed distribution (such as A in Figure 1.13) will tend to have larger deviations from the mean, and hence a larger variance. In comparing two distributions with similar means, therefore, we could examine their variances to see which of the two has the greater degree of dispersion. With grouped data the formula becomes

$$\sigma^2 = \frac{\Sigma f(x - \mu)^2}{\Sigma f} \qquad (1.15)$$

The calculation of the variance is shown in Table 1.9 and from this we obtain

$$\sigma^2 = \frac{1\ 001\ 772\ 261.83}{17\ 636} = 56\ 802.69$$

This calculated value is before translating back into the original units of measurement, as was done for the mean by multiplying by 1000. In the case of the variance, however, we must multiply by 1 000 000 which is the *square* of 1000. The variance is therefore 56 802 690 000. Multiplying by the square of 1000 is a consequence of using squared deviations in the variance formula (see Appendix 1B on E and V operators for more details of this).

One needs to be a little careful about the units of measurement therefore. If the mean is reported at 146.984 then it is appropriate to report the variance as 56 802.69. If the mean is reported as 146 984 then the variance should be reported as 56 802 690 000. Note that it is only the presentation that changes: the underlying facts are the same.

The standard deviation

In what units is the variance measured? As we have used a squaring procedure in the calculation, we end up with something like 'squared' £s, which is not very

Table 1.9 The calculation of the variance of wealth

Range	Mid-point x (£000)	Frequency, f	Deviation $(x - \mu)$	$(x - \mu)^2$	$f(x - \mu)^2$
0	5.0	2448	−142.0	20 159.38	49 350 158.77
10 000−	17.5	1823	−129.5	16 766.04	30 564 482.57
25 000−	32.5	1375	−114.5	13 106.52	18 021 469.99
40 000−	45.0	480	−102.0	10 400.68	4 992 326.62
50 000−	55.0	665	−92.0	8461.01	5 626 568.95
60 000−	70.0	1315	−77.0	5926.49	7 793 339.80
80 000−	90.0	1640	−57.0	3247.15	5 325 317.93
100 000−	125.0	2151	−22.0	483.28	1 039 544.38
150 000−	175.0	2215	28.0	784.91	1 738 579.16
200 000−	250.0	1856	103.0	10 612.35	19 696 526.45
300 000−	400.0	1057	253.0	64 017.23	67 666 217.05
500 000−	750.0	439	603.0	363 628.63	159 632 966.88
1 000 000−	1500.0	122	1353.0	1 830 653.04	223 339 670.45
2 000 000−	3000.0	50	2853.0	8 139 701.86	406 985 092.85
Total		17 636			1 001 772 261.83

convenient. Because of this, we define the square root of the variance to be the standard deviation, which is therefore back in £s. The standard deviation is therefore given by

$$\sigma = \sqrt{\frac{\Sigma(x - \mu)^2}{N}} \qquad (1.16)$$

or, for grouped data

$$\sigma = \sqrt{\frac{\Sigma f(x - \mu)^2}{N}} \qquad (1.17)$$

These are simply the square roots of equations (1.14) and (1.15). The standard deviation of wealth is therefore $\sqrt{56\,802.69} = 238.333$. This is in £000, so the standard deviation is actually £238 333 (note that this is the square root of 56 802 690 000, as it should be). On its own the standard deviation (and the variance) is not easy to interpret since it is not something we have an intuitive feel for, unlike the mean. It is more useful when used in a comparative setting. This will be illustrated later on.

The variance and standard deviation of a sample

As with the mean, a different symbol is used to distinguish a variance calculated from the population and one calculated from a sample. In addition, the sample variance is calculated using a slightly different formula from the one for the population variance. The sample variance is denoted by s^2 and its formula is given by equations (1.18) and (1.19) below

$$s^2 = \frac{\Sigma(x - \bar{x})^2}{n - 1} \qquad (1.18)$$

and, for grouped data

$$s^2 = \frac{\sum f(x - \bar{x})^2}{n - 1}$$

(1.19)

where n is the sample size. The reason $n - 1$ is used in the denominator rather than n (as one might expect) is the following. Our real interest is in the population variance, and the sample variance is an estimate of it. The former is measured by the dispersion around μ, and the sample variance should ideally be measured around μ also. However, μ is unknown, so $\bar{x}$ is used instead. But the variation of the sample observations around $\bar{x}$ tends to be smaller than that around μ. Using $n - 1$ rather than n in the formula compensates for this and the result is an unbiased[5] (i.e. correct on average) estimate of the population variance.

Using the correct formula is more important the smaller is the sample size, as the proportionate difference between $n - 1$ and n increases. For example, if $n = 10$, the adjustment amounts to 10% of the variance; when $n = 100$ the adjustment is only 1%.

The sample standard deviation is given by the square root of equation (1.18) or (1.19).

Worked example 1.6 The variance and standard deviation

We continue with the previous worked example, relating to students' marks. The variance and standard deviation can be calculated as:

X	f	fx	x − μ	(x − μ)²	f(x − μ)²
13	5	65	−2.81	7.89	39.45
14	13	182	−1.81	3.27	42.55
15	29	435	−0.81	0.65	18.98
16	33	528	0.19	0.04	1.20
17	17	289	1.19	1.42	24.11
18	8	144	2.19	4.80	38.40
19	4	76	3.19	10.18	40.73
20	1	20	4.19	17.56	17.56
Totals	110	1739			222.99

The mean is calculated as $1739/110 = 15.81$ and from this the deviations column $(x - \mu)$ is calculated (so $-2.81 = 13 - 15.81$, etc.).

The variance is calculated as $\sum f(x - \mu)^2/(n - 1) = 222.99/109 = 2.05$. The standard deviation is therefore 1.43, the square root of 2.05. (Calculations are shown to two decimal places but have been calculated using exact values.)

For distributions which are approximately symmetric and bell-shaped (i.e. the observations are clustered around the mean) there is an approximate relationship between the standard deviation and the inter-quartile range. This rule of thumb is that the IQR is 1.3 times the standard deviation. In this case, $1.3 \times 1.43 = 1.86$, close to the value calculated earlier, 2.

---

[5] The concept of *bias* is treated in more detail in Chapter 4.

Alternative formulae for calculating the variance and standard deviation

The following formulae give the same answers as equations (1.14) to (1.17) but are simpler to calculate, either by hand or using a spreadsheet. For the population variance one can use

$$\sigma^2 = \frac{\sum x^2}{N} - \mu^2 \tag{1.20}$$

or, for grouped data

$$\sigma^2 = \frac{\sum fx^2}{\sum f} - \mu^2 \tag{1.21}$$

The calculation of the variance using equation (1.21) is shown in Figure 1.14.

Figure 1.14
Descriptive statistics
calculated using *Excel*

	A	B	C	D	E	F	G	H	I
1			WEALTH DATA 2003						
2									
3	Wealth	Mid-point	Frequency						
4	Range	x	f	fx	fx squared		Summary statistics		
5	0	5.0	2 448	12 240.0	61 200.00				
6	10 000	17.5	1 823	31 902.5	558 293.75		Mean	146.984	
7	25 000	32.5	1 375	44 687.5	1 452 343.75		Variance	56 802.691	
8	40 000	45.0	480	21 600.0	972 000.00		Std devn	238.333	
9	50 000	55.0	665	36 575.0	2 011 625.00		Coef varn	1.621	
10	60 000	70.0	1 315	92 050.0	6 443 500.00				
11	80 000	90.0	1 640	147 600.0	13 284 000.00				
12	100 000	125.0	2 151	268 875.0	33 609 375.00				
13	150 000	175.0	2 215	387 625.0	67 834 375.00				
14	200 000	250.0	1 856	464 000.0	116 000 000.00				
15	300 000	400.0	1 057	422 800.0	169 120 000.00				
16	500 000	750.0	439	329 250.0	246 937 500.00				
17	1 000 000	1 500.0	122	183 000.0	274 500 000.00				
18	2 000 000	3 000.0	50	150 000.0	450 000 000.00				
19									
20	Totals		17 636	2 592 205.0	1 382 784 212.50				
21									
22									
23									

The sample variance can be calculated using

$$s^2 = \frac{\sum x^2 - n\bar{x}^2}{n - 1} \tag{1.22}$$

or, for grouped data

$$s^2 = \frac{\sum fx^2 - n\bar{x}^2}{n - 1} \tag{1.23}$$

The standard deviation may of course be obtained as the square root of these formulae.

Using a calculator or computer for calculation

Electronic calculators and (particularly) computers have simplified the calculation of the mean, etc. Figure 1.14 shows how to set out the above calculations in a spreadsheet (*Microsoft Excel* in this case) including some of the appropriate cell formulae.

The variance in this case is calculated using the formula $\sigma^2 = \dfrac{\sum fx^2}{\sum f} - \mu^2$, which is the formula given in equation (1.21) above. Note that it gives the same result as that calculated in the text.

The following formulae are contained in the cells:

D5:	= C5*B5	to calculate f times x
E5:	= D5*B5	to calculate f times x^2
C20:	= SUM(C5:C18)	to sum the frequencies
H6:	= D20/C20	calculates $\sum fx/\sum f$
H7:	= E20/C20 − H6^2	calculates $\sum fx^2/\sum f - \mu^2$
H8:	= SQRT(H7)	calculates σ
H9:	= H8/H6	calculates σ/μ

The coefficient of variation

The measures of dispersion examined so far are all measures of absolute dispersion and, in particular, their values depend upon the units in which the variable is measured. It is therefore difficult to compare the degrees of dispersion of two variables which are measured in different units. For example, one could not compare wealth in the UK with that in Germany if the former uses £s and the latter euros for measurement. Nor could one compare the wealth distribution in one country between two points in time because inflation alters the value of the currency over time. The solution is to use a measure of relative dispersion, which is independent of the units of measurement. One such measure is the coefficient of variation, defined as

$$\text{Coefficient of variation} = \frac{\sigma}{\mu} \qquad (1.24)$$

i.e. the standard deviation divided by the mean. Whenever the units of measurement are changed, the effect upon the mean and the standard deviation is the same, hence the coefficient of variation is unchanged. For the wealth distribution its value is 238.333/146.984 = 1.621, i.e. the standard deviation is 162% of the mean. This may be compared directly with the coefficient of variation of a different wealth distribution to see which exhibits a greater relative degree of dispersion.

Independence of units of measurement

It is worth devoting a little attention to this idea that some summary measures are independent of the units of measurement and some are not, as it occurs quite often in statistics and is not often appreciated at first. A statistic that is independent of the units of measurement is one which is unchanged even when the units of measurement are changed. It is therefore more useful in general than a statistic which is not independent, since one can use it to make comparisons, or judgements, without worrying about how it was measured.

The mean is not independent of the units of measurement. If we are told the average income in the UK is 20 000, for example, we need to know whether it is measured in pounds sterling, euros or even dollars. The underlying level of income is the same, of course, but it is measured differently. By contrast, the rate of growth (described in detail shortly) is independent of the units of measurement. If we are told it is 3% per annum, it would be the same whether it were calculated in pounds, euros or dollars. If told that the rate of growth in the US is 2% per annum, we can immediately conclude that the UK is growing faster, no further information is needed.

Most measures we have encountered so far, such as the mean and variance, do depend on units of measurement. The coefficient of variation is one that does not. We now go on to describe another means of measuring dispersion that avoids the units of measurement problem.

The standard deviation of the logarithm

Another solution to the problem of different units of measurement is to use the logarithm[6] of wealth rather than the actual value. The reason why this works can best be illustrated by an example. Suppose that between 1997 and 2003 each individual's wealth doubled, so that $X_i^{2003} = 2X_i^{1997}$, where X_i^t indicates the wealth of individual i in year t. It follows that the standard deviation of wealth in 2003, X^{2003}, is therefore exactly twice that of 1997, X^{1997}. Taking logs, we have $\ln X_i^{2003} = \ln 2 + \ln X_i^{1997}$, so it follows that the distribution of $\ln X^{2003}$ is the same as that of $\ln X^{1997}$, except that it is shifted to the right by $\ln 2$ units. The variances (and hence standard deviations) of the two logarithmic distributions must therefore be the same, indicating no change in the *relative* dispersion of the two wealth distributions.

The standard deviation of the logarithm of wealth is calculated from the data in Table 1.10. The variance turns out to be

Table 1.10 The calculation of the standard deviation of the logarithm of wealth

Range	Mid-point x (£000)	ln (x)	Frequency, f	fx	fx²
0–	5.0	1.609	2448	3939.9	6341.0
10 000–	17.5	2.862	1823	5217.8	14 934.4
25 000–	32.5	3.481	1375	4786.7	16 663.7
40 000–	45.0	3.807	480	1827.2	6955.5
50 000–	55.0	4.007	665	2664.9	10 679.0
60 000–	70.0	4.248	1315	5586.8	23 735.4
80 000–	90.0	4.500	1640	7379.7	33 207.2
100 000–	125.0	4.828	2151	10 385.7	50 145.4
150 000–	175.0	5.165	2215	11 440.0	59 085.2
200 000–	250.0	5.521	1856	10 247.8	56 583.0
300 000–	400.0	5.991	1057	6333.0	37 943.8
500 000–	750.0	6.620	439	2906.2	19 239.3
1 000 000–	1500.0	7.313	122	892.2	6524.9
2 000 000–	3000.0	8.006	50	400.3	3205.1
Totals			17 636	74 008.2	345 243.0

Note: Use the 'ln' key on your calculator or the = LN() function in a spreadsheet to obtain natural logarithms of the data. You should obtain ln 5 = 1.609, ln 17.5 = 2.862, etc.

---

[6] See Appendix 1C if you are unfamiliar with logarithms. Note that we use the natural logarithm here, but the effect would be the same using logs to base 10.

$$\sigma^2 = \frac{345\ 243.0}{17\ 636} = \left(\frac{74\ 008.2}{17\ 636}\right)^2 = 1.966$$

and the standard deviation $\sigma = 1.402$.

For comparison, the standard deviation of log income in 1979 (discussed in more detail later on) is 1.31, so there appears to have been a slight increase in relative dispersion over this time period.

Measuring deviations from the mean: z-scores

Imagine the following problem. A man and a woman are arguing over their career records. The man says he earns more than she does, so is more successful. The woman replies that women are discriminated against and that, relative to women, she is doing better than the man is, relative to other men. Can the argument be resolved?

Suppose the data are as follows: the average male salary is £19 500, the average female salary £16 800. The standard deviation of male salaries is £4750, for women it is £3800. The man's salary is £31 375 while the woman's is £26 800. The man is therefore £11 875 above the mean, the woman £10 000. However, women's salaries are less dispersed than men's, so the woman has done well to reach £26 800.

One way to resolve the problem is to calculate the z-score, which gives the salary in terms of the *number of standard deviations from the mean*. Thus for the man, the z-score is

$$z = \frac{X - \mu}{\sigma} = \frac{31\ 375 - 19\ 500}{4750} = 2.50 \tag{1.25}$$

Thus the man is 2.5 standard deviations above the male mean salary. For the woman the calculation is

$$z = \frac{26\ 800 - 16\ 800}{3800} = 2.632 \tag{1.26}$$

The woman is 2.632 standard deviations above her mean and therefore wins the argument – she is nearer the top of her distribution than is the man and so is more of an outlier. Actually, this probably will not end the argument, but is the best the statistician can do! The z-score is an important concept which will be used again later in the book when we cover hypothesis testing (Chapter 5).

Chebyshev's inequality

Use of the z-score leads on naturally to Chebyshev's inequality, which tells us about the proportion of observations that fall into the tails of any distribution, regardless of its shape. The theorem is expressed as follows

At least $(1 - 1/k^2)$ of the observations in any distribution
lie within k standard deviations of the mean $\tag{1.27}$

If we take the female wage distribution given above, we can ask what proportion of women lie beyond 2.632 standard deviations from the mean (in both tails of the distribution). Setting $k = 2.632$, then $(1 - 1/k^2) = (1 - 1/2.632^2) = 0.8556$.

So at least 85% of women have salaries within ±2.632 standard deviations of the mean, i.e. between £6 800 (= 16 800 − 2.632 × 3800) and £26 800 (= 16 800 + 2.632 × 3800). 15% of women therefore lie outside this range.

Chebyshev's inequality is a very conservative rule since it applies to *any* distribution; if we know more about the shape of a particular distribution (for example, men's heights follow a Normal distribution − see Chapter 3) then we can make a more precise statement. In the case of the Normal distribution, over 99% of men are within 2.632 standard deviations of the average height, because there is a concentration of observations near the centre of the distribution.

We can also use Chebyshev's inequality to investigate the inter-quartile range. The formula (1.27) implies that 50% of observations lie within $\sqrt{2}$ = 1.41 standard deviations of the mean, a more conservative value than our previous 1.3.

Exercise 1.4

(a) For the data in Exercise 2, calculate the inter-quartile range, the variance and the standard deviation.

(b) Calculate the coefficient of variation.

(c) Check if the relationship between the IQR and the standard deviation stated in the text is approximately true for this distribution.

(d) Approximately how much of the distribution lies within one standard deviation either side of the mean? How does this compare with the prediction from Chebyshev's inequality?

Measuring skewness

The skewness of a distribution is the third characteristic that was mentioned earlier, in addition to location and dispersion. The wealth distribution is heavily skewed to the right, or positively skewed; it has its long tail in the right-hand end of the distribution. A measure of skewness gives a numerical indication of how asymmetric is the distribution.

One measure of skewness, known as the coefficient of skewness, is

$$\frac{\sum f(x - \mu)^3}{N\sigma^3} \tag{1.28}$$

and it is based upon *cubed* deviations from the mean. The result of applying formula (1.28) is positive for a right-skewed distribution (such as wealth), zero for a symmetric one, and negative for a left-skewed one. Table 1.11 shows the calculation for the wealth data (some rows are omitted for brevity). From this we obtain

$$\frac{\sum f(x - \mu)^3}{N} = \frac{1\ 563\ 796\ 357\ 499}{17\ 636} = 88\ 670\ 693.89$$

and dividing by σ^3 gives $\dfrac{88\ 670\ 693.89}{13\ 537\ 964} = 6.550$, which is positive, as expected.

The measure of skewness is much less useful in practical work than measures of location and dispersion, and even knowing the value of the coefficient does not always give much idea of the shape of the distribution: two quite different distributions can share the same coefficient. In descriptive work it is probably better to draw the histogram itself.

Table 1.11 Calculation of the skewness of the wealth data

Range	Mid-point x (£000)	Frequency f	Deviation x − μ	$(x − μ)^3$	$f(x − μ)^3$
0	5.0	2448	−142.0	−2 862 304	−7 006 919 444
10 000	17.5	1823	−129.5	−2 170 929	−3 957 603 101
⋮		⋮		⋮	⋮
1 000 000	1500.0	122	1353.0	2 476 903 349	302 182 208 638
2 000 000	3000.0	50	2853.0	23 222 701 860	1 161 135 092 991
Totals		17 636	4457.2	25 927 167 232	1 563 796 357 499

Comparison of the 2003 and 1979 distributions of wealth

Some useful lessons may be learned by comparing the 2003 distribution with its counterpart from 1979. This covers the period of Conservative government starting with Mrs Thatcher in 1979 up until the first six years of Labour administration. This shows how useful the various summary statistics are when it comes to comparing two different distributions. The wealth data for 1979 are given in Problem 1.5 below, where you are asked to confirm the following calculations.

Average wealth in 1979 was £16 399, about one-ninth of its 2003 value. The average increased substantially therefore (at about 10% per annum, on average), but some of this was due to inflation rather than a real increase in the quantity of assets held. In fact, between 1979 and 2003 the retail price index rose from 52.0 to 181.3, i.e. it increased approximately three and a half times. Thus the nominal[7] increase (i.e. in cash terms, before any adjustment for rising prices) in wealth is made up of two parts: (i) an inflationary part which more than tripled measured wealth and (ii) a real part, consisting of a 2.5 fold increase (thus $3.5 \times 2.5 = 9$, approximately). Price indexes are covered in Chapter 10 where it is shown more formally how to divide a nominal increase into price and real (quantity) components. It is likely that the extent of the real increase in wealth is overstated here due to the use of the retail price index rather than an index of asset prices. A substantial part of the increase in asset values over the period is probably due to the very rapid rise in house prices (houses form a significant part of the wealth of many households).

The standard deviation is similarly affected by inflation. The 1979 value is 25 552 compared to 2003's 238 333, which is about nine times larger. The spread of the distribution appears to have increased therefore (even if we take account of the general price effect). Looking at the coefficient of variation, however, shows that it has increased from 1.56 to 1.62 which is a modest difference. The spread of the distribution *relative to its mean* has not changed by much. This is confirmed by calculating the standard deviation of the logarithm: for 1979 this gives a figure of 1.31, slightly smaller than the 2003 figure (of 1.40).

---

[7] This is a different meaning of the term 'nominal' from that used earlier to denote data measured on a nominal scale, i.e. data grouped into categories without an obvious ordering. Unfortunately, both meanings of the word are in common (statistical) usage, although it should be obvious from the context which use is meant.

The measure of skewness for the 1979 data comes out as 5.723, smaller that the 2003 figure (of 6.550). This suggests that the 1979 distribution is less skewed than is the 1994 one. Again, these two figures can be directly compared because they do not depend upon the units in which wealth is measured. However, the relatively small difference is difficult to interpret in terms of how the shape of the distribution has changed.

The box and whiskers diagram

Having calculated these various summary statistics we can now return to a useful graphical method of presentation. This is the box and whiskers diagram (sometimes called a box plot) which shows the median, quartiles and other aspects of a distribution on a single diagram. Figure 1.15 shows the box plot for the wealth data.

Wealth is measured on the vertical axis. The rectangular box stretches (vertically) from the first to third quartile and therefore encompasses the middle half of the distribution. The horizontal line through it is at the median and lies less than halfway up the box. This tells us that there is a degree of skewness even within the central half of the distribution, although it does not appear very severe. The two 'whiskers' extend above and below the box as far as the highest and lowest observations, *excluding outliers*. An outlier is defined to be any observation which is more than 1.5 times the inter-quartile range (which is the same as the height of the box) above or below the box. Earlier we found the IQR to be 153 517 and the upper quartile to be 180 022, so an (upper) outlier lies beyond

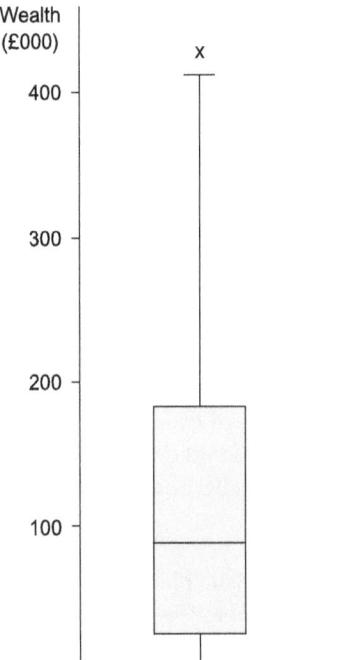

Figure 1.15
Box plot of the wealth distribution

180 022 + 1.5 × 153 517 = 410 298. There are no outliers below the box as wealth cannot fall below zero. The top whisker is thus substantially longer than the bottom one, and indicates the extent of dispersion towards the tails of the distribution. The crosses indicate the outliers and in reality extend far beyond those shown in the diagram.

A simple diagram thus reveals a lot of information about the distribution. Other boxes and whiskers could be placed alongside in the same diagram (perhaps representing other countries) making comparisons straightforward. Some statistical software packages, such as *SPSS* and *STATA*, can generate box plots from the original data, without the need for the user to calculate the median, etc. However, spreadsheet packages do not yet have this useful facility.

Time-series data: investment expenditures 1973–2005

The data on the wealth distribution give a snapshot of the situation at particular points in time, and comparisons can be made between the 1979 and 2003 snapshots. Often, however, we wish to focus on the time-path of a variable and therefore we use time-series data. The techniques of presentation and summarising are slightly different than for cross-section data. As an example, we use data on investment in the UK for the period 1973–2005. These data were taken from Statbase (http://www.statistics.gov.uk/statbase/) although you can find the data in *Economic Trends Annual Supplement*. Investment expenditure is important to the economy because it is one of the primary determinants of growth. Until recent years, the UK economy's growth record had been poor by international standards and lack of investment may have been a cause. The variable studied here is total gross (i.e. before depreciation is deducted) domestic fixed capital formation, measured in £m. The data are shown in Table 1.12.

It should be remembered that the data are in current prices so that the figures reflect price increases as well as changes in the volume of physical investment. The series in Table 1.12 thus shows the actual amount of cash that was

Table 1.12 UK investment, 1973–2005

Year	Investment	Year	Investment	Year	Investment
1973	15 227	1984	58 589	1995	118 031
1974	18 134	1985	64 400	1996	126 593
1975	21 856	1986	68 546	1997	133 620
1976	25 516	1987	78 996	1998	151 083
1977	28 201	1988	96 243	1999	156 344
1978	32 208	1989	111 324	2000	161 468
1979	38 211	1990	114 300	2001	165 472
1980	43 238	1991	105 179	2002	173 525
1981	43 331	1992	101 111	2003	178 751
1982	47 394	1993	101 153	2004	194 491
1983	51 490	1994	108 534	2005	205 843

Note: Time-series data consist of observations on one or more variables over several time periods. The observations can be daily, weekly, monthly, quarterly or, as here, annually.

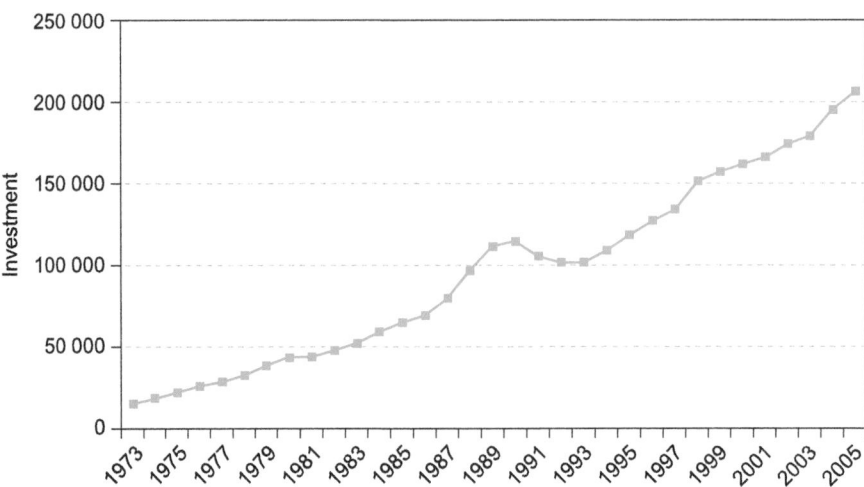

Figure 1.16
Time-series graph of
investment in the UK,
1973–2005

Note: The *X, Y* coordinates are the values {year, investment}; the first data point has the
coordinates {1973, 15 227}, for example.

spent each year on investment. The techniques used below for summarising the investment data could equally well be applied to a series showing the volume of investment.

First of all we can use graphical techniques to gain an insight into the characteristics of investment. Figure 1.16 shows a time-series graph of investment. The graph plots the time periods on the horizontal axis and the investment variable on the vertical.

Plotting the data in this way brings out clearly some key features of the series:

● The trend in investment is upwards, with only a few years in which there was either no increase or a decrease.

● There is a 'hump' in the data in the late 1980s/early 1990s, before the series returns to its trend. Something unusual must have happened around that time. If we want to know what factors determine investment (or the effect of investment upon other economic magnitudes) we should get some useful insights from this period of the data.

● The trend is slightly non-linear – it follows an increasingly steep curve over time. This is essentially because investment grows by a *percentage* or *proportionate* amount each year. As we shall see shortly, it grows by about 8.5% each year. Therefore, as the level of investment increases each year, so does the increase in the level, giving a non-linear graph.

● Successive values of the investment variable are similar in magnitude, i.e. the value in year t is similar to that in $t - 1$. Investment does not change from £40bn in one year to £10bn the next, then back to £50bn, for instance. In fact, the value in one year appears to be based on the value in the previous year, plus (in general) 8.5% or so. We refer to this phenomenon as serial correlation and it is one of the aspects of the data that we might wish to investigate. The *ordering* of the data matters, unlike the case with cross-section data where the ordering is usually irrelevant. In deciding how to model investment behaviour, we might focus on *changes* in investment from year to year.

Table 1.13 **The change in investment**

Year	Δ Investment	Year	Δ Investment	Year	Δ Investment
1973	2880	1984	7099	1995	9497
1974	2907	1985	5811	1996	8562
1975	3722	1986	4146	1997	7027
1976	3660	1987	10 450	1998	17 463
1977	2685	1988	17 247	1999	5261
1978	4007	1989	15 081	2000	5124
1979	6003	1990	2976	2001	4004
1980	5027	1991	−9121	2002	8053
1981	93	1992	−4068	2003	5226
1982	4063	1993	42	2004	15 740
1983	4096	1994	7381	2005	11 352

Note: The change in investment is obtained by taking the difference between successive observations. For example, 2907 is the difference between 18 134 and 15 227.

- The series seems 'smoother' in the earlier years (up to perhaps 1986) and exhibits greater volatility later on. In other words, there are greater fluctuations *around* the trend in the later years. We could express this more formally by saying that the variance of investment around its trend appears to change (increase) over time. This is known as heteroscedasticity; a constant variance is termed homoscedasticity.

We may gain further insight into how investment evolves over time by focusing on the *change* in investment from year to year. If we denote investment in year t by I_t then the change in investment, ΔI_t, is given by $I_t - I_{t-1}$. Table 1.13 shows the changes in investment each year and Figure 1.17 provides a time-series graph.

The series is made up of mainly positive values, indicating that investment increases over time. It also shows that the increase grows each year, with perhaps some greater volatility (of the increase) towards the end of the period. The graph also shows dramatically the change that occurred around 1990.

Figure 1.17
Time-series graph of the change in investment

Outliers

Graphing data also allows you to see outliers (unusual observations). Outliers might be due to an error in inputting the data (e.g. typing 97 instead of 970) or because something unusual happened (e.g. the investment figure for 1991). Either of these should be apparent from an appropriate graph. For example, the graph of the change in investment highlights the 1991 figure. In the case of a straight-forward error you should obviously correct it. If you are satisfied that the outlier is not simply a typo, you might want to think about the possible reasons for its existence and whether it distorts the descriptive picture you are trying to paint.

Another useful way of examining the data is to look at the logarithm of investment. This transformation has the effect of straightening out the non-linear investment series. Table 1.14 shows the transformed values and Figure 1.18 graphs the series. In this case we use the natural (base e) logarithm.

Table 1.14 The logarithm of investment and the change in the logarithm

Year	ln Investment	Δ ln Investment	Year	ln Investment	Δ ln Investment	Year	ln Investment	Δ ln Investment
1973	9.631	0.210	1984	10.978	0.129	1995	11.679	0.084
1974	9.806	0.175	1985	11.073	0.095	1996	11.749	0.070
1975	9.992	0.187	1986	11.135	0.062	1997	11.803	0.054
1976	10.147	0.155	1987	11.277	0.142	1998	11.926	0.123
1977	10.247	0.100	1988	11.475	0.197	1999	11.960	0.034
1978	10.380	0.133	1989	11.620	0.146	2000	11.992	0.032
1979	10.551	0.171	1990	11.647	0.026	2001	12.017	0.024
1980	10.674	0.124	1991	11.563	−0.083	2002	12.064	0.048
1981	10.677	0.002	1992	11.524	−0.039	2003	12.094	0.030
1982	10.766	0.090	1993	11.524	0.000	2004	12.178	0.084
1983	10.849	0.083	1994	11.595	0.070	2005	12.235	0.057

Note: For 1973, 9.631 is the natural logarithm of 15 227 , i.e. ln 15 227 = 9.631.

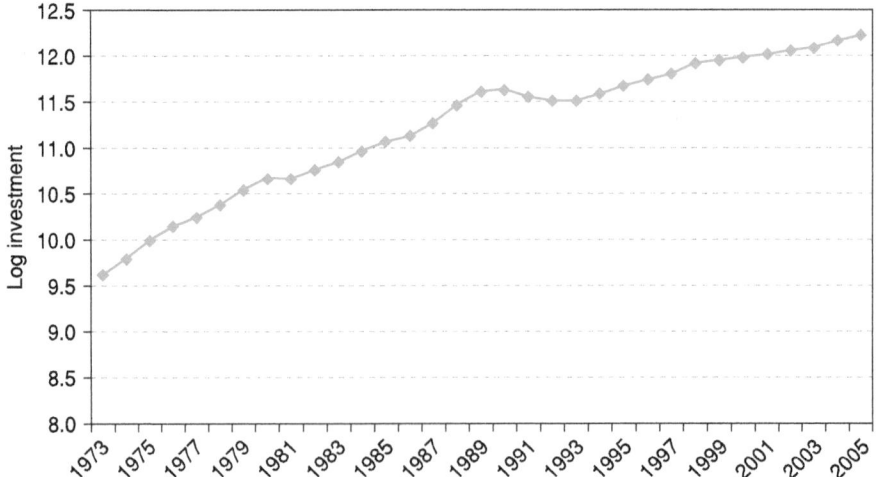

Figure 1.18
Time-series graph of the logarithm of investment expenditures

This new series is much smoother than the original one (as is usually the case when taking logs) and is helpful in showing the long-run trend, though it tends to mask some of the volatility of investment. The slope of the graph gives a close approximation to the average rate of growth of investment over the period (expressed as a decimal). This is calculated as follows

$$slope = \frac{change\ in\ (\ln)\ investment}{number\ of\ years} = \frac{12.235 - 9.631}{32} = 0.081 \qquad (1.29)$$

i.e. 8.1% per annum. Note that although there are 33 observations, there are only 32 years of growth. A word of warning: you must use natural (base e) logarithms, not logarithms to the base 10, for this calculation to work. Remember also that the growth of the *volume* of investment will be less than 8.1% per annum, because part of it is due to price increases.

The logarithmic presentation is useful when comparing two different data series: when graphed in logs it is easy to see which is growing faster – just see which series has the steeper slope.

A corollary of equation (1.29) is that change in the natural logarithm of investment from one year to the next represents the *percentage* change in the data over that year. For example, the natural logarithm of investment in 1973 is 9.631, while in 1974 it is 9.806. The difference is 0.175, so the rate of growth is 17.5%. Remember that this is an approximation and the result of a quick and easy calculation. It is reasonably accurate up to a figure of about 20%.

Finally we can graph the difference of the logarithm, as we graphed the difference of the level. This is shown in Figure 1.19 (the calculations are in Table 1.14).

This is quite revealing. It shows the series fluctuating about the value of approximately 0.08 (the average calculated in equation (1.29) above), with a slight downwards trend. Furthermore, the series does not seem to show increasing volatility over time, as the others did. The graph therefore demonstrates that in *proportionate* terms there is no increasing volatility; the variance of the series around 0.08 does not change much over time (although 1991 still seems to be an 'unusual' observation).

Figure 1.19
Time-series graph of the difference of the logarithmic series

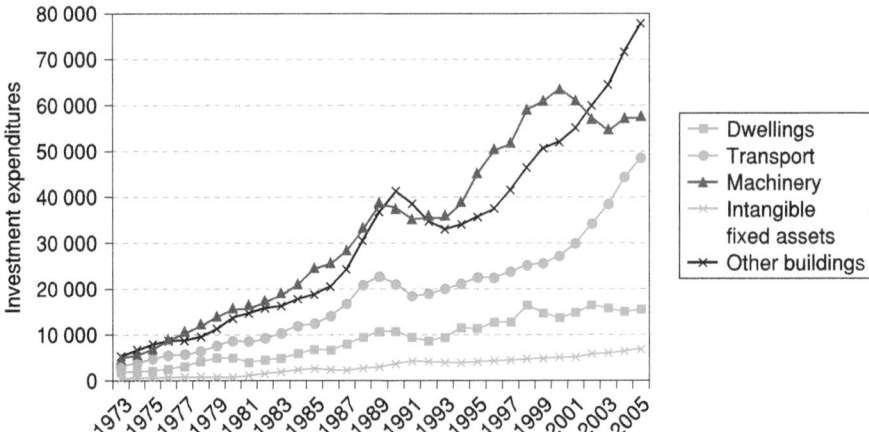

Figure 1.20
A multiple time-series
graph of investment

Graphing multiple series

Investment is made up of different categories: the table in Problem 1.14 presents investment data under four different headings: dwellings; transport; machinery; intangible fixed assets; and other buildings. Together they make up total investment. It is often useful to show all of the series together on one graph. Figure 1.20 shows a multiple time-series graph of the investment data.

Construction of this type of graph is straightforward; it is just an extension of the technique for presenting a single series. The chart shows that all investment categories have increased over time in a fairly similar way, including the hump then fall around 1990. It is noticeable, however, that investment in machinery fell significantly around 2000 while other categories, particularly dwellings, continued to increase. It is difficult from the graph to tell which categories have increased most rapidly over time: the 1973 values are relatively small and hard to distinguish. In fact, it is the 'intangible fixed assets' category (the smallest one) that has increased fastest in proportionate terms. This is easier to observe with a few numerical calculations (covered later in this chapter) rather than trying to read a cramped graph.

One could also produce a multiple series graph of the logarithms of the variables and also of the change, as was done for the total investment series. Since the log transformation tends to squeeze the values (on the *y*-axis) closer together (compare Figures 1.16 and 1.18) it might be easier to see the relative rates of growth of the series using this method. This is left as an exercise for the reader.

Another complication arises when the series are of different orders of magnitude and it is difficult to make all the series visible on the chart. In this case you can chart some of the series against a second vertical scale, on the right-hand axis. An example is shown in Figure 1.21, plotting the (total) investment data with the interest rate, which has much smaller numerical values. If the same axis were used for both series, the interest rate would appear as a horizontal line coinciding with the *x*-axis. This would reveal no useful information to the viewer.

It would usually be inappropriate to use this technique on data such as the investment categories graphed in Figure 1.20. Those are directly comparable to each other and to magnify one of the series by plotting it on a separate axis risks

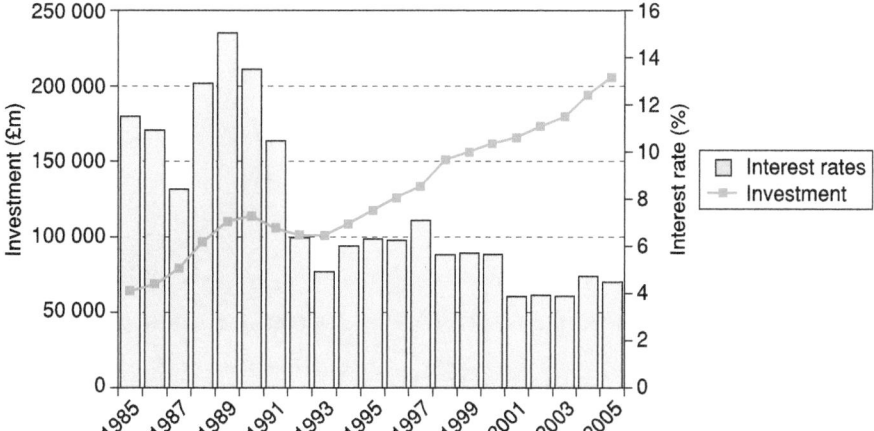

Figure 1.21
Time-series graph using
two vertical scales:
investment (LH scale)
and the interest rate
(RH scale), 1985–2005

Figure 1.21
Time-series graph using
two vertical scales:
investment (LH scale)
and the interest rate
(RH scale), 1985–2005

distorting the message for the reader. However, investment and interest rates are measured in inherently different ways and one cannot directly compare their sizes, hence it is acceptable to use separate axes. The graph allows one to observe the *movements* of the series together and hence perhaps infer something about the relationship between them. The rising investment and falling interest rate possibly suggest an inverse relationship between them.

Overlapping the ranges of the data series

The graph below, taken from the *Treasury Briefing*, February 1994, provides a nice example of how to plot multiple time-series and compare them. The aim is to compare the recessions and recoveries of 1974–78, 1979–83 and 1990–93. Instead of plotting time on the horizontal axis, the number of quarters since the start of each recession is used, so that the series overlap. This makes it easy to see the depth of the last recession and the long time before recovery commenced. By contrast, the 1974–78 recession ended quite quickly and recovery was quite rapid.

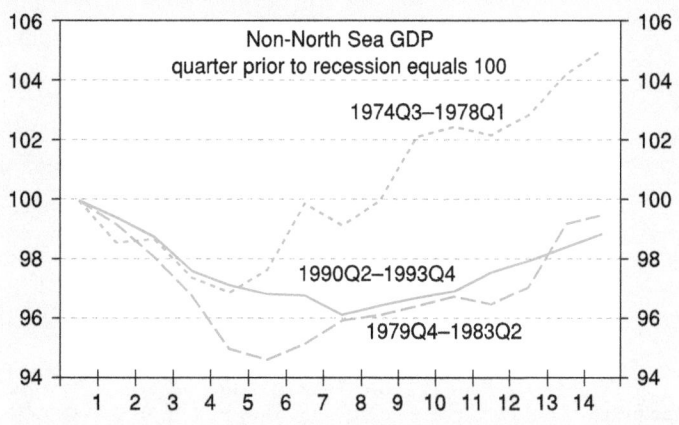

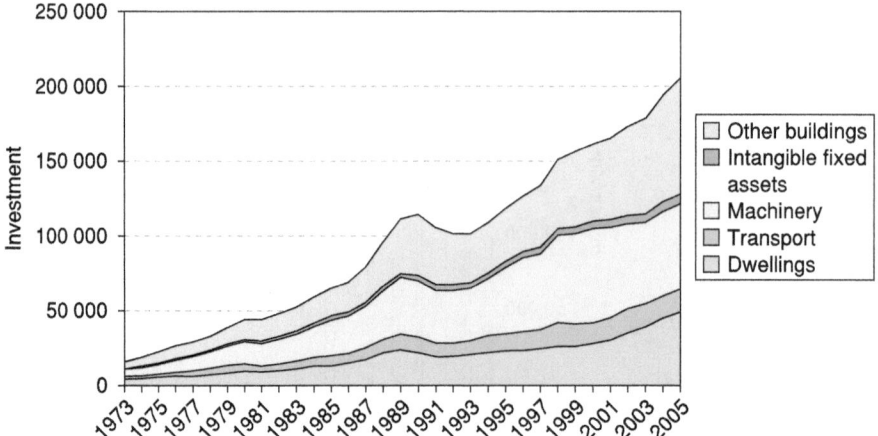

Figure 1.22
Area graph of
investment categories,
1973–2005

The investment categories may also be illustrated by means of an area graph, which plots the four series stacked one on top of the other, as illustrated in Figure 1.22.

This shows, for example, the 'dwellings' and 'machinery' categories each take up about one quarter of total investment. This is easier to see from the area graph than from the multiple series graph in Figure 1.20.

'Chart junk'

With modern computer software it is easy to get carried away and produce a chart that actually hides more than it reveals. There is a great temptation to add some 3D effects, liven it up with a bit of colour, rotate and tilt the viewpoint, etc. This sort of stuff is generally known as 'chart junk'. As an example, look at Figure 1.23 which is an alternative to the area graph in Figure 1.22 above. It was fun to create, but it does not get the message across at all! Taste is of course personal, but moderation is usually an essential part of it.

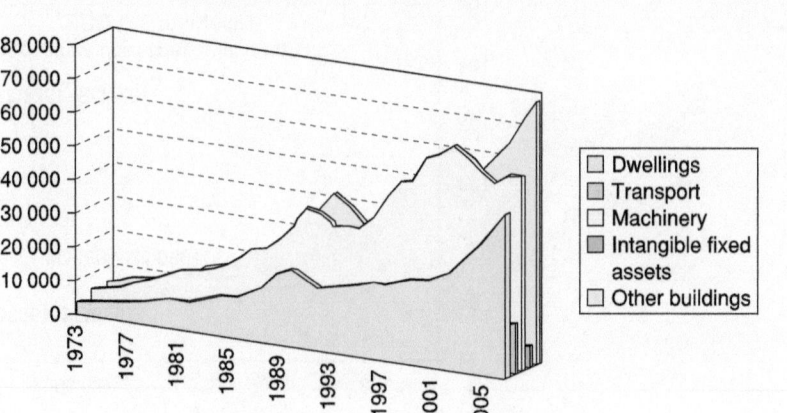

Figure 1.23
Over-the-top graph of
investment

Exercise 1.5

Given the following data:

	1990	1991	1992	1993	1994	1995	1996	1997	1998	1999
Profit	50	60	25	−10	10	45	60	50	20	40
Sales	300	290	280	255	260	285	300	310	300	330

(a) Draw a multiple time series graph of the two variables. Label both axes appropriately and provide a title for the graph.

(b) Adjust the graph by using the right-hand axis to measure profits, the left-hand axis sales. What difference does this make?

Numerical summary statistics

The graphs have revealed quite a lot about the data already, but we can also calculate numerical descriptive statistics as we did for the cross-section data. First we consider the mean, then the variance and standard deviation.

The mean of a time series

We could calculate the mean of investment itself, but would this be helpful? Because the series is trended, it passes through the mean at some point between 1973 and 2005, but never returns to it. The mean of the series is actually £95.103bn, which is not very informative since it tells nothing about its value today, for instance. The problem is that the variable is trended, so that the mean is not typical of the series. The annual increase in investment is also trended, so is subject to the same criticism (see Figure 1.17).

It is better in this case to calculate the average growth rate, as this is more likely to be representative of the whole time period. It seems more reasonable to say that a series is growing at (for example) 8% per annum than that it is growing at 5000 per annum. The average growth rate was calculated in equation (1.29) as 8.1% per annum, by measuring the slope of the graph of the log investment series. That was stated to be an approximate answer. We can obtain an accurate value in the following way:

(1) Calculate the overall growth factor of the series, i.e. x_T/x_1 where x_T is the final observation and x_1 is the initial observation. This is $\dfrac{x_T}{x_1} = \dfrac{205\ 843}{15\ 227}$ = 13.518, i.e. investment expenditure is 13.5 times larger in 2005 than in 1973.

(2) Take the $T − 1$ root of the growth factor. Since $T = 33$ we calculate $\sqrt[32]{13.518}$ = 1.085. (This can be performed on a scientific calculator by raising 13.518 to the power 1/32, i.e. $13.518^{(1/32)} = 1.085$.)

(3) Subtract 1 from the result in the previous step, giving the growth rate as a decimal. In this case we have 1.085 − 1 = 0.085.

Thus the average growth rate of investment is 8.5% per annum, rather than the 8.1% calculated earlier.

The power of compound growth

The *Economist* magazine provided some amusing and interesting examples of how a $1 investment can grow over time. They assumed that an investor (they named her Felicity Foresight, for reasons that become obvious) started with $1 in 1900 and had the foresight or luck to invest, each year, in the best performing asset of the year. Sometimes she invested in equities, some years in gold and so on. By the end of the century she had amassed $9.6 quintillion ($9.6 \times 10^{18}$, more than world gross domestic product (GDP), so highly unrealistic). This is equivalent to an average annual growth rate of 55%. In contrast, Henry Hindsight did the same, but invested in the *previous year's* best asset. This might be thought more realistic. Unfortunately, his $1 turned into only $783, a still respectable annual growth rate of 6.9%. This, however, is beaten by the strategy of investing in the previous year's *worst* performing asset (what goes down must come up . . .). This turned $1 into $1730, a return of 7.7%. Food for thought!

Source: The Economist, 12 February 2000, p. 111.

Note that we could also obtain the accurate answer from our earlier calculation as follows:

- the slope of the graph is 0.0814 (from equation (1.29) above, but to four decimal places for accuracy);
- calculate the anti-log (e^x) of this: $e^{0.0814} = 1.085$;
- subtract 1, giving a growth rate of $1.085 - 1 = 0.085 = 8.5\%$ (p.a.).

Note that, as the calculated growth rate is based only upon the initial and final observations, it could be unreliable if either of these two values is an outlier. With a sufficient span of time, however, this is unlikely to be a serious problem.

The geometric mean

In calculating the average growth rate of investment we have implicitly calculated the geometric mean of a series. If we have a series of n values, then their geometric mean is calculated as the nth root of the *product* of the values, i.e.

$$geometric\ mean = \sqrt[n]{\prod_{i=1}^{n} x_i} \qquad (1.30)$$

The x values in this case are the growth factors in each year, as in Table 1.15 (the values in intermediate years are omitted). The 'Π' symbol is similar to the use of Σ, but means 'multiply together' rather than 'add up'.

The product of the 32 growth factors is 13.518 (the same as is obtained by dividing the final observation by the initial one – why?) and the 32nd root of this is 1.085. This latter figure, 1.085, is the geometric mean of the growth factors and from it we can derive the growth rate of 8.5% p.a. by subtracting 1.

Whenever one is dealing with growth data (or any series that is based on a multiplicative process) one should use the geometric mean rather than the arithmetic mean to get the answer. However, using the arithmetic mean in this case generally gives only a small error, as is indicated below.

Table 1.15 Calculation of the geometric mean – annual growth factors

	Investment	Growth factors	
1973	15 227		
1974	18 134	1.191	(= 18 134/15 227)
1975	21 856	1.205	(= 21 856/18 134)
1976	25 516	1.167	Etc.
⋮	⋮	⋮	
2002	173 525	1.049	
2003	178 751	1.030	
2004	194 491	1.088	
2005	205 843	1.058	

Note: Each growth factor simply shows the ratio of that year's investment to the previous year's.

Another approximate way of obtaining the average growth rate

We have seen that when calculating rates of growth one should use the geometric mean, but if the growth rate is reasonably small then taking the arithmetic mean of the growth factors will give approximately the right answer. The arithmetic mean of the growth factors is

$$\frac{1.191 + 1.205 + \ldots + 1.088 + 1.058}{32} = 1.087$$

giving an estimate of the growth rate of $1.087 - 1 = 0.087 = 8.7\%$ p.a. – close to the correct value. Note also that one could equivalently take the average of the annual growth rates (0.191, 0.205, etc.), giving 0.087, to obtain the same result. Use of the arithmetic mean is justified in this context if one needs only an approximation to the right answer and annual growth rates are reasonably small. It is usually quicker and easier to calculate the arithmetic rather than geometric mean, especially if one does not have a computer to hand.

By now you might be feeling a little overwhelmed by the various methods we have used, all to get an idea of the average – methods which give similar but not always identical answers. Let us summarise the findings:

(a) measuring the slope of the log graph: gives approximately the right answer;
(b) transforming the slope using the formula $e^b - 1$: gives the precise answer (b is the measured slope);
(c) calculating $\sqrt[T-1]{\dfrac{x_T}{x_1}} - 1$: gives the precise answer (as in (b));
(d) calculating the geometric mean of the growth factors: gives the precise answer;
(e) calculating the arithmetic mean of the growth factors: gives approximately the right answer (although not the same approximation as (a) above).

Remember also that the 'precise' answer could be slightly misleading if either initial or final value is an outlier.

Compound interest

The calculations we have performed relating to growth rates are analogous to computing compound interest. If we invest £100 at a rate of interest of 10% per annum, then the investment will grow at 10% p.a. (assuming all the interest is reinvested). Thus after one year the total will have grown to £100 × 1.1 (£110), after two years to £100 × 1.1^2 (£121) and after t years to £100 × 1.1^t. The general formula for the terminal value S_t of a sum S_0 invested for t years at a rate of interest r is

$$S_t = S_0(1 + r)^t \tag{1.31}$$

where r is expressed as a decimal. Rearranging (1.31) to make r the subject yields

$$r = \sqrt[t]{S_t \big/ S_0} - 1 \tag{1.32}$$

which is precisely the formula for the average growth rate. To give a further example: suppose an investment fund turns an initial deposit of £8000 into £13 500 over 12 years. What is the average rate of return on the investment? Setting $S_0 = 8$, $S_t = 13.5$, $t = 12$ and using equation (1.32) we obtain

$$r = \sqrt[12]{13.5 \big/ 8} - 1 = 0.045$$

or 4.5% per annum.

Formula (1.32) can also be used to calculate the depreciation rate and the amount of annual depreciation on a firm's assets. In this case, S_0 represents the initial value of the asset, S_t represents the final or scrap value, and the annual rate of depreciation (as a negative number) is given by r from equation (1.32).

The variance of a time series

How should we describe the variance of a time series? The variance of the investment data can be calculated, but it would be uninformative in the same way as the mean. As the series is trended, and this is likely to continue in the longer run, the variance is in principle equal to infinity. The calculated variance would be closely tied to the sample size: the larger it is, the larger the variance. Again it makes more sense to calculate the variance of the growth rate, which has little trend in the long run.

This variance can be calculated from the formula

$$s^2 = \frac{\sum(x - \bar{x})^2}{n - 1} = \frac{\sum x^2 - n\bar{x}^2}{n - 1} \tag{1.33}$$

where $\bar{x}$ is the average rate of growth. The calculation is set out in Table 1.16 using the right-hand formula in equation (1.33).

The variance is therefore

$$s^2 = \frac{0.3990 - 32 \times 0.087^2}{31} = 0.0051$$

and the standard deviation is 0.071, the square root of the variance. The coefficient of variation is

Table 1.16 Calculation of the variance of the growth rate

Year	Investment	Growth rate	
		x	x^2
1974	18 134	0.191	0.036
1975	21 856	0.205	0.042
1976	25 516	0.167	0.028
⋮	⋮	⋮	⋮
2002	173 525	0.049	0.002
2003	178 751	0.030	0.001
2004	194 491	0.088	0.008
2005	205 843	0.058	0.003
Totals		2.7856	0.3990

$$cv = \frac{0.071}{0.087} = 0.816$$

i.e. the standard deviation of the growth rate is about 80% of the mean.

Note three things about this calculation: first, we have used the arithmetic mean (using the geometric mean makes very little difference); second, we have used the formula for the sample variance since the period 1974–2005 constitutes a sample of all the possible data we could collect; and third, we could have equally used the growth factors for the calculation of the variance (why?).

> ### Worked example 1.7
>
> Given the following data
>
> | Year | 1999 | 2000 | 2001 | 2002 | 2003 |
> |---|---|---|---|---|---|
> | Price of a laptop PC | 1100 | 900 | 800 | 750 | 700 |
>
> we can work out the average rate of price growth per annum as follows. The overall growth factor is $\frac{700}{1100} = 0.6363$. The fact that this number is less than one simply reflects the fact that the price has fallen over time. It has fallen to 64% of its original value. To find the annual rate, we take the fourth root of 0.6363 (four years of growth). Hence we obtain $\sqrt[4]{0.6363} = 0.893$, i.e. each year the price falls to 89% of its value the previous year. This implies price is falling at $0.893 - 1 = -0.107$, or approximately an 11% fall each year.
>
> We can see if the fall is more or less the same, by calculating each year's growth factor. These are:
>
> | Year | 1999 | 2000 | 2001 | 2002 | 2003 |
> |---|---|---|---|---|---|
> | Laptop price | 1100 | 900 | 800 | 750 | 700 |
> | Growth factor | – | 0.818 | 0.889 | 0.9375 | 0.933 |
> | Price fall | – | −19% | −11% | −6% | −7% |
>
> The price fall was larger in the earlier years, in percentage as well as abso-lute terms. Calculating the standard deviation of the values in the final row →

provides a measure of the variability from year to year. The variance is given by

$$s^2 = \frac{(19-11)^2 + (11-11)^2 + (6-11)^2 + (7-11)^2}{3} = 30.7$$

and the standard deviation is then 5.54%. (The calculations are shown rounded but the answer is accurate.)

Exercise 1.6

(a) Using the data in Exercise 1.5, calculate the average level of profit over the time period and the average growth rate of profit over the period. Which appears more useful?

(b) Calculate the variance of profit and compare it to the variance of sales.

Graphing bivariate data: the scatter diagram

The analysis of investment is an example of the use of univariate methods: only a single variable is involved. However, we often wish to examine the relationship between two (or sometimes more) variables and we have to use bivariate (or multivariate) methods. To illustrate the methods involved we shall examine the relationship between investment expenditures and gross domestic product (GDP). Economics tells us to expect a positive relationship between these variables, higher GDP is usually associated with higher investment. Table 1.17 provides data on GDP for the UK.

A scatter diagram (also called an XY chart) plots one variable (in this case investment) on the y axis, the other (GDP) on the x axis, and therefore shows the relationship between them. For example, one can see whether high values of one variable tend to be associated with high values of the other. Figure 1.24 shows the relationship for investment and GDP.

The chart shows a strong linear relationship between the two variables, apart from a curious dip in the middle. This reflects the sharp fall in investment after 1990, which is *not* matched by a fall in GDP (if it were, the XY chart would show

Table 1.17 **GDP data**

Year	GDP	Year	GDP	Year	GDP
1973	74 020	1984	324 633	1995	719 747
1974	83 793	1985	355 269	1996	765 152
1975	105 864	1986	381 782	1997	811 194
1976	125 203	1987	420 211	1998	860 796
1977	145 663	1988	469 035	1999	906 567
1978	167 905	1989	514 921	2000	953 227
1979	197 438	1990	558 160	2001	996 987
1980	230 800	1991	587 080	2002	1 048 767
1981	253 154	1992	611 974	2003	1 110 296
1982	277 198	1993	642 656	2004	1 176 527
1983	302 973	1994	680 978	2005	1 224 715

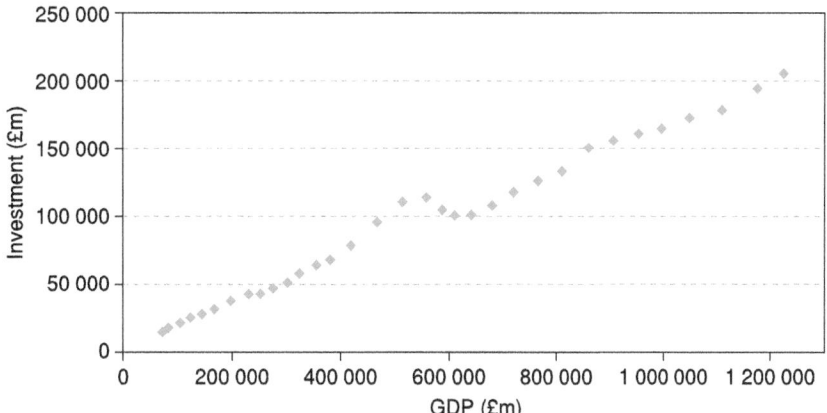

Figure 1.24
Scatter diagram of investment (vertical axis) against GDP (horizontal axis) (nominal values)

Note: The (x, y) coordinates of each point are given by the values of investment and GDP respectively. Thus the first (1973) data point is drawn 15 227 units above the horizontal axis and 74 020 units from the vertical one.

a linear relationship without the dip). It is important to recognise the difference between the time-series plot and the *XY* chart. Because of inflation later observations tend to be towards the top right of the *XY* chart (both investment and GDP are increasing over time) but this does not *have* to happen; if both variables fluctuated up and down, later observations could be at the bottom left (or centre, or anywhere). By contrast, in a time series plot, later observations are always further to the right.

Note that both variables are in nominal terms, i.e. they make no correction for inflation over the time period. This may be seen algebraically: investment expenditure is made up of the *volume* of investment (I) times its *price* (P_I). Similarly, nominal GDP is real GDP (Y) times its price (P_Y). Thus the scatter diagram actually charts $P_I \times I$ against $P_Y \times Y$. It is likely that the two prices follow a similar trend over time and that this dominates the movements in real investment and GDP. The chart then shows the relationship between a mixture of prices and quantities, when the more interesting relationship is between the *quantities* of investment and output.

Figure 1.25 shows the relationship between the quantities of investment and output, i.e. after the strongly trending price effects have been removed. It is not so straightforward as the nominal graph. There is now a 'knot' of points in the centre where perhaps both (real) investment and GDP fluctuated up and down. Overall it is clear that something 'interesting' happened around 1990 that merits additional investigation.

Chapter 10, on index numbers, explains in detail how to derive real variables from nominal ones, as we have done here, and generally describes how to correct for the effects of inflation on economic magnitudes.

Exercise 1.7

(a) Once again using the data from Exercise 1.5, draw an *XY* chart with profits on the vertical axis, sales on the horizontal axis. Choose the scale of the axes appropriately.

(b) (If using Excel to produce graphs) Right click on the graph, choose 'Add trendline' and choose a linear trend. This gives the 'line of best fit' (covered in detail in Chapter 7). What does this appear to show?

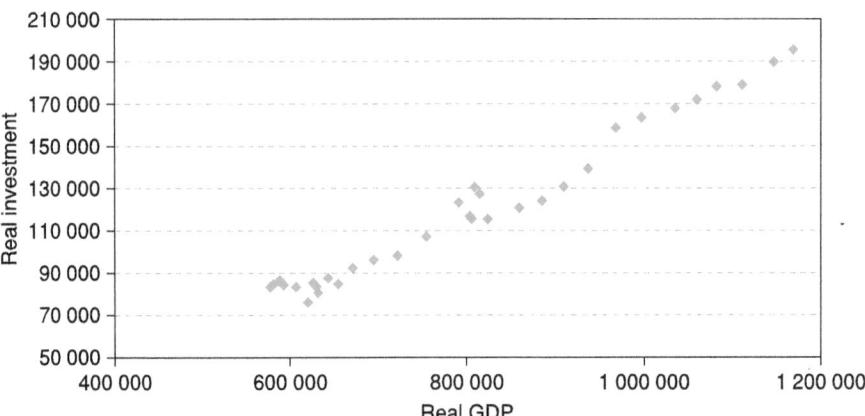

Figure 1.25
The relationship between real investment and real output

Data transformations

In analysing employment and investment data in the examples above we have often changed the variables in some way in order to bring out the important characteristics. In statistics one usually works with data that have been transformed in some way rather than using the original numbers. It is therefore worth summarising the main data transformations available, providing justifications for their use and exploring the implications of such adjustments to the original data. We briefly deal with the following transformations:

- rounding;
- grouping;
- dividing or multiplying by a constant;
- differencing;
- taking logarithms;
- taking the reciprocal;
- deflating.

Rounding

Rounding improves readability. Too much detail can confuse the message, so rounding the answer makes it more memorable. To give an example, the average wealth holding calculated earlier in this chapter is actually £146 983.726 (to three decimal places). It would be absurd to present it in this form, however. We do not know for certain that this figure is accurate (in fact, it almost certainly is not). There is a spurious degree of precision which might mislead the reader. How much should this be rounded for presentational purposes therefore? Remember that the figures have already been effectively rounded by allocation to classes of width 10 000 or more (all observations have been rounded to the mid-point of the interval). However, much of this rounding is offsetting, i.e. numbers rounded up offset those rounded down, so the mean is reasonably accurate. Rounding to £147 000 makes the figure much easier to remember, and is only a change of 0.01% (147 000/146 984 = 1.000 111), so is a reasonable compromise. In the text above, the answer was not rounded to such an extent since the purpose was to highlight the methods of calculation.

Inflation in Zimbabwe

'Zimbabwe's rate of inflation surged to 3731.9%, driven by higher energy and food costs, and amplified by a drop in its currency, official figures show.'
BBC news online, 17 May 2007.

Whether official or not, it is impossible that the rate of inflation is known with such accuracy (to one decimal place!), especially when prices are rising so fast. It would be more reasonable to report a figure of 3700% in this case. Sad to say, inflation rose even further in subsequent months.

Rounding is a 'trap door' function: you cannot obtain the original value from the transformed (rounded) value. Therefore, if you are going to need the original value in further calculations you should not round your answer. Furthermore, small rounding errors can cumulate, leading to a large error in the final answer. Therefore, you should *never* round an intermediate answer, only the final one. Even if you only round the intermediate answer by a small amount, the final answer could be grossly inaccurate. Try the following: calculate $60.29 \times 30.37 - 1831$ both before and after rounding the first two numbers to integers. In the first case you obtain 0.0073, in the second −31.

Grouping

When there is too much data to present easily, grouping solves the problem, although at the cost of hiding some of the information. The examples relating to education and unemployment and to wealth used grouped data. Using the raw data would have given us far too much information, so grouping is a first stage in data analysis. Grouping is another trap door transformation: once it is done you cannot recover the original information.

Dividing/multiplying by a constant

This transformation is carried out to make numbers more readable or to make calculation simpler by removing trailing zeros. The data on wealth were divided by 1000 to ease calculation; otherwise the fx^2 column would have contained extremely large values. Some summary statistics (e.g. the mean) will be affected by the transformation, but not all (e.g. the coefficient of variation). Try to remember which are affected! E and V operators (see Appendix 1B) can help. The transformation is easy to reverse.

Differencing

In time-series data there may be a trend, and it is better to describe the features of the data relative to the trend. The result may also be more economically meaningful, for example governments are often more concerned about the growth of output than about its level. Differencing is one way of eliminating the trend (see Chapter 11 for other methods of detrending data). Differencing was used for the investment data for both of these reasons. One of the implications of differencing is that information about the *level* of the variable is lost.

◯ Taking logarithms

Taking logarithms is used to linearise a non-linear series, in particular one that is growing at a fairly constant rate. It is often easier to see the important features of such a series if the logarithm is graphed rather than the raw data. The logarithmic transformation is also useful in regression (see Chapter 9) because it yields estimates of elasticities (e.g. of demand). Taking the logarithm of the investment data linearised the series and tended to smooth it. The inverses of the logarithmic transformations are 10^x (for common logarithms) and e^x (for natural logarithms) so one can recover the original data.

◯ Taking the reciprocal

The reciprocal of a variable might have a useful interpretation and provide a more intuitive explanation of a phenomenon. The reciprocal transformation will also turn a linear series into a non-linear one. The reciprocal of turnover in the labour market (i.e. the number leaving unemployment divided by the number unemployed) gives an idea of the duration of unemployment. If a half of those unemployed find work each year (turnover = 0.5) then the average duration of unemployment is 2 years (= 1/0.5). If a graph of turnover shows a linear decline over time, then the average duration of unemployment will be rising, at a faster and faster rate. Repeating the reciprocal transformation recovers the original data.

◯ Deflating

Deflating turns a nominal series into a real one, i.e. one that reflects changes in quantities without the contamination of price changes. This is dealt with in more detail in Chapter 10. It is often more meaningful in economic terms to talk about a real variable than a nominal one. Consumers are more concerned about their real income than about their money income, for example.

Confusing real and nominal variables is dangerous! For example, someone's nominal (money) income may be rising yet their real income falling (if prices are rising faster than money income). It is important to know which series you are dealing with (this is a common failing among students new to statistics and economics). An income series that is growing at 2–3% per annum is probably a real series; one that is growing at 10% per annum or more is likely to be nominal.

Guidance to the student: how to measure your progress

Now you have reached the end of the chapter your work is not yet over! It is very unlikely that you have fully understood everything after one read through. What you should do now is:

- Check back over the learning outcomes at the start of the chapter. Do you feel you have achieved them? For example, can you list the various different data types you should be able to recognise (the first learning outcome)?
- Read the chapter summary below to help put things in context. You should recognise each topic and be aware of the main issues, techniques, etc., within them. There should be no surprises or gaps!
- Read the list of key terms. You should be able to give a brief and precise definition or description of each one. Do not worry if you cannot remember all the formulae (although you should try to memorise simple ones such as that for the mean).
- Try out the problems (most important!). Answers to odd-numbered problems are at the back of the book, so you can check your answers. There is more detail for some of the answers on the book's web site.

From all of this you should be able to work out whether you have really mastered the chapter. Do not be surprised if you have not – it will take more than one reading. Go back over those parts where you feel unsure of your knowledge. Use these same learning techniques for each chapter of the book.

Summary

- Descriptive statistics are useful for summarising large amounts of information, highlighting the main features but omitting the detail.
- Different techniques are suited to different types of data, e.g. bar charts for cross-section data and rates of growth for time series.
- Graphical methods, such as the bar chart, provide a picture of the data. These give an informal summary but they are unsuitable as a basis for further analysis.
- Important graphical techniques include the bar chart, frequency distribution, relative and cumulative frequency distributions, histogram and pie chart. For time-series data a time-series chart of the data is informative.
- Numerical techniques are more precise as summaries. Measures of location (such as the mean), of dispersion (the variance) and of skewness form the basis of these techniques.
- Important numerical summary statistics include the mean, median and mode; variance, standard deviation and coefficient of variation; coefficient of skewness.
- For bivariate data the scatter diagram (or *XY* graph) is a useful way of illustrating the data.
- Data are often transformed in some way before analysis, for example by taking logs. Transformations often make it easier to see key features of the data in graphs and sometimes make summary statistics easier to interpret. For example, with time-series data the average rate of growth may be more appropriate than the mean of the series.

Key terms and concepts

bar chart	mode
box and whiskers plot	outliers
coefficient of variation	pie chart
compound growth	quantiles
cross-section data	relative and cumulative frequencies
cross-tabulation	scatter diagram (XY chart)
data transformation	skewness
frequencies	standard deviation
frequency table	time-series data
histogram	variance
mean	z-score
median	

Reference

Atkinson, A. B. *The Economics of Inequality*, 1983, 2nd edn., Oxford University Press.

Problems

Some of the more challenging problems are indicated by highlighting the problem number in colour.

1.1 The following data show the education and employment status of women aged 20–29 (from the *General Household Survey*):

	Higher education	A levels	Other qualification	No qualification	Total
In work	209	182	577	92	1060
Unemployed	12	9	68	32	121
Inactive	17	34	235	136	422
Sample	238	225	880	260	1603

(a) Draw a bar chart of the numbers in work in each education category. Can this be easily compared with the similar diagram for in Figure 1.1?

(b) Draw a stacked bar chart using all the employment states, similar to Figure 1.3. Comment upon any similarities and differences from the diagram in the text.

(c) Convert the table into (column) percentages and produce a stacked bar chart similar to Figure 1.4. Comment upon any similarities and differences.

(d) Draw a pie chart showing the distribution of educational qualifications of those in work and compare it to Figure 1.5 in the text.

1.2 The data below show the median weekly earnings (in £s) of those in full-time employment in Great Britain in 1992, by category of education.

	Degree	Other higher education	A level	GCSE A–C	GCSE D–G	None
Males	433	310	277	242	226	220
Females	346	278	201	183	173	146

(a) In what fundamental way do the data in this table differ from those in Problem 1.1?

(b) Construct a bar chart showing male and female earnings by education category. What does it show?

(c) Why would it be inappropriate to construct a stacked bar chart of the data? How should one graphically present the combined data for males and females? What extra information is necessary for you to do this?

1.3 Using the data from Problem 1.1:

(a) Which education category has the highest proportion of women in work? What is the proportion?

(b) Which category of employment status has the highest proportion of women with a degree? What is the proportion?

1.4   Using the data from Problem 1.2:

(a) What is the premium, in terms of median earnings, of a degree over A levels? Does this differ between men and women?

(b) Would you expect *mean* earnings to show a similar picture? What differences, if any, might you expect?

1.5   The distribution of marketable wealth in 1979 in the UK is shown in the table below (taken from *Inland Revenue Statistics*, 1981, p. 105):

Range	Number 000s	Amount £m
0–	1606	148
1000–	2927	5985
3000–	2562	10 090
5000–	3483	25 464
10 000–	2876	35 656
15 000–	1916	33 134
20 000–	3425	104 829
50 000–	621	46 483
100 000–	170	25 763
200 000–	59	30 581

Draw a bar chart and histogram of the data (assume the final class interval has a width of 200 000). Comment on the differences between the two. Comment on any differences between this histogram and the one for 1994 given in the text.

1.6   The data below show the number of manufacturing plants in the UK in 1991/92 arranged according to employment:

Number of employees	Number of firms
1–	95 409
10–	15 961
20–	16 688
50–	7229
100–	4504
200–	2949
500–	790
1000–	332

Draw a bar chart and histogram of the data (assume the mid-point of the last class interval is 2000). What are the major features apparent in each and what are the differences?

1.7   Using the data from Problem 1.5:

(a) Calculate the mean, median and mode of the distribution. Why do they differ?

(b) Calculate the inter-quartile range, variance, standard deviation and coefficient of variation of the data.

(c) Calculate the skewness of the distribution.

(d) From what you have calculated, and the data in the chapter, can you draw any conclusions about the degree of inequality in wealth holdings, and how this has changed?

(c) What would be the effect upon the mean of assuming the final class width to be £10m? What would be the effects upon the median and mode?

1.8 Using the data from Problem 1.6:

(a) Calculate the mean, median and mode of the distribution. Why do they differ?

(b) Calculate the inter-quartile range, variance, standard deviation and coefficient of variation of the data.

(c) Calculate the coefficient of skewness of the distribution.

1.9 A motorist keeps a record of petrol purchases on a long journey, as follows:

Petrol station	1	2	3
Litres purchased	33	40	25
Price per litre	55.7	59.6	57.0

Calculate the average petrol price for the journey.

1.10 Demonstrate that the weighted average calculation given in equation (1.9) is equivalent to finding the total expenditure on education divided by the total number of pupils.

1.11 On a test taken by 100 students, the average mark is 65, with variance 144. Student A scores 83, student B scores 47.

(a) Calculate the z-scores for these two students.

(b) What is the maximum number of students with a score either better than A's or worse than B's?

(c) What is the maximum number of students with a score better than A's?

1.12 The average income of a group of people is £8000. 80% of the group have incomes within the range £6000–10 000. What is the minimum value of the standard deviation of the distribution?

1.13 The following data show car registrations in the UK during 1970–91 (source: *ETAS*, 1993, p. 57):

Year	Registrations	Year	Registrations	Year	Registrations
1970	91.4	1978	131.6	1986	156.9
1971	108.5	1979	142.1	1987	168.0
1972	177.6	1980	126.6	1988	184.2
1973	137.3	1981	124.5	1989	192.1
1974	102.8	1982	132.1	1990	167.1
1975	98.6	1983	150.5	1991	133.3
1976	106.5	1984	146.6	–	–
1977	109.4	1985	153.5	–	–

(a) Draw a time-series graph of car registrations. Comment upon the main features of the series.

(b) Draw time-series graphs of the change in registrations, the (natural) log of registrations, and the change in the ln. Comment upon the results.

1.14   The table below shows the different categories of investment, 1986–2005.

Year	Dwellings	Transport	Machinery	Intangible fixed assets	Other buildings
1986	14 140	6527	25 218	2184	20 477
1987	16 548	7872	28 225	2082	24 269
1988	21 097	9227	32 614	2592	30 713
1989	22 771	10 624	38 417	2823	36 689
1990	21 048	10 571	37 776	3571	41 334
1991	18 339	9051	35 094	4063	38 632
1992	18 826	8420	35 426	3782	34 657
1993	19 886	9315	35 316	3648	32 988
1994	21 155	11 395	38 426	3613	33 945
1995	22 448	11 036	45 012	3939	35 596
1996	22 516	12 519	50 102	4136	37 320
1997	23 928	12 580	51 465	4249	41 398
1998	25 222	16 113	58 915	4547	46 286
1999	25 700	14 683	60 670	4645	50 646
2000	27 394	13 577	63 535	4966	51 996
2001	29 806	14 656	60 929	5016	55 065
2002	34 499	16 314	57 152	5588	59 972
2003	38 462	15 592	54 441	5901	64 355
2004	44 299	14 939	57 053	6395	71 805
2005	48 534	15 351	57 295	6757	77 906

Use appropriate graphical techniques to analyse the properties of any one of the investment series. Comment upon the results.

1.15   Using the data from Problem 1.13:

(a) Calculate the average rate of growth of the series.

(b) Calculate the standard deviation around the average growth rate.

(c) Does the series appear to be more or less volatile than the investment figures used in the chapter? Suggest reasons.

1.16   Using the data from Problem 1.14:

(a) Calculate the average rate of growth of the series for dwellings.

(b) Calculate the standard deviation around the average growth rate.

(c) Does the series appear to be more or less volatile than the investment figures used in the chapter? Suggest reasons.

1.17   How would you *expect* the following time-series variables to look when graphed? (e.g. Trended? Linear trend? Trended up or down? Stationary? Homoscedastic? Auto-correlated? Cyclical? Anything else?)

(a) Nominal national income.

(b) Real national income.

(c) The nominal interest rate.

1.18 How would you expect the following time-series variables to look when graphed?

(a) The price level.

(b) The inflation rate.

(c) The £/$ exchange rate.

1.19 (a) A government bond is issued, promising to pay the bearer £1000 in five years' time. The prevailing market rate of interest is 7%. What price would you expect to pay now for the bond? What would its price be after two years? If, after two years, the market interest rate jumped to 10%, what would the price of the bond be?

(b) A bond is issued which promises to pay £200 per annum over the next five years. If the prevailing market interest rate is 7%, how much would you be prepared to pay for the bond? Why does the answer differ from the previous question? (Assume interest is paid at the end of each year.)

1.20 A firm purchases for £30 000 a machine that is expected to last for 10 years, after which it will be sold for its scrap value of £3000. Calculate the average rate of depreciation per annum, and calculate the written-down value of the machine after one, two and five years.

1.21 Depreciation of BMW and Mercedes cars is given in the following table:

Age	BMW 525i	Mercedes 200E
Current	22 275	21 900
1 year	18 600	19 700
2 years	15 200	16 625
3 years	12 600	13 950
4 years	9750	11 600
5 years	8300	10 300

(a) Calculate the average rate of depreciation of each type of car.

(b) Use the calculated depreciation rates to estimate the value of the car after 1, 2, etc., years of age. How does this match the actual values?

(c) Graph the values and estimated values for each car.

1.22 A bond is issued which promises to pay £400 per annum in perpetuity. How much is the bond worth now, if the interest rate is 5%? (Hint: the sum of an infinite series of the form

$$\frac{1}{1 + r} + \frac{1}{(1 + r)^2} + \frac{1}{(1 + r)^3} + \cdots$$

is $1/r$, as long as $r > 0$.)

1.23 Demonstrate, using Σ notation, that $E(x + k) = E(x) + k$.

1.24 Demonstrate, using Σ notation, that $V(kx) = k^2 V(x)$.

1.25 Criticise the following statistical reasoning. The average price of a dwelling is £54 150. The average mortgage advance is £32 760. So purchasers have to find £21 390, that is, about 40% of the purchase price. On any basis that is an enormous outlay which young couples, in particular, who are buying a house for the first time would find incredibly difficult, if not impossible, to raise.

1.26 Criticise the following statistical reasoning. Among arts graduates 10% fail to find employment. Among science graduates only 8% remain out of work. Therefore, science graduates are better than arts graduates. (Hint: imagine there are two types of job: popular and unpopular. Arts graduates tend to apply for the former, scientists for the latter.)

1.27 **Project 1**: Is it true that the Conservative government in the UK 1979–1997 lowered taxes, while the Labour government 1997–2007 raised them?

You should gather data that you think are appropriate to the task, summarise them as necessary and write a brief report of your findings. You might like to consider the following points:

- Should one consider tax revenue, or revenue as a proportion of gross national product (GNP)?
- Should one distinguish between tax rates and the tax base (i.e. what is taxed)?
- Has the balance between direct and indirect taxation changed?
- Have different sections of the population fared differently?

You might like to consider other points, and do the problem for a different country. Suitable data sources for the UK are: *Inland Revenue Statistics*, *UK National Accounts*, *Annual Abstract of Statistics* or *Financial Statistics*.

1.28 **Project 2**: Is the employment and unemployment experience of the UK economy worse than that of its competitors? Write a report on this topic in a similar manner to the project above. You might consider rates of unemployment in the UK and other countries; trends in unemployment in each of the countries; the growth in employment in each country; the structure of employment (e.g. full-time/part-time) and unemployment (e.g. long-term/short-term).

You might use data for a number of countries, or concentrate on two in more depth. Suitable data sources are: *OECD Main Economic Indicators*; *European Economy* (published by the European Commission); *Employment Gazette*.

Answers to exercises

Exercise 1.1

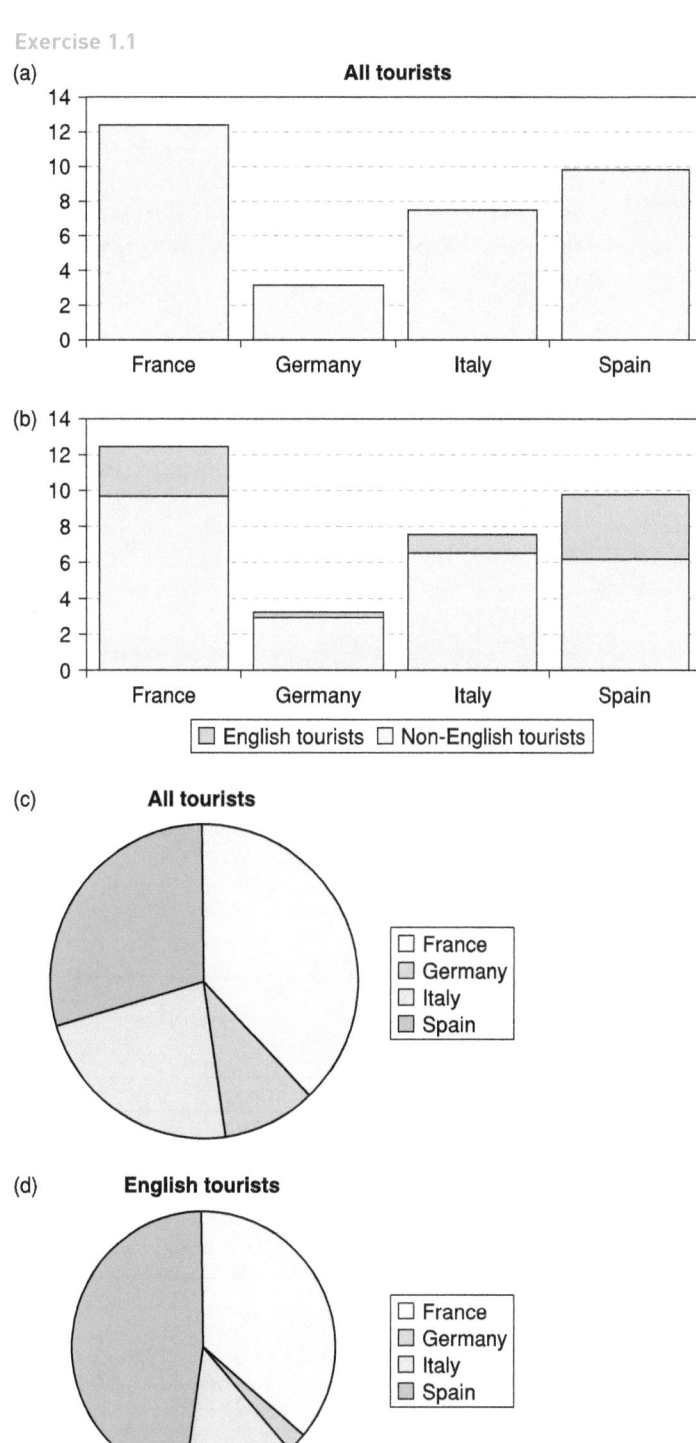

It is clear the English are more likely to visit Spain than are other nationalities.

Exercise 1.2

(a) Bar chart

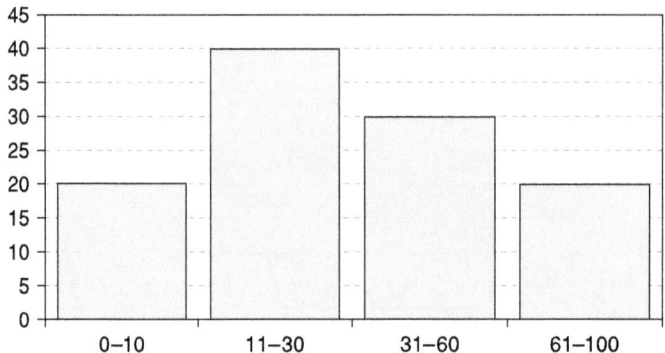

Histogram

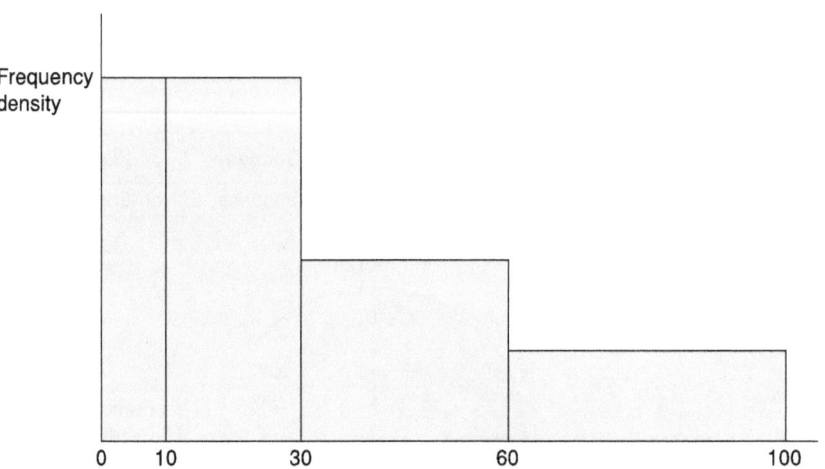

Exercise 1.3

(a)

	Midpoint, x	Frequency, f	fx
0–10	5	20	100
11–30	20	40	800
31–60	45	30	1350
60–100	80	20	1600
–	–	110	3850

Hence the mean = 3850/110 = 35.

The median is contained in the 11–30 group and is 35/40 of the way through the interval (20 + 35 moves us to observation 55). Hence the median is 11 + 35/40 × 19 = 27.625.

The mode is anywhere in the 0–30 range; the frequency density is the same throughout this range.

(b)

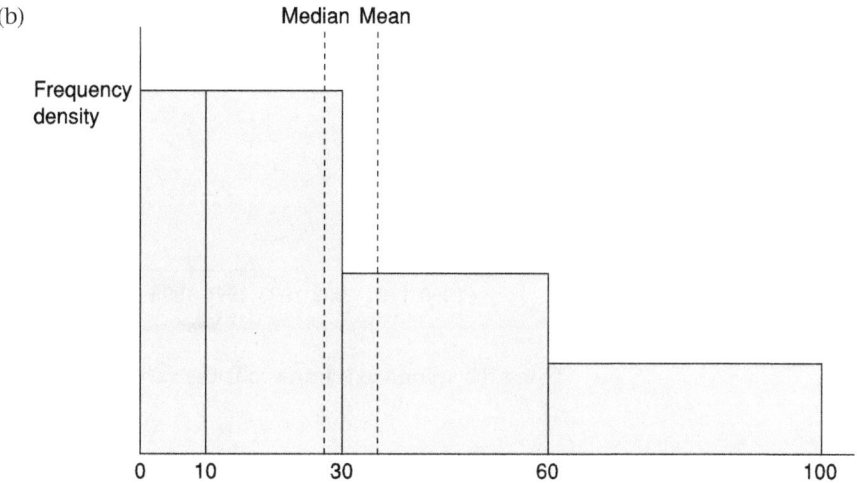

Exercise 1.4

(a) Q1 relates to observation 27.5 (= 110/4). This observation lies in the 11–30 range. There are 20 observations in the first class interval, so Q1 will relate to observation 7.5 in the second interval. Hence we need to go 7.5/40 of the way through the interval. This gives $11 + (7.5/40) \times 19 = 14.6$. Similarly, Q3 is 22.5/30 of the way through the third interval, yielding $Q3 = 31 + 22.5/30 \times 29 = 52.8$. The IQR is therefore 38, approximately. For the variance we obtain $\sum fx = 3850$ and $\sum fx^2 = 205\,250$. The variance is therefore $\sigma^2 = 205\,250/110 - 35^2 = 640.9$ and the standard deviation 25.3.

(b) CV = 25.3/35 = 0.72.

(c) $1.3 \times 25.3 = 32.9$, not far from the IQR value of 38.

(d) 1 standard deviation either side of the mean takes us from 9.7 up to 60.3. This contains all 70 observations in the second and third intervals plus perhaps one from the first interval. Thus we obtain approximately 71 observations within this range. Chebyshev's inequality does not help us here as it is not defined for $k \leq 1$.

Exercise 1.5

(a)

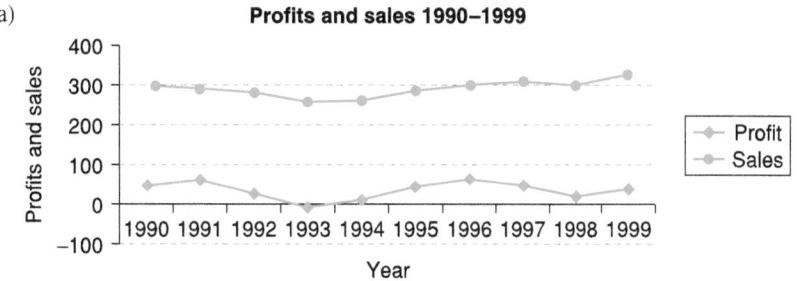

Profits and sales 1990–1999

(b)

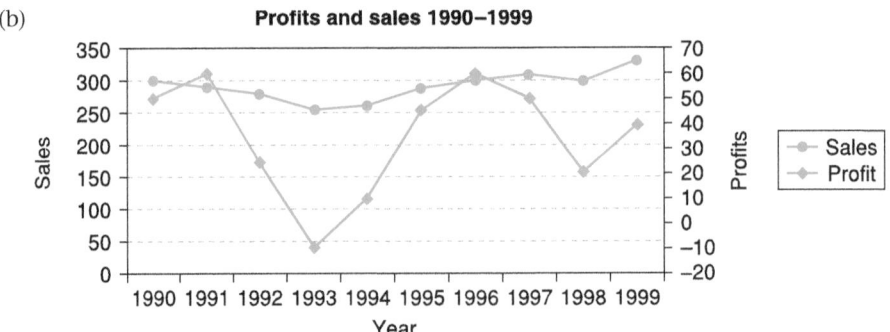

Using the second axis brings out the variability of profits relative to sales.

Exercise 1.6

(a) The average profit is 35. The average rate of growth is calculated by comparing the end values 50 and 40, over the 10-year period. The ratio is 0.8. Taking the ninth root of this (nine years of growth) gives $\sqrt[9]{0.8} = 0.926$ so the annual rate of growth is $0.976 - 1 = -2.4\%$.

(b) The variances are (using the sample variance formula): for profits, $\Sigma(x - \mu)^2 = 4800$ and dividing by 9 gives 533.3. For sales, the mean is 291 and $\Sigma(x - \mu)^2 = 4540$. The variance is therefore $4540/9 = 504.4$. This is similar in absolute size to the variance of profits, but relative to the mean it is much smaller.

Exercise 1.7

(a/b)

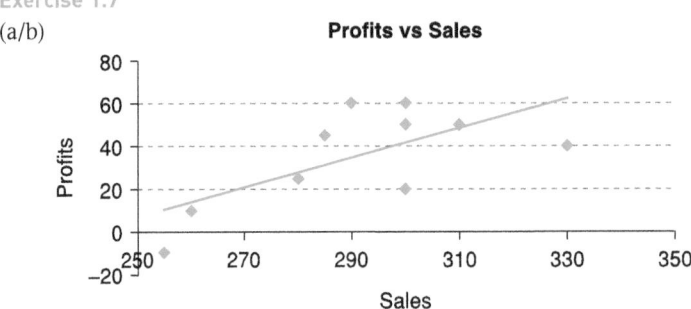

The trend line seems to show a positive relationship between the variables: higher profits are associated with higher sales.

Appendix 1A Σ notation

The Greek symbol Σ (capital sigma) means 'add up' and is a shorthand way of writing what would otherwise be long algebraic expressions. Instead of writing out each term in the series, we provide a template, or typical term of the series, with instructions about how many terms there are.

For example, given the following observations on x:

x_1	x_2	x_3	x_4	x_5
3	5	6	4	8

then

$$\sum_{i=1}^{5} x_i = x_1 + x_2 + x_3 + x_4 + x_5 = 3 + 5 + 6 + 4 + 8 = 26$$

The template is simply x in this case, representing a number to be added in the series. To expand the sigma expression, the subscript i is replaced by successive integers, beginning with the one below the Σ sign and ending with the one above it (1 to 5 in the example above). Hence the instruction is to add the terms x_1 to x_5. Similarly

$$\sum_{i=2}^{4} x_i = x_2 + x_3 + x_4 = 5 + 6 + 4 = 15$$

The instruction tells us to add up only the second, third and fourth terms of the series. When it is clear what range of values i takes (usually when we are to add all available values), the formula can be simplified to $\sum_i x_i$ or $\sum x_i$ or even $\sum x$.

When frequencies are associated with each of the observations, as in the data below:

i	1	2	3	4	5
x_i	3	5	6	4	8
f_i	2	2	4	3	1

then

$$\sum_{i=1}^{i=5} f_i x_i = f_1 x_1 + \ldots + f_5 x_5 = 2 \times 3 + 2 \times 5 + \ldots + 1 \times 8 = 60$$

And also

$$\sum f_i = 2 + 2 + 4 + 3 + 1 = 12$$

Thus the sum of the 12 observations is 60 and the mean is

$$\frac{\sum fx}{\sum f} = \frac{60}{12} = 5$$

We are not limited just to adding the x values. For example, we might wish to square each observation before adding them together. This is expressed as

$$\sum x^2 = x_1^2 + x_2^2 + \ldots + x_5^2 = 150$$

Note that this is different from

$$(\sum x)^2 = (x_1 + x_2 + \ldots + x_5)^2 = 676$$

Part of the formula for the variance calls for the following calculation

$$\sum fx^2 = f_1 x_1^2 + f_2 x_2^2 + \ldots + f_5 x_5^2 = 2 \times 3^2 + 2 \times 5^2 + \ldots + 1 \times 8^2 = 324$$

Using $\sum$ notation we can see the effect of transforming x by dividing by 1000, as was done in calculating the average level of wealth. Instead of working with x we used kx, where $k = 1/1000$. In finding the mean we calculated

$$\frac{\sum kx}{N} = \frac{kx_1 + kx_2 + \ldots}{N} = \frac{k(x_1 + x_2 + \ldots)}{N} = k\frac{\sum x}{N} \qquad (1.34)$$

So, to find the mean of the original variable x, we had to divide by k again, i.e. multiply by 1000. In general, whenever each observation in a sum is multiplied by a constant, the constant can be taken outside the summation operator, as in equation (1.34) above.

Problems on $\sum$ notation

1A.1   Given the following data on x_i: {4, 6, 3, 2, 5}, evaluate

$$\sum x_i, \ \sum x_i^2, \ (\sum x_i)^2, \ \sum(x_i - 3), \ \sum x_i - 3, \ \sum_{i=2}^{4} x_i$$

1A.2   Given the following data on x_i: {8, 12, 6, 4, 10}, evaluate

$$\sum x_i, \ \sum x_i^2, \ (\sum x_i)^2, \ \sum(x_i - 3), \ \sum x_i - 3, \ \sum_{i=2}^{4} x_i$$

1A.3   Given the following frequencies, f_i, associated with the x values in Problem 1A.1: {5, 3, 3, 8, 5}, evaluate

$$\sum fx, \ \sum fx^2, \ \sum f(x - 3), \ \sum fx - 3$$

1A.4   Given the following frequencies, f_i, associated with the x values in Problem 1A.2: {10, 6, 6, 16, 10}, evaluate

$$\sum fx, \ \sum fx^2, \ \sum f(x - 3), \ \sum fx - 3$$

1A.5   Given the pairs of observations on x and y

x	4	3	6	8	12
y	3	9	1	4	3

evaluate $\sum xy, \ \sum x(y - 3), \ \sum(x + 2)(y - 1)$

1A.6 Given the pairs of observations on x and y

x	3	7	4	1	9
y	1	2	5	1	2

evaluate Σxy, $\Sigma x(y-2)$, $\Sigma(x-2)(y+1)$.

1A.7 Demonstrate that

$$\frac{\Sigma f(x-k)}{\Sigma f} = \frac{\Sigma fx}{\Sigma f} - k$$

where k is a constant.

1A.8 Demonstrate that

$$\frac{\Sigma f(x-\mu)^2}{\Sigma f} = \frac{\Sigma fx^2}{\Sigma f} - \mu^2$$

Appendix 1B E and V operators

These operators are an extremely useful form of notation that we shall make use of later in the book. It is quite easy to keep track of the effects of data transformations using them. There are a few simple rules for manipulating them that allow some problems to be solved quickly and elegantly.

$E(x)$ is the mean of a distribution and $V(x)$ is its variance. We showed above in equation (1.34) that multiplying each observation by a constant k multiplies the mean by k. Thus we have

$$E(kx) = kE(x) \tag{1.35}$$

Similarly, if a constant is added to every observation the effect is to add that constant to the mean (see Problem 1.23)

$$E(x + a) = E(x) + a \tag{1.36}$$

(Graphically, the whole distribution is shifted a units to the right and hence so is the mean.) Combining equations (1.35) and (1.36)

$$E(kx + a) = kE(x) + a \tag{1.37}$$

Similarly for the variance operator it can be shown that

$$V(x + k) = V(x) \tag{1.38}$$

Proof

$$V(x + k) = \frac{\Sigma((x+k) - (\mu+k))^2}{N} = \frac{\Sigma((x-\mu) + (k-k))^2}{N} = \frac{\Sigma(x-\mu)^2}{N} = V(x)$$

(A shift of the whole distribution leaves the variance unchanged.) Also

$$V(kx) = k^2 V(x) \tag{1.39}$$

(See Problem 1.24 above.) This is why, when the wealth figures were divided by 1000, the variance became divided by 1000^2. Applying (1.38) and (1.39)

$$V(kx + a) = k^2V(x) \qquad (1.40)$$

Finally we should note that V itself can be expressed in terms of E

$$V(x) = E(x - E(x))^2 \qquad (1.41)$$

Appendix 1C   Using logarithms

Logarithms are less often used now that cheap electronic calculators are available. Formerly logarithms were an indispensable aid to calculation. However, the logarithmic transformation is useful in other contexts in statistics and economics so its use is briefly set out here.

The logarithm (to the base 10) of a number x is defined as the power to which 10 must be raised to give x. For example, $10^2 = 100$, so the log of 100 is 2 and we write $\log_{10} 100 = 2$ or simply $\log 100 = 2$.

Similarly, the log of 1000 is 3 ($1000 = 10^3$), of 10 000 it is 4, etc. We are not restricted to integer (whole number) powers of 10, so for example $10^{2.5} = 316.227766$ (try this if you have a scientific calculator), so the log of 316.227766 is 2.5. Every number x can therefore be represented by its logarithm.

Multiplication of two numbers

We can use logarithms to multiply two numbers x and y, based on the property[8]

$$\log xy = \log x + \log y$$

For example, to multiply 316.227766 by 10

$$\log(316.227766 \times 10) = \log 316.227766 + \log 10$$
$$= 2.5 + 1$$
$$= 3.5$$

The *anti-log* of 3.5 is given by $10^{3.5} = 3162.27766$ which is the answer.

Taking the anti-log (i.e. 10 raised to a power) is the inverse of the log transformation. Schematically we have

$$x \to \text{take logarithms} \to a\ (= \log x) \to \text{raise 10 to the power } a \to x$$

Division

To divide one number by another we subtract the logs. For example, to divide 316.227766 by 100

$$\log(316.227766/100) = \log 316.227766 - \log 100$$
$$= 2.5 - 2$$
$$= 0.5$$

and $10^{0.5} = 3.16227766$.

---

[8] This is equivalent to saying $10^x \times 10^y = 10^{x+y}$.

Powers and roots

Logarithms simplify the process of raising a number to a power. To find the square of a number, multiply the logarithm by 2, e.g. to find 316.227766^2:

$$\log(316.227766^2) = 2 \log(316.227766) = 5$$

and $10^5 = 100\ 000$.

To find the square root of a number (equivalent to raising it to the power $\frac{1}{2}$) divide the log by 2. To find the nth root, divide the log by n. For example, in the text we have to find the 32nd root of 13.518

$$\frac{\log(13.518)}{32} = \frac{1.1309}{32} = 0.0353$$

and $10^{0.0353} = 1.085$.

Common and natural logarithms

Logarithms to the base 10 are known as common logarithms but one can use any number as the base. *Natural* logarithms are based on the number e (= 2.71828 . . .) and we write ln x instead of log x to distinguish them from common logarithms. So, for example

$$\ln 316.227766 = 5.756462732$$

since $e^{5.756462732} = 316.227766$.

Natural logarithms can be used in the same way as common logarithms and have the similar properties. Use the 'ln' key on your calculator just as you would the 'log' key, but remember that the inverse transformation is e^x rather than 10^x.

Problems on logarithms

1C.1 Find the common logarithms of: 0.15, 1.5, 15, 150, 1500, 83.7225, 9.15, –12.

1C.2 Find the log of the following values: 0.8, 8, 80, 4, 16, –37.

1C.3 Find the natural logarithms of: 0.15, 1.5, 15, 225, –4.

1C.4 Find the ln of the following values: 0.3, e, 3, 33, –1.

1C.5 Find the anti-log of the following values: –0.823909, 1.1, 2.1, 3.1, 12.

1C.6 Find the anti-log of the following values: –0.09691, 2.3, 3.3, 6.3.

1C.7 Find the anti-ln of the following values: 2.70805, 3.70805, 1, 10.

1C.8 Find the anti-ln of the following values: 3.496508, 14, 15, –1.

1C.9 Evaluate: $\sqrt[2]{10}, \sqrt[4]{3.7}, 4^{1/4}, 12^{-3}, 25^{-3/2}$.

1C.10 Evaluate: $\sqrt[3]{30}, \sqrt[6]{17}, 8^{1/4}, 15^0, 12^0, 3^{-1/3}$.

2

Probability

Learning outcomes

By the end of this chapter you should be able to:

- understand the essential concept of the probability of an event occurring;

- appreciate that the probability of a combination of events occurring can be calculated using simple arithmetic rules (the addition and multiplication rules);

- understand that a probability can depend upon the outcome of other events (conditional probability);

- know how to make use of probability theory to help make decisions in situations of uncertainty.

Complete your diagnostic test for Chapter 2 now to create your personal study plan. Exercises with an icon ? are also available for practice in MathXL with additional supporting resources.

Probability theory and statistical inference

In October 1985 Mrs Evelyn Adams of New Jersey, USA, won $3.9 m in the State lottery at odds of 1 in 3 200 000. In February 1986 she won again, although this time only (!) $1.4 m at odds of 1 in 5 200 000. The odds against both these wins were calculated at about 1 in 17 300 bn. Mrs Adams is quoted as saying 'They say good things come in threes, so . . .'.

The above story illustrates the principles of probability at work. The same principles underlie the theory of statistical inference, which is the task of drawing conclusions (inferences) about a population from a sample of data drawn from that population. For example, we might have a survey which shows that 30% of a sample of 100 families intend to take a holiday abroad next year. What can we conclude from this about *all* families? The techniques set out in this and subsequent chapters show how to accomplish this.

Why is knowledge of probability necessary for the study of statistical inference? In order to be able to say something about a population on the basis of some sample evidence we must first examine how the sample data are collected. In many cases, the sample is a random one, i.e. the observations making up the sample are chosen at random from the population. If a second sample were selected it would almost certainly be different from the first. Each member of the population has a particular probability of being in the sample (in simple random sampling the probability is the same for all members of the population). To understand sampling procedures, and the implications for statistical inference, we must therefore first examine the theory of probability.

As an illustration of this, suppose we wish to know if a coin is fair, i.e. equally likely to fall heads or tails. The coin is tossed 10 times and 10 heads are recorded. This constitutes a random sample of tosses of the coin. What can we infer about the coin? *If* it is fair, the probability of getting ten heads is 1 in 1024, so a fairly unlikely event seems to have happened. We might reasonably infer therefore that the coin is biased towards heads.

The definition of probability

The first task is to define precisely what is meant by probability. This is not as easy as one might imagine and there are a number of different schools of thought on the subject. Consider the following questions:

- What is the probability of 'heads' occurring on the toss of a coin?
- What is the probability of a driver having an accident in a year of driving?
- What is the probability of a country such as Peru defaulting on its international loan repayments (as Mexico did in the 1980s)?

We shall use these questions as examples when examining the different schools of thought on probability.

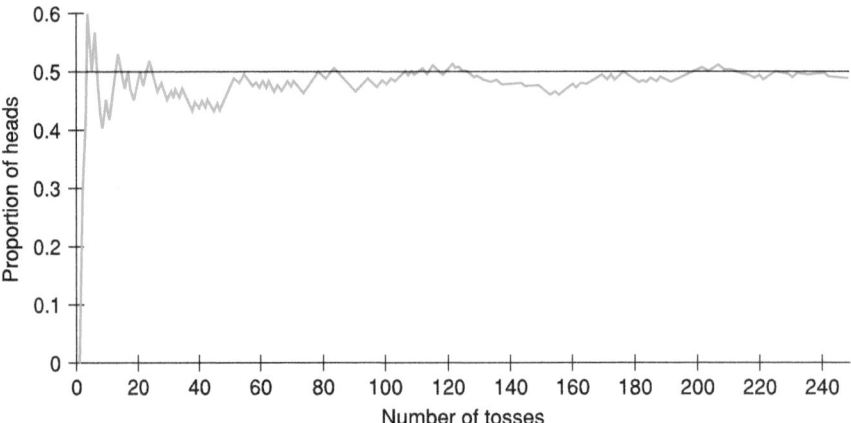

Figure 2.1
The proportion of
heads in 250 tosses
of a fair coin

The frequentist view

Considering the first question above, the frequentist view would be that the probability is equal to the proportion of heads obtained from a coin in the long run, i.e. if the coin were tossed many times. The first few results of such an experiment might be

H, T, T, H, H, H, T, H, T, . . .

After a while, the proportion of heads settles down at some particular fraction and subsequent tosses will individually have an insignificant effect upon the value. Figure 2.1 shows the result of tossing a coin 250 times and recording the proportion of heads (actually, this was simulated on a computer: life is too short to do it for real).

This shows the proportion settling down at a value of about 0.50, which indicates an unbiased coin (or rather, an unbiased computer in this case!). This value is the probability, according to the frequentist view. To be more precise, the probability is defined as the proportion of heads obtained as the number of tosses *approaches infinity*. In general we can define Pr(H), the probability of event H (in this case heads) occurring, as

$$\Pr(H) = \frac{\text{number of occurrences of } H}{\text{number of trials}}, \text{ as the number of trials approaches infinity.}$$

In this case, each toss of the coin constitutes a trial.

This definition gets round the obvious question of how many trials are needed before the probability emerges, but means that the probability of an event cannot strictly be obtained in finite time.

Although this approach appears attractive in theory, it does have its problems. One could not actually toss the coin an infinite number of times. Or, what if one took a different coin, would the results from the first coin necessarily apply to the second?

Perhaps more seriously, the definition is of less use for the second and third questions posed above. Calculating the probability of an accident is not too problematic: it may be defined as the proportion of all drivers having an accident during the year. However, this may not be relevant for a *particular* driver, since drivers vary so much in their accident records. And how would you answer the third question? There is no long run that we can appeal to. We cannot re-run history over and over again to see in what proportion of cases the country defaults. Yet this is what lenders want to know and credit-rating agencies have to assess. Maybe another approach is needed.

The subjective view

According to the subjective view, probability is a degree of belief that someone holds about the likelihood of an event occurring. It is inevitably subjective and therefore some argue that it should be the degree of belief that it is *rational* to hold, but this just shifts the argument to what is meant by 'rational'. Some progress can be made by distinguishing between prior and posterior beliefs. The former are those held before any evidence is considered; the latter are the modified probabilities in the light of the evidence. For example, one might initially believe a coin to be fair (the prior probability of heads is one-half), but not after seeing only five heads in fifty tosses (the posterior probability would be less than a half).

Although it has its attractions, this approach (which is the basis of Bayesian statistics) also has its drawbacks. It is not always clear how one should arrive at the prior beliefs, particularly when one really has no prior information. Also, these methods often require the use of sophisticated mathematics, which may account for the limited use made of them. The development of more powerful computers and user-friendly software may increase the popularity of the Bayesian approach.

There is not universal agreement therefore as to the precise definition of probability. We do not have space here to explore the issue further, so we will ignore the problem! The probability of an event occurring will be defined as a certain value and we will not worry about the precise origin or meaning of that value. This is an axiomatic approach: we simply state what the probability is, without justifying it, and then examine the consequences.

Exercise 2.1

(a) Define the probability of an event according to the frequentist view.

(b) Define the probability of an event according to the subjective view.

Exercise 2.2

For the following events, suggest how their probability might be calculated. In each case, consider whether you have used the frequentist or subjective view of probability (or possibly some mixture).

(a) The Republican party winning the next US election.

(b) The number 5 being the first ball drawn in next week's lottery.

(c) A repetition of the 2004 Asian tsunami.

(d) Your train home being late.

Probability theory: the building blocks

We start with a few definitions, to establish a vocabulary that we will subsequently use.

- An experiment is an action such as flipping a coin, which has a number of possible outcomes or events, such as heads or tails.
- A trial is a single performance of the experiment, with a single outcome.
- The sample space consists of all the possible outcomes of the experiment. The outcomes for a single toss of a coin are {heads, tails}, for example, and these constitute the sample space for a toss of a coin. The outcomes in the sample space are mutually exclusive, which means that the occurrence of one rules out all the others. One cannot have both heads and tails in a single toss of a coin. As a further example, if a single card is drawn at random from a pack, then the sample space may be drawn as in Figure 2.2. Each point represents one card in the pack and there are 52 points altogether. (The sample space could be set out in alternative ways. For instance, one could write a list of all the cards: ace of spades, king of spades, . . . , two of clubs. One can choose the representation most suitable for the problem at hand.)
- With each outcome in the sample space we can associate a probability, which is the chance of that outcome occurring. The probability of heads is one-half; the probability of drawing the ace of spades from a pack of cards is one in 52, etc.

There are restrictions upon the probabilities we can associate with the outcomes in the sample space. These are needed to ensure that we do not come up with self-contradictory results; for example, it would be odd to arrive at the conclusion that we could expect heads more than half the time *and* tails more than half the time. To ensure our results are always consistent, the following rules apply to probabilities:

- The probability of an event must lie between 0 and 1, i.e.

$$0 \leqslant \Pr(A) \leqslant 1, \text{ for any event } A \tag{2.1}$$

The explanation is straightforward. If A is certain to occur it occurs in 100% of all trials and so its probability is 1. If A is certain not to occur then its probability is 0, since it never happens however many trials there are. As one cannot be more certain than certain, probabilities of less than 0 or more than 1 can never occur, and equation (2.1) follows.

- The sum of the probabilities associated with all the outcomes in the sample space is 1. Formally

$$\sum P_i = 1 \tag{2.2}$$

Figure 2.2
The sample space for drawing from a pack of cards

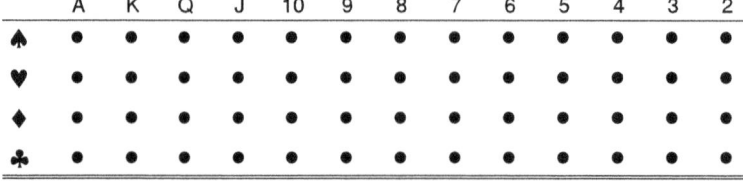

	A	K	Q	J	10	9	8	7	6	5	4	3	2
♠	•	•	•	•	•	•	•	•	•	•	•	•	•
♥	•	•	•	•	•	•	•	•	•	•	•	•	•
♦	•	•	•	•	•	•	•	•	•	•	•	•	•
♣	•	•	•	•	•	•	•	•	•	•	•	•	•

where P_i is the probability of event i occurring. This follows from the fact that one, and only one, of the outcomes *must* occur, since they are mutually exclusive and also exhaustive, i.e. they define all the possibilities.

● Following on from equation (2.2) we may define the complement of an event as everything in the sample space apart from that event. The complement of heads is tails, for example. If we write the complement of A as not-A then it follows that $\text{Pr}(A) + \text{Pr}(\text{not-}A) = 1$ and hence

$$\text{Pr}(\text{not-}A) = 1 - \text{Pr}(A) \tag{2.3}$$

Compound events

Most practical problems require the calculation of the probability of a set of outcomes rather than just a single one, or the probability of a series of outcomes in separate trials. For example, the probability of drawing a spade at random from a pack of cards encompasses 13 points in the sample space (one for each spade). This probability is 13 out of 52, or one-quarter, which is fairly obvious; but for more complex problems the answer is not immediately evident. We refer to such sets of outcomes as compound events. Some examples are getting a five *or* a six on a throw of a die or drawing an ace *and* a queen to complete a 'straight' in a game of poker.

It is sometimes possible to calculate the probability of a compound event by examining the sample space, as in the case of drawing a spade above. However, in many cases this is not so, for the sample space is too complex or even impossible to write down. For example, the sample space for three draws of a card from a pack consists of over 140 000 points! (A typical point might be, for example, the ten of spades, eight of hearts and three of diamonds.) An alternative method is needed. Fortunately there are a few simple rules for manipulating probabilities which help us to calculate the probabilities of compound events.

If the previous examples are examined closely it can be seen that outcomes are being compounded using the words 'or' and 'and': '. . . five *or* six on a single throw . . .'; '. . . an ace *and* a queen . . .'. 'And' and 'or' act as operators, and compound events are made up of simple events compounded by these two operators. The following rules for manipulating probabilities show how to use these operators and thus how to calculate the probability of a compound event.

The addition rule

This rule is associated with 'or'. When we want the probability of one outcome *or* another occurring, we add the probabilities of each. More formally, the probability of A or B occurring is given by

$$\text{Pr}(A \text{ or } B) = \text{Pr}(A) + \text{Pr}(B) \tag{2.4}$$

So, for example, the probability of a five or a six on a roll of a die is

$$\text{Pr}(5 \text{ or } 6) = \text{Pr}(5) + \text{Pr}(6) = 1/6 + 1/6 = 1/3 \tag{2.5}$$

This answer can be verified from the sample space, as shown in Figure 2.3. Each dot represents a simple event (one to six). The compound event is made up of two of the six points, shaded in Figure 2.3, so the probability is 2/6 or 1/3.

However, equation (2.4) is not a general solution to this type of problem, i.e. it does not *always* work, as can be seen from the following example. What is the probability of a queen or a spade in a single draw from a pack of cards? $\Pr(Q) =$ 4/52 (four queens in the pack) and $\Pr(S) = 13/52$ (13 spades), so applying equation (2.4) gives

$$\Pr(Q \text{ or } S) = \Pr(Q) + \Pr(S) = 4/52 + 13/52 = 17/52 \qquad (2.6)$$

However, if the sample space is examined, the correct answer is found to be 16/52, as in Figure 2.4. The problem is that one point in the sample space (the one representing the queen of spades) is double-counted, once as a queen and again as a spade. The event 'drawing a queen *and* a spade' is possible, and gets double-counted. Equation (2.4) has to be modified by subtracting the probability of getting a queen *and* a spade, to eliminate this double counting. The correct answer is obtained from

$$\begin{aligned} \Pr(Q \text{ or } S) &= \Pr(Q) + \Pr(S) - \Pr(Q \text{ and } S) \\ &= 4/52 + 13/52 - 1/52 \\ &= 16/52 \end{aligned} \qquad (2.7)$$

The general rule is therefore

$$\Pr(A \text{ or } B) = \Pr(A) + \Pr(B) - \Pr(A \text{ and } B) \qquad (2.8)$$

Rule (2.4) worked for the die example because $\Pr(5 \text{ and } 6) = 0$ since a five and a six cannot simultaneously occur. The double counting did not affect the calculation of the probability.

In general, therefore, one should use equation (2.8), but when two events are mutually exclusive the rule simplifies to equation (2.4).

The multiplication rule

The multiplication rule is associated with use of the word 'and' to combine events. Consider a mother with two children. What is the probability that they are both boys? This is really a compound event: a boy on the first birth *and* a boy on the second. Assume that in a single birth a boy or girl is equally likely, so $\Pr(\text{boy}) = \Pr(\text{girl}) = 0.5$. Denote by $\Pr(B1)$ the probability of a boy on the first birth and by $\Pr(B2)$ the probability of a boy on the second. Thus the question asks for $\Pr(B1 \text{ and } B2)$ and this is given by

$$Pr(B1 \text{ and } B2) = Pr(B1) \times Pr(B2) = 0.5 \times 0.5$$
$$= 0.25$$

(2.9)

Intuitively, the multiplication rule can be understood as follows. One-half of mothers have a boy on their first birth and of these, one-half will again have a boy on the second. Therefore a quarter (a half of one-half) of mothers have two boys.

Like the addition rule, the multiplication rule requires slight modification before it can be applied generally and give the right answer in all circumstances. The example assumes first and second births to be independent events, i.e. that having a boy on the first birth does not affect the probability of a boy on the second. This assumption is not always valid.

Write $Pr(B2|B1)$ to indicate the probability of the event $B2$ *given* that the event $B1$ has occurred. (This is known as the conditional probability, more precisely the probability of $B2$ conditional upon $B1$.) Let us drop the independence assumption and suppose the following

$$Pr(B1) = Pr(G1) = 0.5$$

(2.10)

i.e. boys and girls are equally likely on the first birth, and

$$Pr(B2|B1) = Pr(G2|G1) = 0.6$$

(2.11)

i.e. a boy is more likely to be followed by another boy, and a girl by another girl. (It is easy to work out $Pr(B2|G1)$ and $Pr(G2|B1)$. What are they?)

Now what is the probability of two boys? Half of all mothers have a boy first, and of these, 60% have another boy. Thus 30% (60% of 50%) of mothers have two boys. This is obtained from the rule

$$Pr(B1 \text{ and } B2) = Pr(B1) \times Pr(B2|B1)$$
$$= 0.5 \times 0.6$$
$$= 0.3$$

(2.12)

Thus in general we have

$$Pr(A \text{ and } B) = Pr(A) \times Pr(B|A)$$

(2.13)

which simplifies to

$$Pr(A \text{ and } B) = Pr(A) \times Pr(B)$$

(2.14)

if A and B are independent.

Independence may therefore be defined as follows: two events, A and B, are independent if the probability of one occurring is not influenced by the fact of the other having occurred. Formally, if A and B are independent then

$$Pr(B|A) = Pr(B|\text{not } A) = Pr(B)$$

(2.15)

and

$$Pr(A|B) = Pr(A|\text{not } B) = Pr(A)$$

(2.16)

The concept of independence is an important one in statistics, as it usually simplifies problems considerably. If two variables are known to be independent then we can analyse the behaviour of one without worrying about what is happening to the other variable. For example, sales of computers are independent of temperature, so if one is trying to predict sales next month one does not need to worry about the weather. In contrast, ice cream sales do depend on the weather, so predicting sales accurately requires one to forecast the weather first.

Intuition does not always work with probabilities!

Counter-intuitive results frequently arise in probability, which is why it is wise to use the rules to calculate probabilities in tricky situations, rather than rely on intuition. Take the following questions:

- What is the probability of obtaining two heads (HH) in two tosses of a coin?
- What is the probability of obtaining tails followed by heads (TH)?
- If a coin is tossed until either HH or TH occurs, what are the probabilities of each sequence occurring first?

The answers to the first two are easy: $\frac{1}{2} \times \frac{1}{2} = \frac{1}{4}$ in each case. You might therefore conclude that each sequence is equally likely to be the first observed, but you would be wrong!

Unless HH occurs on the first two tosses, then TH *must* occur first. HH is therefore the first sequence *only* if it occurs on the first two tosses, which has a probability of $\frac{1}{4}$. The probability that TH is first is therefore $\frac{3}{4}$. The probabilities are unequal, a strange result. Now try the same thing with HHH and THH and three tosses of a coin.

Combining the addition and multiplication rules

More complex problems can be solved by suitable combinations of the addition and multiplication formulae. For example, what is the probability of a mother having one child of each sex? This could occur in one of two ways: a girl followed by a boy or a boy followed by a girl. It is important to note that these are two different routes to the same outcome. Therefore we have (assuming non-independence according to equation (2.11))

$$
\begin{aligned}
\Pr(1 \text{ girl}, 1 \text{ boy}) &= \Pr((G1 \text{ and } B2) \text{ or } (B1 \text{ and } G2)) \\
&= \Pr(G1) \times \Pr(B2|G1) + \Pr(B1) \times \Pr(G2|B1) \\
&= (0.5 \times 0.4) + (0.5 \times 0.4) \\
&= 0.4
\end{aligned}
$$

The answer can be checked if we remember equation (2.2) stating that probabilities must sum to 1. We have calculated the probability of two boys (0.3) and of a child of each sex (0.4). The only other possibility is of two girls. This probability must be 0.3, the same as two boys, since boys and girls are treated symmetrically in this problem (even with the non-independence assumption). The sum of the three possibilities (two boys, one of each or two girls) is therefore $0.3 + 0.4 + 0.3 = 1$, as it should be. This is often a useful check to make, especially if one is unsure that one's calculations are correct.

Note that the problem would have been different if we had asked for the probability of the mother having one girl with a younger brother.

Tree diagrams

The preceding problem can be illustrated using a tree diagram, which often helps to clarify a problem. A tree diagram is an alternative way of enumerating

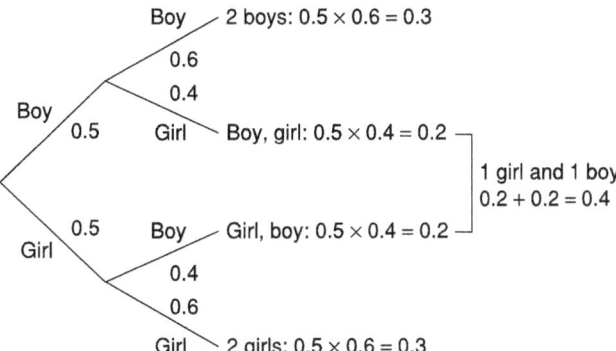

Figure 2.5
Tree diagram for a
family with two children

all possible outcomes in the sample space, with the associated probabilities. The diagram for two children is shown in Figure 2.5.

The diagram begins at the left and the first node shows the possible alternatives (boy, girl) at that point and the associated probabilities (0.5, 0.5). The next two nodes show the alternatives and probabilities for the second birth, given the sex of the first child. The final four nodes show the possible results: {boy, boy}; {boy, girl}; {girl, boy}; and {girl, girl}.

To find the probability of two girls, using the tree diagram, follow the lowest path, multiplying the probabilities along it to give $0.5 \times 0.6 = 0.3$. To find the probability of one child of each sex it is necessary to follow all the routes which lead to such an outcome. There are two in this case: leading to boy, girl and to girl, boy. Each of these has a probability of 0.2, obtained by multiplying the probabilities along that branch of the tree. Adding these together (since either one *or* the other leads to the desired outcome) yields the answer, giving $0.2 + 0.2 = 0.4$. This provides a graphical alternative to the formulae used above and may help comprehension.

The tree diagram can obviously be extended to cover third and subsequent children although the number of branches rapidly increases (in geometric progression). The difficulty then becomes not just the calculation of the probability attached to each outcome, but sorting out which branches should be taken into account in the calculation. Suppose we consider a family of five children of whom three are girls. To simplify matters we again assume independence of probabilities. The appropriate tree diagram has $2^5 = 32$ end-points, each with probability 1/32. How many of these relate to families with three girls and two boys, for example? One can draw the diagram and count them, yielding the answer 10, but it takes considerable time and is prone to error. Far better would be to use a formula. To develop this, we use the ideas of combinations and permutations.

Combinations and permutations

How can we establish the number of ways of having three girls and two boys in a family of five children? One way would be to write down all the possible orderings:

GGGBB GGBGB GGBBG GBGGB GBGBG
GBBGG BGGGB BGGBG BGBGG BBGGG

This shows that there are 10 such orderings, so the probability of three girls and two boys in a family of five children is 10/32. In more complex problems this soon becomes difficult or impossible. The record number of children born to a British mother is 39 (!) of whom 32 were girls. The appropriate tree diagram has over five thousand billion 'routes' through it, and drawing one line (i.e. for one child) per second would imply 17 433 years to complete the task! Rather than do this, we use the combinatorial formula to find the answer. Suppose there are n children, r of them girls, then the number of orderings, denoted nCr, is obtained from[1]

$$nCr = \frac{n!}{r!(n-r)!}$$

$$= \frac{n \times (n-1) \times \ldots \times 1}{\{r \times (r-1) \times \ldots \times 1\} \times \{(n-r) \times (n-r-1) \times \ldots \times 1\}} \tag{2.17}$$

In the above example $n = 5$, $r = 3$ so the number of orderings is

$$5C3 = \frac{5 \times 4 \times 3 \times 2 \times 1}{\{3 \times 2 \times 1\} \times \{2 \times 1\}} = 10 \tag{2.18}$$

If there were four girls out of five children then the number of orderings or combinations would be

$$5C4 = \frac{5 \times 4 \times 3 \times 2 \times 1}{\{4 \times 3 \times 2 \times 1\} \times 1} = 5 \tag{2.19}$$

This gives five possible orderings, i.e. the single boy could be the first, second, third, fourth or fifth born.

Why does this formula work? Consider five empty places to fill, corresponding to the five births in chronological order. Take the case of three girls (call them Amanda, Bridget and Caroline for convenience) who have to fill three of the five places. For Amanda there is a choice of five empty places. Having 'chosen' one, there remain four for Bridget, so there are $5 \times 4 = 20$ possibilities (i.e. ways in which these two could choose their places). Three remain for Caroline, so there are 60 (= $5 \times 4 \times 3$) possible orderings in all (the two boys take the two remaining places). Sixty is the number of permutations of three *named* girls in five births. This is written $5P3$ or in general nPr. Hence

$$5P3 = 5 \times 4 \times 3$$

or in general

$$nPr = n \times (n-1) \times \ldots \times (n-r+1) \tag{2.20}$$

A simpler formula is obtained by multiplying and dividing by $(n-r)!$

$$nPr = \frac{n \times (n-r) \times \ldots \times (n-r+1) \times (n-r)!}{(n-r)!} = \frac{n!}{(n-r)!} \tag{2.21}$$

---

[1] $n!$ is read 'n factorial' and is defined as the product of all the integers up to and including n. Thus, for example, $3! = 3 \times 2 \times 1 = 6$.

What is the difference between *nPr* and *nCr*? The latter does not distinguish between the girls; the two cases Amanda, Bridget, Caroline, boy, boy and Bridget, Amanda, Caroline, boy, boy are effectively the same (three girls followed by two boys). So *nPr* is larger by a factor representing the number of ways of ordering the three girls. This factor is given by $r! = 3 \times 2 \times 1 = 6$ (any of the three girls could be first, either of the other two second, and then the final one). Thus to obtain *nCr* one must divide *nPr* by $r!$, giving (2.17).

Exercise 2.3

(a) A dart is thrown at a dartboard. What is the sample space for this experiment?

(b) An archer has a 30% chance of hitting the bull's eye on the target. What is the complement to this event and what is its probability?

(c) What is the probability of two mutually exclusive events both occurring?

(d) A spectator reckons there is a 70% probability of an American rider winning the Tour de France and a 40% probability of Frenchman winning. Comment.

Exercise 2.4

(a) For the archer in Exercise 2.3(b) what is the probability that she hits the target with one (and only one) of two arrows?

(b) What is the probability that she hits the target with both arrows?

(c) Explain the importance of the assumption of independence for the answers to both parts (a) and (b) of this exercise.

(d) If the archer becomes more confident after a successful shot (i.e. her probability of a shot on target rises to 50%) and less confident (probability falls to 20%) after a miss, how would this affect the answers to parts (a) and (b)?

Exercise 2.5

(a) Draw the tree diagrams associated with Exercise 2.4. You will need one for the case of independence of events, one for non-independence.

(b) Extend the diagram (assuming independence) to a third arrow. Use this to mark out the paths with two successful shots out of three. Calculate the probability of two hits out of three shots.

(c) Repeat part (b) for the case of non-independence. For this you may assume that a hit raises the problem of success with the next arrow to 50%. A miss lowers it to 20%.

Exercise 2.6

(a) Show how the answer to Exercise 2.5(b) may be arrived at using algebra, including the use of the combinatorial formula.

(b) Repeat part (a) for the non-independence case.

Bayes' theorem

Bayes' theorem is a factual statement about probabilities, which in itself is uncontroversial. However, the use and interpretation of the result is at the heart of the difference between classical and Bayesian statistics. The theorem itself is easily derived from first principles. Equation (2.22) is similar to equation (2.13) covered earlier when discussing the multiplication rule

$$\Pr(A \text{ and } B) = \Pr(A|B) \times \Pr(B) \tag{2.22}$$

hence

$$\Pr(A|B) = \frac{\Pr(A \text{ and } B)}{\Pr(B)} \tag{2.23}$$

Expanding both top and bottom of the right-hand side

$$\Pr(A|B) = \frac{\Pr(B|A) \times \Pr(A)}{\Pr(B|A) \times \Pr(A) + \Pr(B|\text{not } A) \times \Pr(\text{not } A)} \tag{2.24}$$

Equation (2.24) is known as Bayes' theorem and is a statement about the probability of the event A, conditional upon B having occurred. The following example demonstrates its use.

Two bags contain red and yellow balls. Bag A contains six red and four yellow balls, bag B has three red and seven yellow balls. A ball is drawn at random from one bag and turns out to be red. What is the probability that it came from bag A? Since bag A has relatively more red balls to yellow balls than does bag B, it seems bag A ought to be favoured. The probability should be more than 0.5. We can check if this is correct.

Denoting

$\Pr(A) = 0.5$ (the probability of choosing bag A at random) $= \Pr(B)$

$\Pr(R|A) = 0.6$ (the probability of selecting a red ball from bag A), etc.

we have

$$\Pr(A|R) = \frac{\Pr(R|A) \times \Pr(A)}{\Pr(R|A) \times \Pr(A) + \Pr(R|B) \times \Pr(B)} \tag{2.25}$$

using Bayes' theorem. Evaluating this gives

$$\Pr(A|R) = \frac{0.6 \times 0.5}{0.6 \times 0.5 + 0.3 \times 0.5} \tag{2.26}$$

$$= \frac{2}{3}$$

(You can check that $\Pr(B|R) = \frac{1}{3}$ so that the sum of the probabilities is 1.) As expected, this result is greater than 0.5.

Bayes' theorem can be extended to cover more than two bags: if there are five bags, for example, labelled A to E, then

$$\Pr(A|R) = \frac{\Pr(R|A) \times \Pr(A)}{\Pr(R|A) \times \Pr(A) + \Pr(R|B) \times \Pr(B) + \ldots + \Pr(R|E) \times \Pr(E)} \tag{2.27}$$

In Bayesian language, $\Pr(A)$, $\Pr(B)$, etc., are known as the prior (to the drawing of the ball) probabilities, $\Pr(R|A)$, $\Pr(R|B)$, etc., are the likelihoods and $\Pr(A|R)$, $\Pr(B|R)$, etc., are the posterior probabilities. Bayes' theorem can alternatively be expressed as

$$\text{posterior probability} = \frac{\text{likelihood} \times \text{prior probability}}{\sum(\text{likelihoods} \times \text{prior probabilites})} \tag{2.28}$$

This is illustrated below, by reworking the above example.

	Prior probabilities	Likelihoods	Prior × likelihood	Posterior probabilities
A	0.5	0.6	0.30	0.30/0.45 = 2/3
B	0.5	0.3	0.15	0.15/0.45 = 1/3
Total			0.45	

The general version of Bayes' theorem may be stated as follows. If there are n events labelled $E_1, \ldots, E_n$ then the probability of the event E_i occurring, given the sample evidence S, is

$$\Pr(E_i|S) = \frac{\Pr(S|E_i) \times \Pr(E_i)}{\sum(\Pr(S|E_i) \times \Pr(E_i))} \tag{2.29}$$

As stated earlier, dispute arises over the interpretation of Bayes' theorem. In the above example there is no difficulty because the probability statements can be interpreted as relative frequencies. If the experiment of selecting a bag at random and choosing a ball from it were repeated many times, then of those occasions when a red ball is selected, in two-thirds of them bag A will have been chosen. However, consider an alternative interpretation of the symbols:

A: a coin is fair;
B: a coin is unfair;
R: the result of a toss is a head.

Then, given a toss (or series of tosses) of a coin, this evidence can be used to calculate the probability of the coin being fair. But this makes no sense according to the frequentist school: either the coin is fair or not; it is not a question of probability. The calculated value must be interpreted as a degree of belief and be given a subjective interpretation.

Exercise 2.7

(a) Repeat the 'balls in the bag' exercise from the text, but with bag A containing five red and three yellow balls, bag B containing one red and two yellow balls. The single ball drawn is red. Before doing the calculation, predict which bag is more likely to be the source of the drawn ball. Explain why.

(b) Bag A now contains 10 red and six yellow balls (i.e. twice as many as before, but in the same proportion). Does this alter the answer you obtained in part (a)?

(c) Set out your answer to part (b) in the form of prior probabilities and likelihoods, in order to obtain the posterior probability.

Decision analysis

The study of probability naturally leads on to the analysis of decision making where risk is involved. This is the realistic situation facing most firms and the use of probability can help to illuminate the problem. To illustrate the topic, we use the example of a firm facing a choice of three different investment projects. The uncertainty that the firm faces concerns the interest rate at which to discount the future flows of income. If the interest/discount rate is high then projects which have income far in the future become less attractive relative to

Table 2.1 Data for decision analysis: present values of three investment projects at different interest rates (£000)

Project	Future interest rate			
	4%	5%	6%	7%
A	1475	1363	1200	1115
B	1500	1380	1148	1048
C	1650	1440	1200	810
Probability	0.1	0.4	0.4	0.1

projects with more immediate returns. A low rate reverses this conclusion. The question is: which project should the firm select? As we shall see, there is no unique, right answer to the question but, using probability theory we can see why the answer might vary.

Table 2.1 provides the data required for the problem. The three projects are imaginatively labelled A, B and C. There are four possible states of the world, i.e. future scenarios, each with a different interest rate, as shown across the top of the table. This is the only source of uncertainty, otherwise the states of the world are identical. The figures in the body of the table show the present value of each income stream at the given discount rate.

Present value

The present value of future income is its value today and is obtained using the interest rate. For example, if the interest rate is 10%, the present value (i.e. today) of £110 received in one year's time is £100. In other words, one could invest £100 today at 10% and have £110 in one year's time. £100 today and £110 next year are equivalent.

The present value of £110 received in two years' time is smaller since one has to wait longer to receive it. It is calculated as £110/1.1^2 = 90.91. Again, £90.91 invested at 10% per annum will yield £110 in two years' time. After one year it is worth £90.91 × 1.1 = 100 and after a second year that £100 becomes £110. Notice that, if the interest rate rises, the present value falls. For example, if the interest rate is 20%, £110 next year is worth only £110/1.2 = 91.67 today.

The present value of £110 in one year's time and another £110 in two years' time is £110/1.1 + £110/1.1^2 = £190.91. The present value of more complicated streams of income can be calculated by extension of this principle. In the example used in the text you do not need to worry about how the present value is arrived at. Before reading on you may wish to do Exercise 2.8 to practise calculation of present value.

Thus, for example, if the interest rate turns out to be 4% then project A has a present value of £1 475 000 while B's is £1 500 000. If the discount rate turns out to be 5% the PV for A is £1 363 000 while for B it has changed to £1 380 000. Obviously, as the discount rate rises, the present value of the return falls. (Alternatively, we could assume that a higher interest rate increases the cost of borrowing to finance the project, which reduces its profitability.) We assume that each project requires a (certain) initial outlay of £1 100 000 with which the *PV* should be compared.

The final row of the table shows the probabilities which the firm attaches to each interest rate. These are obviously someone's subjective probabilities and are symmetric around a central value of 5.5%.

Exercise 2.8

(a) At an interest or discount rate of 10%, what is the present value of £1200 received in one year's time?

(b) If the interest rate rises to 15%, how is the present value altered? The interest rate has risen by 50% (from 10% to 15%): how has the present value changed?

(c) At an interest rate of 10% what is the present value of £1200 received in (i) two years' time and (ii) five years' time?

(d) An income of £500 is received at the end of years one, two and three (i.e. £1500 in total). What is its present value? Assume r = 10%.

(e) Project *A* provides an income of £300 after one year and another £600 after two years. Project *B* provides £400 and £488 at the same times. At a discount rate of 10% which project has the higher present value? What happens if the discount rate rises to 20%?

Decision criteria: maximising the expected value

We need to decide how a decision is to be made on the basis of these data. The first criterion involves the expected value of each project. Because of the uncertainty about the interest rate there is no single present value for each project. We therefore calculate the expected value, using the E operator which was introduced in Chapter 1. In other words, we find the expected present value of each project, by taking a weighted average of the *PV* figures, the weights being the probabilities. The project with the highest expected return is chosen.

The expected values are calculated in Table 2.2. The highest expected present value is £1 302 000, associated with project *C*. On this criterion therefore, *C* is chosen. Is this a wise choice? If the business always uses this rule to evaluate many projects then in the long run it will earn the maximum profits. However, you may notice that if the interest rate turns out to be 7% then *C* would be the *worst* project to choose in this case and the firm would make a substantial loss in such circumstances. Project *C* is the most sensitive to the discount rate (it has the greatest *variance* of *PV* values of the three projects) and therefore the firm faces more risk by opting for *C*. There is a trade-off between risk and return.

Table 2.2 **Expected values of the three projects**

Project	Expected value
A	1284.2
B	1266.0
C	1302.0

Note: 1284.2 is calculated as 1475 × 0.1 + 1363 × 0.4 + 1200 × 0.4 + 1115 × 0.1. This is the weighted average of the four *PV* values. A similar calculation is performed for the other projects.

Table 2.3 **The maximin criterion**

Project	Minimum
A	1115
B	1048
C	810
Maximum	1115

Perhaps some alternative criteria should be looked at. These we look at next, in particular the maximin, maximax and minimax regret strategies.

Maximin, maximax and minimax regret

The maximin criterion looks at the worst-case scenario for each project and then selects the project which does best in these circumstances. It is inevitably a pessimistic or cautious view therefore. Table 2.3 illustrates the calculation. This time we observe that project A is preferred. In the worst case (which occurs when $r = 7\%$ for all projects) then A does best, with a PV of £1 115 000 and therefore a slight profit. The maximin criterion may be a good one in business where managers tend to over-optimism. Calculating the maximin may be a salutary exercise, even if it is not the ultimate deciding factor.

The opposite criterion is the optimistic one where the maximax criterion is used. In this case one looks at the *best* circumstances for each project and chooses the best-performing project. Each project does best when the interest rate is at its lowest level, 3%. Examining the first column of Table 2.1 shows that project C (PV = 1650) performs best and is therefore chosen. Given the earlier warning about over-optimistic managers, this may not be suitable as the sole criterion for making investment decisions.

A final criterion is that of minimax regret. If project B were chosen but the interest rate turns out to be 7% then we would regret not having chosen A, the best project under these circumstances. Our *regret* would be the extent of the difference between the two, a matter of $1115 - 1048 = 67$. Similarly, the regret if we had chosen C would be $1115 - 810 = 305$. We can calculate these regrets at the other interest rates too, always comparing the PV of a project with the best PV given that interest rate. This gives us Table 2.4.

The final column of the table shows the maximum regret for each project. The minimax regret criterion is to choose the minimum of these figures. This is

Table 2.4 **The costs of taking the wrong decision**

Project	4%	5%	6%	7%	Maximum
A	175	77	0	0	175
B	150	60	52	67	150
C	0	0	0	305	305
Minimum					150

given at the bottom of the final column; it is 150 which is associated with project *B*. A justification for using this criterion might be that you do not want to fall too far behind your competitors. If other firms are facing similar investment decisions, then the regret table shows the difference in *PV* (and hence profits) if they choose the best project while you do not. Choosing the minimax regret solution ensures that you will not fall too far behind. During the internet bubble of the 1990s it was important to gain market share and keep up with, or surpass, your competitors. The minimax regret strategy might be a useful tool during such times.

You will probably have noticed that we have managed to find a justification for choosing all three projects! No one project comes out best on all criteria. Nevertheless, the analysis might be of some help: if the investment project is one of many small, independent investments the firm is making, then this would justify use of the expected value criterion. On the other hand, if this is a big, one-off project which could possibly bankrupt the firm if it goes wrong, then the maximin criterion would be appropriate.

The expected value of perfect information

Often a firm can improve its knowledge about future possibilities via research, which costs money. This effectively means buying information about the future state of the world. The question arises: how much should a firm pay for such information? Perfect information would reveal the future state of the world with certainty – in this case, the future interest rate. In that case you could be sure of choosing the right project given each state of the world. If interest rates turn out to be 4%, the firm would invest in *C*, if 7% in *A*, and so on.

In such circumstances, the firm would expect to earn

$$(0.1 \times 1650) + (0.4 \times 1440) + (0.4 \times 1200) + (0.1 \times 1115) = 1332.5$$

i.e. the probability of each state of the world is multiplied by the *PV* of the *best* project for that state. This gives a figure which is greater than the expected value calculated earlier, without perfect information, 1302. The expected value of perfect information is therefore the difference between these two, 30.5. This sets a *maximum* to the value of information, for it is unlikely in the real world that any information about the future is going to be perfect.

Exercise 2.9

(a) Evaluate the three projects detailed in the table below, using the criteria of expected value, maximin, maximax and minimax regret. The probability of a 4% interest rate is 0.3, of 6% is 0.4 and of 8% is 0.3.

Project	4%	6%	8%
A	100	80	70
B	90	85	75
C	120	60	40

(b) What would be the value of perfect information about the interest rate?

Summary

- The theory of probability forms the basis of statistical inference: the drawing of inferences on the basis of a random sample of data. The reason for this is the probability basis of random sampling.
- A convenient definition of the probability of an event is the number of times the event occurs divided by the number of trials (occasions when the event could occur).
- For more complex events, their probabilities can be calculated by combining probabilities, using the addition and multiplication rules.
- The probability of events A or B occurring is calculated according to the addition rule.
- The probability of A and B occurring is given by the multiplication rule.
- If A and B are not independent, then $Pr(A$ and $B) = Pr(A) \times Pr(B|A)$, where $Pr(B|A)$ is the probability of B occurring given that A has occurred (the conditional probability).
- Tree diagrams are a useful technique for enumerating all the possible paths in series of probability trials, but for large numbers of trials the huge number of possibilities makes the technique impractical.
- For experiments with a large number of trials (e.g. obtaining 20 heads in 50 tosses of a coin) the formulae for combinations and permutations can be used.
- The combinatorial formula nCr gives the number of ways of combining r similar objects among n objects, e.g. the number of orderings of three girls (and hence implicitly two boys also) in five children.
- The permutation formula nPr gives the number of orderings of r distinct objects among n, e.g. three named girls among five children.
- Bayes' theorem provides a formula for calculating a conditional probability, e.g. the probability of someone being a smoker, given they have been diagnosed with cancer. It forms the basis of Bayesian statistics, allowing us to calculate the probability of a hypothesis being true, based on the sample evidence and prior beliefs. Classical statistics disputes this approach.
- Probabilities can also be used as the basis for decision making in conditions of uncertainty, using as decision criteria expected value maximisation, maximin, maximax or minimax regret.

Key terms and concepts

addition rule	minimax
Bayes' theorem	minimax regret
combinations	multiplication rule
complement	mutually exclusive
compound event	outcome or event
conditional probability	permutations
exhaustive	probability experiment
expected value of perfect information	probability of an event
frequentist approach	sample space
independent events	subjective approach
maximin	tree diagram

Problems

Some of the more challenging problems are indicated by highlighting the problem number in colour.

2.1 Given a standard pack of cards, calculate the following probabilities:

(a) drawing an ace;

(b) drawing a court card (i.e. jack, queen or king);

(c) drawing a red card;

(d) drawing three aces without replacement;

(e) drawing three aces with replacement.

2.2 The following data give duration of unemployment by age, in July 1986.

Age	Duration of unemployment (weeks)				Total (000s)	Economically active (000s)
	≤8	8–26	26–52	>52		
		(Percentage figures)				
16–19	27.2	29.8	24.0	19.0	273.4	1270
20–24	24.2	20.7	18.3	36.8	442.5	2000
25–34	14.8	18.8	17.2	49.2	531.4	3600
35–49	12.2	16.6	15.1	56.2	521.2	4900
50–59	8.9	14.4	15.6	61.2	388.1	2560
≥60	18.5	29.7	30.7	21.4	74.8	1110

The 'economically active' column gives the total of employed (not shown) plus unemployed in each age category.

(a) In what sense may these figures be regarded as probabilities? What does the figure 27.2 (top-left cell) mean following this interpretation?

(b) Assuming the validity of the probability interpretation, which of the following statements are true?

(i) The probability of an economically active adult aged 25–34, drawn at random, being unemployed is 531.4/3600.

(ii) If someone who has been unemployed for over one year is drawn at random, the probability that they are aged 16–19 is 19%.

(iii) For those aged 35–49 who became unemployed before July 1985, the probability of their still being unemployed is 56.2%.

(iv) If someone aged 50–59 is drawn at random from the economically active population, the probability of their being unemployed for eight weeks or less is 8.9%.

(v) The probability of someone aged 35–49 drawn at random from the economically active population being unemployed for between 8 and 26 weeks is 0.166 × 521.2/4900.

(c) A person is drawn at random from the population and found to have been unemployed for over one year. What is the probability that they are aged between 16 and 19?

2.3 'Odds' in horserace betting are defined as follows: 3/1 (three-to-one against) means a horse is expected to win once for every three times it loses; 3/2 means two wins out of five races; 4/5 (five to four *on*) means five wins for every four defeats, etc.

(a) Translate the above odds into 'probabilities' of victory.

(b) In a three-horse race, the odds quoted are 2/1, 6/4, and 1/1. What makes the odds different from probabilities? Why are they different?

(c) Discuss how much the bookmaker would expect to win in the long run at such odds, assuming each horse is backed equally.

2.4 (a) Translate the following odds to 'probabilities': 13/8, 2/1 *on*, 100/30.

(b) In the 2.45 race at Plumpton on 18/10/94 the odds for the five runners were:

Philips Woody	1/1
Gallant Effort	5/2
Satin Noir	11/2
Victory Anthem	9/1
Common Rambler	16/1

Calculate the 'probabilities' and their sum.

(c) Should the bookmaker base his odds on the true probabilities of each horse winning, or on the amount bet on each horse?

2.5 How might you estimate the probability of Peru defaulting on its debt repayments next year?

2.6 How might you estimate the probability of a corporation reneging on its bond payments?

2.7 Judy is 33, unmarried and assertive. She is a graduate in political science, and involved in union activities and anti-discrimination movements. Which of the following statements do you think is more probable?

(a) Judy is a bank clerk.

(b) Judy is a bank clerk, active in the feminist movement.

2.8 In March 1994 a news item revealed that a London 'gender' clinic (which reportedly enables you to choose the sex of your child) had just set up in business. Of its first six births, two were of the 'wrong' sex. Assess this from a probability point of view.

2.9 A newspaper advertisement reads 'The sex of your child predicted, or your money back!' Discuss this advertisement from the point of view of (a) the advertiser and (b) the client.

2.10 'Roll six sixes to win a Mercedes!' is the announcement at a fair. You have to roll six dice. If you get six sixes you win the car, valued at £20 000. The entry ticket costs £1. What is your expected gain or loss on this game? The organisers of the fair have to take out insurance against the car being won. This costs £250 for the day. Does this seem a fair premium? If not, why not?

2.11 At another stall, you have to toss a coin numerous times. If a head does not appear in 20 tosses you win £1 bn. The entry fee for the game is £100.

(a) What are your expected winnings?

(b) Would you play?

2.12   A four-engine plane can fly as long as at least two of its engines work. A two-engine plane flies as long as at least one engine works. The probability of an individual engine failure is 1 in 1000.

   (a) Would you feel safer in a four- or two-engine plane, and why? Calculate the probabilities of an accident for each type.

   (b) How much safer is one type than the other?

   (c) What crucial assumption are you making in your calculation? Do you think it is valid?

2.13   Which of the following events are independent?

   (a) Two flips of a fair coin.

   (b) Two flips of a biased coin.

   (c) Rainfall on two successive days.

   (d) Rainfall on St Swithin's day and rain one month later.

2.14   Which of the following events are independent?

   (a) A student getting the first two questions correct in a multiple-choice exam.

   (b) A driver having an accident in successive years.

   (c) IBM and Dell earning positive profits next year.

   (d) Arsenal Football Club winning on successive weekends.

   How is the answer to (b) reflected in car insurance premiums?

2.15   Manchester United beat Liverpool 4–2 at soccer, but you do not know the order in which the goals were scored. Draw a tree diagram to display all the possibilities and use it to find (a) the probability that the goals were scored in the order L, MU, MU, MU, L, MU, and (b) the probability that the score was 2–2 at some stage.

2.16   An important numerical calculation on a spacecraft is carried out independently by three computers. If all arrive at the same answer, it is deemed correct. If one disagrees, it is overruled. If there is no agreement then a fourth computer does the calculation and, if its answer agrees with any of the others, it is deemed correct. The probability of an individual computer getting the answer right is 99%. Use a tree diagram to find:

   (a) the probability that the first three computers get the right answer;

   (b) the probability of getting the right answer;

   (c) the probability of getting no answer;

   (d) the probability of getting the wrong answer.

2.17   The French national lottery works as follows. Six numbers from the range 0 to 49 are chosen at random. If you have correctly guessed all six you win the first prize. What are your chances of winning if you are only allowed to choose six numbers? A single entry like this costs €1. For €210 you can choose 10 numbers and you win if the six selected numbers are among them. Is this better value than the single entry?

2.18   The UK national lottery works as follows. You choose six (different) numbers in the range 1 to 49. If all six come up in the draw (in any order) you win the first prize, expected to be around £2m (which could be shared if someone else chooses the six winning numbers).

(a) What is your chance of winning with a single ticket?

(b) You win a second prize if you get five out of six right, *and* your final chosen number matches the 'bonus' number in the draw (also in the range 1 to 49). What is the probability of winning a second prize?

(c) Calculate the probabilities of winning a third, fourth or fifth prize, where a third prize is won by matching five out of the six numbers, a fourth prize by matching four out of six and a fifth prize by matching three out of six.

(d) What is the probability of winning a prize?

(e) The prizes are as follows:

Prize	Value	
First	£2 m	(expected, possibly shared)
Second	£100 000	(expected, for each winner)
Third	£1500	(expected, for each winner)
Fourth	£65	(expected, for each winner)
Fifth	£10	(guaranteed, for each winner)

Comment upon the distribution of the fund between first, second, etc., prizes.

(f) Why is the fifth prize guaranteed whereas the others are not?

(g) In the first week of the lottery, 49 million tickets were sold. There were 1 150 000 winners, of which 7 won (a share of) the jackpot, 39 won a second prize, 2139 won a third prize and 76 731 a fourth prize. Are you surprised by these results or are they as you would expect?

2.19   A coin is either fair or has two heads. You initially assign probabilities of 0.5 to each possibility. The coin is then tossed twice, with two heads appearing. Use Bayes' theorem to work out the posterior probabilities of each possible outcome.

2.20   A test for AIDS is 99% successful, i.e. if you are HIV+ it will detect it in 99% of all tests, and if you are not, it will again be right 99% of the time. Assume that about 1% of the population are HIV+. You take part in a random testing procedure, which gives a positive result. What is the probability that you are HIV+? What implications does your result have for AIDS testing?

2.21   (a) Your initial belief is that a defendant in a court case is guilty with probability 0.5. A witness comes forward claiming he saw the defendant commit the crime. You know the witness is not totally reliable and tells the truth with probability p. Use Bayes' theorem to calculate the posterior probability that the defendant is guilty, based on the witness's evidence.

(b) A second witness, equally unreliable, comes forward and claims she saw the defendant commit the crime. Assuming the witnesses are not colluding, what is your posterior probability of guilt?

(c) If $p < 0.5$, compare the answers to (a) and (b). How do you account for this curious result?

2.22   A man is mugged and claims that the mugger had red hair. In police investigations of such cases, the victim was able correctly to identify the assailant's hair colour 80% of the time. Assuming that 10% of the population have red hair, what is the probability that the assailant in this case did, in fact, have red hair? Guess the answer first, then find the right answer using Bayes' theorem. What are the implications of your results for juries' interpretation of evidence in court, particularly in relation to racial minorities?

2.23   A firm has a choice of three projects, with profits as indicated below, dependent upon the state of demand.

Project	Demand		
	Low	Middle	High
A	100	140	180
B	130	145	170
C	110	130	200
Probability	0.25	0.45	0.3

(a) Which project should be chosen on the expected value criterion?

(b) Which project should be chosen on the maximin and maximax criteria?

(c) Which project should be chosen on the minimax regret criterion?

(d) What is the expected value of perfect information to the firm?

2.24   A firm can build a small, medium or large factory, with anticipated profits from each dependent upon the state of demand, as in the table below.

Factory	Demand		
	Low	Middle	High
Small	300	320	330
Medium	270	400	420
Large	50	250	600
Probability	0.3	0.5	0.2

(a) Which project should be chosen on the expected value criterion?

(b) Which project should be chosen on the maximin and maximax criteria?

(c) Which project should be chosen on the minimax regret criterion?

(d) What is the expected value of perfect information to the firm?

2.25   There are 25 people at a party. What is the probability that there are at least two with a birthday in common?

Hint: the *complement* is (much) easier to calculate.

2.26   This problem is tricky, but amusing. Three gunmen, A, B and C, are shooting at each other. The probabilities that each will hit what they aim at are respectively 1, 0.75, 0.5. They take it in turns to shoot (in alphabetical order) and continue until only one is left alive. Calculate the probabilities of each winning the contest. (Assume they draw lots for the right to shoot first.)

Hint 1: Start with one-on-one gunfights, e.g. the probability of A beating B, or of B beating C.

Hint 2: You'll need the formula for the sum of an infinite series, given in Chapter 1.

2.27 The BMAT test (see http://www.ucl.ac.uk/lapt/bmat/) is an on-line test for prospective medical students. It uses 'certainty based marking'. After choosing your answer from the alternatives available, you then have to give your level of confidence that your answer is correct: low, medium or high. If you choose low, you get one mark for the correct answer, zero if it is wrong. For medium confidence you get +2 or –2 marks for correct or incorrect answers. If you choose high, you get +3 or –6.

   (a) If you are 60% confident your answer is correct (i.e. you think there is a 60% probability you are right), which certainty level should you choose?

   (b) Over what range of probabilities is 'medium' the best choice?

   (c) If you were 85% confident, how many marks would you expect to lose by opting for one of the wrong choices?

2.28 A multiple choice test involves 20 questions, with four choices for each answer.

   (a) If you guessed the answers to all questions at random, what mark out of 20 would you expect to get?

   (b) If you know the correct answer to eight of the questions, what is your expected score out of 20?

   (c) The examiner wishes to correct the bias due to students guessing answers. They decide to award a negative mark for incorrect answers (with 1 for a correct answer and 0 for no answer given). What negative mark would ensure that the overall mark out of 20 is a true reflection of the student's ability?

Answers to exercises

Answer in text.

(a) A subjective view would have to be taken, informed by such things as opinion polls.

(b) 1/49, a frequentist view. Some people do add their own subjective evaluations (e.g. that 5 must come up as it has not been drawn for several weeks) but these are often unwarranted according to the frequentist approach.

(c) A mixture of objective and subjective criteria might be used here. Historical data on the occurrence of tsunamis might give a (frequentist) baseline figure, to which might be added subjective considerations such as the amount of recent seismic activity.

(d) A mixture again. Historical data give a benchmark (possibly of little relevance) while immediate factors such as the weather might alter one's subjective judgement. (As I write it is snowing outside, which seems to have a huge impact on British trains!)

(a) 1, 2, 3, . . . , 20, 21 (a triple seven), 22 (double eleven), 24, 25 (outer bull), 26, 27, 28, 30, 32, 33, 34, 36, 38, 39, 40, 42, 45, 48, 50, 51, 54, 57, 60. Or it could miss altogether!

(b) The complement is missing the target, with probability $1 - 0.3 = 70\%$.

(c) Zero, it is impossible.

(d) Impossible, the probabilities sum to more than one.

(a) $0.3 \times 0.7 + 0.7 \times 0.3 = 0.42$. This is a hit followed by a miss or a miss followed by a hit.

(b) $0.3 \times 0.3 = 0.09$.

(c) It is assumed that the probability of the second arrow hitting the target is the same as the first. Altering this assumption would affect both answers.

(d) Part (a) becomes $0.3 \times (1 - 0.5) + 0.7 \times 0.2 = 0.29$. Part (b) becomes $0.3 \times 0.5 = 0.15$.

(a) Independent case:

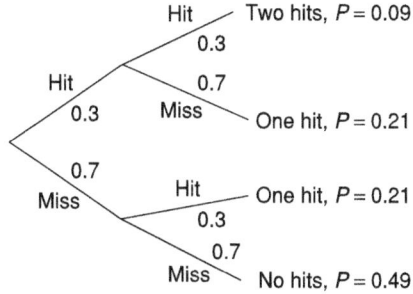

Dependent case:

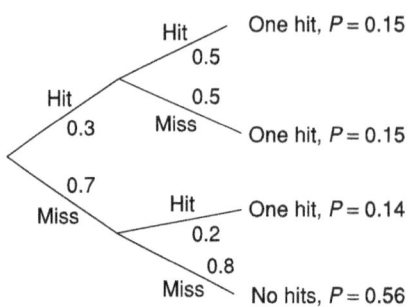

(b)

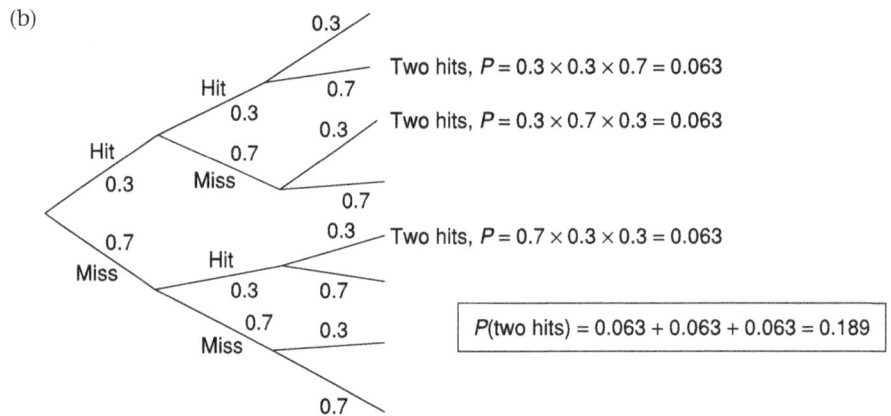

P(two hits) = 0.063 + 0.063 + 0.063 = 0.189

(c)

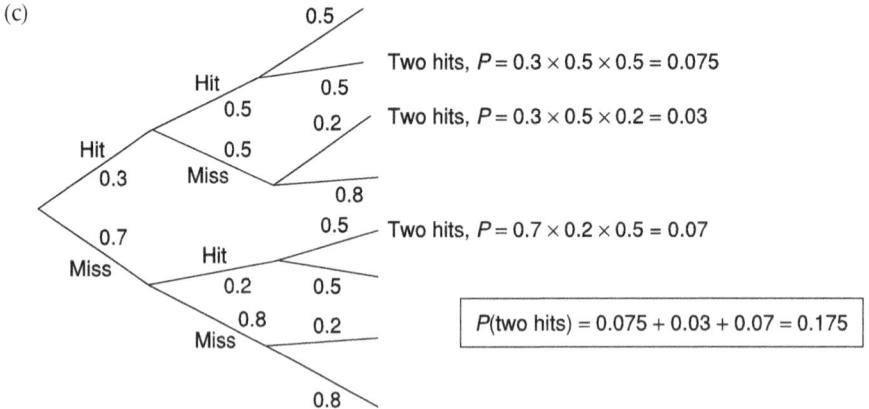

P(two hits) = 0.075 + 0.03 + 0.07 = 0.175

Exercise 2.6

(a) Pr(2 hits) = Pr(H and H and M) × 3C2 = 0.3 × 0.3 × 0.7 × 3 = 0.189.

(b) This cannot be done using the combinatorial formula, because of the non-independence of probabilities. Instead one has to calculate Pr(H and H and M) + Pr(H and M and H) + Pr(M and H and H), yielding the answer 0.175.

Exercise 2.7

(a) Bag A has proportionately more red balls than bag B, hence should be the favoured bag from which the single red ball was drawn. Performing the calculation

$$\Pr(A|R) = \frac{\Pr(R|A) \times \Pr(A)}{\Pr(R|A) \times \Pr(A) + \Pr(R|B) \times \Pr(B)}$$

$$= -\frac{0.625 \times 0.5}{0.625 \times 0.5 + 0.5 \times 0.5} = 0.556$$

(b) The result is the same, as $\Pr(R|A) = 0.625$ as before. The number of balls does not enter the calculation.

(c)	Prior probabilities	Likelihoods	Prior × likelihood	Posterior probabilities
A	0.5	0.625	0.3125	0.3125/0.5625 = 0.556
B	0.5	0.5	0.25	0.25/0.5625 = 0.444
Total			0.5625	

Exercise 2.8

(a) $1200/1.1 = 1090.91$.

(b) $1200/1.15 = 1043.48$. The PV has only changed by 4.3%. This is calculated as $1.1/1.15 - 1 = -0.043$.

(c) $1200/1.1^2 = 991.74$; $1200/1.1^5 = 745.11$.

(d) $PV = 500/1.1 + 500/1.1^2 + 500/1.1^3 = 1243.43$.

(e) At 10%: project A yields a PV of $300/1.1 + 600/1.1^2 = 768.6$. Project B yields $400/1.1 + 488/1.1^2 = 766.9$. At 20% the PVs are 666.7 and 672.2, reversing the rankings. A's large benefits in year 2 are penalised by the higher discount rate.

Exercise 2.9

(a) Project	Expected value	Minimum	Maximum
A	$0.3 \times 100 + 0.4 \times 80 + 0.3 \times 70 = 83$	70	100
B	$0.3 \times 90 + 0.4 \times 85 + 0.3 \times 75 = 83.5$	75	90
C	$0.3 \times 120 + 0.4 \times 60 + 0.3 \times 40 = 72$	40	120

The maximin is 75, associated with project B and the maximax is 120, associated with project C. The regret values are given by

	4%	6%	8%	Max
A	20	5	5	20
B	30	0	0	30
C	0	25	35	35
			Min	20

The minimax regret is 20, associated with project A.

(b) With perfect information the firm could earn $0.3 \times 120 + 0.4 \times 85 + 0.3 \times 75 = 92.5$. The highest expected value is 83.5, so the value of perfect information is $92.5 - 83.5 = 9$.

3

Probability distributions

Learning
outcomes

By the end of this chapter you should be able to:

- recognise that the result of most probability experiments (e.g. the score on a die) can be described as a random variable;

- appreciate how the behaviour of a random variable can often be summarised by a probability distribution (a mathematical formula);

- recognise the most common probability distributions and be aware of their uses;

- solve a range of probability problems using the appropriate probability distribution.

Complete your diagnostic test for Chapter 3 now to create your personal study plan. Exercises with an icon ② are also available for practice in MathXL with additional supporting resources.

Introduction

In this chapter the probability concepts introduced in Chapter 2 are generalised by using the idea of a probability distribution. A probability distribution lists, in some form, all the possible outcomes of a probability experiment and the probability associated with each one. For example, the simplest experiment is tossing a coin, for which the possible outcomes are heads or tails, each with probability one-half. The probability distribution can be expressed in a variety of ways: in words, or in a graphical or mathematical form. For tossing a coin, the graphical form is shown in Figure 3.1, and the mathematical form is

$$\Pr(H) = \tfrac{1}{2}$$
$$\Pr(T) = \tfrac{1}{2}$$

The different forms of presentation are equivalent, but one might be more suited to a particular purpose.

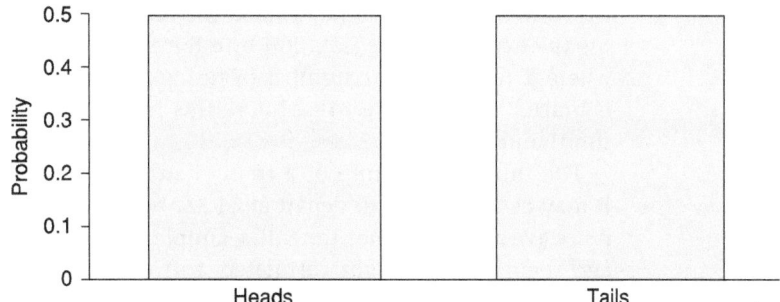

Figure 3.1
The probability distribution for the toss of a coin

Some probability distributions occur often and so are well known. Because of this they have names so we can refer to them easily; for example, the Binomial distribution or the Normal distribution. In fact, each constitutes a *family* of distributions. A single toss of a coin gives rise to one member of the Binomial distribution family; two tosses would give rise to another member of that family. These two distributions differ in the number of tosses. If a biased coin were tossed, this would lead to yet another Binomial distribution, but it would differ from the previous two because of the different probability of heads.

Members of the Binomial family of distributions are distinguished either by the number of tosses or by the probability of the event occurring. These are the two parameters of the distribution and tell us all we need to know about the distribution. Other distributions might have different numbers of parameters, with different meanings. Some distributions, for example, have only one parameter. We will come across examples of different types of distribution throughout the rest of this book.

In order to understand fully the idea of a probability distribution a new concept is first introduced, that of a random variable. As will be seen later in the chapter, an important random variable is the sample mean, and to understand how to draw inferences from the sample mean it is important to recognise it as a random variable.

Random variables

Examples of random variables have already been encountered in Chapter 2, for example, the result of the toss of a coin, or the number of boys in a family of five children. A random variable is one whose outcome or value is the result of chance and is therefore unpredictable, although the range of possible outcomes and the probability of each outcome may be known. It is impossible to know in advance the outcome of a toss of a coin for example, but it must be either heads or tails, each with probability one-half. The number of heads in 250 tosses is another random variable, which can take any value between zero and 250, although values near 125 are the most likely. You are very unlikely to get 250 heads from tossing a fair coin!

Intuitively, most people would 'expect' to get 125 heads from 250 tosses of the coin, since heads comes up half the time on average. This suggests we could use the expected value notation introduced in Chapter 1 and write $E(X) = 125$, where X represents the number of heads obtained from 250 tosses. This usage is indeed valid and we will explore this further below. It is a very convenient shorthand notation.

The time of departure of a train is another example of a random variable. It may be timetabled to depart at 11.15, but it probably (almost certainly!) will not leave at exactly that time. If a sample of ten basketball players were taken, and their average height calculated, this would be a random variable. In this latter case, it is the process of taking a sample that introduces the variability which makes the resulting average a random variable. If the experiment were repeated, a different sample and a different value of the random variable would be obtained.

The above examples can be contrasted with some things which are *not* random variables. If one were to take *all* basketball players and calculate their average height, the result would not be a random variable. This time there is no sampling procedure to introduce variability into the result. If the experiment were repeated the same result would be obtained, since the same people would be measured the second time (this assumes that the population does not change, of course). Just because the value of something is unknown does not mean it qualifies as a random variable. This is an important distinction to bear in mind, since it is legitimate to make probability statements about random variables ('the probability that the average height of a sample of basketball players is over 195 cm is 60%') but not about parameters ('the probability that the Pope is over six feet is 60%'). Here again there is a difference of opinion between frequentist and subjective schools of thought. The latter group would argue that it is possible to make probability statements about the Pope's height. It is a way of expressing lack of knowledge about the true value. The frequentists would say the Pope's height is a fact that we do not happen to know; that does not make it a random variable.

The Binomial distribution

One of the simplest distributions which a random variable can have is the Binomial. The Binomial distribution arises whenever the underlying probability experiment has just two possible outcomes, for example heads or tails from the toss of a coin. Even if the coin is tossed many times (so one could end up with one, two, three . . . , etc., heads in total) the *underlying* experiment has only two outcomes, so the Binomial distribution should be used. A counter-example would be the rolling of die, which has six possible outcomes (in this case the Multinomial distribution, not covered in this book, would be used). Note, however, that if we were interested only in rolling a six or not, we *could* use the Binomial by defining the two possible outcomes as 'six' and 'not-six'. It is often the case in statistics that by suitable transformation of the data we can use different distributions to tackle the same problem. We will see more of this later in the chapter.

The Binomial distribution can therefore be applied to the type of problem encountered in the previous chapter, concerning the sex of children. It provides a general formula for calculating the probability of r boys in n births or, in more general terms, the probability of r 'successes' in n trials.[1] We shall use it to calculate the probabilities of 0, 1, . . . , 5 boys in five births.

For the Binomial distribution to apply we first need to assume independence of successive events and we shall assume that, for any birth

$$\Pr(\text{boy}) = P = \tfrac{1}{2}$$

It follows that

$$\Pr(\text{girl}) = 1 - \Pr(\text{boy}) = 1 - P = \tfrac{1}{2}$$

Although we have $P = \tfrac{1}{2}$ in this example, the Binomial distribution can be applied for any value of P between 0 and 1.

First we consider the case of $r = 5$, $n = 5$, i.e. five boys in five births. This probability is found using the multiplication rule

$$\Pr(r = 5) = P \times P \times P \times P \times P = P^5 = (\tfrac{1}{2})^5 = 1/32$$

The probability of four boys (and then implicitly one girl) is

$$\Pr(r = 4) = P \times P \times P \times P \times (1 - P) = 1/32$$

But this gives only one possible ordering of the four boys and one girl. Our original statement of the problem did not specify a particular ordering of the children. There are five possible orderings (the single girl could be in any of five positions in rank order). Recall that we can use the combinatorial formula nCr to calculate the number of orderings, giving $5C4 = 5$. Hence the probability of four boys and one girl in any order is 5/32. Summarising, the formula for four boys and one girl is

$$\Pr(r = 4) = 5C4 \times P^4 \times (1 - P)$$

----

[1] The identification of a boy with 'success' is a purely formal one and is not meant to be pejorative!

For three boys (and two girls) we obtain

$$\Pr(r = 3) = 5C3 \times P^3 \times (1 - P)^2 = 10 \times 1/8 \times 1/4 = 10/32$$

In a similar manner

$$\Pr(r = 2) = 5C2 \times P^2 \times (1 - P)^3 = 10/32$$

$$\Pr(r = 1) = 5C1 \times P^1 \times (1 - P)^4 = 5/32$$

$$\Pr(r = 0) = 5C0 \times P^0 \times (1 - P)^5 = 1/32$$

As a check on our calculations we may note that the sum of the probabilities equals 1, as they should do, as we have enumerated all possibilities.

A fairly clear pattern emerges. The probability of r boys in n births is given by

$$\Pr(r) = nCr \times P^r \times (1 - P)^{n-r}$$

and this is known as the Binomial formula or distribution. The Binomial distribution is appropriate for analysing problems with the following characteristics:

- There is a number (n) of trials.
- Each trial has only two possible outcomes, 'success' (with probability P) and 'failure' (probability $1 - P$) and the outcomes are independent between trials.
- The probability P does not change between trials.

The probabilities calculated by the Binomial formula may be illustrated in a diagram, as shown in Figure 3.2. This is very similar to the relative frequency distribution which was introduced in Chapter 1. That distribution was based on empirical data (to do with wealth) while the Binomial probability distribution is a theoretical construction, built up from the basic principles of probability theory.

As stated earlier, the Binomial is, in fact, a family of distributions and each member of this family is distinguished by two parameters, n and P. The Binomial is thus a distribution with two parameters, and once their values are known the distribution is completely determined (i.e. $\Pr(r)$ can be calculated for all values of r). To illustrate the difference between members of the family of the Binomial distribution, Figure 3.3 presents three other Binomial distributions, for different values of P and n. It can be seen that for the value of $P = \frac{1}{2}$ the

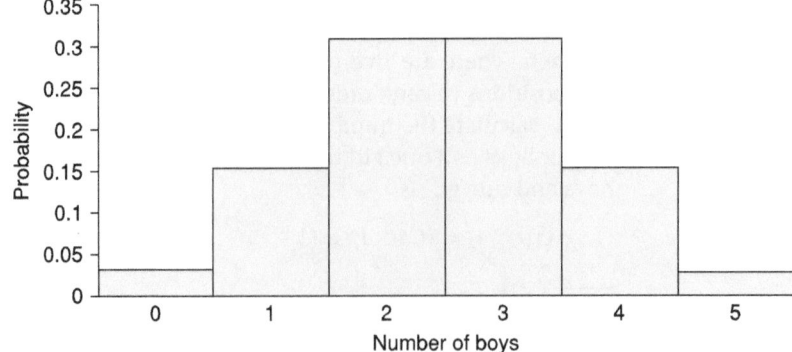

Figure 3.2
Probability distribution of the number of boys in five children

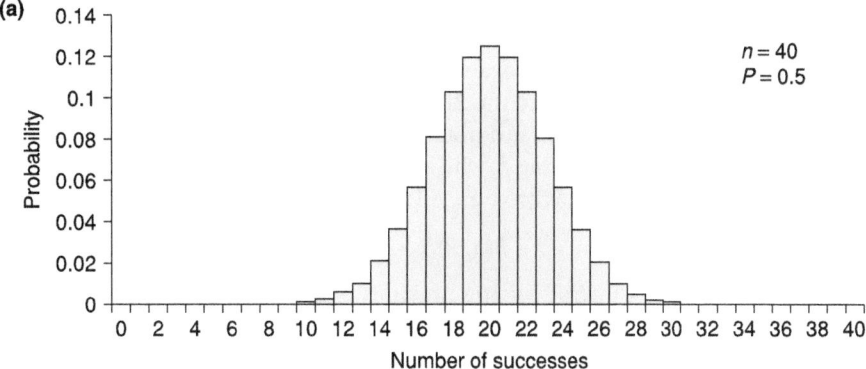

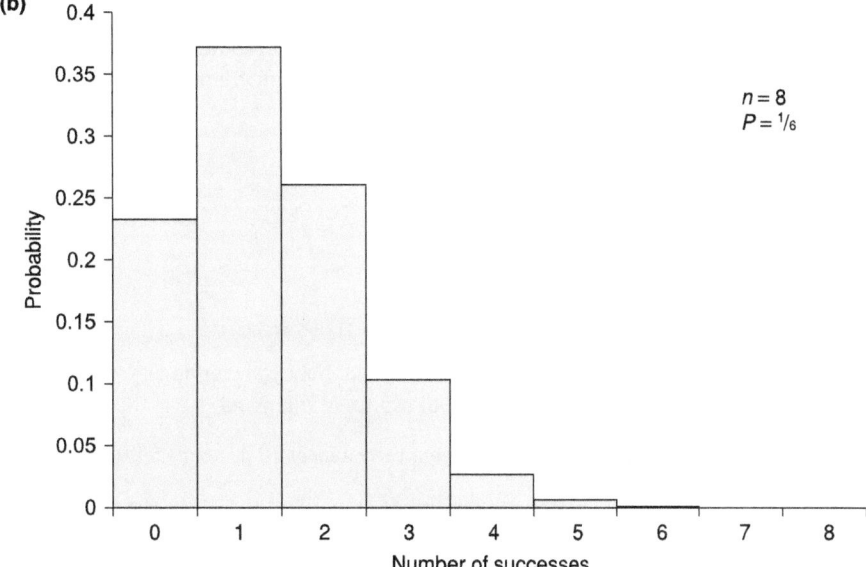

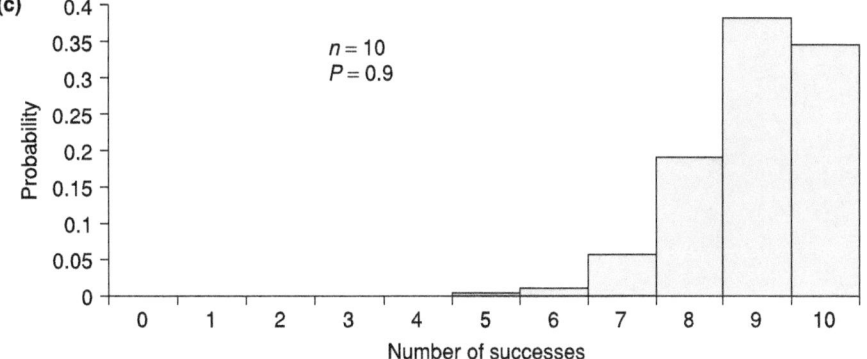

Figure 3.3
Binomial distributions
with different
parameter values

distribution is symmetric, while for all other values it is skewed to either the left or the right. Part (b) of the figure illustrates the distribution relating to the worked example of rolling a die, described below.

Since the Binomial distribution depends only upon the two values n and P, a shorthand notation can be used, rather than using the formula itself. A random variable r, which has a Binomial distribution with the parameters n and P, can be written in general terms as

$$r \sim B(n, P) \qquad\qquad (3.1)$$

Thus for the previous example of children, where r represents the number of boys

$$r \sim B(5, \tfrac{1}{2})$$

This is simply a brief and convenient way of writing down the information available; it involves no new problems of a conceptual nature. Writing

$$r \sim B(n, P)$$

is just a shorthand for

$$\Pr(r) = nCr \times P^r \times (1 - P)^{n-r}$$

Teenage weapons

This is a nice example of how knowledge of the Binomial distribution can help our interpretation of events in the news.

'One in five teens carry weapon'. (link on main BBC news web site 23 July 2007)

Following the link to the text of the story, we read:

'One in five young teenagers say that their friends are carrying knives and weapons, says a major annual survey of schoolchildren's health and wellbeing'.

With concerns about knife crime among teenagers, this survey shows that a fifth of youngsters are 'fairly sure' or 'certain' that their male friends are carrying a weapon.'

Notice, incidentally, how the story subtly changes. The headline suggests 20% of teenagers carry a weapon. The text then says this is what *young* teenagers report of their *friends*. It then reveals that some are only 'fairly sure' and that it applies to boys, not girls. By now our suspicions should be aroused. What is the truth?

Note that you are more likely to know someone who carries a weapon than to carry one yourself. Let p be the proportion who truly carry a weapon. Assume also that each person has 10 friends. What is the probability that a person, selected at random, has no friends who carry a weapon? Assuming independence, this is given by $(1 - p)^{10}$. Hence the probability of at least one friend with a weapon is $1 - (1 - p)^{10}$. This is proportion of people who will report having at least one friend with a weapon. How does this vary with p? This is set out in the following table:

p	P(⩾ 1 friend with weapon) $1 - (1 - p)^{10}$
0.0%	0%
0.5%	5%
1.0%	10%
1.5%	14%
2.0%	18%
2.5%	22%
3.0%	26%
3.5%	30%
4.0%	34%

Thus a true proportion of just over 2% carrying weapons will generate a report suggesting 20% know someone carrying a weapon! This is much less alarming (and less newsworthy) than in the original story.

You might like to test the assumptions. What happens if there are more than 10 friends assumed? What happens if events are not independent, i.e. having one friend with a weapon increases the probability of another friend with a weapon?

The mean and variance of the Binomial distribution

In Chapter 1 we calculated the mean and variance of a set of data, of the distribution of wealth. The picture of that distribution (Figure 1.9) looks not too dissimilar to one of the Binomial distributions shown in Figure 3.3 above. This suggests that we can calculate the mean and variance of a Binomial distribution, just as we did for the empirical distribution of wealth. Calculating the mean would provide the answer to a question such as 'If we have a family with five children, how many do we expect to be boys?'. Intuitively the answer seems clear, 2.5 (even though such a family could not exist!). The Binomial formula allows us to confirm this intuition.

The mean and variance are most easily calculated by drawing up a relative frequency table based on the Binomial frequencies. This is shown in Table 3.1 for the values $n = 5$ and $P = \frac{1}{2}$. Note that r is equivalent to x in our usual notation and Pr(r), the relative frequency, is equivalent to $f(x)/\Sigma f(x)$. The mean of this distribution is given by

$$E(r) = \frac{\Sigma r \times \text{Pr}(r)}{\Sigma \text{Pr}(r)} = \frac{80/32}{32/32} = 2.5 \qquad (3.2)$$

Table 3.1 Calculating the mean and variance of the Binomial distribution

r	Pr(r)	$r \times$ Pr(r)	$r^2 \times$ Pr(r)
0	1/32	0	0
1	5/32	5/32	5/32
2	10/32	20/32	40/32
3	10/32	30/32	90/32
4	5/32	20/32	80/32
5	1/32	5/32	25/32
Totals	32/32	80/32	240/32

and the variance is given by

$$V(r) = \frac{\sum r^2 \times \Pr(r)}{\sum \Pr(r)} - \mu^2 = \frac{240/32}{32/32} - 2.5^2 = 1.25 \qquad (3.3)$$

The mean value tells us that in a family of five children we would expect, on average, two and a half boys. Obviously no single family can be like this; it is the average over all such families. The variance is more difficult to interpret intuitively, but it tells us something about how the number of boys in different families will be spread around the average of 2.5.

There is a quicker way to calculate the mean and variance of the Binomial distribution. It can be shown that the mean can be calculated as nP, i.e. the number of trials times the probability of success. For example, in a family with five children and an equal probability that each child is a boy or a girl, then we expect $nP = 5 \times \frac{1}{2} = 2.5$ to be boys.

The variance can be calculated as $nP(1 - P)$. This gives $5 \times \frac{1}{2} \times \frac{1}{2} = 1.25$, as found above by extensive calculation.

> Worked example 3.1 **Rolling a die**

If a die is thrown four times, what is the probability of getting two or more sixes? This is a problem involving repeated experiments (rolling the die) with but two types of outcome for each roll: success (a six) or failure (anything but a six). Note that we combine several possibilities (scores of 1, 2, 3, 4 or 5) together and represent them all as failure. The probability of success (one-sixth) does not vary from one experiment to another, and so use of the Binomial distribution is appropriate. The values of the parameters are $n = 4$ and $P = 1/6$. Denoting by r the random variable 'the number of sixes in four rolls of the die' then

$$r \sim B(4, \tfrac{1}{6})$$

Hence

$$\Pr(r) = nCr \times P^r(1 - P)^{(n-r)}$$

where $P = \frac{1}{6}$ and $n = 4$. The probabilities of two, three and four sixes are then given by

$$\Pr(r = 2) = 4C2(\tfrac{1}{6})^2(\tfrac{5}{6})^2 = 0.116$$
$$\Pr(r = 3) = 4C3(\tfrac{1}{6})^3(\tfrac{5}{6})^1 = 0.015$$
$$\Pr(r = 4) = 4C4(\tfrac{1}{6})^4(\tfrac{5}{6})^0 = 0.00077$$

Since these events are mutually exclusive, the probabilities can simply be added together to achieve the desired result, which is 0.132, or 13.2%. This is the probability of two or more sixes in four rolls of a die.

This result can be illustrated diagrammatically as part of the area under the appropriate Binomial distribution, shown in Figure 3.4.

The shaded areas represent the probabilities of two or more sixes and together their area represents 13.2% of the whole distribution. This illustrates an important principle: that probabilities can be represented by areas under an appropriate probability distribution. We shall see more of this later.

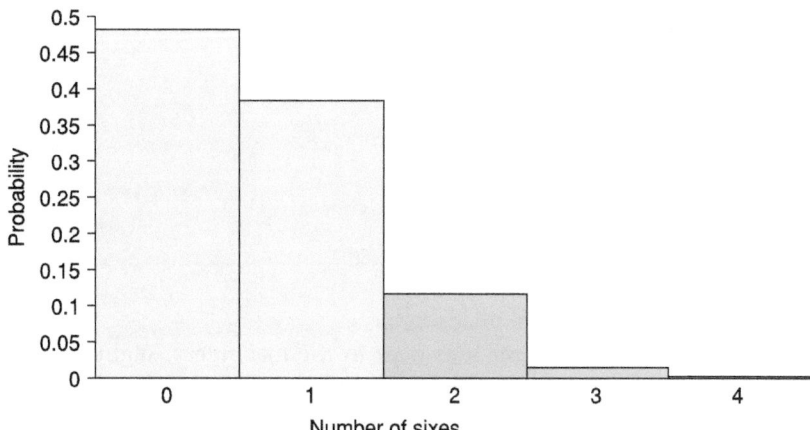

Figure 3.4
Probability of two or more
sixes in four rolls of a die

Exercise 3.1

(a) The probability of a randomly drawn individual having blue eyes is 0.6. What is the probability that four people drawn at random all have blue eyes?

(b) What is the probability that two of the sample of four have blue eyes?

(c) For this particular example, write down the Binomial formula for the probability of r blue-eyed individuals, for $r = 0 \ldots 4$. Confirm that the probabilities sum to one.

Exercise 3.2

(a) Calculate the mean and variance of the number of blue-eyed individuals in the previous exercise.

(b) Draw a graph of this Binomial distribution and on it mark the mean value and the mean value +/− one standard deviation.

Having introduced the concept of probability distributions using the Binomial, we now move on to the most important of all probability distributions – the Normal.

The Normal distribution

The Binomial distribution applies when there are two possible outcomes to an experiment, but not all problems fall into this category. For instance, the (random) arrival time of a train is a continuous variable and cannot be analysed using the Binomial. There are many probability distributions in statistics, developed to analyse different types of problem. Several of them are covered in this book and the most important of them is the Normal distribution, which we now turn to. It was discovered by the German mathematician Gauss in the nineteenth century (hence it is also known as the Gaussian distribution), in the course of his work on regression (see Chapter 7).

Many random variables turn out to be Normally distributed. Men's (or women's) heights are Normally distributed. IQ (the measure of intelligence) is also Normally distributed. Another example is of a machine producing (say) bolts with a nominal length of 5 cm which will actually produce bolts of slightly varying length (these differences would probably be extremely small) due to

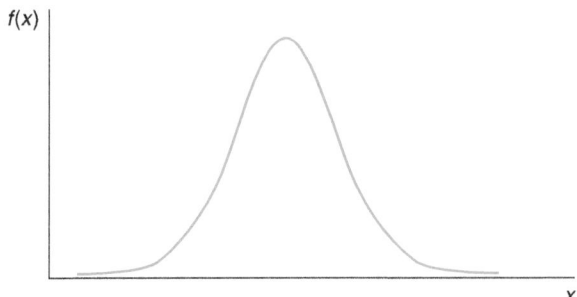

Figure 3.5
The Normal distribution

factors such as wear in the machinery, slight variations in the pressure of the lubricant, etc. These would result in bolts whose length varies, in accordance with the Normal distribution. This sort of process is extremely common, with the result that the Normal distribution often occurs in everyday situations.

The Normal distribution tends to arise when a random variable is the result of many independent, random influences added together, none of which dominates the others. A man's height is the result of many genetic influences, plus environmental factors such as diet, etc. As a result, height is Normally distributed. If one takes the height of men and women together, the result is not a Normal distribution, however. This is because there is one influence which dominates the others: gender. Men are, on average, taller than women. Many variables familiar in economics are not Normal however – incomes, for example (although the logarithm of income is approximately Normal). We shall learn techniques to deal with such circumstances in due course.

Having introduced the idea of the Normal distribution, what does it look like? It is presented below in graphical and then mathematical forms. Unlike the Binomial, the Normal distribution applies to continuous random variables such as height and a typical Normal distribution is illustrated in Figure 3.5. Since the Normal distribution is a continuous one it can be evaluated for all values of x, not just for integers. The figure illustrates the main features of the distribution:

- It is unimodal, having a single, central peak. If this were men's heights it would illustrate the fact that most men are clustered around the average height, with a few very tall and a few very short people.
- It is symmetric, the left and right halves being mirror images of each other.
- It is bell-shaped.
- It extends continuously over all the values of x from minus infinity to plus infinity, although the value of $f(x)$ becomes extremely small as these values are approached (the pages of this book being of only finite width, this last characteristic is not faithfully reproduced!). This also demonstrates that most empirical distributions (such as men's heights) can only be an approximation to the theoretical ideal, although the approximation is close and good enough for practical purposes.

Note that we have labelled the y-axis '$f(x)$' rather than 'Pr(x)' as we did for the Binomial distribution. This is because it is *areas under the curve* that represent probabilities, not the heights. With the Binomial, which is a discrete distribution, one can legitimately represent probabilities by the heights of the bars. For the Normal, although $f(x)$ does not give the probability per se, it does give an indication: you are more likely to encounter values from the middle of the distribution (where $f(x)$ is greater) than from the extremes.

In mathematical terms the formula for the Normal distribution is (x is the random variable)

$$f(x) = \frac{1}{\sigma\sqrt{2\pi}}e^{-\frac{1}{2}\left(\frac{x-\mu}{\sigma}\right)^2} \tag{3.4}$$

The mathematical formulation is not so formidable as it appears. μ and σ are the parameters of the distribution, such as n and P for the Binomial (though they have different meanings); π is 3.1416 and e is 2.7183. If the formula is evaluated using different values of x the values of $f(x)$ obtained will map out a Normal distribution. Fortunately, as we shall see, we do not need to use the mathematical formula in most practical problems.

Like the Binomial, the Normal is a family of distributions differing from one another only in the values of the parameters μ and σ. Several Normal distributions are drawn in Figure 3.6 for different values of the parameters.

Whatever value of μ is chosen turns out to be the centre of the distribution. As the distribution is symmetric, μ is its mean. The effect of varying σ is to narrow (small σ) or widen (large σ) the distribution. σ turns out to be the standard deviation of the distribution. The Normal is another two-parameter family of distributions like the Binomial, and once the mean μ and the standard deviation σ (or equivalently the variance, σ^2) are known the whole of the distribution can be drawn.

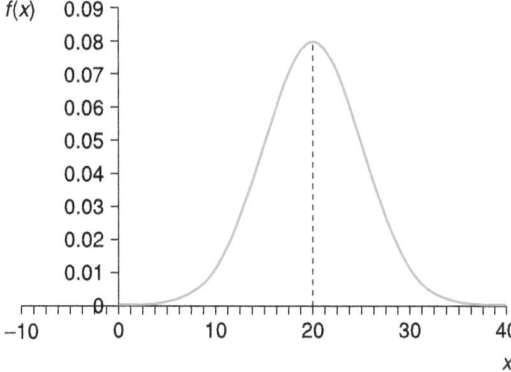

Figure 3.6(a)
The Normal distribution,
$\mu = 20$, $\sigma = 5$

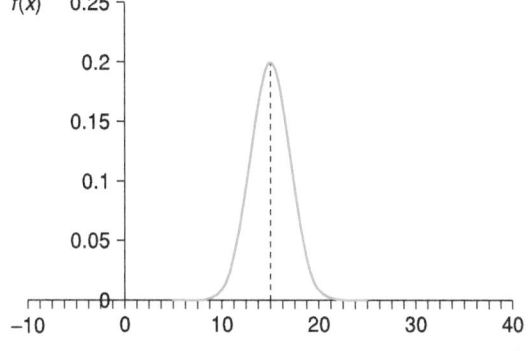

Figure 3.6(b)
The Normal distribution,
$\mu = 15$, $\sigma = 2$

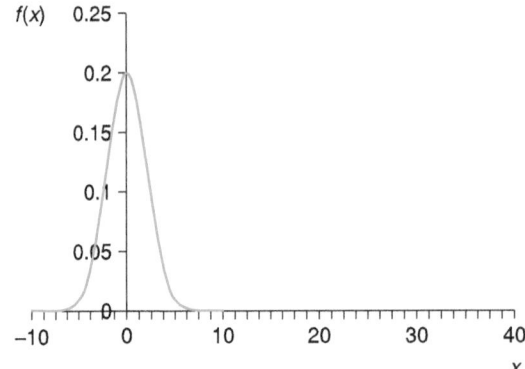

The shorthand notation for a Normal distribution is

$$x \sim N(\mu, \sigma^2) \tag{3.5}$$

meaning 'the variable x is Normally distributed with mean μ and variance σ^2'. This is similar in form to the expression for the Binomial distribution, though the meanings of the parameters are different.

Use of the Normal distribution can be illustrated using a simple example. The height of adult males is Normally distributed with mean height $\mu = 174$ cm and standard deviation $\sigma = 9.6$ cm. Let x represent the height of adult males; then

$$x \sim N(174, 92.16) \tag{3.6}$$

and this is illustrated in Figure 3.7. Note that equation (3.6) contains the variance rather than the standard deviation.

What is the probability that a randomly selected man is taller than 180 cm? If all men are equally likely to be selected, this is equivalent to asking what proportion of men are over 180 cm in height. This is given by the area under the Normal distribution, to the right of $x = 180$, i.e. the shaded area in Figure 3.7. The further from the mean of 174, the smaller the area in the tail of the distribution. One way to find this area would be to make use of equation (3.4), but this requires the use of sophisticated mathematics.

Since this is a frequently encountered problem, the answers have been set out in the tables of the standard Normal distribution. We can simply look up the solution. However, since there is an infinite number of Normal distributions (one for every combination of μ and σ^2) it would be an impossible task to tabulate

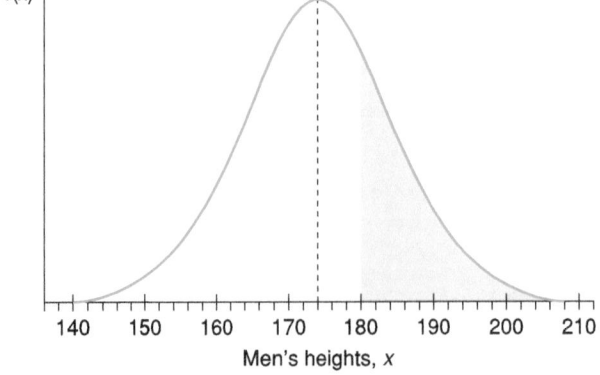

them all. The standard Normal distribution, which has a mean of zero and variance of one, is therefore used to represent all Normal distributions. Before the table can be consulted, therefore, the data have to be transformed so that they accord with the standard Normal distribution.

The required transformation is the z score, which was introduced in Chapter 1. This measures the distance between the value of interest (180) and the mean, measured in terms of standard deviations. Therefore we calculate

$$z = \frac{x - \mu}{\sigma} \qquad (3.7)$$

and z is a Normally distributed random variable with mean 0 and variance 1, i.e. $z \sim N(0, 1)$. This transformation shifts the original distribution μ units to the left and then adjusts the dispersion by dividing through by σ, resulting in a mean of 0 and variance 1. z is Normally distributed because x is Normally distributed. The transformation in equation (3.7) retains the Normal distribution shape, despite the changes to mean and variance. If x followed some other distribution then z would not be Normal either.

It is easy to verify the mean and variance of z using the rules for E and V operators encountered in Chapter 1

$$E(z) = E\left(\frac{x - \mu}{\sigma}\right) = \frac{1}{\sigma}(E(x) - \mu) = 0 \quad (\text{since } E(x) = \mu)$$

$$V(z) = V\left(\frac{x - \mu}{\sigma}\right) = \frac{1}{\sigma^2}V(x) = \frac{\sigma^2}{\sigma^2} = 1$$

Evaluating the z score from our data we obtain

$$z = \frac{180 - 174}{9.6} = 0.63 \qquad (3.8)$$

This shows that 180 is 0.63 standard deviations above the mean, 174, of the distribution. This is a measure of how far 180 is from 174 and allows us to look up the answer in tables. The task now is to find the area under the standard Normal distribution to the right of 0.63 standard deviations above the mean. This answer can be read off directly from the table of the standard Normal distribution, included as Table A2 in the appendix to this book. An excerpt from Table A2 (see page **414**) is presented in Table 3.2.

The left-hand column gives the z score to one place of decimals. The appropriate row of the table to consult is the one for $z = 0.6$, which is shaded. For the second place of decimals (0.03) we consult the appropriate column, also shaded. At their intersection we find the value 0.2643, which is the desired area and

Table 3.2 **Areas of the standard Normal distribution (excerpt from Table A2)**

z	0.00	0.01	0.02	0.03	. . .	0.09
0.0	0.5000	0.4960	0.4920	0.4880	. . .	0.4641
0.1	0.4602	0.4562	0.4522	0.4483	. . .	0.4247
⋮	⋮	⋮	⋮	⋮	. . .	⋮
0.5	0.3085	0.3050	0.3015	0.2981	. . .	0.2776
0.6	0.2743	0.2709	0.2676	0.2643	. . .	0.2451
0.7	0.2420	0.2389	0.2358	0.2327	. . .	0.2148

therefore probability, i.e. 26.43% of the distribution lies to the right of 0.63 standard deviations above the mean. Therefore 26.43% of men are over 180 cm in height.

Use of the standard Normal table is possible because, although there is an infinite number of Normal distributions, they are all fundamentally the same, so that the area to the right of 0.63 standard deviations above the mean is the same for all of them. As long as we measure the distance in terms of standard deviations then we can use the standard Normal table. The process of standardisation turns all Normal distributions into a standard Normal distribution with a mean of zero and a variance of one. This process is illustrated in Figure 3.8.

The area in the right-hand tail is the same for both distributions. It is the standard Normal distribution in Figure 3.8(b), which is tabulated in Table A2. To demonstrate how standardisation turns all Normal distributions into the standard Normal, the earlier problem is repeated but taking all measurements in inches. The answer should obviously be the same. Taking 1 inch = 2.54 cm the figures are

$$x = 70.87 \quad \sigma = 3.78 \quad \mu = 68.50$$

What proportion of men are over 70.87 inches in height? The appropriate Normal distribution is now

$$x \sim N(68.50, 3.78^2) \tag{3.9}$$

The z score is

$$z = \frac{70.87 - 68.50}{3.78} = 0.63 \tag{3.10}$$

which is the same z score as before and therefore gives the same probability.

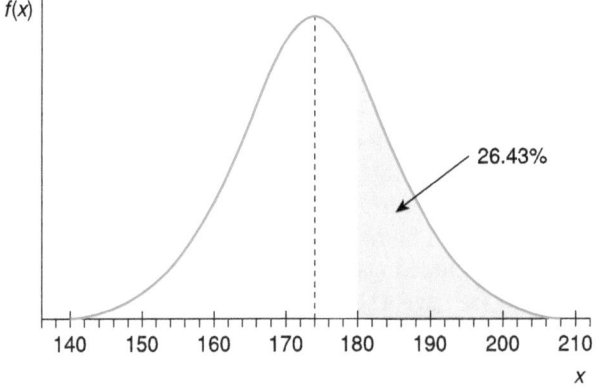

Figure 3.8(a)
The Normal distribution

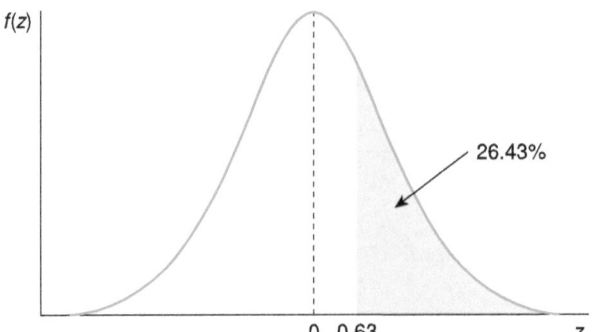

Figure 3.8(b)
The standard Normal distribution corresponding to Figure 3.8(a)

Worked example 3.2

Packets of cereal have a nominal weight of 750 grams, but there is some variation around this as the machines filling the packets are imperfect. Let us assume that the weights follow a Normal distribution. Suppose that the standard deviation around the mean of 750 is 5 grams. What proportion of packets weigh more than 760 grams?

Summarising our information, we have $x \sim N(750, 25)$, where x represents the weight. We wish to find $\Pr(x > 760)$. To be able to look up the answer, we need to measure the distance between 760 and 750 in terms of standard deviations. This is

$$z = \frac{760 - 750}{5}$$
$$= 2.0$$

Looking up $z = 2.0$ in Table A2 reveals an area of 0.0228 in the tail of the distribution. Thus 2.28% of packets weigh more than 760 grams.

Since a great deal of use is made of the standard Normal tables, it is worth working through a couple more examples to reinforce the method. We have so far calculated that $\Pr(z > 0.63) = 0.2643$. Since the total area under the graph equals one (i.e. the sum of probabilities must be one), the area to the left of $z = 0.63$ must equal 0.7357, i.e. 73.57% of men are under 180 cm. It is fairly easy to manipulate areas under the graph to arrive at any required area. For example, what proportion of men are between 174 and 180 cm in height? It is helpful to refer to Figure 3.9 at this point.

The size of area A is required. Area B has already been calculated as 0.2643. Since the distribution is symmetric the area A + B must equal 0.5, since 174 is at the centre (mean) of the distribution. Area A is therefore 0.5 − 0.2643 = 0.2357. 23.57% is the desired result.

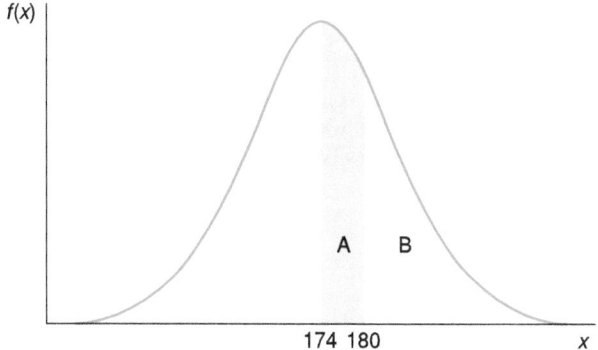

Figure 3.9
The proportion of men between 174 cm and 180 cm in height

Using software to find areas under the standard Normal distribution

If you use a spreadsheet program you can look up the z-distribution directly and hence dispense with tables. In *Excel*, for example, the function '=NORMSDIST(0.63)' gives the answer 0.7357, i.e. the area to the *left* of the z score. The area in the right-hand tail is then obtained by subtracting this value from 1, i.e. 1 − 0.7357 = 0.2643. Entering the formula '= 1 − NORMSDIST(0.63)' in a cell will give the area in the right-hand tail directly.

As a final exercise consider the question of what proportion of men are between 166 and 178 cm tall. As shown in Figure 3.10 area C + D is wanted. The only way to find this is to calculate the two areas separately and then add them together. For area D the z score associated with 178 is

$$z_D = \frac{178 - 174}{9.6} = 0.42 \tag{3.11}$$

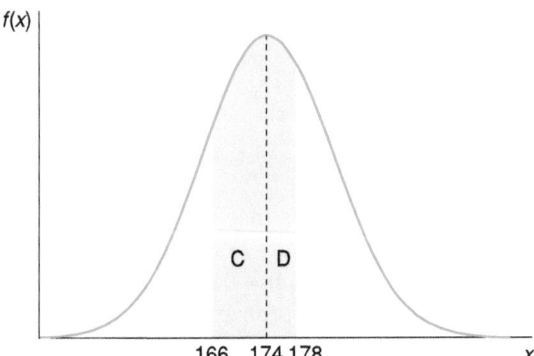

Figure 3.10
The proportion of men between 166 cm and 178 cm in height

Table A2 (see page **414**) indicates that the area in the right-hand tail, beyond z = 0.42, is 0.3372, so area D = 0.5 − 0.3372 = 0.1628. For C, the z score is

$$z_C = \frac{166 - 174}{9.6} = -0.83 \tag{3.12}$$

The minus sign indicates that it is the left-hand tail of the distribution, below the mean, which is being considered. Since the distribution is symmetric, it is the same as if it were the right-hand tail, so the minus sign may be ignored when consulting the table. Looking up z = 0.83 in Table A2 gives an area of 0.2033 in the tail, so area C is therefore 0.5 − 0.2033 = 0.2967. Adding areas C and D gives 0.1628 + 0.2967 = 0.4595. So nearly half of all men are between 166 and 178 cm in height.

An alternative interpretation of the results obtained above is that if a man is drawn at random from the adult population, the probability that he is over 180 cm tall is 26.43%. This is in line with the frequentist school of thought. Since 26.43% of the population is over 180 cm in height, that is the probability of a man over 180 cm being drawn at random.

Exercise 3.3
(?)

(a) The random variable x is distributed Normally, with x ~ N(40, 36). Find the probability that x > 50.

(b) Find Pr(x < 45).

(c) Find Pr(36 < x < 44).

Exercise 3.4

The mean +/– 0.67 standard deviations cuts off 25% in each tail of the Normal distribution. Hence the middle 50% of the distribution lies within +/– 0.67 standard deviations of the mean. Use this fact to calculate the inter-quartile range for the distribution $x \sim N(200, 256)$.

Exercise 3.5

As suggested in the text, the logarithm of income is approximately Normally distributed. Suppose the log (to the base 10) of income has the distribution $x \sim N(4.18, 2.56)$. Calculate the inter-quartile range for x and then take anti-logs to find the inter-quartile range of income.

The sample mean as a Normally distributed variable

One of the most important concepts in statistical inference is the probability distribution of the mean of a random sample, since we often use the sample mean to tell us something about an associated population. Suppose that, from the population of adult males, a random sample of size $n = 36$ is taken, their heights measured and the mean height of the sample calculated. What can we infer from this about the true average height of the population? To do this, we need to know about the statistical properties of the sample mean. The sample mean is a random variable because of the chance element of random sampling (different samples would yield different values of the sample mean). Since the sample mean is a random variable it must have associated with it a probability distribution.

We therefore need to know, first, what is the appropriate distribution and, second, what are its parameters. From the definition of the sample mean we have

$$\bar{x} = \frac{1}{n}(x_1 + x_2 + \ldots + x_n) \tag{3.13}$$

where each observation, x_i, is itself a Normally distributed random variable, with $x_i \sim N(\mu, \sigma^2)$, because each comes from the parent distribution with such characteristics. (We stated earlier that men's heights are Normally distributed.) We now make use of the following theorem to demonstrate that $\bar{x}$ is Normally distributed:

Theorem **Any linear combination of independent, Normally distributed random variables is itself Normally distributed.**

A linear combination of two variables x_1 and x_2 is of the form $w_1x_1 + w_2x_2$ where w_1 and w_2 are constants. This can be generalised to any number of x values. It is clear that the sample mean satisfies these conditions and is a linear combination of the individual x values (with the weight on each observation equal to $1/n$). As long as the observations are independently drawn, therefore, the sample mean is Normally distributed.

We now need the parameters (mean and variance) of the distribution. For this we use the E and V operators once again

$$E(\bar{x}) = \frac{1}{n}(E(x_1) + E(x_2) + \ldots + E(x_n)) = \frac{1}{n}(\mu + \mu + \ldots + \mu) = \frac{1}{n}n\mu = \mu \tag{3.14}$$

$$V(\bar{x}) = V\left(\frac{1}{n}[x_1 + x_2 + \ldots + x_n]\right)$$ (3.15)

$$= \frac{1}{n^2}(V(x_1) + V(x_2) + \ldots + V(x_n))$$

$$= \frac{1}{n^2}(\sigma^2 + \sigma^2 + \ldots + \sigma^2)$$

$$= \frac{1}{n^2}n\sigma^2 = \frac{\sigma^2}{n}$$

Putting all this together, we have[2]

$$\bar{x} \sim N\left(\mu, \frac{\sigma^2}{n}\right)$$ (3.16)

This we may summarise in the following theorem:

Theorem | **The sample mean, $\bar{x}$, drawn from a population which has a Normal distribution with mean μ and variance σ^2, has a sampling distribution which is Normal, with mean μ and variance σ^2/n, where n is the sample size.**

The meaning of this theorem is as follows. First of all it is assumed that the population from which the samples are to be drawn is itself Normally distributed (this assumption will be relaxed in a moment), with mean μ and variance σ^2. From this population many samples are drawn, each of sample size n, and the mean of each sample is calculated. The samples are independent, meaning that the observations selected for one sample do not influence the selection of observations in the other samples. This gives many sample means, $\bar{x}_1$, $\bar{x}_2$, etc. If these sample means are treated as a new set of observations, then the probability distribution of these observations can be derived. The theorem states that this distribution is Normal, with the sample means centred around μ, the population mean, and with variance σ^2/n. The argument is set out diagrammatically in Figure 3.11.

Intuitively this theorem can be understood as follows. If the height of adult males is a Normally distributed random variable with mean $\mu = 174$ cm and

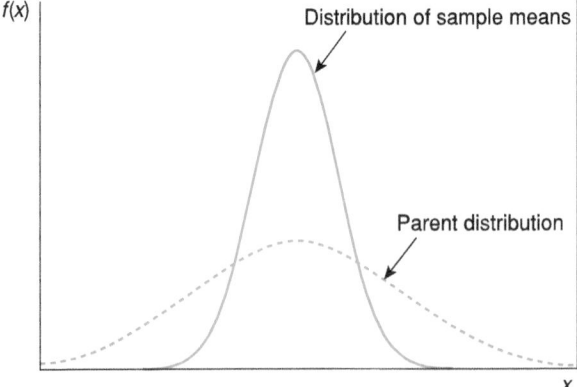

Figure 3.11
The parent distribution and the distribution of sample means

Note: The distribution of $\bar{x}$ is drawn for a sample size of $n = 9$. A larger sample size would narrow the $\bar{x}$ distribution; a smaller sample size would widen it.

---

[2] Don't worry if you didn't follow the derivation of this formula, just accept that it is correct.

variance $\sigma^2 = 92.16$, then it would be expected that a random sample of (say) nine males would yield a sample mean height of around 174 cm, perhaps a little more, perhaps a little less. In other words, the sample mean is centred around 174 cm, or the mean of the distribution of sample means is 174 cm.

The larger is the size of the individual samples (i.e. the larger n), the closer the sample mean would tend to be to 174 cm. For example, if the sample size is only two, a sample of two very tall people is quite possible, with a high sample mean as a result, well over 174 cm, e.g. 182 cm. But if the sample size were 20, it is very unlikely that 20 very tall males would be selected and the sample mean is likely to be much closer to 174. This is why the sample size n appears in the formula for the variance of the distribution of the sample mean, σ^2/n.

Note that, once again, we have transformed one (or more) random variables, the x_i values, with a particular probability distribution into another random variable, $\bar{x}$, with a (slightly) different distribution. This is common practice in statistics: transforming a variable will often put it into a more useful form, for example one whose probability distribution is well known.

The above theorem can be used to solve a range of statistical problems. For example, what is the probability that a random sample of nine men will have a mean height greater than 180 cm? The height of all men is known to be Normally distributed with mean $\mu = 174$ cm and variance $\sigma^2 = 92.16$. The theorem can be used to derive the probability distribution of the sample mean. For the population we have

$$\bar{x} \sim N(\mu, \sigma^2), \text{ i.e. } \bar{x} \sim N(174, 92.16)$$

Hence for the sample mean

$$\bar{x} \sim N(\mu, \sigma^2/n), \text{ i.e. } \bar{x} \sim N(174, 92.16/9)$$

This is shown diagrammatically in Figure 3.12.

To answer the question posed, the area to the right of 180, shaded in Figure 3.11, has to be found. This should by now be a familiar procedure. First the z score is calculated

$$z = \frac{\bar{x} - \mu}{\sqrt{\sigma^2/n}} = \frac{180 - 174}{\sqrt{92.16/9}} = 1.88 \tag{3.17}$$

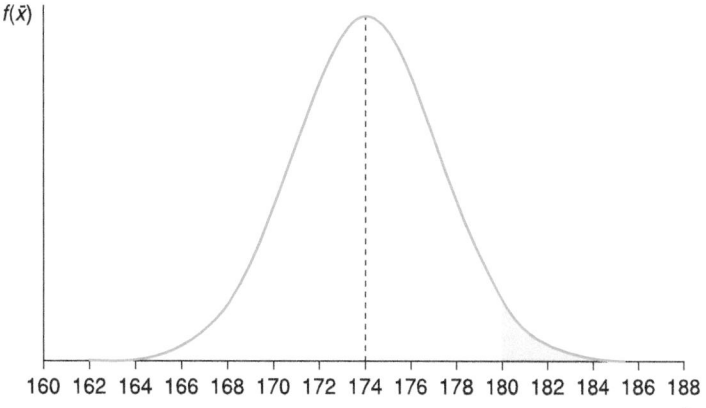

Figure 3.12
The proportion of sample means greater than $\bar{x} = 180$

Note that the z score formula is subtly different because we are dealing with the sample mean $\bar{x}$ rather than x itself. In the numerator we use $\bar{x}$ rather than x and in the denominator we use σ^2/n, not σ^2. This is because $\bar{x}$ has a variance σ^2/n, not σ^2, which is the population variance. $\sqrt{\sigma^2/n}$ is known as the standard error, to distinguish it from σ, the standard deviation of the population. The principle behind the z score is the same however: it measures how far is a sample mean of 180 from the population mean of 174, measured in terms of standard deviations.

Looking up the value of $z = 1.88$ in Table A2 gives an area of 0.0311 in the right-hand tail of the Normal distribution. Thus 3.11% of sample means will be greater than or equal to 180 cm when the sample size is nine. The desired probability is therefore 3.11%.

As this probability is quite small, we might consider the reasons for this. There are two possibilities:

(a) through bad luck, the sample collected is not very representative of the population as a whole;
(b) the sample is representative of the population, but the population mean is not 174 cm after all.

Only one of these two possibilities can be correct. How to decide between them will be taken up later on, in Chapter 5 on hypothesis testing.

It is interesting to examine the difference between the answer for a sample size of nine (3.11%) and the one obtained earlier for a single individual (26.43%). The latter may be considered as a sample of size one from the population. The examples illustrate the fact that the larger the sample size, the closer the sample mean is likely to be to the population mean. Thus larger samples tend to give better estimates of the population mean.

Oil reserves

An interesting application of probability distributions is to the estimation of oil reserves. The quantity of oil in an oil field is not known for certain, but is subject to uncertainty. The *proven* oil reserve of a field is the amount recoverable with probability of 90% (known as P90 in the oil industry). One can then add up the proven oil reserves around the world to get a total of proven reserves.

However, using probability theory we can see this might be misleading. Suppose we have 50 fields, where the recoverable quantity of oil is distributed as $x \sim N(100, 81)$ in each. From tables we note that $\bar{x} - 1.28s$ cuts off the bottom 10% of the Normal distribution, 88.48 in this case. This is the proven reserve for a field. Summing across the 50 fields gives 4424 as total reserves. But is there a 90% probability of recovering at least this amount?

Using the first theorem above, the total quantity of oil y is distributed Normally, with mean $E(y) = E(x_1) + \ldots + E(x_{50}) = 5000$ and variance $V(y) = V(x_1) + \ldots + V(x_{50}) = 4050$, assuming independence of the oil fields. Hence we have $y \sim N(5000, 4050)$. Again, the bottom 10% is cut off by $\bar{y} - 1.28s$, which is 4919. This is 11% larger than the 4424 calculated above. Adding up the proven reserves of each field individually underestimates the true total proven reserves. In fact, the probability of total proven reserves being greater than 4424 is almost 100%.

Note that the numbers given here are for illustration purposes and don't reflect the actual state of affairs. The principle of the calculation is correct however.

Sampling from a non-Normal population

The previous theorem and examples relied upon the fact that the population followed a Normal distribution. But what happens if it is not Normal? After all, it is not known for certain that the heights of all adult males are exactly Normally distributed, and there are many populations which are not Normal (e.g. wealth, as shown in Chapter 1). What can be done in these circumstances? The answer is to use another theorem about the distribution of sample means (presented without proof). This is known as the Central Limit Theorem:

Theorem

> **The sample mean $\bar{x}$, drawn from a population with mean μ and variance σ^2, has a sampling distribution which approaches a Normal distribution with mean μ and variance σ^2/n, as the sample size approaches infinity.**

This is very useful, since it drops the assumption that the population is Normally distributed. Note that the distribution of sample means is only Normal as long as the sample size is infinite; for any finite sample size the distribution is only approximately Normal. However, the approximation is close enough for practical purposes if the sample size is larger than 25 or so observations. If the population distribution is itself nearly Normal then a smaller sample size would suffice. If the population distribution is particularly skewed then more than 25 observations would be desirable. Twenty-five observations constitutes a rule of thumb that is adequate in most circumstances. This is another illustration of statistics as an inexact science. It does not provide absolutely clear-cut answers to questions but, used carefully, helps us to arrive at sensible conclusions.

As an example of the use of the Central Limit Theorem, we return to the wealth data of Chapter 1. Recall that the mean level of wealth was 146.984 (measured in £000) and the variance 56 803. Suppose that a sample of $n = 50$ people were drawn from this population. What is the probability that the sample mean is greater than 160 (i.e. £160 000)?

On this occasion we know that the parent distribution is highly skewed so it is fortunate that we have 50 observations. This should be ample for us to justify applying the Central Limit Theorem. The distribution of $\bar{x}$ is therefore

$$\bar{x} \sim N(\mu, \sigma^2/n) \tag{3.18}$$

and, inserting the parameter values, this gives[3]

$$\bar{x} \sim N(146.984, 56\ 803/50) \tag{3.19}$$

To find the area beyond a sample mean of 160, the z score is first calculated

$$z = \frac{160 - 146.984}{\sqrt{56\ 803/50}} = 0.39 \tag{3.20}$$

Referring to the standard Normal tables, the area in the tail is then found to be 34.83%. This is the desired probability. So there is a probability of 34.83% of finding a mean of £160 000 or greater with a sample of size 50. This demonstrates

---

[3] Note that if we used 146 984 for the mean we would have 56 803 000 000 as the variance. Using £000 keeps the numbers more manageable. The z score is the same in both cases.

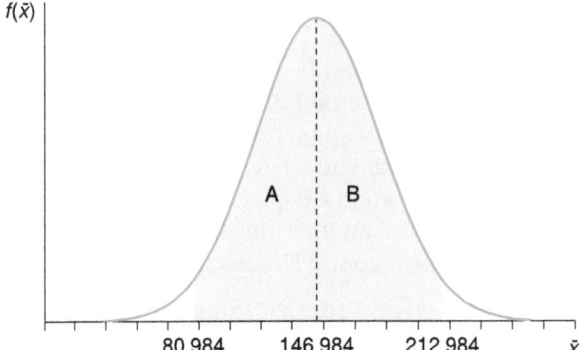

Figure 3.13
The probability of $\bar{x}$ lying within £66 000 either side of £146 984

that there is quite a high probability of getting a sample mean which is a relatively long way from £146 984. This is a consequence of the high degree of dispersion in the distribution of wealth.

Extending this example, we can ask what is the probability of the sample mean lying within, say, £66 000 either side of the true mean of £146 984 (i.e. between £80 984 and £212 984)? Figure 3.13 illustrates the situation, with the desired area shaded. By symmetry, areas A and B must be equal, so we only need find one of them. For B, we calculate the z score

$$z = \frac{212.984 - 146.984}{\sqrt{56\,803/50}} = 1.958 \tag{3.21}$$

From the standard Normal table, this cuts off approximately 2.5% in the upper tail, so area B = 0.475. Areas A and B together make up 95% of the distribution, therefore. There is thus a 95% probability of the sample mean falling within the range [80 984, 212 984] and we call this the 95% probability interval for the sample mean. We write this

$$\Pr(80\,984 \leqslant \bar{x} \leqslant 212\,984) = 0.95 \tag{3.22}$$

or, in terms of the formulae we have used[4]

$$\Pr(\mu - 1.96\sqrt{\sigma^2/n} \leqslant \bar{x} \leqslant \mu + 1.96\sqrt{\sigma^2/n}) = 0.95 \tag{3.23}$$

The 95% probability interval and the related concept of the 95% confidence interval (which will be introduced in Chapter 4) play important roles in statistical inference. We deliberately designed the example above to arrive at an answer of 95% for this reason.

Exercise 3.6

(a) If x is distributed as $x \sim N(50, 64)$ and samples of size $n = 25$ are drawn, what is the distribution of the sample mean $\bar{x}$?

(b) If the sample size doubles to 50, how is the standard error of $\bar{x}$ altered?

(c) Using the sample size of 25, (i) what is the probability of $\bar{x} > 51$? (ii) What is $\Pr(\bar{x} < 48)$? (iii) What is $\Pr(49 < \bar{x} < 50.5)$?

---

[4] 1.96 is the precise value cutting off 2.5% in each tail.

The relationship between the Binomial and Normal distributions

Many statistical distributions are related to one another in some way. This means that many problems can be solved by a variety of different methods (using different distributions), though usually one is more convenient or more accurate than the others. This point may be illustrated by looking at the relationship between the Binomial and Normal distributions.

Recall the experiment of tossing a coin repeatedly and noting the number of heads. We said earlier that this can be analysed via the Binomial distribution. But note that the number of heads, a random variable, is influenced by many independent random events (the individual tosses) added together. Furthermore, each toss counts equally, none dominates. These are just the conditions under which a Normal distribution arises, so it looks like there is a connection between the two distributions.

This idea is correct. Recall that if a random variable r follows a Binomial distribution then

$r \sim B(n, P)$

and the mean of the distribution is nP and the variance $nP(1 - P)$. It turns out that as n increases, the Binomial distribution becomes approximately the same as a Normal distribution with mean nP and variance $nP(1 - P)$. This approximation is sufficiently accurate as long as $nP > 5$ and $n(1 - P) > 5$, so the approximation may not be very good (even for large values of n) if P is very close to zero or one. For the coin tossing experiment, where $P = 0.5$, 10 tosses should be sufficient. Note that this approximation is good enough with only 10 observations even though the underlying probability distribution is nothing like a Normal distribution.

To demonstrate, the following problem is solved using both the Binomial and Normal distributions. Forty students take an exam in statistics which is simply graded pass/fail. If the probability, P, of any individual student passing is 60%, what is the probability of at least 30 students passing the exam?

The sample data are

$$P = 0.6$$
$$1 - P = 0.4$$
$$n = 40$$

Binomial distribution method

To solve the problem using the Binomial distribution it is necessary to find the probability of exactly 30 students passing, plus the probability of 31 passing, plus the probability of 32 passing, etc., up to the probability of 40 passing (the fact that the events are mutually exclusive allows this). The probability of 30 passing is

$$\Pr(r = 30) = nCr \times P^r(1 - P)^{n-r}$$
$$= 40C^{30} \times 0.6^{30} \times 0.4^{10}$$
$$= 0.020$$

(*Note*: This calculation assumes that the probabilities are independent, i.e. no copying!) This by itself is quite a tedious calculation, but Pr(31), Pr(32), etc., still have to be calculated. Calculating these and summing them gives the result of 3.52% as the probability of at least 30 passing. (It would be a useful exercise for you to do, if only to appreciate how long it takes.)

Normal distribution method

As stated above, the Binomial distribution can be approximated by a Normal distribution with mean nP and variance $nP(1 - P)$. nP in this case is 24 (40×0.6) and $n(1 - P)$ is 16, both greater than 5, so the approximation can be safely used. Thus

$$r \sim N(nP, nP(1 - P))$$

and inserting the parameter values gives

$$r \sim N(24, 9.6)$$

The usual methods are then used to find the appropriate area under the distribution. However, before doing so, there is one adjustment to be made (this only applies when approximating the Binomial distribution by the Normal). The Normal distribution is a continuous one while the Binomial is discrete. Thus 30 in the Binomial distribution is represented by the area under the Normal distribution between 29.5 and 30.5. 31 is represented by 30.5 to 31.5, etc. Thus it is the area under the Normal distribution to the right of 29.5, not 30, which must be calculated. This is known as the continuity correction. Calculating the z score gives

$$z = \frac{29.5 - 24}{\sqrt{9.6}} = 1.78 \tag{3.24}$$

This gives an area of 3.75%, not far off the correct answer as calculated by the Binomial distribution. The time saved and ease of calculation would seem to be worth the slight loss in accuracy.

Other examples can be constructed to test this method, using different values of P and n. Small values of n, or values of nP or $n(1 - P)$ less than 5, will give poor results, i.e. the Normal approximation to the Binomial will not be very good.

Exercise 3.7

(a) A coin is tossed 20 times. What is the probability of more than 14 heads? Perform the calculation using both the Binomial and Normal distributions, and compare results.

(b) A biased coin, for which $\Pr(H) = 0.7$ is tossed 6 times. What is the probability of more than 4 heads? Compare Binomial and Normal methods in this case. How accurate is the Normal approximation?

(c) Repeat part (b) but for more than 5 heads.

The Poisson distribution

The section above showed how the Binomial distribution could be approximated by a Normal distribution under certain circumstances. The approximation does not work particularly well for very small values of P, when nP is less than 5. In these circumstances the Binomial may be approximated instead by the Poisson distribution, which is given by the formula

$$\Pr(x) = \frac{\mu^x e^{-\mu}}{x!} \tag{3.25}$$

where μ is the mean of the distribution (similar to μ for the Normal distribution and nP for the Binomial). Like the Binomial, but unlike the Normal, the Poisson is a discrete probability distribution, so that equation (3.25) is only defined for integer values of x. Furthermore, it is applicable to a series of trials which are independent, as in the Binomial case.

The use of the Poisson distribution is appropriate when the probability of 'success' is very small and the number of trials large. Its use is illustrated by the following example. A manufacturer gives a two-year guarantee on the TV screens it makes. From past experience it knows that 0.5% of its screens will be faulty and fail within the guarantee period. What is the probability that of a consignment of 500 screens (a) none will be faulty, (b) more than three are faulty?

The mean of the Poisson distribution in this case is $\mu = 2.5$ (0.5% of 500). Therefore

$$\Pr(x = 0) = \frac{2.5^0 e^{-2.5}}{0!} = 0.082 \tag{3.26}$$

giving a probability of 8.2% of no failures. The answer to this problem via the Binomial method is

$$\Pr(r = 0) = 0.995^{500} = 0.0816$$

Thus the Poisson method gives a reasonably accurate answer. The Poisson approximation to the Binomial is satisfactory if nP is less than about 7.

The probability of more than three screens expiring is calculated as

$$\Pr(x > 3) = 1 - \Pr(x = 0) - \Pr(x = 1) - \Pr(x = 2) - \Pr(x = 3)$$

$$\Pr(x = 1) = \frac{2.5^1 e^{-2.5}}{1!} = 0.205$$

$$\Pr(x = 2) = \frac{2.5^2 e^{-2.5}}{2!} = 0.256$$

$$\Pr(x = 3) = \frac{2.5^3 e^{-2.5}}{3!} = 0.214$$

So

$$\Pr(x > 3) = 1 - 0.082 - 0.205 - 0.256 - 0.214 = 0.242$$

Thus there is a probability of about 24% of more than three failures. The Binomial calculation is much more tedious, but gives an answer of 24.2% also.

The Poisson distribution is also used in problems where events occur over time, such as goals scored in a football match (see Problem 3.25) or queuing-type problems (e.g. arrivals at a bank cash machine). In these problems, there is no natural 'number' of trials but it is clear that, if we take a short interval of time, the probability of an event occurring is small. We can then consider the number of trials to be the number of time intervals. This is illustrated by the following example. A football team scores, on average, two goals every game (you can vary the example by using your own favourite team plus their scoring record!). What is the probability of the team scoring zero or one goal during a game?

The mean of the distribution is 2, so we have, using the Poisson distribution

$$Pr(x = 0) = \frac{2^0 e^{-2}}{0!} = 0.135$$

$$Pr(x = 1) = \frac{2^1 e^{-2}}{1!} = 0.271$$

You should continue to calculate the probabilities of 2 or more goals and verify that the probabilities sum to 1.

A queuing-type problem is the following. If a shop receives, on average, 20 customers per hour, what is the probability of no customers within a five-minute period while the owner takes a coffee break?

The average number of customers per five-minute period is $20 \times 5/60 = 1.67$. The probability of a free five-minute spell is therefore

$$Pr(x = 0) = \frac{1.67^0 e^{-1.67}}{0!} = 0.189$$

a probability of about 19%. Note that this problem cannot be solved by the Binomial method since n and P are not known separately, only their product.

Exercise 3.8

?

(a) The probability of winning a prize in a lottery is 1 in 50. If you buy 50 tickets, what is the probability that (i) 0 tickets win, (ii) 1 ticket wins, (iii) 2 tickets win. (iv) What is the probability of winning at least one prize?

(b) On average, a person buys a lottery ticket in a supermarket every 5 minutes. What is the probability that 10 minutes will pass with no buyers?

Railway accidents

Andrew Evans of University College, London, used the Poisson distribution to examine the numbers of fatal railway accidents in Britain between 1967 and 1997. Since railway accidents are, fortunately, rare, the probability of an accident in any time period is very small and so use of the Poisson distribution is appropriate. He found that the average number of accidents has been falling over time and by 1997 had reached 1.25 per annum. This figure is therefore used as the mean μ of the Poisson distribution, and we can calculate the probabilities of 0, 1, 2, etc., accidents each year. Using $\mu = 1.25$ and inserting this into equation 3.26 we obtain the following table:

Number of accidents	0	1	2	3	4	5	6
Probability	0.287	0.358	0.224	0.093	0.029	0.007	0.002

and this distribution can be graphed:

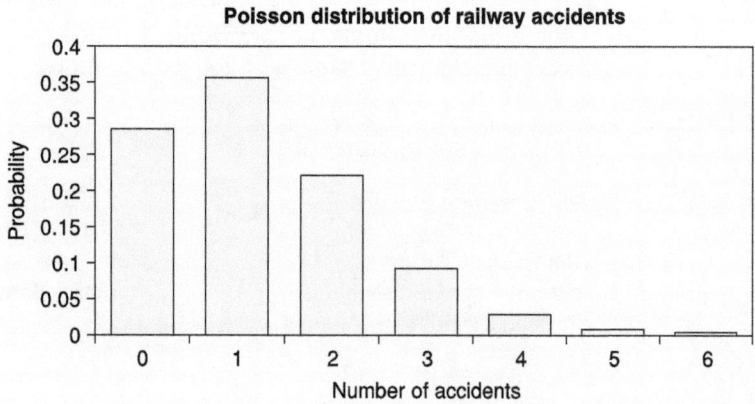

Poisson distribution of railway accidents

Thus the most likely outcome is one fatal accident per year and anything over four is extremely unlikely. In fact, Evans found that the Poisson was not a perfect fit to the data: the actual variation was less than that predicted by the model.

Source: A. W. Evans, Fatal train accidents on Britain's mainline railways, *J. Royal Statistical Society, Series A*, 2000, **163** (1), 99–119.

Summary

- The behaviour of many random variables (e.g. the result of the toss of a coin) can be described by a probability distribution (in this case, the Binomial distribution).

- The Binomial distribution is appropriate for problems where there are only two possible outcomes of a chance event (e.g. heads/tails, success/failure) and the probability of success is the same each time the experiment is conducted.

- The Normal distribution is appropriate for problems where the random variable has the familiar bell-shaped distribution. This often occurs when the variable is influenced by many, independent factors, none of which dominates the others. An example is men's heights, which are Normally distributed.

- The Poisson distribution is used in circumstances where there is a very low probability of 'success' and a high number of trials.

- Each of these distributions is actually a family of distributions, differing in the parameters of the distribution. Both the Binomial and Normal distributions have two parameters: n and P in the former case, μ and σ^2 in the latter. The Poisson distribution has one parameter, its mean μ.

- The mean of a random sample follows a Normal distribution, because it is influenced by many independent factors (the sample observations), none of which dominates in the calculation of the mean. This statement is always true if the population from which the sample is drawn follows a Normal distribution.

● If the population is not Normally distributed then the Central Limit Theorem states that the sample mean is Normally distributed in large samples. In this case 'large' means a sample of about 25 or more.

Key terms and concepts

Binomial distribution	probability distribution
Central Limit Theorem	random variable
Normal distribution	standard error
parameters of a distribution	standard Normal distribution
Poisson distribution	

Problems

Some of the more challenging problems are indicated by highlighting the problem number in colour.

3.1 Two dice are thrown and the sum of the two scores is recorded. Draw a graph of the resulting probability distribution of the sum and calculate its mean and variance. What is the probability that the sum is 9 or greater?

3.2 Two dice are thrown and the absolute difference of the two scores recorded. Graph the resulting probability distribution and calculate its mean and variance. What is the probability that the absolute difference is 4 or more?

3.3 Sketch the probability distribution for the likely time of departure of a train. Locate the timetabled departure time on your chart.

3.4 A train departs every half hour. You arrive at the station at a completely random moment. Sketch the probability distribution of your waiting time. What is your expected waiting time?

3.5 Sketch the probability distribution for the number of accidents on a stretch of road in one day.

3.6 Sketch the probability distribution for the number of accidents on the same stretch of road in one year. How and why does this differ from your previous answer?

3.7 Six dice are rolled and the number of sixes is noted. Calculate the probabilities of 0, 1, . . ., 6 sixes and graph the probability distribution.

3.8 If the probability of a boy in a single birth is $\frac{1}{2}$ and is independent of the sex of previous babies then the number of boys in a family of 10 children follows a Binomial distribution with mean 5 and variance 2.5. In each of the following instances, describe how the distribution of the number of boys differs from the Binomial described above.

(a) The probability of a boy is $\frac{6}{10}$.

(b) The probability of a boy is $\frac{1}{2}$ but births are not independent. The birth of a boy makes it more than an even chance that the next child is a boy.

(c) As (b) above, except that the birth of a boy makes it less than an even chance that the next child will be a boy.

(d) The probability of a boy is $\frac{6}{10}$ on the first birth. The birth of a boy makes it a more than even chance that the next baby will be a boy.

3.9   A firm receives components from a supplier in large batches, for use in its production process. Production is uneconomic if a batch containing 10% or more defective components is used. The firm checks the quality of each incoming batch by taking a sample of 15 and rejecting the whole batch if more than one defective component is found.

(a) If a batch containing 10% defectives is delivered, what is the probability of its being accepted?

(b) How could the firm reduce this probability of erroneously accepting bad batches?

(c) If the supplier produces a batch with 3% defective, what is the probability of the firm sending back the batch?

(d) What role does the assumption of a 'large' batch play in the calculation?

3.10 The UK record for the number of children born to a mother is 39, 32 of them girls. Assuming the probability of a girl in a single birth is 0.5 and that this probability is independent of previous births:

(a) Find the probability of 32 girls in 39 births (you'll need a scientific calculator or a computer to help with this!).

(b) Does this result cast doubt on the assumptions?

3.11 Using equation (3.5) describing the Normal distribution and setting $\mu = 0$ and $\sigma^2 = 1$, graph the distribution for the values $x = -2, -1.5, -1, -0.5, 0, 0.5, 1, 1.5, 2$.

3.12 Repeat the previous Problem for the values $\mu = 2$ and $\sigma^2 = 3$. Use values of x from -2 to $+6$ in increments of 1.

3.13 For the standard Normal variable z, find

(a) $\Pr(z > 1.64)$

(b) $\Pr(z > 0.5)$

(c) $\Pr(z > -1.5)$

(d) $\Pr(-2 < z < 1.5)$

(e) $\Pr(z = -0.75)$.

For (a) and (d), shade in the relevant areas on the graph you drew for Problem 3.11.

3.14 Find the values of z which cut off

(a) the top 10%

(b) the bottom 15%

(c) the middle 50%

of the standard Normal distribution.

3.15 If $x \sim N(10, 9)$ find

(a) $\Pr(x > 12)$

(b) $\Pr(x < 7)$

(c) $\Pr(8 < x < 15)$

(d) $\Pr(x = 10)$.

3.16 IQ (the intelligence quotient) is Normally distributed with mean 100 and standard deviation 16.

(a) What proportion of the population has an IQ above 120?

(b) What proportion of the population has IQ between 90 and 110?

(c) In the past, about 10% of the population went to university. Now the proportion is about 30%. What was the IQ of the 'marginal' student in the past? What is it now?

3.17 Ten adults are selected at random from the population and their IQ measured. (Assume a population mean of 100 and s.d. of 16 as in Problem 3.16.)

(a) What is the probability distribution of the sample average IQ?

(b) What is the probability that the average IQ of the sample is over 110?

(c) If many such samples were taken, in what proportion would you expect the average IQ to be over 110?

(d) What is the probability that the average IQ lies within the range 90 to 110? How does this answer compare to the answer to part (b) of Problem 16? Account for the difference.

(e) What is the probability that a random sample of ten university students has an average IQ greater than 110?

(f) The first adult sampled has an IQ of 150. What do you expect the average IQ of the sample to be?

3.18 The average income of a country is known to be £10 000 with standard deviation £2500. A sample of 40 individuals is taken and their average income calculated.

(a) What is the probability distribution of this sample mean?

(b) What is the probability of the sample mean being over £10 500?

(c) What is the probability of the sample mean being below £8000?

(d) If the sample size were 10, why could you not use the same methods to find the answers to (a)–(c)?

3.19 A coin is tossed 10 times. Write down the distribution of the number of heads:

(a) exactly, using the Binomial distribution;

(b) approximately, using the Normal distribution;

(c) Find the probability of four or more heads, using both methods. How accurate is the Normal method, with and without the continuity correction?

3.20 A machine producing electronic circuits has an average failure rate of 15% (they're difficult to make). The cost of making a batch of 500 circuits is £8400 and the good ones sell for £20 each. What is the probability of the firm making a loss on any one batch?

3.21 An experienced invoice clerk makes an error once in every 100 invoices, on average.

(a) What is the probability of finding a batch of 100 invoices without error?

(b) What is the probability of finding such a batch with more than two errors?

Calculate the answers using both the Binomial and Poisson distributions. If you try to solve the problem using the Normal method, how accurate is your answer?

3.22   A firm employing 100 workers has an average absenteeism rate of 4%. On a given day, what is the probability of (a) no workers, (b) one worker, (c) more than six workers being absent?

3.23   **(Computer project)** This problem demonstrates the Central Limit Theorem at work. In your spreadsheet, use the =*RAND*() function to generate a random sample of 25 observations (I suggest entering this function in cells A4:A28, for example). Copy these cells across 100 columns, to generate 100 samples. In row 29, calculate the mean of each sample. Now examine the distribution of these sample means.

   (*Hint*: you will find the *RAND*() function recalculates automatically every time you perform an operation in the spreadsheet. This makes it difficult to complete the analysis. The solution is to copy and then use 'Edit, Paste Special, Values' to create a copy of the values of the sample means. These will remain stable.)

   (a) What distribution would you expect them to have?

   (b) What is the parent distribution from which the samples are drawn?

   (c) What are the parameters of the parent distribution and of the sample means?

   (d) Do your results accord with what you would expect?

   (e) Draw up a frequency table of the sample means and graph it. Does it look as you expected?

   (f) Experiment with different sample sizes and with different parent distributions to see the effect that these have.

3.24   **(Project)** An extremely numerate newsagent (with a spreadsheet program, as you will need) is trying to work out how many copies of a newspaper he should order. The cost to him per copy is 15p, which he then sells at 45p. Sales are distributed Normally with an average daily sale of 250 and variance 625. Unsold copies cannot be returned for credit or refund; he has to throw them away, losing 15p per copy.

   (a) What do you think the seller's objective should be?

   (b) How many copies should he order?

   (c) What happens to the *variance* of profit as he orders more copies?

   (d) Calculate the probability of selling *more than X* copies. (Create an extra column in the spreadsheet for this.) What is the value of this probability at the optimum number of copies ordered?

   (e) What would the price–cost ratio have to be to justify the seller ordering *X* copies?

   (f) The wholesaler offers a sale or return deal, but the cost per copy is 16p. Should the seller take up this new offer?

   (g) Are there other considerations which might influence the seller's decision?

   Hints:

   Set up your spreadsheet as follows:

   Col. A: (cells A10:A160) 175, 176, . . . up to 325 in unit increments (to represent sales levels).

   Col. B: (cells B10:B160) the probability of sales falling between 175 and 176, between 176 and 177, etc., up to 325 – 326. (*Excel* has the '= NORMDIST()' function to do this – see the help facility.)

   Col. C: (cells C10:C160) total cost (= 0.15 × number ordered. Put the latter in cell F3 so you can reference it and change its value).

Col. D: (cells D10:D160) total revenue ('=MIN(sales, number ordered) × 0.45').

Col. E: profit (revenue − cost).

Col. F: profit × probability (i.e. col. E × col. B).

Cell F161: the sum of F10:F160 (this is the expected profit).

Now vary the number ordered (cell F3) to find the maximum value in F161. You can also calculate the variance of profit fairly simply, using an extra column.

3.25 **(Project)** Using a weekend's football results from the Premier (or other) league, see if the number of goals per game can be adequately modelled by a Poisson process. First calculate the average number of goals per game for the whole league, then derive the distribution of goals per game using the Poisson distribution. Do the actual numbers of goals per game follow this distribution? You might want to take several weeks' results to obtain more reliable results.

Answers to exercises

(a) $0.6^4 = 0.1296$ or 12.96%.

(b) $0.6^2 \times 0.4^2 \times 4C2 = 0.3456$.

(c) $\Pr(r) = 0.6^r \times 0.4^{4-r}4Cr$. The probabilities of $r = 0 \ldots 4$ are respectively 0.0256, 0.1536, 0.3456, 0.3456, 0.1296, which sum to one.

(a)

r	$P(r)$	$r \times P(r)$	$r^2 \times P(r)$
0	0.0256	0	0
1	0.1536	0.1536	0.1536
2	0.3456	0.6912	1.3824
3	0.3456	1.0368	3.1104
4	0.1296	0.5184	2.0736
Totals	1	2.4	6.72

The mean = 2.4/1 = 2.4 and the variance = $6.72/1 - 2.4^2 = 0.96$. Note that these are equal to nP and $nP(1 - P)$.

(b)

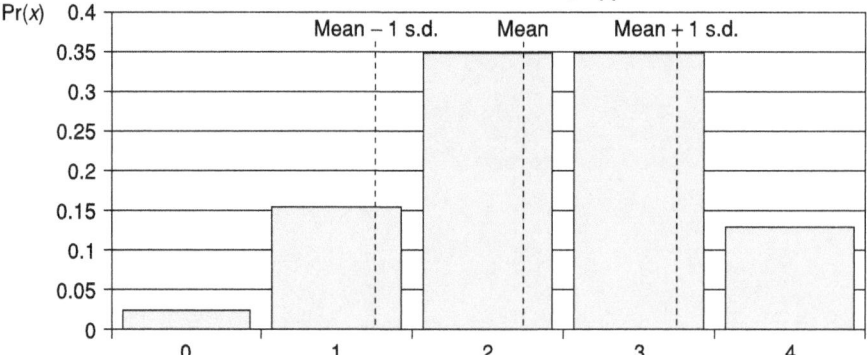

(a) $z = (50 - 40)/\sqrt{36} = 1.67$ and the area beyond $z = 1.67$ is 4.75%.

(b) $z = -0.83$ so area is 20.33%.

(c) This is symmetric around the mean, $z = \pm 0.67$ and the area within these two bounds is 49.72%.

To obtain the IQR we need to go 0.67 s.d.s above and below the mean, giving $200 \pm 0.67 \times 16 = [189.28, 210.72]$.

The IQR (in logs) is within $4.18 \pm 0.67 \times \sqrt{2.56} = [3.11, 5.25]$. Translated out of logs (using 10^x) yields [1288.2, 177 827.9].

Exercise 3.6

(a) $e \sim N(50, 64/25)$.

(b) The s.e. gets smaller. It is $1/\sqrt{2}$ times its previous value.

(c) (i) $z = (51 - 50)/\sqrt{(64/25)} = 0.625$. Hence area in tail = 26.5%. (ii) $z = -1.25$, hence area = 10.56%. (iii) z values are -0.625 and $+0.3125$, giving tail areas of 26.5% and 37.8%, totalling 64.3%. The area between the limits is therefore 35.7%.

Exercise 3.7

(a) Binomial method: $\Pr(r) = 0.5^r \times 0.5^{(20-r)} \times 20Cr$. This gives probabilities of 15, 16, etc., heads of 0.0148, 0.0046, etc., which total 0.0207 or 2.1%. By the Normal approximation, $r \sim N(10, 5)$ and $z = (14.5 - 10)/\sqrt{5} = 2.01$. The area in the tail is then 2.22%, not far off the correct value (a 10% error). Note that $nP = 10 = n(1 - P)$.

(b) Binomial method: $\Pr(5 \text{ or } 6 \text{ heads}) = 0.302 + 0.118 = 0.420$ or 42%. By the Normal, $r \sim N(4.2, 1.26)$, $z = 0.267$ and the area is 39.36%, still reasonably close to the correct answer despite the fact that $n(1 - P) = 1.8$.

(c) By similar methods the answers are 11.8% (Binomial) and 12.3% (Normal).

Exercise 3.8

(a) (i) $\mu = 1$ in this case $(1/50 \times 50)$ so $\Pr(x = 0) = 1^0 e^{-1}/0! = 0.368$. (ii) $\Pr(x = 1) = 1^1 e^{-1}/1! = 0.368$. (iii) $1^2 e^{-1}/2! = 0.184$. (iv) $1 - 0.368 = 0.632$.

(b) The average number of customer per 10 minutes is 2 (= 10/5). Hence $\Pr(x = 0) = 2^0 e^{-2}/0! = 0.135$.

5

Hypothesis testing

Contents

Learning outcomes

By the end of this chapter you should be able to:

- understand the philosophy and scientific principles underlying hypothesis testing;
- appreciate that hypothesis testing is about deciding whether a hypothesis is true or false on the basis of a sample of data;
- recognise the type of evidence which leads to a decision that the hypothesis is false;
- carry out hypothesis tests for a variety of statistical problems;
- recognise the relationship between hypothesis testing and a confidence interval;
- recognise the shortcomings of hypothesis testing.

Complete your diagnostic test for Chapter 5 now to create your personal study plan. Exercises with an icon ? *are also available for practice in MathXL with additional supporting resources.*

Introduction

This chapter deals with issues very similar to those of the previous chapter on estimation, but examines them in a different way. The estimation of population parameters and the testing of hypotheses about those parameters are similar techniques (indeed they are formally equivalent in a number of respects), but there are important differences in the interpretation of the results arising from each method. The process of estimation is appropriate when measurement is involved, such as measuring the true average expenditure on food; hypothesis testing is better when decision making is involved, such as whether to accept that a supplier's products are up to a specified standard. Hypothesis testing is also used to make decisions about the truth or otherwise of different theories, such as whether rising prices are caused by rising wages; and it is here that the issues become contentious. It is sometimes difficult to interpret correctly the results of hypothesis tests in these circumstances. This is discussed further later in this chapter.

The concepts of hypothesis testing

In many ways hypothesis testing is analogous to a criminal trial. In a trial there is a defendant who is *initially presumed innocent*. The *evidence* against the defendant is then presented and, if the jury finds this convincing *beyond all reasonable doubt*, he is found guilty; the presumption of innocence is overturned. Of course, mistakes are sometimes made: an innocent person is convicted or a guilty person set free. Both of these errors involve costs (not only in the monetary sense), either to the defendant or to society in general, and the errors should be avoided if at all possible. The laws under which the trial is held may help avoid such errors. The rule that the jury must be convinced 'beyond all reasonable doubt' helps to avoid convicting the innocent, for instance.

The situation in hypothesis testing is similar. First there is a maintained or null hypothesis which is initially *presumed* to be true. The empirical evidence, usually data from a random sample, is then gathered and assessed. If the evidence seems inconsistent with the null hypothesis, i.e. it has a low probability of occurring *if* the hypothesis were true, then the null hypothesis is *rejected* in favour of an alternative. Once again there are two types of error one can make, either rejecting the null hypothesis when it is really true, or not rejecting it when in fact it is false. Ideally one would like to avoid both types of error.

An example helps to clarify the issues and the analogy. Suppose that you are thinking of taking over a small business franchise. The current owner claims the weekly turnover of each existing franchise is £5000 and at this level you are willing to take on a franchise. You would be more cautious if the turnover is less than this figure. You examine the books of 26 franchises chosen at random and find that the average turnover was £4900 with standard deviation £280. What do you do?

The null hypothesis in this case is that average weekly turnover is £5000 (or more; that would be even more to your advantage). The alternative hypothesis is that turnover is strictly less than £5000 per week. We may write these more succinctly as follows

$$H_0: \mu = 5000$$
$$H_1: \mu < 5000$$

H_0 is conventionally used to denote the null hypothesis, H_1 the alternative. Initially, H_0 is presumed to be true and this presumption will be tested using the sample evidence. Note that the sample evidence is *not* used as part of the hypothesis.

You have to decide whether the owner's claim is correct (H_0) or not (H_1). The two types of error you could make are as follows:

- **Type I error** – reject H_0 when it is in fact true. This would mean missing a good business opportunity.
- **Type II error** – not rejecting H_0 when it is in fact false. You would go ahead and buy the business and then find out that it is not as attractive as claimed. You would have overpaid for the business.

The situation is set out in Figure 5.1.

Obviously a good decision rule would give a good chance of making a correct decision and rule out errors as far as possible. Unfortunately it is impossible completely to eliminate the possibility of errors. As the decision rule is changed to reduce the probability of a Type I error, the probability of making a Type II error inevitably increases. The skill comes in balancing these two types of error.

Again a diagram is useful in illustrating this. Assuming that the null hypothesis is true, then the sample observations are drawn from a population with mean 5000 and some variance, which we shall assume is accurately measured by the sample variance. The distribution of $\bar{x}$ is then given by

$$\bar{x} \sim N(\mu, \sigma^2/n) \text{ or}$$
$$\bar{x} \sim N(5000, 280^2/26)$$

(5.1)

Under the alternative hypothesis the distribution of $\bar{x}$ would be the same except that it would be centred on a value less than 5000. These two situations are illustrated in Figure 5.2. The distribution of $\bar{x}$ under H_1 is shown by a dashed curve to signify that its exact position is unknown, only that it lies to the left of the distribution under H_0.

A decision rule amounts to choosing a point or dividing line on the horizontal axis in Figure 5.2. If the sample mean lies to the left of this point then H_0 is rejected (the sample mean is too far away from H_0 for it to be credible) in favour of H_1 and you do not buy the firm. If $\bar{x}$ lies above this decision point then H_0 is not rejected and you go ahead with the purchase. Such a decision point is

		True situation	
		H_0 true	H_0 false
Decision	Accept H_0	Correct decision	Type II error
	Reject H_0	Type I error	Correct decision

Figure 5.1
The two different types of error

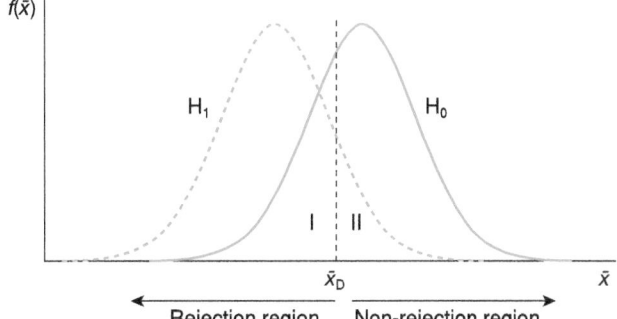

Figure 5.2
The sampling
distributions of $\bar{x}$
under H_0 and H_1

shown in Figure 5.2, denoted by $\bar{x}_D$. To the left of $\bar{x}_D$ lies the rejection (of H_0) region; to the right lies the non-rejection region.

Based on this point, we can see the probabilities of Type I and Type II errors. The area under the H_0 distribution to the left of $\bar{x}_D$, labelled I, shows the probability of rejecting H_0 given that it is in fact true: a Type I error. The area under the H_1 distribution to the right of $\bar{x}_D$, labelled II, shows the probability of a Type II error: not rejecting H_0 when it is in fact false (and H_1 is true).

Shifting the decision line to the right or left alters the balance of these probabilities. Moving the line to the right increases the probability of a Type I error but reduces the probability of a Type II error. Moving the line to the left has the opposite effect.

The Type I error probability can be calculated for any value of $\bar{x}_D$. Suppose we set $\bar{x}_D$ to a value of 4950. Using the distribution of $\bar{x}$ given in equation (5.1) above, the area under the distribution to the left of 4950 is obtained using the z score

$$z = \frac{\bar{x}_D - \mu}{\sqrt{s^2/n}} = \frac{4950 - 5000}{\sqrt{280^2/26}} = -0.91 \tag{5.2}$$

From the tables of the standard Normal distribution we find that the probability of a Type I error is 18.1%. Unfortunately, the Type II error probability cannot be established because the exact position of the distribution under H_1 is unknown. Therefore we cannot decide on the appropriate position of $\bar{x}_D$ by some balance of the two error probabilities.

The convention therefore is to set the position of $\bar{x}_D$ by using a Type I error probability of 5%, known as the significance level[1] of the test. In other words, we are prepared to accept a 5% probability of rejecting H_0 when it is, in fact, true. This allows us to establish the position of $\bar{x}_D$. From Table A2 (see page **414**) we find that $z = -1.64$ cuts off the bottom 5% of the distribution, so the decision line should be 1.64 standard errors below 5000. The value -1.64 is known as the critical value of the test. We therefore obtain

$$\bar{x}_D = 5000 - 1.64\sqrt{280^2/26} = 4910 \tag{5.3}$$

---

[1] The term **size** of the test is also used, not to be confused with the sample size. We use the term 'significance level' in this text.

Since the sample mean of 4900 lies below 4910 we reject H_0 *at the 5% significance level* or equivalently we reject *with 95% confidence*. The significance level is generally denoted by the symbol α and the complement of this, given by $1 - \alpha$, is known as the confidence level (as used in the confidence interval).

An equivalent procedure would be to calculate the z score associated with the sample mean, known as the test statistic, and then compare this to the critical value of the test. This allows the hypothesis testing procedure to be broken down into five neat steps.

(1) Write down the null and alternative hypotheses:

H_0: $\mu = 5000$
H_1: $\mu < 5000$

(2) Choose the significance level of the test, conventionally $\alpha = 0.05$ or 5%.
(3) Look up the critical value of the test from statistical tables, based on the chosen significance level. $z^* = 1.64$ is the critical value in this case.

(4) Calculate the test statistic

$$z = \frac{\bar{x} - \mu}{\sqrt{s^2/n}} = \frac{-100}{\sqrt{280^2/26}} = -1.82 \tag{5.4}$$

(5) Decision rule. Compare the test statistic with the critical value: if $z < -z^*$ reject H_0 in favour of H_1. Since $-1.82 < -1.64$ H_0 is rejected with 95% confidence. Note that we use $-z^*$ here (rather than $+z^*$) because we are dealing with the left-hand tail of the distribution.

Worked example 5.1

A sample of 100 workers found the average overtime hours worked in the previous week was 7.8, with standard deviation 4.1 hours. Test the hypothesis that the average for all workers is 5 hours or less.

We can set out the five steps of the answer as follows:

(1) H_0: $\mu = 5$
H_1: $\mu > 5$
(2) Significance level, $\alpha = 5\%$.
(3) Critical value $z^* = 1.64$.
(4) Test statistic

$$z = \frac{\bar{x} - \mu}{\sqrt{s^2/n}} = \frac{7.8 - 5}{\sqrt{4.1^2/100}} = 6.8$$

(5) Decision rule: $6.8 > 1.64$ so we reject H_0 in favour of H_1. Note that in this case we are dealing with the right-hand tail of the distribution (positive values of z and z^*). Only high values of $\bar{x}$ reject H_0.

One-tail and two-tail tests

In the above example the rejection region for the test consisted of one tail of the distribution of $\bar{x}$, since the buyer was only concerned about turnover being less

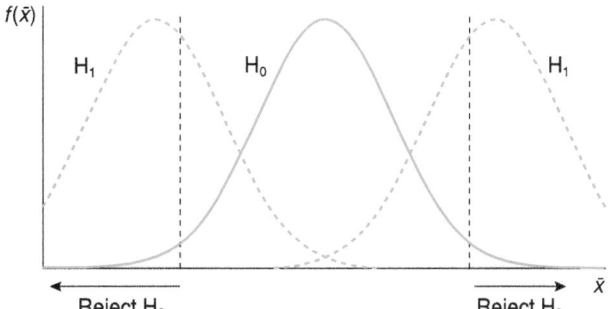

Figure 5.3
A two-tail hypothesis
test

than claimed. For this reason it is known as a one-tail test. Suppose now that an accountant is engaged to sell the franchise and wants to check the claim about turnover before advertising the business for sale. In this case she would be concerned about turnover being either below *or* above 5000.

This would now become a two-tail test with the null and alternative hypotheses being

$$H_0: \mu = 5000$$
$$H_1: \mu \neq 5000$$

Now there are two rejection regions for the test. Either a very low sample mean *or* a very high one will serve to reject the null hypothesis. The situation is presented graphically in Figure 5.3.

The distribution of $\bar{x}$ under H_0 is the same as before, but under the alternative hypothesis the distribution could be shifted either to the left or to the right, as depicted. If the significance level is still chosen to be 5%, then the complete rejection region consist of the *two* extremes of the distribution under H_0, containing 2.5% in each tail (hence 5% in total). This gives a Type I error probability of 5% as before.

The critical value of the test therefore becomes $z^* = 1.96$, the value which cuts off 2.5% in each tail of the standard Normal distribution. Only if the test statistic falls into one of the rejection regions beyond 1.96 standard errors from the mean is H_0 rejected.

Using data from the previous example, the test statistic remains $z = -1.82$ so that the null hypothesis cannot be rejected in this case, as -1.82 does not fall beyond -1.96. To recap, the five steps of the test are:

(1) $H_0: \mu = 5000$
      $H_1: \mu \neq 5000$
(2) Choose the significance level: $\alpha = 0.05$.
(3) Look up the critical value: $z^* = 1.96$.
(4) Evaluate the test statistic

$$z = \frac{-100}{\sqrt{280^2/26}} = -1.82$$

(5) Compare test statistic and critical values: if $z < -z^*$ or $z > z^*$ reject H_0 in favour of H_1. In this case $-1.82 > -1.96$ so H_0 cannot be rejected with 95% confidence.

One- and two-tail tests therefore differ only at steps 1 and 3. Note that we have come to different conclusions according to whether a one- or two-tail test was used, with the same sample evidence. There is nothing wrong with this, however, for there are different interpretations of the two results. If the investor always uses his rule, he will miss out on 5% of good investment opportunities, when sales are (by chance) low. He will never miss out on a good opportunity because the investment appears too good (i.e. sales by chance are very high). For the accountant, 5% of the firms with sales averaging £5000 will not be advertised as such, *either* because sales appear too low *or* because they appear too high.

It is tempting on occasion to use a one-tail test because of the sample evidence. For example, the accountant might look at the sample evidence above and decide that the franchise operation can only have true sales less than or equal to 5000. Therefore a one-tail test is used. This is a dangerous practice, since the sample evidence is being used to help formulate the hypothesis, which is then tested on that same evidence. This is going round in circles; the hypothesis should be chosen *independently* of the evidence, which is then used to test it. Presumably the accountant would also use a one-tail test (with $H_1: \mu > 5000$ as the alternative hypothesis) if it was noticed that the sample mean were *above* the hypothesised value. In effect therefore the 10% significance level would be used, not the 5% level, since there would be 5% in each tail of the distribution. A Type I error would be made on 10% of all occasions rather than 5%.

It is acceptable to use a one-tail test when you have *independent* information about what the alternative hypothesis should be, or you are not concerned about one side of the distribution (such as the investor) and can effectively add that into the null hypothesis. Otherwise, it is safer to use a two-tail test.

Exercise 5.1

(a) Two political parties are debating crime figures. One party says that crime has increased compared to the previous year. The other party says it has not. Write down the null and alternative hypotheses.

(b) Explain the two types of error that could be made in this example and the possible costs of each type of error.

Exercise 5.2

?

(a) We test the hypothesis $H_0: \mu = 100$ against $H_1: \mu > 100$ by rejecting H_0 if our sample mean is greater than 108. If in fact $\bar{x} \sim N(100, 900/25)$, what is the probability of making a Type I error?

(b) If we wanted a 5% Type I error probability, what decision rule should we adopt?

(c) If we knew that μ could only take on the values 100 (under H_0) or 112 (under H_1) what would be the Type II error probability using the decision rule in part (a)?

Exercise 5.3

?

Test the hypothesis $H_0: \mu = 500$ versus $H_1: \mu \neq 500$ using the evidence $\bar{x} = 530$, $s = 90$ from a sample of size $n = 30$.

The choice of significance level

We justified the choice of the 5% significance level by reference to convention. This is usually a poor argument for anything, but it does have some justification. In an ideal world we would have precisely specified null *and* alternative hypotheses (e.g. we would test $H_0: \mu = 5000$ against $H_1: \mu = 4500$, these being the only possibilities). Then we could calculate the probabilities of both Type I *and* Type II errors, for any given decision rule. We could then choose the optimal decision rule, which gives the best compromise between the two types of error. This is reflected in a court of law. In criminal cases, the jury must be convinced of the prosecution's case beyond reasonable doubt, because of the cost of committing a Type I error. In a civil case (libel, for example) the jury need only be convinced *on the balance of probabilities*. In a civil case, the costs of Type I and Type II error are more evenly balanced and so the burden of proof is lessened.

However, in practice we usually do not have the luxury of two well-specified hypotheses. As in the example, the null hypothesis is precisely specified (it has to be or the test could not be carried out) but the alternative hypothesis is imprecise (sometimes called a composite hypothesis because it encompasses a range of values). Statistical inference is often used not so much as an aid to decision making but to provide evidence for or against a particular theory, to alter one's degree of belief in the truth of the theory. For example, an economic theory might assert that rising prices are caused by rising wages (the cost–push theory of inflation). The null and alternative hypotheses would be:

H_0: there is no connection between rising wages and rising prices;
H_1: there is some connection between rising wages and rising prices.

(Note that the null has 'no connection', since this is a precise statement. 'Some connection' is too vague to be the null hypothesis.) Data could be gathered to test this hypothesis (the appropriate methods will be discussed in the chapters on correlation and regression). But what decision rests upon the result of this test? It could be thought that government might make a decision to impose a prices and incomes policy, but if every academic study of inflation led to the imposition or abandonment of a prices and incomes policy there would have been an awful lot of policies! (In fact, there *were* a lot of such policies, but not as many as the number of studies of inflation.) No single study is decisive ('more research is needed' is a very common phrase) but each does influence the climate of opinion which may eventually lead to a policy decision. But if a hypothesis test is designed to influence opinion, how is the significance level to be chosen?

It is difficult to trade off the costs of Type I and Type II errors and the probability of making those errors. A Type I error in this case means concluding that rising wages do cause rising prices when, in fact, they do not. So what would be the cost of this error, i.e. imposing a prices and incomes policy when, in fact, it is not needed? It is extremely difficult, if not impossible, to put a figure on it. It would depend on what type of prices and incomes policy were imposed – would wages be frozen or allowed to rise with productivity, how fast would prices be allowed to rise, would company dividends be frozen? The costs of the Type II error would also be problematic (not imposing a needed prices and incomes policy), for they would depend, among other things, on what alternative policies might be adopted.

The 5% significance level really does depend upon convention therefore, it cannot be justified by reference to the relative costs of Type I and Type II errors (it is too much to believe that everyone does consider these costs and independently arrives at the conclusion that 5% is the appropriate significance level!). However, the 5% convention does impose some sort of discipline upon research;

it sets some kind of standard which all theories (hypotheses) should be measured against. Beware the researcher who reports that a particular hypothesis is rejected at the 8% significance level; it is likely that the significance level was chosen so that the hypothesis could be rejected, which is what the researcher was hoping for in the first place!

The Prob-value approach

Suppose a result is significant at the 4.95% level (i.e. it just meets the 5% convention and the null hypothesis is rejected). A *very* slight change in the sample data could have meant the result being significant at only the 5.05% level, and the null hypothesis not being rejected. Would we really be happy to alter our belief completely on such fragile results? Most researchers (but not all!) would be cautious if their results were only just significant (or fell just short of significance).

This suggests an alternative approach: the significance level of the test statistic could be reported and the reader could make his own judgements about it. This is known as the Prob-value approach, the Prob-value being the significance level of the calculated test statistic. For example, the calculated test statistic for the investor problem was $z = -1.82$ and the associated Prob-value is obtained from Table A2 (see page **414**) as 3.44%, i.e. -1.82 cuts off 3.44% in one tail of the standard Normal distribution. This means that the null hypothesis can be rejected at the 3.44% significance level or, alternatively expressed, with 96.56% confidence.

Notice that Table A2 gives the Prob-value for a one-tail test; for a two-tail test the Prob-value should be doubled. Thus for the accountant, using the two-tail test, the significance level is 6.88% and this is the level at which the null hypothesis can be rejected. Alternatively we could say we reject the null with 93.12% confidence. This does not meet the standard 5% criterion (for the significance level) which is most often used, so would result in non-rejection of the null.

An advantage of using the Prob-value approach is that many statistical software programs routinely provide the Prob-value of a calculated test statistic. If one understands the use of Prob-values then one does not have to look up tables (this applies to any distribution, not just the Normal), which can save a lot of time.

To summarise, one rejects the null hypothesis if either:

- (Method 1) – the test statistic **is greater than** the critical value, i.e. $z > z^*$, or
- (Method 2) – the Prob-value associated with the test statistic **is less than** the significance level, i.e. $P < 0.05$ (if the 5% significance level is used).

I have found that many students initially find this confusing, because of the opposing inequality in the two versions (greater than and less than). For example, a program might calculate a hypothesis test and report the result as '$z = 1.4$ (P value $= 0.162$)'. The first point to note is that most software programs report the Prob-value for a two-tail test by default. Hence, assuming a 5% significance level, in this case we cannot reject H_0 because $z = 1.4 < 1.96$ or equivalently because $0.162 > 0.05$, against a two-tailed alternative (i.e. H_1 contains $\neq$).

If you wish to conduct a one-tailed test you have to halve the reported Prob-value, becoming 0.081 in this example. This is again greater than 5%, so the hypothesis is still accepted, even against a one-sided alternative (H_1 contains > or <). Equivalently, one could compare 1.4 with the one-tail critical value, 1.64, showing non-rejection of the null, but one has to look up the standard Normal table with this method. Computers cannot guess whether a one- or two-sided test is wanted, so take the conservative option and report the two-sided value. The correction for a one-sided test has to be done manually.

Significance, effect size and power

Researchers usually look for 'significant' results. Academic papers report that 'the results are significant' or that 'the coefficient is significantly different from zero at the 5% significance level'. It is vital to realise that the word 'significant' is used here in the *statistical* sense and not in its everyday sense of being *important*. Something can be statistically significant yet still unimportant.

Suppose that we have some more data about the business examined earlier. Data for 100 franchises have been uncovered, revealing an average weekly turnover of £4975 with standard deviation £143. Can we reject the hypothesis that the average weekly turnover is £5000? The test statistic is

$$z = \frac{4975 - 5000}{\sqrt{143^2/100}} = -1.75$$

Since this is less than $-z^* = -1.64$ the null is rejected with 95% confidence. True average weekly turnover is less than £5000. However, the difference is only £25 per week, which is 0.5% of £5000. Common sense would suggest that the difference may be unimportant, even if it is significant in the statistical sense. One should not interpret statistical results in terms of significance alone, therefore; one should also look at the size of the difference (sometimes known as the effect size) and ask whether it is important or not. This is a mistake made by even experienced researchers; a review of articles in the prestigious *American Economic Review* reported that 82% of them confused statistical significance for economic significance in some way (McCloskey and Ziliak, 2004).

This problem with hypothesis testing paradoxically grows worse as the sample size increases. For example, if 250 observations reveal average sales of 4985 with standard deviation 143, the null would (just) be rejected at 5% significance. In fact, given a large enough sample size we can virtually guarantee to reject the null hypothesis even before we have gathered the data. This can be seen from equation (5.4) for the z score test statistic: as n grows larger, the test statistic also inevitably increases.

A good way to remember this point is to appreciate that it is the *evidence* which is significant, not the size of the effect. Strictly, it is better to say '. . . there is significant evidence of difference between . . .' than '. . . there is a significant difference between . . .'.

A related way of considering the effect of increasing sample size is via the concept of the power of a test. This is defined as

Power of a test = $1 - \text{Pr(Type II error)} = 1 - \beta$ (5.5)

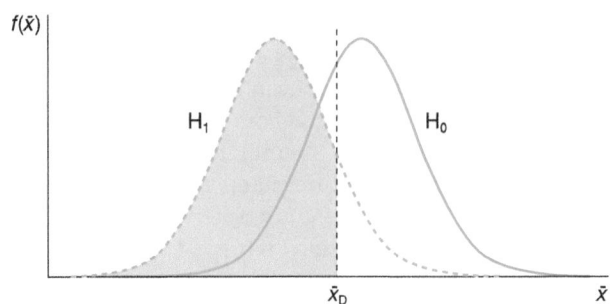

Figure 5.4
The power of a test

where β is the symbol conventionally used to indicate the probability of a Type II error. As a Type II error is defined as not rejecting H_0 when false (equivalent to rejecting H_1 when true), power is the probability of rejecting H_0 when false (if H_0 is false, it must be *either* accepted *or* rejected; hence these probabilities sum to one). This is one of the correct decisions identified earlier, associated with the lower right-hand box in Figure 5.1, that of correctly rejecting a false null hypothesis. The power of a test is therefore given by the area under the H_1 distribution, to the left of the decision line, as illustrated (shaded) in Figure 5.4 (for a one-tail test).

It is generally desirable to maximise the power of a test, as long as the probability of a Type I error is not raised in the process. There are essentially three ways of doing this.

- Avoid situations where the null and alternative hypotheses are very similar, i.e. the hypothesised means are not far apart (a small effect size).
- Use a large sample size. This reduces the sampling variance of $\bar{x}$ (under both H_0 and H_1) so the two distributions become more distinct.
- Use good sampling methods which have small sampling variances. This has a similar effect to increasing the sample size.

Unfortunately, in economics and business the data are very often given in advance and there is little or no control possible over the sampling procedures. This leads to a neglect of consideration of power, unlike in psychology, for example, where the experiment can often be designed by the researcher. The gathering of sample data will be covered in detail in Chapter 9.

Exercise 5.4   If a researcher believes the cost of making a Type I error is much greater than the cost of a Type II error, should they choose a 5% or 1% significance level? Explain why.

Exercise 5.5   (a) A researcher uses *Excel* to analyse data and test a hypothesis. The program

reports a test statistic of $z = 1.77$ (P value = 0.077). Would you reject the null hypothesis if carrying out (i) a one-tailed test (ii) a two-tailed test? Use the 5% significance level.

(b) Repeat part (a) using a 1% significance level.

Further hypothesis tests

We now proceed to consider a number of different types of hypothesis test, all involving the same principles but differing in details of their implementation. This is similar to the exposition in the last chapter covering, in turn, tests of a proportion, tests of the difference of two means and proportions, and finally problems involving small sample sizes.

Testing a proportion

A car manufacturer claims that no more than 10% of its cars should need repairs in the first three years of their life, the warranty period. A random sample of 50 three-year-old cars found that 8 had required attention. Does this contradict the maker's claim?

   This problem can be handled in a very similar way to the methods used for a mean. The key, once again, is to recognise the sample proportion as a random variable with an associated probability distribution. From Chapter 4 (equation (4.9)), the sampling distribution of the sample proportion in large samples is given by

$$p \sim N\left(\pi, \frac{\pi(1-\pi)}{n}\right) \qquad (5.6)$$

In this case $\pi = 0.10$ (under the null hypothesis, the maker's claim). The sample data are

$p = 8/50 = 0.16$
$n = 50$

Thus 16% of the sample required attention within the warranty period. This is substantially higher than the claimed 10%, but is this just because of a bad sample or does it reflect the reality that the cars are badly built? The hypothesis test is set out along the same lines as for a sample mean.

(1) H_0: $\pi = 0.10$
     H_1: $\pi > 0.10$

     (The only concern is the manufacturer not matching its claim.)
(2) Significance level: $\alpha = 0.05$.
(3) The critical value of the one-tail test at the 5% significance level is $z^* = 1.64$, obtained from the standard Normal table.
(4) The test statistic is

$$z = \frac{p - \pi}{\sqrt{\dfrac{\pi(1-\pi)}{n}}} = \frac{0.16 - 0.10}{\sqrt{\dfrac{0.1 \times 0.9}{50}}} = 1.41$$

(5) Since the test statistic is less than the critical value, it falls into the non-rejection region. The null hypothesis is not rejected by the data. The manufacturer's claim is not unreasonable.

Note that for this problem, the rejection region lies in the *upper* tail of the distribution because of the 'greater than' inequality in the alternative hypothesis. The null hypothesis is therefore rejected in this case if $z > z^*$.

Do children prefer branded goods only because of the name?

Researchers at Johns Hopkins Bloomberg School of Public Health in Maryland found young children were influenced by the packaging of foods. 63 children were offered two identical meals, save that one was still in its original packaging (from MacDonalds). 76% of the children preferred the branded French fries.

Is this evidence significant? The null hypothesis is $H_0: \pi = 0.5$ versus $H_1: \pi > 0.5$. The test statistic for this hypothesis test is

$$z = \frac{p - \pi}{\sqrt{\dfrac{\pi(1 - \pi)}{n}}} = \frac{0.76 - 0.50}{\sqrt{\dfrac{0.5 \times 0.5}{63}}} = 4.12$$

which is greater than the critical value of $z^* = 1.64$. Hence we conclude that children are influenced by the packaging or brand name.

(*Source: New Scientist*, 11 August 2007.)

Testing the difference of two means

Suppose a car company wishes to compare the performance of its two factories producing an identical model of car. The factories are equipped with the same machinery but their outputs might differ due to managerial ability, labour relations, etc. Senior management wishes to know if there is any difference between the two factories. Output is monitored for 30 days, chosen at random, with the following results:

	Factory 1	Factory 2
Average daily output	420	408
Standard deviation of daily output	25	20

Does this produce sufficient evidence of a real difference between the factories, or does the difference between the samples simply reflect random differences such as minor breakdowns of machinery? The information at our disposal may be summarised as

$$\bar{x}_1 = 420 \qquad \bar{x}_2 = 408$$
$$s_1 = 25 \qquad s_2 = 20$$
$$n_1 = 30 \qquad n_2 = 30$$

The hypothesis test to be conducted concerns the difference between the factories' outputs, so the appropriate random variable to examine is $\bar{x}_1 - \bar{x}_2$. From Chapter 4 (equation (4.12)), this has the following distribution, in large samples

$$\bar{x}_1 - \bar{x}_2 \sim N\left(\mu_1 - \mu_2, \frac{\sigma_1^2}{n_1} + \frac{\sigma_2^2}{n_2}\right) \qquad (5.7)$$

The population variances, σ_1^2 and σ_2^2, may be replaced by their sample estimates, s_1^2 and s_1^2, if the former are unknown, as here. The hypothesis test is therefore as follows.

(1) H_0: $\mu_1 - \mu_2 = 0$
    H_1: $\mu_1 - \mu_2 \neq 0$

The null hypothesis posits no real difference between the factories. This is a two-tail test since there is no a priori reason to believe one factory is better than the other, apart from the sample evidence.

(2) Significance level: $\alpha = 1\%$. This is chosen since the management does not want to interfere unless it is really confident of some difference between the factories. In order to favour the null hypothesis, a lower significance level than the conventional 5% is set.

(3) The critical value of the test is $z^* = 2.57$. This cuts off 0.5% in each tail of the standard Normal distribution.

(4) The test statistic is

$$z = \frac{(\bar{x}_1 - \bar{x}_2) - (\mu_1 - \mu_2)}{\sqrt{\dfrac{s_1^2}{n_1} + \dfrac{s_2^2}{n_2}}} = \frac{(420 - 408) - 0}{\sqrt{\dfrac{25^2}{30} + \dfrac{20^2}{30}}} = 2.05$$

Note that this is of the same form as in the single-sample cases. The hypothesised value of the difference (zero in this case) is subtracted from the sample difference and this is divided by the standard error of the random variable.

(5) Decision rule: $z < z^*$ so the test statistic falls into the non-rejection region. There does not appear to be a significant difference between the two factories.

A number of remarks about this example should be made. First, it should be noted that it is not necessary for the two sample sizes to be equal (although they are in the example). For example, 45 days' output from factory 1 and 35 days' from factory 2 could have been sampled. Second, the values of s_1^2 and s_2^2 do not have to be equal. They are respectively estimates of σ_1^2 and σ_2^2 and, although the null hypothesis asserts that $\mu_1 = \mu_2$, it does not assert that the variances are equal. Management wants to know if the *average* levels of output are the same; it is not concerned about daily fluctuations in output. A test of the hypothesis of equal variances is set out in Chapter 6.

The final point to consider is whether all the necessary conditions for the correct application of this test have been met. The example noted that the 30 days were chosen at random. If the 30 days sampled were consecutive we might doubt whether the observations were truly independent. Low output on one day (e.g. due to a mechanical breakdown) might influence the following day's output (e.g. if a special effort were made to catch up on lost production).

Testing the difference of two proportions

The general method should by now be familiar, so we will proceed by example for this case. Suppose that, in a comparison of two holiday companies' customers, of the 75 who went with Happy Days Tours, 45 said they were satisfied, while 48 of the 90 who went with Fly by Night Holidays were satisfied. Is there a significant difference between the companies?

This problem can be handled by a hypothesis test on the difference of two sample proportions. The procedure is as follows. The sample evidence is

$$p_1 = 45/75 = 0.6 \qquad n_1 = 75$$
$$p_2 = 48/90 = 0.533 \qquad n_2 = 90$$

The hypothesis test is carried out as follows

(1) $H_0: \pi_1 - \pi_2 = 0$
    $H_1: \pi_1 - \pi_2 \neq 0$

(2) Significance level: $\alpha = 5\%$.
(3) Critical value: $z^* = 1.96$.
(4) Test statistic: The distribution of $p_1 - p_2$ is

$$p_1 - p_2 \sim N\left(\pi_1 - \pi_2, \frac{\pi_1(1 - \pi_1)}{n_1} + \frac{\pi_2(1 - \pi_2)}{n_2}\right)$$

so the test statistic is

$$z = \frac{(p_1 - p_2) - (\pi_1 - \pi_2)}{\sqrt{\dfrac{\pi_1(1 - \pi_1)}{n_1} + \dfrac{\pi_2(1 - \pi_2)}{n_2}}} \qquad (5.8)$$

However, π_1 and π_2 in the denominator of equation (5.8) have to be replaced by estimates from the samples. They cannot simply be replaced by p_1 and p_2 because these are unequal; to do so would contradict the null hypothesis that they *are* equal. Since the null hypothesis is assumed to be true (for the moment), it doesn't make sense to use a test statistic which explicitly supposes the null hypothesis to be false. Therefore π_1 and π_2 are replaced by an estimate of their common value which is denoted $\hat{\pi}$ and whose formula is

$$\hat{\pi} = \frac{n_1 p_1 + n_2 p_2}{n_1 + n_2} \qquad (5.9)$$

i.e. a weighted average of the two sample proportions. This yields

$$\hat{\pi} = \frac{75 \times 0.6 + 90 \times 0.533}{75 + 90} = 0.564$$

This, in fact, is just the proportion of all customers who were satisfied, 93 out of 165. The test statistic therefore becomes

$$z = \frac{0.6 - 0.533 - 0}{\sqrt{\dfrac{0.564 \times (1 - 0.564)}{75} + \dfrac{0.564 \times (1 - 0.564)}{90}}} = 0.86$$

(5) The test statistic is less than the critical value so the null hypothesis cannot be rejected with 95% confidence. There is not sufficient evidence to demonstrate a difference between the two companies' performance.

Are women better at multi-tasking?

The conventional wisdom is 'yes'. However, the concept of multi-tasking originated in computing and, in that domain it appears men are more likely to multi-task. Oxford Internet Surveys (http://www.oii.ox.ac.uk/microsites/oxis/) asked a sample of 1578 people if they multi-tasked while on-line (e.g. listening to music, using the phone). 69% of men said they did compared to 57% of women. Is this difference statistically significant?

The published survey does not give precise numbers of men and women respondents for this question, so we will assume equal numbers (the answer is not very sensitive to this assumption). We therefore have the test statistic

$$z = \frac{0.69 - 0.57 - 0}{\sqrt{\dfrac{0.63 \times (1 - 0.63)}{789} + \dfrac{0.63 \times (1 - 0.63)}{789}}} = 4.94$$

(0.63 is the overall proportion of multi-taskers.) The evidence is significant and clearly suggests this is a genuine difference: men are the multi-taskers!

Exercise 5.6

(?)

A survey of 80 voters finds that 65% are in favour of a particular policy. Test the hypothesis that the true proportion is 50%, against the alternative that a majority is in favour.

Exercise 5.7

(?)

A survey of 50 teenage girls found that on average they spent 3.6 hours per week chatting with friends over the internet. The standard deviation was 1.2 hours. A similar survey of 90 teenage boys found an average of 3.9 hours, with standard deviation 2.1 hours. Test if there is any difference between boys' and girls' behaviour.

Exercise 5.8

(?)

One gambler on horse racing won on 23 of his 75 bets. Another won on 34 out of 95. Is the second person a better judge of horses, or just luckier?

Hypothesis tests with small samples

As with estimation, slightly different methods have to be employed when the sample size is small ($n < 25$) and the population variance is unknown. When both of these conditions are satisfied the t distribution must be used rather than the Normal, so a t test is conducted rather than a z test. This means consulting tables of the t distribution to obtain the critical value of a test, but otherwise the methods are similar. These methods will be applied to hypotheses about sample means only, since they are inappropriate for tests of a sample proportion, as was the case in estimation.

Testing the sample mean

A large chain of supermarkets sells 5000 packets of cereal in each of its stores each month. It decides to test-market a different brand of cereal in 15 of its stores. After a month the 15 stores have sold an average of 5200 packets each, with a standard deviation of 500 packets. Should all supermarkets switch to selling the new brand?

The sample information is

$$\bar{x} = 5200, \; s = 500, \; n = 15$$

From Chapter 4 the distribution of the sample mean from a small sample when the population variance is unknown is based upon

$$\frac{\bar{x} - \mu}{\sqrt{s^2/n}} \sim t_v \tag{5.10}$$

with $v = n - 1$ degrees of freedom. The hypothesis test is based on this formula and is conducted as follows:

(1) H_0: $\mu = 5000$
    H_1: $\mu > 5000$
    (Only an improvement in sales is relevant.)
(2) Significance level: $\alpha = 1\%$ (chosen because the cost of changing brands is high).
(3) The critical value of the t distribution for a one-tail test at the 1% significance level with $v = n - 1 = 14$ degrees of freedom is $t^* = 2.62$.
(4) The test statistic is

$$t = \frac{\bar{x} - \mu}{\sqrt{s^2/n}} = \frac{5200 - 5000}{\sqrt{500^2/15}} = 1.55$$

(5) The null hypothesis is not rejected since the test statistic, 1.55, is less than the critical value, 2.62. It would probably be unwise to switch over to the new brand of cereals.

Testing the difference of two means

A survey of 20 British companies found an average annual expenditure on research and development of £3.7m with a standard deviation of £0.6m. A survey of 15 similar German companies found an average expenditure on research and development of £4.2m with standard deviation £0.9m. Does this evidence lend support to the view often expressed that Britain does not invest enough in research and development?

This is a hypothesis about the difference of two means, based on small sample sizes. The test statistic is again based on the t distribution, i.e.

$$\frac{(\bar{x}_1 - \bar{x}_2) - (\mu_1 - \mu_2)}{\sqrt{\dfrac{S^2}{n_1} + \dfrac{S^2}{n_2}}} \sim t_v \tag{5.11}$$

where S^2 is the pooled variance (as given in equation (4.23)) and the degrees of freedom are given by $v = n_1 + n_2 - 2$.

The hypothesis test procedure is as follows:

(1) H_0: $\mu_1 - \mu_2 = 0$
    H_1: $\mu_1 - \mu_2 < 0$
(2) Significance level: $\alpha = 5\%$.

(3) The critical value of the t distribution at the 5% significance level for a one-tail test with $v = n_1 + n_2 - 2 = 33$ degrees of freedom is approximately $t^* = 1.70$.

(4) The test statistic is based on equation (5.11)

$$t = \frac{(\bar{x}_1 - \bar{x}_2) - (\mu_1 - \mu_2)}{\sqrt{\dfrac{S^2}{n_1} + \dfrac{S^2}{n_2}}} = \frac{3.7 - 4.2 - 0}{\sqrt{\dfrac{0.55}{20} + \dfrac{0.55}{15}}} = -1.97$$

where S^2 is the pooled variance, calculated by

$$S^2 = \frac{(n_1 - 1)s_1^2 + (n_2 - 1)s_2^2}{n_1 + n_2 - 2} = \frac{19 \times 0.6^2 + 14 \times 0.9^2}{33} = 0.55$$

(5) The test statistic falls in the rejection region, $t < -t^*$, so the null hypothesis is rejected. The data do support the view that Britain spends less on R&D than Germany.

Exercise 5.9

It is asserted that parents spend, on average, £540 per annum on toys for each child. A survey of 24 parents finds expenditure of £490, with standard deviation £150. Does this evidence contradict the assertion?

Exercise 5.10

A sample of 15 final-year students were found to spend on average 15 hours per week in the university library, with standard deviation 3 hours. A sample of 20 freshers found they spend on average 9 hours per week in the library, standard deviation 5 hours. Is this sufficient evidence to conclude that finalists spend more time in the library?

Are the test procedures valid?

A variety of assumptions underlie each of the tests which we have applied above and it is worth considering in a little more detail whether these assumptions are justified. This will demonstrate that one should not rely upon the statistical tests alone; it is important to retain one's sense of judgement.

The first test concerned the weekly turnover of a series of franchise operations. To justify the use of the Normal distribution underlying the test, the sample observations must be independently drawn. The random errors around the true mean turnover figure should be independent of each other. This might not be the case if, for example, similar events could affect the turnover figures of all franchises.

If one were using time-series data, as in the car factory comparison, similar issues arise. Do the 30 days represent independent observations or might there be an autocorrelation problem (e.g. if the sample days were close together in time)? Suppose that factory 2 suffered a breakdown of some kind which took three days to fix. Output would be reduced on three successive days and factory 2 would almost inevitably appear less efficient than factory 1. A look at the individual sample observations might be worthwhile, therefore, to see if there are unusual patterns. It would have been altogether better if the samples had been collected on randomly chosen days over a longer time period to reduce the danger of this type of problem.

If the two factories both obtain their supplies from a common, but limited, source then the output of one factory might not be independent of the output of the other. A high output of one factory would tend to be associated with a low output from the other, which has little to do with their relative efficiencies. This might leave the average difference in output unchanged but might increase the variance substantially (either a very high positive value of $\bar{x}_1 - \bar{x}_2$ or a very high negative value is obtained). This would lead to a low value of the test statistic and the conclusion of no difference in output. Any real difference in efficiency is masked by the common supplier problem. If the two samples are not independent then the distribution of $\bar{x}_1 - \bar{x}_2$ may not be Normal.

Hypothesis tests and confidence intervals

Formally, two-tail hypothesis tests and confidence intervals are equivalent. Any value that lies within the 95% confidence interval around the sample mean cannot be rejected as the 'true' value using the 5% significance level in a hypothesis test using the same sample data. For example, our by now familiar accountant could construct a confidence interval for the firm's sales. This yields the 95% confidence interval

$$[4792, 5008] \tag{5.12}$$

Notice that the hypothesised value of 5000 is within this interval and that it was not rejected by the hypothesis test carried out earlier. As long as the same confidence level is used for both procedures, they are equivalent.

Having said this, their interpretation is different. The hypothesis test forces us into the reject/do not reject dichotomy, which is rather a stark choice. We have seen how it becomes more likely that the null hypothesis is rejected as the sample size increases. This problem does not occur with estimation. As the sample size increases the confidence interval becomes narrower (around the unbiased point estimate) which is entirely beneficial. The estimation approach also tends to emphasise importance over significance in most people's minds. With a hypothesis test one might know that turnover is significantly different from 5000 without knowing how far from 5000 it actually is.

On some occasions a confidence interval is inferior to a hypothesis test, however. Consider the following case. In the UK only 17 out of 465 judges are women (3.7%).[2] The Equal Opportunities Commission commented that since the appointment system is so secretive it is impossible to tell if there is discrimination or not. What can the statistician say about this? No discrimination (in its broadest sense) would mean half of all judges would be women. Thus the hypotheses are

---

[2] This figure is somewhat out of date now, but it is still a useful example.

H_0: $\pi = 0.5$ (no discrimination)
H_1: $\pi < 0.5$ (discrimination against women)

The sample data are $p = 0.037$, $n = 465$. The z score is

$$z = \frac{p - \pi}{\sqrt{\dfrac{\pi(1 - \pi)}{n}}} = \frac{0.037 - 0.5}{\sqrt{\dfrac{0.5 \times 0.5}{465}}} = -19.97$$

This is clearly significant (*and* 3.7% is a long way from 50%!) so the null hypothesis is rejected. There is some form of discrimination somewhere against women (unless women choose not to be judges). But a confidence interval estimate of the 'true' proportion of female judges would be meaningless. To what population is this 'true' proportion related?

The lesson from all this is that there exist differences between confidence intervals and hypothesis tests, despite their formal similarity. Which technique is more appropriate is a matter of judgement for the researcher. With hypothesis testing, the rejection of the null hypothesis at some significance level might actually mean a small (and unimportant) deviation from the hypothesised value. It should be remembered that the rejection of the null hypothesis based on a large sample of data is also consistent with the true value and hypothesised value possibly being quite close together.

Independent and dependent samples

The following example illustrates the differences between independent samples (as encountered so far) and dependent samples where slightly different methods of analysis are required. The example also illustrates how a particular problem can often be analysed by a variety of statistical methods.

A company introduces a training programme to raise the productivity of its clerical workers, which is measured by the number of invoices processed per day. The company wants to know if the training programme is effective. How should it evaluate the programme? There is a variety of ways of going about the task, as follows:

- Take two (random) samples of workers, one trained and one not trained, and compare their productivity.
- Take a sample of workers and compare their productivity before and after training.
- Take two samples of workers, one to be trained and the other not. Compare the improvement of the trained workers with any change in the other group's performance over the same time period.

We shall go through each method in turn, pointing out any possible difficulties.

Two independent samples

Suppose a group of 10 workers is trained and compared to a group of 10 non-trained workers, with the following data being relevant

$$\bar{x}_T = 25.5 \qquad \bar{x}_N = 21.0$$
$$s_T = 2.55 \qquad s_N = 2.91$$
$$n_T = 10 \qquad n_N = 10$$

Thus, trained workers process 25.5 invoices per day compared to only 21 by non-trained workers. The question is whether this is significant, given that the sample sizes are quite small.

The appropriate test here is a t test of the difference of two sample means, as follows:

$$H_0: \mu_T - \mu_N = 0$$
$$H_1: \mu_T - \mu_N > 0$$

$$t = \frac{25.5 - 21.0}{\sqrt{\dfrac{7.49}{10} + \dfrac{7.49}{10}}} = 3.68$$

(7.49 is S^2, the pooled variance). The t statistic leads to rejection of the null hypothesis; the training programme does seem to be effective.

One problem with this test is that the two samples might not be truly random and thus not properly reflect the effect of the training programme. Poor workers might have been reluctant (and thus refused) to take part in training, departmental managers might have selected better workers for training as some kind of reward, or simply better workers may have volunteered. In a well-designed experiment this should not be allowed to happen, of course, but we do not rule out the possibility. There is also the 5% (significance level) chance of unrepresentative samples being selected and a Type I error occurring.

Paired samples

This is the situation where a sample of workers is tested before and after training. The sample data are as follows:

Worker	1	2	3	4	5	6	7	8	9	10
Before	21	24	23	25	28	17	24	22	24	27
After	23	27	24	28	29	21	24	25	26	28

In this case, the observations in the two samples are paired and this has implications for the method of analysis. One *could* proceed by assuming these are two independent samples and conduct a t test. The summary data and results are

$$\bar{x}_B = 23.50 \qquad \bar{x}_A = 25.5$$
$$s_B = 3.10 \qquad s_A = 2.55$$
$$n_B = 10 \qquad n_A = 10$$

The resulting test statistic is $t_{18} = 1.58$ which is not significant at the 5% level.

There are two problems with this test and its result. First, the two samples are not truly independent, since the before and after measurements refer to the same group of workers. Second, nine out of 10 workers in the sample have shown an improvement, which is odd in view of the result found above, of no significant improvement. If the training programme really has no effect, then the probability of a single worker showing an improvement is $\frac{1}{2}$. The probability of nine or more workers showing an improvement is, by the Binomial method, $(\frac{1}{2})^{10} \times 10C9 + (\frac{1}{2})^{10}$, which is about one in a hundred. A very unlikely event seems to have occurred.

The t test used above is inappropriate because it does not make full use of the information in the sample. It does not reflect the fact, for example, that the before and after scores, 21 and 23, relate to the same worker. The Binomial calculation above does reflect this fact. A re-ordering of the data would not affect the t test result, but would affect the Binomial, since a different number of workers would now show an improvement. Of course, the Binomial does not use all the sample information either – it dispenses with the actual productivity data for each worker and replaces it with 'improvement' or 'no improvement'. It disregards the amount of improvement for each worker.

The best use of the sample data comes by measuring the improvement for each worker, as follows (if a worker had deteriorated, this would be reflected by a negative number):

Worker	1	2	3	4	5	6	7	8	9	10
Improvement	2	3	1	3	1	4	0	3	2	1

These new data can be treated by single sample methods, and account is taken both of the actual data values and of the fact that the original samples were dependent (re-ordering of the data would produce different improvement figures). The summary statistics of the new data are as follows

$$\bar{x} = 2.00, \; s = 1.247, \; n = 10$$

The null hypothesis of no improvement can now be tested as follows

$$H_0: \mu = 0$$
$$H_1: \mu > 0$$

$$t = \frac{2.0 - 0}{\sqrt{\dfrac{1.247^2}{10}}} = 5.07$$

This is significant at the 5% level so the null hypothesis of no improvement is rejected. The correct analysis of the sample data has thus reversed the previous conclusion. It is perhaps surprising that treating the same data in different ways leads to such a difference in the results. It does illustrate the importance of using the appropriate method.

Matters do not end here, however. Although we have discovered an improvement, this might be due to other factors apart from the training programme. For example, if the before and after measurements were taken on different days of the week (that Monday morning feeling . . .), or if one of the days were sunnier, making people feel happier and therefore more productive, this would bias the results. These may seem trivial examples but these effects do exist, for example the 'Friday afternoon car', which has more faults than the average.

The way to solve this problem is to use a control group, so called because extraneous factors are controlled for, in order to isolate the effects of the factor under investigation. In this case, the productivity of the control group would be measured (twice) at the same times as that of the training group, though no training would be given to them. Ideally, the control group would be matched on other factors (e.g. age) to the treatment group to avoid other factors influencing the results. Suppose that the average improvement of the control group were 0.5 invoices per day with standard deviation 1.0 (again for a group of 10). This can be compared with the improvement of the training group via the two-sample t test, giving

$$t = \frac{2.0 - 0.5}{\sqrt{\dfrac{1.13^2}{10} + \dfrac{1.13^2}{10}}} = 2.97$$

(1.13^2 is the pooled variance). This confirms the finding that the training programme is of value.

Exercise 5.11

A group of students' marks on two tests, before and after instruction, were as follows:

Student	1	2	3	4	5	6	7	8	9	10	11	12
Before	14	16	11	8	20	19	6	11	13	16	9	13
After	15	18	15	11	19	18	9	12	16	16	12	13

Test the hypothesis that the instruction had no effect, using both the independent sample and paired sample methods. Compare the two results.

Discussion of hypothesis testing

The above exposition has served to illustrate how to carry out a hypothesis test and the rationale behind it. However, the methodology has been subject to criticism and it is important to understand this since it gives a greater insight into the meaning of the results of a hypothesis test.

In the previous examples the problem has often been posed as a decision-making one, yet we noted that in many instances no decision is actually taken and therefore it is difficult to justify a particular significance level. Bayesian statisticians would argue that their methods do not suffer from this problem, since the result of their analysis (termed a posterior probability) gives the degree of belief which the researcher has in the truth of the null hypothesis. However, this posterior probability does in part depend upon the prior probability (i.e. before the statistical analysis) that the researcher attaches to the null hypothesis. As noted in Chapter 2, the derivation of the prior probabilities can be difficult.

In practice, most people do not regard the results of a hypothesis test as all-or-nothing proof, but interpret the result on the basis of the quality of the data, the care the researcher has taken in analysing the data, personal experience and a multitude of other factors. Both schools of thought, classical and Bayesian, introduce subjectivity into the analysis and interpretation of data: classical statisticians in the choice of the significance level (and choice of one- or two-tail test), Bayesians in their choice of prior probabilities. It is not clear which method is superior, but classical methods have the advantage of being simpler.

Another criticism of hypothesis testing is that it is based on weak methodological foundations. The philosopher Karl Popper argued that theories should be rigorously tested against the evidence, and that strenuous efforts should be made to try to falsify the theory or hypothesis. This methodology is not strictly followed in hypothesis testing, where the researcher's favoured hypothesis is usually the alternative. A conclusion in favour of the alternative hypothesis is arrived at by default, because of the failure of the null hypothesis to survive the evidence.

Consider the researcher who believes that health standards have changed in the last decade. This may be tested by gathering data on health and testing the null hypothesis of no change in health standards against the alternative hypothesis of some change. The researcher's theory thus becomes the alternative hypothesis and is never actually tested against the data. No attempt is made to falsify the (alternative) hypothesis; it is accepted by default if the null hypothesis falls. *Only* the null hypothesis is ever tested.

A further problem is the asymmetry between the null and alternative hypotheses. The null hypothesis is that there is *exactly* no change in health standards whereas the alternative hypothesis contains all other possibilities, from a large deterioration to a large improvement. The dice seem loaded against the null hypothesis. Indeed, as noted earlier, if a large enough sample is taken the null hypothesis is almost certain to be rejected, because there is bound to have been *some* change, however, small. The large sample size leads to a small standard error (σ^2/n) and thus a large z score. This suggests that the significance level of a test should decrease as the sample size increases.

These particular problems are avoided by the technique of estimation, which measures the size of the change and focuses attention upon that, rather than upon some accept/reject decision. As the sample size increases, the confidence interval narrows and an improved measure of the true change in health standards is obtained. Zero (i.e. no change in health standards) might be in the confidence interval or it might not; it is not the central issue. We might say that an estimate tells us what the value of a population parameter *is*, while a hypothesis test tells us what it is *not*. Thus the techniques of estimation and hypothesis testing put different emphasis upon interpretation of the results, even though they are formally identical.

Summary

- Hypothesis testing is the set of procedures for deciding whether a hypothesis is true or false. When conducting the test we presume the hypothesis, termed the null hypothesis, is true until it is proved false on the basis of some sample evidence.

- If the null is proved false, it is rejected in favour of the alternative hypothesis. The procedure is conceptually similar to a court case, where the defendant is presumed innocent until the evidence proves otherwise.

- Not all decisions turn out to be correct and there are two types of error that can be made. A Type I error is to reject the null hypothesis when it is in fact true. A Type II error is not to reject the null when it is false.

- Choosing the appropriate decision rule (for rejecting the null hypothesis) is a question of trading off Type I and Type II errors. Because the alternative hypothesis is imprecisely specified, the probability of a Type II error usually cannot be specified.

- The rejection region for a test is therefore chosen to give a 5% probability of making a Type I error (sometimes a 1% probability is chosen). The critical value of the test statistic (sometimes referred to as the critical value of the test) is the value which separates the acceptance and rejection regions.

- The decision is based upon the value of a test statistic, which is calculated from the sample evidence and from information in the null hypothesis

$$\left(\text{e.g. } z = \frac{\bar{x} - \mu}{s/\sqrt{n}} \right)$$

- The null hypothesis is rejected if the test statistic falls into the rejection region for the test (i.e. it exceeds the critical value).

- For a two-tail test there are two rejection regions, corresponding to very high and very low values of the test statistic.

- Instead of comparing the test statistic to the critical value, an equivalent procedure is to compare the Prob-value of the test statistic with the significance level. The null is rejected if the Prob-value is less than the significance level.

- The power of a test is the probability of a test correctly rejecting the null hypothesis. Some tests have low power (e.g. when the sample size is small) and therefore are not very useful.

Key terms and concepts

alternative hypothesis	paired samples
critical value	power
effect size	Prob-value
independent samples	rejection region
null or maintained hypothesis	significance level
one- and two-tail tests	Type I and Type II errors

Reference

D. McCloskey, and S. Ziliak, Size matters: the standard error of regressions in the *American Economic Review, Journal of Socio-Economics*, 2004, **33**, 527–546.

Problems

Some of the more challenging problems are indicated by highlighting the problem number in colour.

5.1 Answer true or false, with reasons if necessary.

(a) There is no way of reducing the probability of a Type I error without simultaneously increasing the probability of a Type II error.

(b) The probability of a Type I error is associated with an area under the distribution of $\bar{x}$ assuming the null hypothesis to be true.

(c) It is always desirable to minimise the probability of a Type I error.

(d) A larger sample, *ceteris paribus*, will increase the power of a test.

(e) The significance level is the probability of a Type II error.

(f) The confidence level is the probability of a Type II error.

5.2 Consider the investor in the text, seeking out companies with weekly turnover of at least £5000. He applies a one-tail hypothesis test to each firm, using the 5% significance level. State whether each of the following statements is true or false (or not known) and explain why.

(a) 5% of his investments are in companies with less than £5000 turnover.

(b) 5% of the companies he *fails* to invest in have turnover greater than £5000 per week.

(c) He invests in 95% of all companies with turnover of £5000 or over.

5.3 A coin which is either fair or has two heads is to be tossed twice. You decide on the following decision rule: if two heads occur you will conclude it is a two-headed coin, otherwise you will presume it is fair. Write down the null and alternative hypotheses and calculate the probabilities of Type I and Type II errors.

5.4 In comparing two medical treatments for a disease, the null hypothesis is that the two treatments are equally effective. Why does making a Type I error not matter? What significance level for the test should be set as a result?

5.5 A firm receives components from a supplier, which it uses in its own production. The components are delivered in batches of 2000. The supplier claims that there are only 1% defective components on average from its production. However, production occasionally becomes out of control and a batch is produced with 10% defective components. The firm wishes to intercept these low-quality batches, so a sample of size 50 is taken from each batch and tested. If two or more defectives are found in the sample then the batch is rejected.

(a) Describe the two types of error the firm might make in assessing batches of components.

(b) Calculate the probability of each type of error given the data above.

(c) If instead, samples of size 30 were taken and the batch rejected if one or more rejects were found, how would the error probabilities be altered?

(d) The firm can alter the two error probabilities by choice of sample size and rejection criteria. How should it set the relative sizes of the error probabilities

  (i)   if the product might affect consumer safety?
  (ii) if there are many competitive suppliers of components?
  (iii) if the costs of replacement under guarantee are high?

5.6   Computer diskettes, which do not meet the quality required for high-density (1.44 Mb) diskettes, are sold as double-density diskettes (720 kb) for 80p each. High-density diskettes are sold for £1.20 each. A firm samples 30 diskettes from each batch of 1000 and if any fail the quality test the whole batch is sold as double-density diskettes. What are the types of error possible and what is the cost to the firm of a Type I error?

5.7   Testing the null hypothesis that $\mu = 10$ against $\mu > 10$, a researcher obtains a sample mean of 12 with standard deviation 6 from a sample of 30 observations. Calculate the z score and the associated Prob-value for this test.

5.8   Given the sample data $\bar{x} = 45$, $s = 16$, $n = 50$, at what level of confidence can you reject H_0: $\mu = 40$ against a two-sided alternative?

5.9   What is the power of the test carried out in Problem 5.3?

5.10 Given the two hypotheses

$$H_0: \mu = 400$$
$$H_1: \mu = 415$$

and $\sigma^2 = 1000$ (for both hypotheses):

(a) Draw the distribution of $\bar{x}$ under both hypotheses.

(b) If the decision rule is chosen to be: reject H_0 if $\bar{x} \geqslant 410$ from a sample of size 40, find the probability of a Type II error and the power of the test.

(c) What happens to these answers as the sample size is increased? Draw a diagram to illustrate.

5.11 Given the following sample data

$$\bar{x} = 15 \quad s^2 = 270 \quad n = 30$$

test the null hypothesis that the true mean is equal to 12, against a two-sided alternative hypothesis. Draw the distribution of $\bar{x}$ under the null hypothesis and indicate the rejection regions for this test.

5.12 From experience it is known that a certain brand of tyre lasts, on average, 15 000 miles with standard deviation 1250. A new compound is tried and a sample of 120 tyres yields an average life of 15 150 miles. Are the new tyres an improvement? Use the 5% significance level.

5.13 Test $H_0: \pi = 0.5$ against $H_0: \pi \neq 0.5$ using $p = 0.45$ from a sample of size $n = 35$.

5.14 Test the hypothesis that 10% of your class or lecture group are left-handed.

5.15 Given the following data from two independent samples

$$\bar{x}_1 = 115 \qquad \bar{x}_2 = 105$$
$$s_1 = 21 \qquad s_2 = 23$$
$$n_1 = 49 \qquad n_2 = 63$$

test the hypothesis of no difference between the population means against the alternative that the mean of population 1 is greater than the mean of population 2.

5.16 A transport company wants to compare the fuel efficiencies of the two types of lorry it operates. It obtains data from samples of the two types of lorry, with the following results:

Type	Average mpg	Std devn	Sample size
A	31.0	7.6	33
B	32.2	5.8	40

Test the hypothesis that there is no difference in fuel efficiency, using the 99% confidence level.

5.17 A random sample of 180 men who took the driving test found that 103 passed. A similar sample of 225 women found that 105 passed. Test whether pass rates are the same for men and women.

5.18 (a) A pharmaceutical company testing a new type of pain reliever administered the drug to 30 volunteers experiencing pain. Sixteen of them said that it eased their pain. Does this evidence support the claim that the drug is effective in combating pain?

(b) A second group of 40 volunteers were given a placebo instead of the drug. Thirteen of them reported a reduction in pain. Does this new evidence cast doubt upon your previous conclusion?

5.19 (a) A random sample of 20 observations yielded a mean of 40 and standard deviation 10. Test the hypothesis that $\mu = 45$ against the alternative that it is not. Use the 5% significance level.

(b) What assumption are you implicitly making in carrying out this test?

5.20 A photo processing company sets a quality standard of no more than 10 complaints per week on average. A random sample of 8 weeks showed an average of 13.6 complaints, with standard deviation 5.3. Is the firm achieving its quality objective?

5.21 Two samples are drawn. The first has a mean of 150, variance 50 and sample size 12. The second has mean 130, variance 30 and sample size 15. Test the hypothesis that they are drawn from populations with the same mean.

5.22 (a) A consumer organisation is testing two different brands of battery. A sample of 15 of brand A shows an average useful life of 410 hours with a standard deviation of 20 hours. For brand B, a sample of 20 gave an average useful life of 391 hours with standard deviation 26 hours. Test whether there is any significant difference in battery life.

(b) What assumptions are being made about the populations in carrying out this test?

5.23 The output of a group of 11 workers before and after an improvement in the lighting in their factory is as follows:

Before	52	60	58	58	53	51	52	59	60	53	55
After	56	62	63	50	55	56	55	59	61	58	56

Test whether there is a significant improvement in performance

(a) assuming these are independent samples,

(b) assuming they are dependent.

5.24 Another group of workers were tested at the same times as those in Problem 5.23, although their department *also* introduced rest breaks into the working day.

Before	51	59	51	53	58	58	52	55	61	54	55
After	54	63	55	57	63	63	58	60	66	57	59

Does the introduction of rest days alone appear to improve performance?

5.25 Discuss in general terms how you might 'test' the following:

(a) astrology;

(b) extra-sensory perception;

(c) the proposition that company takeovers increase profits.

5.26 **(Project)** Can your class tell the difference between tap water and bottled water? Set up an experiment as follows: fill r glasses with tap water and $n - r$ glasses with bottled water. The subject has to guess which is which. If they get more than p correct, you conclude they can tell the difference. Write up a report of the experiment including:

(a) a description of the experimental procedure;

(b) your choice of n, r and p, with reasons;

(c) the power of your test;

(d) your conclusions.

5.27 **(Computer project)** Use the $= RAND( )$ function in your spreadsheet to create 100 samples of size 25 (which are effectively all from the same population). Compute the mean and standard deviation of each sample. Calculate the z score for each sample, using a hypothesised mean of 0.5 (since the $= RAND( )$ function chooses a random number in the range 0 to 1).

(a) How many of the z scores would you expect to exceed 1.96 in absolute value? Explain why.

(b) How many do exceed this? Is this in line with your prediction?

(c) Graph the sample means and comment upon the shape of the distribution. Shade in the area of the graph beyond $z = \pm 1.96$.

Answers to exercises

Exercise 5.1

(a) H_0: crime is the same as last year, H_1: crime has increased.

(b) Type I error – concluding crime has risen, when in fact it has not. Type II – concluding it has not risen, when, in fact, it has. The cost of the former might be employing more police officers which are not in fact warranted; of the latter, not employing more police to counter the rising crime level. (The *Economist* magazine (19 July 2003) reported that 33% of respondents to a survey in the UK felt that crime had risen in the previous two years, only 4% thought that it had fallen. In fact, crime had fallen slightly, by about 2%. A lot of people were making a Type I error, therefore.)

Exercise 5.2

(a) $z = (108 - 100)/\sqrt{36} = 1.33$. The area in the tail beyond 1.33 is 9.18%, which is the probability of a Type I error.

(b) $z = 1.64$ cuts off 5% in the upper tail of the distribution, hence we need the decision rule to be at $\bar{x} + 1.64 \times s/\sqrt{n} = 100 + 1.64 \times \sqrt{36} = 109.84$.

(c) Under H_1: $\mu = 112$, we can write $\bar{x} \sim N(112, 900/25)$. (We assume the same variance under both H_0 and H_1 in this case.) Hence $z = (108 - 112)/\sqrt{36} = -0.67$. This gives an area in the tail of 25.14%, which is the Type II error probability. Usually, however, we do not have a precise statement of the value of μ under H_1 so cannot do this kind of calculation.

Exercise 5.3

$\alpha = 0.05$ (significance level chosen), hence the critical value is $z^* = 1.96$. The test statistic is $z = (530 - 500)/(90/\sqrt{30}) = 1.83 < 1.96$ so H_0 is not rejected at the 5% significance level.

Exercise 5.4

One wants to avoid making a Type I error if possible, i.e. rejecting H_0 when true. Hence set a low significance level (1%) so that H_0 is only rejected by very strong evidence.

Exercise 5.5

(a) (i) Reject. The Prob-value should be halved, to 0.0385, which is less than 5%. Alternatively, $1.77 > 1.64$. (ii) Do not reject, the Prob-value is greater than 5%; equivalently $1.77 < 1.96$.

(b) In this case, the null is not rejected in both cases. In the one-tailed case, $0.0385 > 1\%$, so the null is not rejected.

Exercise 5.6

$$z = \frac{0.65 - 0.5}{\sqrt{\dfrac{0.5 \times 0.5}{80}}} = 2.68 \text{ hence the null is decisively rejected.}$$

Exercise 5.7

We have the data: $\bar{x}_1 = 3.6$, $s_1 = 1.2$, $n_1 = 50$; $\bar{x}_2 = 3.9$, $s_2 = 2.1$, $n_2 = 90$. The null hypothesis is H_0: $\mu_1 = \mu_2$ versus H_1: $\mu_1 \neq \mu_2$. The test statistic is

$$z = \frac{(\bar{x}_1 - \bar{x}_2) - (\mu_1 - \mu_2)}{\sqrt{\dfrac{s_1^2}{n_1} + \dfrac{s_2^2}{n_2}}} = \frac{(3.6 - 3.9) - 0}{\sqrt{\dfrac{1.2^2}{50} + \dfrac{2.1^2}{90}}} = -1.08 < 1.96$$

(absolute value) so the null is not rejected at the 5% significance level.

Exercise 5.8

The evidence is $p_1 = 23/75$, $n_1 = 75$, $p_2 = 34/95$, $n_2 = 95$. The hypothesis to be tested is H_0: $\pi_1 - \pi_2 = 0$ versus H_1: $\pi_1 - \pi_2 < 0$. Before calculating the test statistic we must calculate the pooled variance as

$$\hat{\pi} = \frac{n_1 p_1 + n_2 p_2}{n_1 + n_2} = \frac{75 \times 0.3067 + 95 \times 0.3579}{75 + 95} = 0.3353$$

The test statistic is then

$$z = \frac{0.3067 - 0.3579 - 0}{\sqrt{\dfrac{0.3353 \times (1 - 0.3353)}{75} + \dfrac{0.3353 \times (1 - 0.3353)}{95}}} = -0.70$$

This is less in absolute magnitude than 1.64, the critical value of a one tailed test, so the null is not rejected. The second gambler is just luckier than the first, we conclude. We have to be careful about our interpretation, however: one of the gamblers might prefer longer-odds bets, so wins less often but gets more money each time. Hence this may not be a fair comparison.

Exercise 5.9

We shall treat this as a two-tailed test, although a one-tailed test might be justified if there were other evidence that spending had fallen. The hypothesis is H_0: $\mu = 540$ versus H_1: $\mu \neq 540$. Given the sample evidence, the test statistic is

$$t = \frac{\bar{x} - \mu}{\sqrt{s^2/n}} = \frac{490 - 540}{\sqrt{150^2/24}} = -1.63$$

The critical value of the t distribution for 23 degrees of freedom is 2.069, so the null is not rejected.

Exercise 5.10

The hypothesis to test is H_0: $\mu_F - \mu_N = 0$ versus H_1: $\mu_F - \mu_N > 0$ (F indexes finalists, N the new students). The pooled variance is calculated as

$$S^2 = \frac{(n_1 - 1)s_1^2 + (n_2 - 1)s_2^2}{n_1 + n_2 - 2} = \frac{15 \times 3^2 + 20 \times 5^2}{35} = 18.14$$

The test statistic is

$$t = \frac{(\bar{x}_1 - \bar{x}_2) - (\mu_1 - \mu_2)}{\sqrt{\dfrac{S^2}{n_1} + \dfrac{S^2}{n_2}}} = \frac{15 - 9 - 0}{\sqrt{\dfrac{18.14}{15} + \dfrac{18.14}{20}}} = 4.12$$

The critical value of the t distribution with $15 + 20 - 2 = 33$ degrees of freedom is approximately 1.69 (5% significance level, for a one-tailed test). Thus the null is decisively rejected and we conclude finalists do spend more time in the library.

By the method of independent samples we obtain $\bar{x}_1 = 13$, $\bar{x}_2 = 14.5$, $s_1 = 4.29$, $s_2 = 3.12$, with $n = 12$ in both cases. The test statistic is therefore

$$t = \frac{(\bar{x}_1 - \bar{x}_2) - (\mu_1 - \mu_2)}{\sqrt{\dfrac{S^2}{n_1} + \dfrac{S^2}{n_2}}} = \frac{13 - 14.5 - 0}{\sqrt{\dfrac{14.05}{12} + \dfrac{14.05}{12}}} = -0.98$$

with pooled variance

$$S^2 = \frac{(n_1 - 1)s_1^2 + (n_2 - 1)s_2^2}{n_1 + n_2 - 2} = \frac{11 \times 4.29^2 + 11 \times 3.12^2}{22} = 14.05$$

The null of no effect is therefore accepted. By the method of paired samples, we have a set of improvements as follows:

Student	1	2	3	4	5	6	7	8	9	10	11	12
Improvement	1	2	4	3	−1	−1	3	1	3	0	3	0

The mean of these is 1.5 and the variance is 3. The t statistic is therefore

$$t = \frac{1.5 - 0}{\sqrt{3/12}} = 3$$

This now conclusively rejects the null hypothesis (critical value 1.8), in stark contrast to the former method. The difference arises because 10 out of 12 students have improved or done as well as before, only two have fallen back (slightly). The gain in marks is modest but applies consistently to nearly all candidates.

7

Correlation and regression

Learning outcomes

By the end of this chapter you should be able to:

- understand the principles underlying correlation and regression;
- calculate and interpret a correlation coefficient and relate it to an *XY* graph of the two variables;
- calculate the line of best fit (regression line) and interpret the result;
- recognise the statistical significance of the results, using confidence intervals and hypothesis tests;
- recognise the importance of the units in which the variables are measured and of transformations to the data;
- use computer software (*Excel*) to derive the regression line and interpret the computer output.

Complete your diagnostic test for Chapter 7 now to create your personal study plan. Exercises with an icon ? *are also available for practice in* MathXL *with additional supporting resources.*

Introduction

Correlation and regression are techniques for investigating the statistical relationship between two, or more, variables. In Chapter 1 we examined the relationship between investment and gross domestic product (GDP) using graphical methods (the *XY* chart). Although visually helpful, this did not provide any precise measurement of the strength of the relationship. In Chapter 6 the χ^2 test did provide a test of the significance of the association between two category-based variables, but this test cannot be applied to variables measured on a ratio scale. Correlation and regression fill in these gaps: the strength of the relationship between two (or more) ratio scale variables can be measured and the significance tested.

Correlation and regression are the techniques most often used by economists and forecasters. They can be used to answer such questions as

- Is there a link between the money supply and the price level?
- Do bigger firms produce at lower cost than smaller firms?
- Does instability in a country's export performance hinder its growth?

Each of these questions is about economics or business as much as about statistics. The statistical analysis is part of a wider investigation into the problem; it cannot provide a complete answer to the problem but, used sensibly, is a vital input. Correlation and regression techniques may be applied to time-series or cross-section data. The methods of analysis are similar in each case, although there are differences of approach and interpretation which are highlighted in this chapter and the next.

This chapter begins with the topic of correlation and simple (i.e. two variable) regression, using as an example the determinants of the birth rate in developing countries. In Chapter 8, multiple regression is examined, where a single dependent variable is explained by more than one explanatory variable. This is illustrated using time-series data pertaining to imports into the UK. This shows how a small research project can be undertaken, avoiding the many possible pitfalls along the way. Finally, a variety of useful additional techniques, tips and traps is set out, to help you understand and overcome a number of problems that can arise in regression analysis.

What determines the birth rate in developing countries?

This example follows the analysis in Michael Todaro's book, *Economic Development in the Third World* (3rd edn, pp. 197–200) where he tries to establish which of three variables (gross national product (GNP) per capita, the growth rate per capita or income inequality) is most important in determining a country's birth rate. (This analysis has been dropped from later editions of Todaro's book.) The analysis is instructive as an example of correlation and regression techniques in a number of ways. First, the question is an important one; it was discussed at the UN International Conference on Population and Development in Cairo in 1995. It is felt by many that reducing the birth rate is a vital factor in economic

Table 7.1 Todaro's data on birth rate, GNP, growth and inequality

Country	Birth rate	1981 GNP p.c.	GNP growth	Income ratio
Brazil	30	2200	5.1	9.5
Colombia	29	1380	3.2	6.8
Costa Rica	30	1430	3.0	4.6
India	35	260	1.4	3.1
Mexico	36	2250	3.8	5.0
Peru	36	1170	1.0	8.7
Philippines	34	790	2.8	3.8
Senegal	48	430	−0.3	6.4
South Korea	24	1700	6.9	2.7
Sri Lanka	27	300	2.5	2.3
Taiwan	21	1170	6.2	3.8
Thailand	30	770	4.6	3.3

Source: Adapted from Todaro, M. (1992).

development (birth rates in developed countries average around 12 per 1000 population, in developing countries around 30). Second, Todaro uses the statistical analysis to arrive at an unjustified conclusion (it is always best to learn from others' mistakes).

The data used by Todaro are shown in Table 7.1 using a sample of 12 developing countries. Two points need to be made initially. First, the sample only includes developing countries, so the results will not give an all-embracing explanation of the birth rate. Different factors might be relevant to developed countries, for example. Second, there is the important question of why these particular countries were chosen as the sample and others ignored. The choice of country was, in fact, limited by data availability, and one should ask whether countries with data available are likely to be representative of all countries. Data were, in fact, available for more than 12 countries, so Todaro was selective. You are asked to explore the implications of this in some of the problems at the end of the chapter.

The variables are defined as follows:

Birth rate: the number of births per 1000 population in 1981.
GNP per capita: 1981 gross national product p.c., in US dollars.
Growth rate: the growth rate of GNP p.c. per annum, 1961–1981.
Income ratio: the ratio of the income share of the richest 20% to that of the poorest 40%. A higher value of this ratio indicates greater inequality.

We leave aside the concerns about the sample until later and concentrate now on analysing the figures. The first thing it is useful to do is to graph the variables to see if anything useful is revealed. *XY* graphs are the most suitable in this case and they are shown in Figure 7.1. From these we see a reasonably tidy relationship between the birth rate and the growth rate, with a negative slope; there is a looser relationship with the income ratio, with a positive slope; and there is little discernible pattern (apart from a flat line) in the graph of birth rate against GNP. Todaro asserts that the best relationship is between the birth rate and income inequality. He rejects the growth rate as an important determinant of the birth rate because of the four countries at the top of the chart, which have

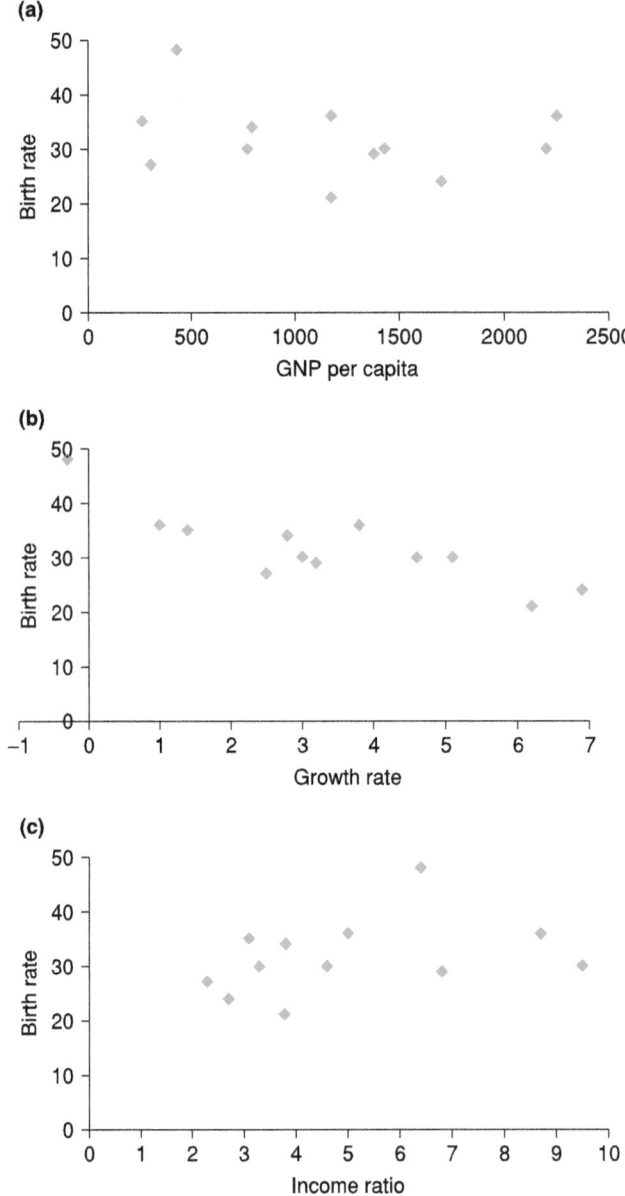

Figure 7.1
Graphs of the birth
rate against (a) GNP,
(b) growth and
(c) income ratio

very different growth rates, yet similar birth rates. In the following sections we
shall see whether Todaro's conclusions are justified.

Correlation

The relationships graphed in Figure 7.1 can first be summarised numerically by
measuring the correlation coefficient between any pair of variables. We illustrate
this by calculating the correlation coefficient between the birth rate (B) and

growth (G), although we also present the results for the other cases. Just as the mean is a number that summarises information about a single variable, so the correlation coefficient is a number which summarises the relationship between two variables.

The different types of possible relationship between any two variables, X and Y, may be summarised as follows:

- High values of X tend to be associated with low values of Y and vice versa. This is termed negative correlation, and appears to be the case for B and G.
- High (low) values of X tend to be associated with high (low) values of Y. This is positive correlation and reflects (rather weakly) the relationship between B and the income ratio (IR).
- No relationship between X and Y exists. High (low) values of X are associated about equally with high and low values of Y. This is zero, or the absence of, correlation. There appears to be little correlation between the birth rate and per capita GNP.

It should be noted that positive correlation does not mean that high values of X are *always* associated with high values of Y, but usually they are. It is also the case that correlation only represents a *linear* relationship between the two variables. As a counter-example, consider the backwards-bending labour supply curve, as suggested by economic theory (higher wages initially encourage extra work effort, but above a certain point the benefit of higher wage rates is taken in the form of more leisure). The relationship is non-linear and the measured degree of correlation between wages and hours of work is likely to be low, even though the former obviously influences the latter.

The sample correlation coefficient, r, is a numerical statistic which distinguishes between the types of cases shown in Figure 7.1. It has the following properties:

- It always lies between -1 and $+1$. This makes it relatively easy to judge the strength of an association.
- A positive value of r indicates positive correlation, a higher value indicating a stronger correlation between X and Y (i.e. the observations lie closer to a straight line). $r = 1$ indicates perfect positive correlation and means that all the observations lie precisely on a straight line with positive slope, as Figure 7.2 illustrates.
- A negative value of r indicates negative correlation. Similar to the above, a larger negative value indicates stronger negative correlation and $r = -1$ signifies perfect negative correlation.

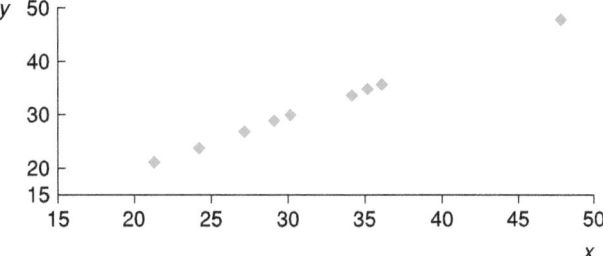

Figure 7.2
Perfect positive
correlation

Table 7.2 Calculation of the correlation coefficient, r

Country	Birth rate Y	GNP growth X	Y^2	X^2	XY
Brazil	30	5.1	900	26.01	153.0
Colombia	29	3.2	841	10.24	92.8
Costa Rica	30	3.0	900	9.00	90.0
India	35	1.4	1225	1.96	49.0
Mexico	36	3.8	1296	14.44	136.8
Peru	36	1.0	1296	1.00	36.0
Philippines	34	2.8	1156	7.84	95.2
Senegal	48	−0.3	2304	0.09	−14.4
South Korea	24	6.9	576	47.61	165.6
Sri Lanka	27	2.5	729	6.25	67.5
Taiwan	21	6.2	441	38.44	130.2
Thailand	30	4.6	900	21.16	138.0
Totals	380	40.2	12 564	184.04	1139.7

Note: In addition to the X and Y variables in the first two columns, three other columns are needed, for X^2, Y^2 and XY values.

- A value of $r = 0$ (or close to it) indicates a lack of correlation between X and Y.
- The relationship is symmetric, i.e. the correlation between X and Y is the same as between Y and X. It does not matter which variable is labelled Y and which is labelled X.

The formula[1] for calculating the correlation coefficient is given in equation (7.1)

$$r = \frac{n\sum XY - \sum X \sum Y}{\sqrt{(n\sum X^2 - (\sum X)^2)(n\sum Y^2 - (\sum Y)^2)}} \tag{7.1}$$

The calculation of r for the relationship between birth rate (Y) and growth (X) is shown in Table 7.2 and equation (7.2). From the totals in Table 7.2 we calculate

$$r = \frac{12 \times 1139.7 - 40.2 \times 380}{\sqrt{(12 \times 184.04 - 40.2^2)(12 \times 12\,564 - 380^2)}} = -0.824 \tag{7.2}$$

This result indicates a fairly strong negative correlation between the birth rate and growth. Countries which have higher economic growth rates also tend to have lower birth rates. The result of calculating the correlation coefficient for the case of the birth rate and the income ratio is $r = 0.35$, which is positive as expected. Greater inequality (higher IR) is associated with a higher birth rate, though the degree of correlation is not particularly strong and less than the correlation with the growth rate. Between the birth rate and GNP per capita the value of r is only −0.26 indicating only a modest degree of correlation. All of this begins to cast doubt upon Todaro's interpretation of the data.

---

[1] The formula for r can be written in a variety of different ways. The one given here is the most convenient for calculation.

Exercise 7.1

(a) Perform the required calculations to confirm that the correlation between the birth rate and the income ratio is 0.35.

(b) In *Excel*, use the = CORREL() function to confirm your calculations in the previous two exercises. (For example, the function = CORREL(A1:A12,B1:B12) would calculate the correlation between a variable *X* in cells A1:A12 and *Y* in cells B1:B12.)

(c) Calculate the correlation coefficient between the birth rate and the growth rate again, but expressing the birth rate per 100 population and the growth rate as a decimal. (In other words, divide *Y* by 10 and *X* by 100.) Your calculation should confirm that changing the units of measurement leaves the correlation coefficient unchanged.

Are the results significant?

These results come from a (small) sample, one of many that could have been collected. Once again we can ask the question, what can we infer about the population (of all developing countries) from the sample? *Assuming* the sample was drawn at random (which may not be justified) we can use the principles of hypothesis testing introduced in Chapter 5. As usual, there are two possibilities.

(1) The truth is that there is no correlation (in the population) and that our sample exhibits such a large (absolute) value by chance.
(2) There really is a correlation between the birth rate and the growth rate and the sample correctly reflects this.

Denoting the true but unknown population correlation coefficient by ρ (the Greek letter 'rho') the possibilities can be expressed in terms of a hypothesis test

$$H_0: \rho = 0$$
$$H_1: \rho \neq 0$$

The test statistic in this case is not *r* itself but a transformation of it

$$t = \frac{r\sqrt{n-2}}{\sqrt{1-r^2}} \tag{7.3}$$

which has a *t* distribution with $n - 2$ degrees of freedom. The five steps of the test procedure are therefore:

(1) Write down the null and alternative hypotheses (shown above).
(2) Choose the significance level of the test: 5% by convention.
(3) Look up the critical value of the test for $n - 2 = 10$ degrees of freedom: $t_{10}^* = 2.228$ for a two-tail test.
(4) Calculate the test statistic using equation (7.3)

$$t = \frac{-0.824\sqrt{12-2}}{\sqrt{1-(-0.824)^2}} = -4.59$$

(5) Compare the test statistic with the critical value. In this case $t < -t_{10}^*$ so H_0 is rejected. There is a less than 5% chance of the sample evidence occurring if the null hypothesis were true, so the latter is rejected. There does appear to be a genuine association between the birth rate and the growth rate.

Performing similar calculations (see Exercise 7.2 below) for the income ratio and for GNP reveals that in both cases the null hypothesis cannot be rejected at the 5% significance level. These observed associations could well have arisen by chance.

Are significant results important?

Following the discussion in Chapter 5, we might ask if a certain value of the correlation coefficient is economically important as well as being significant. We saw earlier that 'significant' results need not be important. The difficulty in this case is that we have little intuitive understanding of the correlation coefficient. Is $\rho = 0.5$ important, for example? Would it make much difference if it were only 0.4?

Our understanding may be helped if we look at some graphs of variables with different correlation coefficients. Three are shown in Figure 7.3. Panel (a) of the figure graphs two variables with a correlation coefficient of 0.2. Visually there seems little association between the variables, yet the correlation coefficient is (just) significant: $t = 2.06$ ($n = 100$ and the Prob-value is 0.046). This is a significant result which does not impress much.

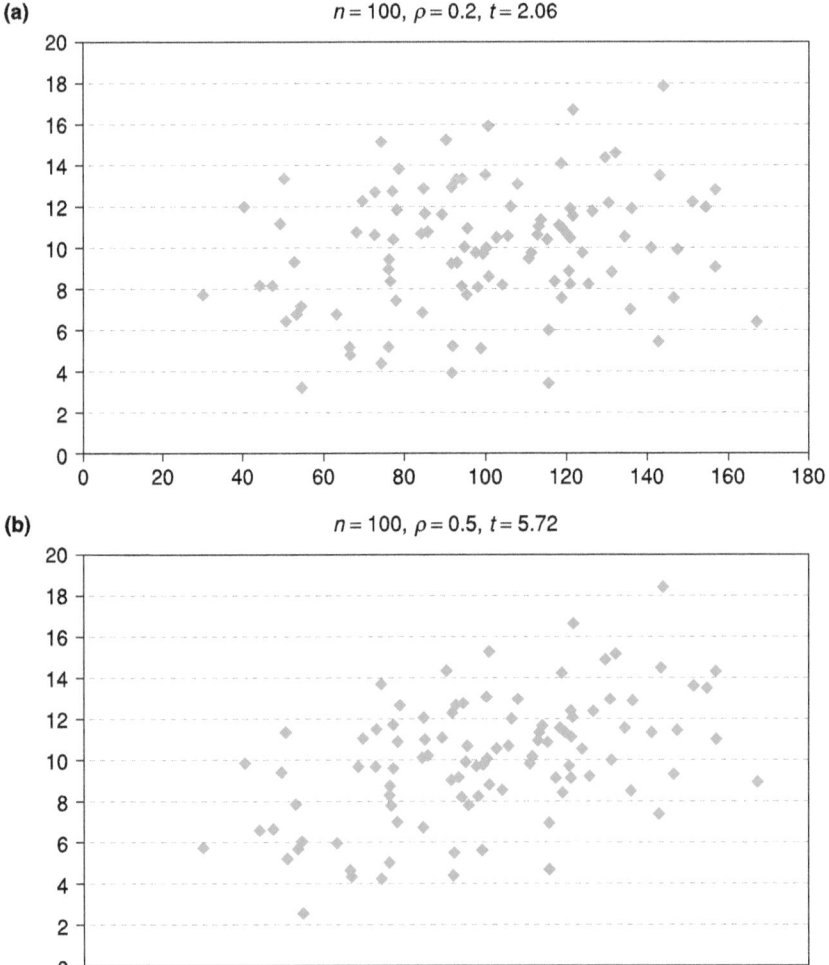

Figure 7.3
Variables with different correlations

(c) $n = 1000$, $\rho = 0.1$, $t = 3.18$

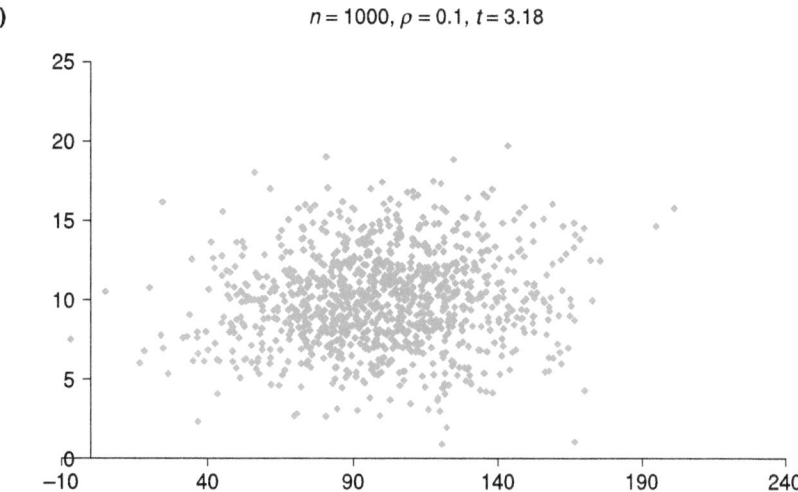

Figure 7.3
(cont'd)

In panel (b) the correlation coefficient is 0.5 and the association seems a little stronger visually, though there is still a substantial scatter of the observations around a straight line. Yet the t statistic in this case is 5.72, highly significant (Prob-value 0.000).

Finally, panel (c) shows an example where $n = 1000$. To the eye this looks much like a random scatter, with no discernable pattern. Yet the correlation coefficient is 0.1 and the t statistic is 3.18, again highly significant (Prob-value = 0.002).

The lessons from this seem fairly clear. What looks like a random scatter on a chart may in fact reveal a relationship between variables which is statistically significant, especially if there are a large number of observations. On the other hand, a high t-statistic and correlation coefficient can still mean there is a lot of variation in the data, revealed by the chart. Panel (b) suggests, for example, that we are unlikely to get a very reliable prediction of the value of y, even if we know the value of x.

Exercise 7.2

(a) Test the hypothesis that there is no association between the birth rate and the income ratio.

(b) Look up the Prob-value associated with the test statistic and confirm that it does not reject the null hypothesis.

Correlation and causality

It is important to test the significance of any result because almost every pair of variables will have a non-zero correlation coefficient, even if they are totally unconnected (the chance of the sample correlation coefficient being *exactly* zero is very, very small). Therefore it is important to distinguish between correlation coefficients which are significant and those which are not, using the t test just outlined. But even when the result is significant one should beware of the danger of 'spurious' correlation. Many variables which clearly cannot be related turn out to be 'significantly' correlated with each other. One now famous example is between the price level and cumulative rainfall. Because they both rise year after year, it is easy to see why they are correlated, yet it is hard to think of a plausible reason why they should be causally related to each other.

Apart from spurious correlation there are four possible reasons for a non-zero value of r.

(1) X influences Y.
(2) Y influences X.
(3) X and Y jointly influence each other.
(4) Another variable, Z, influences both X and Y.

Correlation alone does not allow us to distinguish between these alternatives. For example, wages (X) and prices (Y) are highly correlated. Some people believe this is due to cost–push inflation, i.e. that wage rises lead to price rises. This is case (1) above. Others believe that wages rise to keep up with the cost of living (i.e. rising prices), which is (2). Perhaps a more convincing explanation is (3), a wage–price spiral where each feeds upon the other. Others would suggest that it is the growth of the money supply, Z, which allows both wages and prices to rise. To distinguish between these alternatives is important for the control of inflation, but correlation alone does not allow that distinction to be made.

Correlation is best used therefore as a suggestive and descriptive piece of analysis, rather than a technique which gives definitive answers. It is often a preparatory piece of analysis, which gives some clues to what the data might yield, to be followed by more sophisticated techniques such as regression.

The coefficient of rank correlation

On occasion it is inappropriate or impossible to calculate the correlation coefficient as described above and an alternative approach is required. Sometimes the original data are unavailable but the ranks are. For example, schools may be ranked in terms of their exam results, but the actual pass rates are not available. Similarly, they may be ranked in terms of spending per pupil, with actual spending levels unavailable. Although the original data are missing, one can still test for an association between spending and exam success by calculating the correlation between the ranks. If extra spending improves exam performance, schools ranked higher on spending should also be ranked higher on exam success, leading to a positive correlation.

Second, even if the raw data are available, they may be highly skewed and hence the correlation coefficient may be influenced heavily by a few outliers. In this case, the hypothesis test for correlation may be misleading as it is based on the assumption of underlying Normal distributions for the data. In this case we could transform the values to ranks, and calculate the correlation of the ranks. In a similar manner to the median, described in Chapter 1, this can effectively deal with heavily skewed distributions.

In these cases, it is Spearman's coefficient of rank correlation that is calculated. (The 'standard' correlation coefficient described above is more fully known as Pearson's product-moment correlation coefficient, to distinguish it.) The formula to be applied is the same as before, though there are a few tricks to be learned about constructing the ranks and also the hypothesis test is conducted in a different manner.

Table 7.3 Calculation of Spearman's rank correlation coefficient

Country	Birth rate Y	Growth rate X	Rank Y	Rank X	Y^2	X^2	XY
Brazil	30	5.1	7	3	49	9	21
Colombia	29	3.2	9	6	81	36	54
Costa Rica	30	3.0	7	7	49	49	49
India	35	1.4	4	10	16	100	40
Mexico	36	3.8	2.5	5	6.25	25	12.5
Peru	36	1.0	2.5	11	6.25	121	27.5
Philippines	34	2.8	5	8	25	64	40
Senegal	48	−0.3	1	12	1	144	12
South Korea	24	6.9	11	1	121	1	11
Sri Lanka	27	2.5	10	9	100	81	90
Taiwan	21	6.2	12	2	144	4	24
Thailand	30	4.6	7	4	49	16	28
Totals	–	–	78	78	647.5	650	409

Note: The country with the highest growth rate (South Korea) is ranked 1 for variable X; Taiwan, the next fastest growth nation, is ranked 2, etc. For the birth rate, Senegal is ranked 1, having the highest birth rate, 48. Taiwan has the lowest birth rate and so is ranked 12 for variable Y.

Using the ranks is generally less efficient than using the original data, because one is effectively throwing away some of the information (e.g. by *how much* do countries' growth rates differ). However, there is a trade-off: the rank correlation coefficient is more robust, i.e. it is less influenced by outliers or highly skewed distributions. If one suspects this is a risk, it may be better to use the ranks. This is similar to the situation where the median can prove superior to the mean as a measure of central tendency.

We will calculate the rank correlation coefficient for the data on birth and growth rates, to provide a comparison with the ordinary correlation coefficient calculated earlier. It is unlikely that the distributions of birth or of growth rates is particularly skewed (and we have too few observations to reliably tell) so the Pearson measure might generally be preferred, but we calculate the Spearman coefficient for comparison. Table 7.3 presents the data for birth and growth rates in the form of ranks. Calculating the ranks is fairly straightforward, though there are a couple of points to note.

The country with the highest birth rate has the rank of 1, the next highest 2, and so on. Similarly, the country with the highest growth rate ranks 1, etc. One could reverse a ranking, so the lowest birth rate ranks 1, for example; the direction of ranking can be somewhat arbitrary. This would leave the rank correlation coefficient unchanged in value, but the sign would change (e.g. 0.5 would become −0.5). This could be confusing as we would now have a 'negative' correlation rather than a positive one (though the birth rate variable would now have to be redefined). It is better to use the 'natural' order of ranking for each variable.

Where two or more observations are the same, as are the birth rates of Mexico and Peru, then they are given the same rank, which is the average of the relevant ranking values. For example, both countries are given the rank of 2.5, which is the average of 2 and 3. Similarly, Brazil, Costa Rica and Thailand are all given the rank of 7, which is the average of 6, 7 and 8. The next country, Colombia, is then given the rank of 9.

Excel warning

Microsoft Excel has a *rank()* function built in, which takes a variable and calculates a new variable consisting of the ranks, similar to the above table. However, note that it deals with tied values in a different way. In the example above, Brazil, Costa Rica and Thailand would all be given a rank of 6 by *Excel*, not 7. This then gives a different correlation coefficient to that calculated here. *Excel's* method can be shown to be problematic since, if the rankings are reversed (e.g. the highest growth country is numbered 12 rather than 1) *Excel* gives a different numerical result.

We now apply formula (7.1) to the ranked data, giving

$$r_s = \frac{n\sum XY - \sum X \sum Y}{\sqrt{(n\sum X^2 - (\sum X)^2)(n\sum Y^2 - (\sum Y)^2)}}$$

$$= \frac{12 \times 409 - 78 \times 78}{\sqrt{(12 \times 650 - 78^2)(12 \times 647.5 - 78^2)}} = -0.691$$

This indicates a negative rank correlation between the two variables, as with the standard correlation coefficient ($r = -0.824$), but with a slightly smaller absolute value.

To test the significance of the result a hypothesis test can be performed on the value of ρ_s, the corresponding population parameter

H_0: $\rho_s = 0$
H_1: $\rho_s \neq 0$

This time the t distribution cannot be used (because we are no longer relying on the parent distribution being Normal), but prepared tables of the critical values for ρ_s itself may be consulted; these are given in Table A6 (see page **426**), and an excerpt is given in Table 7.4.

The critical value at the 5% significance level, for $n = 12$, is 0.591. Hence the null hypothesis is rejected if the rank correlation coefficient falls outside the

Table 7.4 **Excerpt from Table A6: Critical values of the rank correlation coefficient**

n	10%	5%	2%	1%
5	0.900			
6	0.829	0.886	0.943	
⋮	⋮	⋮	⋮	⋮
11	0.523	0.623	0.763	0.794
12	0.497	0.591	0.703	0.780
13	0.475	0.566	0.673	0.746

Note: The critical value is given at the intersection of the shaded row and column.

range [−0.591, 0.591], which it does in this case. Thus the null can be rejected with 95% confidence; the data do support the hypothesis of a relationship between the birth rate and growth. This critical value shown in the table is for a two-tail test. For a one-tail test, the significance level given in the top row of the table should be halved.

Exercise 7.3

(a) Rank the observations for the income ratio across countries (highest = 1) and calculate the coefficient of rank correlation with the birth rate.

(b) Test the hypothesis that $\rho_s = 0$.

(c) Reverse the rankings for both variables and confirm that this does not affect the calculated test statistic.

Worked example 7.1

To illustrate all the calculations and bring them together without distracting explanation, we work through a simple example with the following data on X and Y:

Y	17	18	19	20	27	18
X	3	4	7	6	8	5

An XY graph of the data reveals the following picture, which suggests positive correlation:

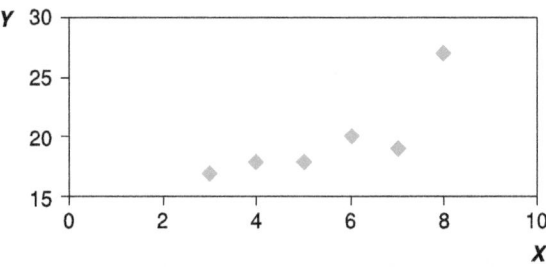

Note that one point appears to be something of an outlier. All the calculations for correlation may be based on the following table:

Obs	Y	X	Y^2	X^2	XY	Rank Y R_Y	Rank X R_X	R_Y^2	R_X^2	$R_X R_Y$
1	17	3	289	9	51	6	6	36	36	36
2	18	4	324	16	72	4.5	5	20.25	25	22.5
3	19	7	361	49	133	3	2	9	4	6
4	20	6	400	36	120	2	3	4	9	6
5	27	8	729	64	216	1	1	1	1	1
6	18	5	324	25	90	4.5	4	20.25	16	18
Totals	119	33	2427	199	682	21	21	90.5	91	89.5

The (Pearson) correlation coefficient r is therefore:

$$r = \frac{n\sum XY - \sum X \sum Y}{\sqrt{(n\sum X^2 - (\sum X)^2)(n\sum Y^2 - (\sum Y)^2)}}$$

$$= \frac{6 \times 682 - 33 \times 119}{\sqrt{(6 \times 199 - 33^2)(6 \times 2427 - 119^2)}} = 0.804$$

The hypothesis $H_0: \rho = 0$ versus $H_1: \rho \neq 0$ can be tested using the t test statistic:

$$t = \frac{r\sqrt{n-2}}{\sqrt{1-r^2}} = \frac{0.804 \times \sqrt{6-2}}{\sqrt{1-0.804^2}} = 2.7$$

which is compared to a critical value of 2.776, so the null hypothesis is not rejected, narrowly. This is largely attributable to the small number of observations and anyway it may be unwise to use the t-distribution on such a small sample. The rank correlation coefficient is calculated as

$$r = \frac{n\sum XY - \sum X \sum Y}{\sqrt{(n\sum X^2 - (\sum X)^2)(n\sum Y^2 - (\sum Y)^2)}}$$

$$= \frac{6 \times 89.5 - 21 \times 21}{\sqrt{(6 \times 91 - 21^2)(6 \times 90.5 - 21^2)}} = 0.928$$

The critical value at the 5% significance level is 0.886, so the rank correlation coefficient *is* significant, in contrast to the previous result. Not too much should be read into this, however; with few observations the ranking process can easily alter the result substantially.

A simpler formula

When the ranks occur without any ties, equation (7.1) simplifies to the following formula:

$$r_s = 1 - \frac{6 \times \sum d^2}{n(n^2 - 1)} \tag{7.4}$$

where d is the difference in the ranks. An example of the use of this formula is given below, using the following data for calculation

Rank Y	Rank X	d	d^2
1	5	−4	16
4	1	3	9
5	2	3	9
6	3	3	9
3	4	−1	1
2	6	−4	16
		Total	60

The differences d and their squared values are shown in the final columns of the table and from these we obtain

$$r_s = 1 - \frac{6 \times 60}{6 \times (6^2 - 1)} = -0.714 \tag{7.5}$$

This is the same answer as would be obtained using the conventional formula (7.1). The verification is left as an exercise. Remember, this formula can only be used if there are no ties in either variable.

Regression analysis

Regression analysis is a more sophisticated way of examining the relationship between two (or more) variables than is correlation. The major differences between correlation and regression are the following:

- Regression can investigate the relationships between two *or more* variables.
- A *direction* of causality is asserted, from the explanatory variable (or variables) to the dependent variable.
- The *influence* of each explanatory variable upon the dependent variable is measured.
- The *significance* of each explanatory variable can be ascertained.

Thus regression permits answers to such questions as:

- Does the growth rate influence a country's birth rate?
- If the growth rate increases, by how much might a country's birth rate be expected to fall?
- Are other variables important in determining the birth rate?

In this example we assert that the direction of causality is from the growth rate (X) to the birth rate (Y) and not vice versa. The growth rate is therefore the explanatory variable (also referred to as the independent or exogenous variable) and the birth rate is the dependent variable (also called the explained or endogenous variable).

Regression analysis describes this causal relationship by fitting a straight line drawn through the data, which best summarises them. It is sometimes called 'the line of best fit' for this reason. This is illustrated in Figure 7.4 for the birth rate and growth rate data. Note that (by convention) the explanatory variable is placed on the horizontal axis, the explained on the vertical. This regression line is downward sloping (its derivation will be explained shortly) for the same

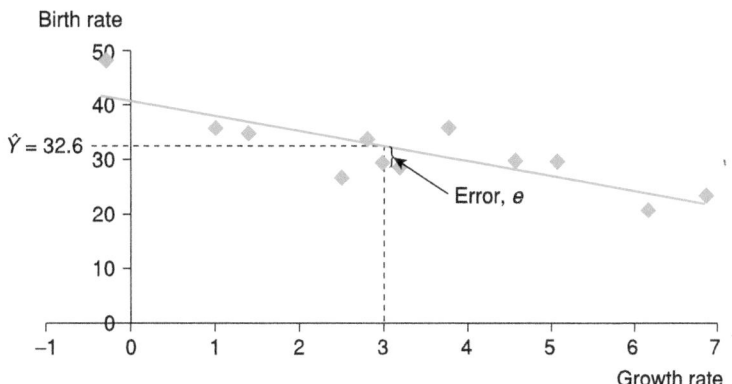

Figure 7.4
The line of best fit

reason that the correlation coefficient is negative, i.e. high values of Y are generally associated with low values of X and vice versa.

Since the regression line summarises knowledge of the relationship between X and Y, it can be used to predict the value of Y given any particular value of X. In Figure 7.4 the value of $X = 3$ (the observation for Costa Rica) is related via the regression line to a value of Y (denoted by $\hat{Y}$) of 32.6. This predicted value is close (but not identical) to the actual birth rate of 30. The difference reflects the absence of perfect correlation between the two variables.

The difference between the actual value, Y, and the predicted value, $\hat{Y}$, is called the error or residual. It is labelled e in Figure 7.4. (*Note*: The italic e denoting the error term should not be confused with the roman letter e, used as the base for natural logarithms (see Appendix 1C to Chapter 1, page **78**). Why should such errors occur? The relationship is never going to be an exact one for a variety of reasons. There are bound to be other factors besides growth which affect the birth rate (e.g. the education of women) and these effects are all subsumed into the error term. There might additionally be simple measurement error (of Y) and, of course, people do act in a somewhat random fashion rather than follow rigid rules of behaviour.

All of these factors fall into the error term and this means that the observations lie around the regression line rather than on it. If there are many of these factors, none of which is predominant, and they are independent of each other, then these errors may be assumed to be Normally distributed about the regression line.

Why not include these factors explicitly? On the face of it this would seem to be an improvement, making the model more realistic. However, the costs of doing this are that the model becomes more complex, calculation becomes more difficult (not so important now with computers) and it is generally more difficult for the reader (or researcher) to interpret what is going on. If the main interest is the relationship between the birth rate and growth, why complicate the model unduly? There is a virtue in simplicity, as long as the simplified model still gives an undistorted view of the relationship. In Chapter 10 on multiple regression the trade-off between simplicity and realism will be further discussed, particularly with reference to the problems which can arise if relevant explanatory variables are omitted from the analysis.

Calculation of the regression line

The equation of the sample regression line may be written

$$\hat{Y}_i = a + bX_i \tag{7.6}$$

where

$\hat{Y}_i$ is the predicted value of Y for observation (country) i
X_i is the value of the explanatory variable for observation i, and
a, b are fixed coefficients to be estimated; a measures the intercept of the regression line on the Y axis, b measures its slope.

This is illustrated in Figure 7.5.

The first task of regression analysis is to find the values of a and b so that the regression line may be drawn. To do this we proceed as follows. The difference between the actual value, Y_i, and its predicted value, $\hat{Y}_i$, is e_i, the error. Thus

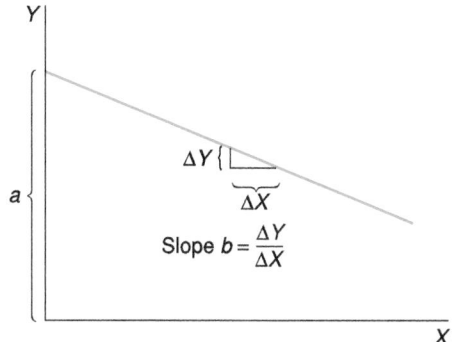

Figure 7.5
Intercept and slope of
the regression line

$$Y_i = \hat{Y}_i + e_i \tag{7.7}$$

Substituting equation (7.6) into equation (7.7) the regression equation can be written

$$Y_i = a + bX_i + e_i \tag{7.8}$$

Equation (7.8) shows that observed birth rates are made up of two components:

(1) that part explained by the growth rate, $a + bX_i$, and
(2) an error component, e_i.

In a good model, part (1) should be large relative to part (2) and the regression line is based upon this principle. The line of best fit is therefore found by finding the values of a and b which *minimise the sum of squared errors* ($\sum e_i^2$) from the regression line. For this reason, this method is known as 'the method of least squares' or simply 'ordinary least squares' (OLS). The use of this criterion will be justified later on, but it can be said in passing that the sum of the errors is not minimised because that would not lead to a unique answer for the values a and b. In fact, there is an infinite number of possible regression lines which all yield a sum of errors equal to zero. Minimising the sum of *squared* errors does yield a unique answer.

The task is therefore to

$$\text{minimise } \sum e_i^2 \tag{7.9}$$

by choice of a and b.

Rearranging equation (7.8) the error is given by

$$e_i = Y_i - a - bX_i \tag{7.10}$$

so equation (7.9) becomes

$$\text{minimise } \sum(Y_i - a - bX_i)^2 \tag{7.11}$$

by choice of a and b.

Finding the solution to equation (7.11) requires the use of differential calculus, and is not presented here. The resulting formulae for a and b are

$$b = \frac{n\sum XY - \sum X \sum Y}{n\sum X^2 - (\sum X)^2} \tag{7.12}$$

and

$$a = \bar{Y} - b\bar{X} \qquad\qquad (7.13)$$

where $\bar{X}$ and $\bar{Y}$ are the mean values of X and Y respectively. The values necessary to evaluate equations (7.12) and (7.13) can be obtained from Table 7.2 which was used to calculate the correlation coefficient. These values are repeated for convenience

$$\sum Y = 380 \qquad \sum Y^2 = 12\ 564$$
$$\sum X = 40.2 \qquad \sum X^2 = 184.04$$
$$\sum XY = 1139.70 \qquad n = 12$$

Using these values we obtain

$$b = \frac{12 \times 1139.70 - 40.2 \times 380}{12 \times 184.04 - 40.2^2} = -2.700$$

and

$$a = \frac{380}{12} - (-2.700) \times \frac{40.2}{12} = 40.711$$

Thus the regression equation can be written, to two decimal places for clarity, as

$$Y_i = 40.71 - 2.70X_i + e_i$$

Interpretation of the slope and intercept

The most important part of the result is the slope coefficient $b = -2.7$ since it measures the effect of X upon Y. This result implies that a unit increase in the growth rate (e.g. from 2% to 3% p.a.) would lower the birth rate by 2.7, for example from 30 births per 1000 population to 27.3. Given that the growth data refer to a 20-year period (1961 to 1981), this increase in the growth rate would have to be sustained over such a time, not an easy task. How big is the effect upon the birth rate? The average birth rate in the sample is 31.67, so a reduction of 2.7 for an average country would be a fall of 8.5% ($2.7/31.67 \times 100$). This is reasonably substantial (although not enough to bring the birth rate down to developed country levels) but would need a considerable, sustained increase in the growth rate to bring it about.

The value of a, the intercept, may be interpreted as the predicted birth rate of a country with zero growth (since $\hat{Y}_i = a$ at $X = 0$). This value of 40.71 is fairly close to that of Senegal, which actually had negative growth over the period and whose birth rate was 48, a little higher than the intercept value. Although a has a sensible interpretation in this case, this is not always so. For example, in a regression of the demand for a good on its price, a would represent demand at zero price, which is unlikely ever to be observed.

Exercise 7.4

(a) Calculate the regression line relating the birth rate to the income ratio.

(b) Interpret the coefficients of this equation.

⬯ Measuring the goodness of fit of the regression line

Having calculated the regression line we now ask whether it provides a good fit for the data, i.e. do the observations tend to lie close to, or far away from, the line? If the fit is poor, perhaps the effect of X upon Y is not so strong after all. Note that even if X has *no* effect upon Y we can still calculate a regression line and its slope coefficient b. Although b is likely to be small, it is unlikely to be exactly zero. Measuring the goodness of fit of the data to the line helps us to distinguish between good and bad regressions.

We proceed by comparing the three competing models explaining the birth rate. Which of them fits the data best? Using the income ratio and the GNP variable gives the following regressions (calculations not shown) to compare with our original model:

for the income ratio (IR): $B = 26.44 + 1.045 \times IR + e$
for GNP: $B = 34.72 - 0.003 \times GNP + e$
for growth: $B = 40.71 - 2.70 \times GROWTH + e$

How can we decide which of these three is 'best' on the basis of the regression equations alone? From Figure 7.1 it is evident that some relationships appear stronger than others, yet this is not revealed by examining the regression equation alone. More information is needed. (You cannot choose the best equation simply by looking at the size of the coefficients. Try to think why.)

The goodness of fit is calculated by comparing two lines: the regression line and the 'mean line' (i.e. a horizontal line drawn at the mean value of Y). The regression line *must* fit the data better (if the mean line were the best fit, that is also where the regression line would be) but the question is how much better? This is illustrated in Figure 7.6, which demonstrates the principle behind the calculation of the coefficient of determination, denoted by R^2 and usually more simply referred to as 'R squared'.

The figure shows the mean value of Y, the calculated sample regression line and an arbitrarily chosen sample observation (X_i, Y_i). The difference between Y_i and $\bar{Y}$ (length $Y_i - \bar{Y}$) can be divided up into:

(1) That part 'explained' by the regression line, $\hat{Y}_i - \bar{Y}$ (i.e. explained by the value of X_i).
(2) The error term $e_i = Y_i - \hat{Y}_i$.

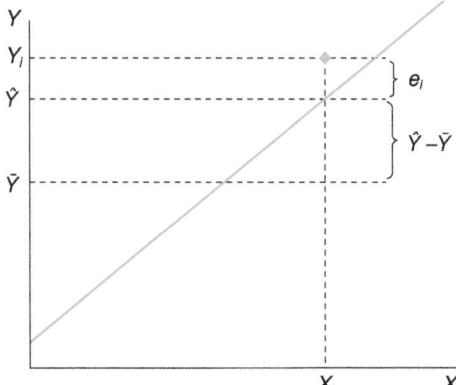

Figure 7.6
The calculation of R^2

In algebraic terms

$$Y_i - \bar{Y} = (Y - \hat{Y}_i) + (\hat{Y}_i - \bar{Y}) \tag{7.14}$$

A good regression model should 'explain' a large part of the differences between the Y_i values and $\bar{Y}$, i.e. the length $\hat{Y}_i - \bar{Y}$ should be large relative to $Y_i - \bar{Y}$. A measure of fit would therefore be $(\hat{Y}_i - \bar{Y})/(Y_i - \bar{Y})$. We need to apply this to all observations, not just a single one. Hence we need to sum this expression over all the sample observations. A problem is that some of the terms would take a negative value and offset the positive terms. To get round this problem we square each of the terms in equation (7.14) to make them all positive, and then sum over the observations. This gives

$\sum(Y_i - \bar{Y})^2$, known as the total sum of squares (TSS)
$\sum(\hat{Y}_i - \bar{Y})^2$, the regression sum of squares (RSS), and
$\sum(Y_i - \hat{Y}_i)^2$, the error sum of squares (ESS)

The measure of goodness of fit, R^2, is then defined as the ratio of the regression sum of squares to the total sum of squares, i.e.

$$R^2 = \frac{\text{RSS}}{\text{TSS}} \tag{7.15}$$

The better the divergences between Y_i and $\bar{Y}$ are explained by the regression line, the better the goodness of fit, and the higher the calculated value of R^2. Further, it is true that

$$\text{TSS} = \text{RSS} + \text{ESS} \tag{7.16}$$

From equations (7.15) and (7.16) we can then see that R^2 must lie between 0 and 1 (note that since each term in equation (7.16) is a sum of squares, none of them can be negative). Thus

$$0 \leqslant R^2 \leqslant 1$$

A value of $R^2 = 1$ indicates that all the sample observations lie exactly on the regression line (equivalent to perfect correlation). If $R^2 = 0$ then the regression line is of no use at all – X does not influence Y (linearly) at all, and to try to predict a value of Y_i one might as well use the mean $\bar{Y}$ rather than the value X_i inserted into the sample regression equation.

To calculate R^2, alternative formulae to those above make the task easier. Instead we use

$$\begin{aligned}
\text{TSS} &= \sum(Y_i - \bar{Y})^2 = \sum Y_i^2 - n\bar{Y}^2 = 12\,564 - 12 \times 31.67^2 = 530.667 \\
\text{ESS} &= \sum(Y_i - \hat{Y})^2 = \sum Y_i^2 - a\sum Y_i - b\sum X_i Y_i \\
&= 12\,564 - 40.711 \times 380 - (-2.7) \times 1139.70 = 170.754 \\
\text{RSS} &= \text{TSS} - \text{ESS} = 530.667 - 170.754 = 359.913
\end{aligned}$$

This gives the result

$$R^2 = \frac{\text{RSS}}{\text{TSS}} = \frac{359.913}{530.667} = 0.678$$

This is interpreted as follows. Countries' birth rates vary around the overall mean value of 31.67. 67.8% of this variation is explained by variation in countries' growth rates. This is quite a respectable figure to obtain, leaving only 32.8% of the variation in Y left to be explained by other factors (or pure random variation). The regression seems to make a worthwhile contribution to explaining why birth rates differ.

It turns out that in simple regression (i.e. where there is only one explanatory variable), R^2 is simply the square of the correlation coefficient between X and Y. Thus for the income ratio and for GNP we have

for IR: $R^2 = 0.35^2 = 0.13$
for GNP: $R^2 = -0.26^2 = 0.07$

This shows, once again, that these other variables are not terribly useful in explaining why birth rates differ. Each of them only explains a small proportion of the variation in Y.

It should be emphasised at this point that R^2 is not the only criterion (or even an adequate one in all cases) for judging the quality of a regression equation and that other statistical measures, set out below, are also required.

Exercise 7.5   (a) Calculate the R^2 value for the regression of the birth rate on the income ratio, calculated in Exercise 7.4.

(?)   (b) Confirm that this result is the same as the square of the correlation coefficient between these two variables, calculated in Exercise 7.1.

Inference in the regression model

So far, regression has been used as a descriptive technique, to measure the relationship between the two variables. We now go on to draw inferences from the analysis about what the *true* regression line might look like. As with correlation, the estimated relationship is in fact a *sample* regression line, based upon data for 12 countries. The estimated coefficients a and b are random variables, since they would differ from sample to sample. What can be inferred about the true (but unknown) regression equation?

The question is best approached by first writing down a true or population regression equation, in a form similar to the sample regression equation

$$Y_i = \alpha + \beta X_i + \varepsilon_i \tag{7.17}$$

As usual, Greek letters denote true, or population, values. Thus α and β are the population *parameters*, of which a and b are (point) estimates, using the method of least squares, and ε is the population error term. If we could observe the individual error terms ε_i then we would be able to get exact values of α and β (even from a sample), rather than just estimates.

Given that a and b are estimates, we can ask about their properties: whether they are unbiased and how precise they are, compared to alternative estimators. Under reasonable assumptions (e.g. see Maddala (2001), Chapter 3) it can be shown that the OLS estimates of the coefficients are unbiased. Thus OLS provides useful point estimates of the parameters (the true values α and β). This is one reason for using the least squares method. It can also be shown that, among the class of linear unbiased estimators, OLS has the minimum variance, i.e. the method provides the most precise estimates. This is another, powerful justification for the use of OLS. So, just as the sample mean provides a more precise estimate of the population mean than does a single observation, the least squares estimates of α and β are the most precise.

Analysis of the errors

To find confidence intervals for α and β we need to know which statistical distribution we should be using, i.e. the distributions of a and b. These can be derived, based on the assumptions that the error term ε in equation (7.17) above is Normally distributed and that the errors are statistically independent of each other. Since we are using cross-section data from countries which are different geographically, politically and socially it seems reasonable to assume the errors are independent.

To check the Normality assumption we can graph the residuals calculated from the sample regression line. If the true errors are Normal it seems likely that these residuals should be approximately Normal also. The residuals are calculated according to equation (7.10) above. For example, to calculate the residual for Brazil we subtract the fitted value from the actual value. The fitted value is calculated by substituting the growth rate into the estimated regression equation, yielding $\hat{Y} = 40.712 - 2.7 \times 5.1 = 26.9$. Subtracting this from the actual value gives $Y_i - \hat{Y} = 30 - 26.9 = 3.1$. Other countries' residuals are calculated in similar manner, yielding the results shown in Table 7.5.

These residuals may then be gathered together in a frequency table (as in Chapter 1) and graphed. This is shown in Figure 7.7.

Although the number of observations is small (and therefore the graph is not a smooth curve) the chart does have the greater weight of frequencies in the centre as one would expect, with less weight as one moves into the tails of the distribution. The assumption that the true error term is Normally distributed does not seem unreasonable.

If the residuals from the sample regression equation appeared distinctly non-Normal (heavily skewed, for example) then one should be wary of constructing confidence intervals using the formulae below. Instead, one might consider transforming the data (see below) before continuing. There are more formal tests for Normality of the residuals but they are beyond the scope of this book. Drawing a graph is an informal alternative, which can be useful, but remember that graphical methods can be misinterpreted.

Table 7.5 Calculation of residuals

	Actual birth rate	Fitted values	Residuals
Brazil	30	26.9	3.1
Colombia	29	32.1	−3.1
Costa Rica	30	32.6	−2.6
⋮	⋮	⋮	⋮
Sri Lanka	27	34.0	−7.0
Taiwan	21	24.0	−3.0
Thailand	30	28.3	1.7

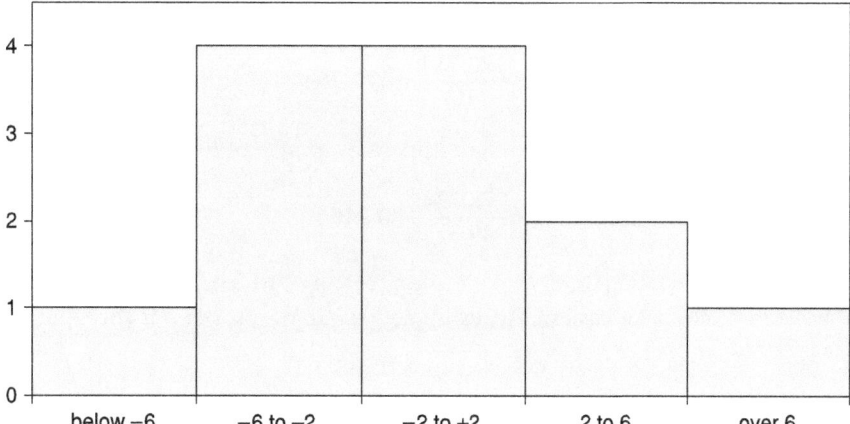

Figure 7.7
Bar chart of residuals
from the regression
equation

If one were using time-series data one should also check the residuals for autocorrelation at this point. This occurs when the error in period t is dependent in some way on the error in the previous period(s) and implies that the method of least squares may not be the best way of estimating the relationship. In this example we have cross-section data, so it is not appropriate to check for autocorrelation, since the ordering of the data does not matter. Chapter 8, on multiple regression, covers this topic.

Confidence interval estimates of α and β

Having checked that the residuals appear reasonably Normal we can proceed with inference. This means finding interval estimates of the parameters α and β and, later on, conducting hypothesis tests. As usual, the 95% confidence interval is obtained by adding and subtracting approximately two standard errors from the point estimate. We therefore need to calculate the standard error of a and of b and we also need to look up tables to find the precise number of standard errors to add and subtract. The principle is just the same as for the confidence interval estimate of the sample mean, covered in Chapter 4.

The estimated sampling variance of b, the slope coefficient, is given by

$$s_b^2 = \frac{s_e^2}{\sum(X_i - \bar{X})^2} \tag{7.18}$$

where

$$s_e^2 = \frac{\sum e_i^2}{n-2} = \frac{\text{ESS}}{n-2} \tag{7.19}$$

is the estimated variance of the error term, ε.

The sampling variance of b measures the uncertainty associated with the estimate. Note that the uncertainty is greater (i) the larger the error variance s_e^2 (i.e. the more scattered the points around the regression line) and (ii) the lower the dispersion of the X observations. When X does not vary much it is then more difficult to measure the effect of changes in X upon Y, and this is reflected in the formula.

First we need to calculate s_e^2. The value of this is

$$s_e^2 = \frac{170.754}{10} = 17.0754 \qquad (7.20)$$

and so the estimated variance of b is

$$s_b^2 = \frac{17.0754}{49.37} = 0.346 \qquad (7.21)$$

(Use $\sum(X_i - \bar{X})^2 = \sum X_i^2 - n\bar{X}^2$ in calculating (7.21) – it makes the calculation easier.) The estimated standard error of b is the square root of (7.21),

$$s_b = \sqrt{0.346} = 0.588 \qquad (7.22)$$

To construct the confidence interval around the point estimate, $b = -2.7$, the t distribution is used (in regression this applies to all sample sizes, not just small ones). The 95% confidence interval is thus given by

$$[b - t_v s_b, \, b + t_v s_b] \qquad (7.23)$$

where t_v is the (two-tail) critical value of the t distribution at the appropriate significance level (5% in this case), with $v = n - 2$ degrees of freedom. The critical value is 2.228. Thus the confidence interval evaluates to

$$[-2.7 - 2.228 \times 0.588, \, -2.7 + 2.228 \times 0.588] = [-4.01, -1.39]$$

Thus we can be 95% confident that the true value of β lies within this range. Note that the interval only includes negative values: we can rule out an upwards-sloping regression line.

For the intercept a, the estimate of the variance is given by

$$s_a^2 = s_e^2 \times \left(\frac{1}{n} + \frac{\bar{X}^2}{\sum(X_i - \bar{X})^2} \right) = 17.0754 \times \left(\frac{1}{12} + \frac{3.35^2}{49.37} \right) = 5.304 \qquad (7.24)$$

and the estimated standard error of a is the square root of this, 2.303. The 95% confidence interval for α, again using the t distribution, is

$$[40.71 - 2.228 \times 2.303, \, 40.71 + 2.228 \times 2.303] = [35.57, 45.84]$$

The results so far can be summarised as follows

$$Y_i = 40.711 - 2.70X_i + e_i$$
s.e. (2.30)   (0.59)
$$R^2 = 0.678 \quad n = 12$$

This conveys, at a glance, all the necessary information to the reader, who can then draw the inferences deemed appropriate. Any desired confidence interval (not just the 95% one) can be quickly calculated with the aid of a set of t tables.

Testing hypotheses about the coefficients

As well as calculating confidence intervals, one can use hypothesis tests as the basis for statistical inference in the regression model. These tests are quickly and easily explained given the information already assembled. Consider the following hypothesis

$$H_0: \beta = 0$$
$$H_1: \beta \neq 0$$

This null hypothesis is interesting because it implies no influence of X upon Y at all (i.e. the slope of the true regression line is flat and Y_i can be equally well predicted by $\bar{Y}$). The alternative hypothesis asserts that X does in fact influence Y.

The procedure is in principle the same as in Chapter 5 on hypothesis testing. We measure how many standard deviations separate the observed value of b from the hypothesised value. If this is greater than an appropriate critical value we reject the hypothesis. The test statistic is calculated using the formula

$$t = \frac{b - \beta}{s_b} = \frac{-2.7 - 0}{0.588} = -4.59 \tag{7.25}$$

Thus the sample coefficient b differs by 4.59 standard errors from its hypothesised value $\beta = 0$. This is compared to the critical value of the t distribution, using $n - 2$ degrees of freedom. Since $t < -t_{10}^*$ ($= -2.228$), in this case the null hypothesis is rejected with 95% confidence. X does have some influence on Y. Similar tests using the income ratio and GDP to attempt to explain the birth rate show that in neither case is the slope coefficient significantly different from zero, i.e. neither of these variables appears to influence the birth rate.

Rule of thumb for hypothesis tests

A quick and reasonably accurate method for establishing whether a coefficient is significantly different from zero is to see if it is at least twice its standard error. If so, it is significant. This works because the critical value (at 95%) of the t distribution for reasonable sample sizes is about 2.

Sometimes regression results are presented with the t statistic (as calculated above), rather than the standard error, below each coefficient. This implicitly assumes that the hypothesis of interest is that the coefficient is zero. This is not always appropriate: in the consumption function a test for the marginal propensity to consume being equal to 1 might be of greater relevance, for example. In a demand equation, one might want to test for unit elasticity. For this reason, it is better to present the standard errors rather than the t statistics.

Note that the test statistic $t = -4.59$ is exactly the same result as in the case of testing the correlation coefficient. This is no accident, for the two tests are equivalent. A non-zero slope coefficient means there is a relationship between X and Y which also means the correlation coefficient is non-zero. Both null hypotheses are rejected.

Testing the significance of R^2: the F test

Another check of the quality of the regression equation is to test whether the R^2 value, calculated earlier, is significantly greater than zero. This is a test using the F distribution and turns out once again to be equivalent to the two previous tests $H_0: \beta = 0$ and $H_0: \rho = 0$, conducted in previous sections, using the t distribution.

The null hypothesis for the test is $H_0: R^2 = 0$, implying once again that X does not influence Y (hence equivalent to $\beta = 0$). The test statistic is

$$F = \frac{R^2/1}{(1 - R^2)/(n - 2)} \tag{7.26}$$

or equivalently

$$F = \frac{RSS/1}{ESS/(n - 2)} \tag{7.27}$$

The F statistic is therefore the ratio of the regression sum of squares to the error sum of squares, each divided by their degrees of freedom (for the RSS there is one degree of freedom because of the one explanatory variable, for the ESS there are $n - 2$ degrees of freedom). A high value of the F statistic rejects H_0 in favour of the alternative hypothesis, $H_1: R^2 > 0$. Evaluating (7.26) gives

$$F = \frac{0.678/1}{(1 - 0.678)/10} = 21.078 \tag{7.28}$$

The critical value of the F distribution at the 5% significance level, with $v_1 = 1$ and $v_2 = 10$, is $F_{1,10}^* = 4.96$. The test statistic exceeds this, so the regression as a whole is significant. It is better to use the regression model to explain the birth rate than to use the simpler model which assumes all countries have the same birth rate (the sample average).

As stated before, this test is equivalent to those carried out before using the t distribution. The F statistic is, in fact, the square of the t statistic calculated earlier ($-4.59^2 = 21.078$) and reflects the fact that, in general

$$F_{1,n-2} = t_{n-2}^2$$

The Prob-value associated with both statistics is the same (approximately 0.001 in this case) so both tests reject the null at the same level of significance. However, in multiple regression with more than one explanatory variable, the relationship no longer holds and the tests do fulfil different roles, as we shall see in the next chapter.

Exercise 7.6

(a) For the regression of the birth rate on the income ratio, calculate the standard errors of the coefficients and hence construct 95% confidence intervals for both.

(b) Test the hypothesis that the slope coefficient is zero against the alternative that it is not zero.

(c) Test the hypothesis $H_0: R^2 = 0$.

Interpreting computer output

Having shown how to use the appropriate formulae to derive estimates of the parameters, their standard errors and to test hypotheses, we now present all these results as they would be generated by a computer software package, in this case *Excel*. This removes all the effort of calculation and allows us to concentrate on more important issues such as the interpretation of the results. Table 7.6 shows the computer output.

Table 7.6 **Regression analysis output using** *Excel*

	A	B	C	D	E	F	G	H
25								
26								
27								
28		*Regression Statistics*						
29		Multiple R	0.824					
30		R square	0.678					
31		Adjusted R square	0.646					
32		Standard error	4.132					
33		Observations	12					
34								
35		ANOVA						
36			*df*	*SS*	*MS*	*F*	*Significance F*	
37		Regression	1	359.913	359.913	21.078	0.001	
38		Residual	10	170.754	17.075			
39		Total	11	530.667				
40								
41			*Coefficients*	*Standard Error*	*t Stat*	*P-value*	*Lower 95%*	*Upper 95%*
42		Intercept	40.71	2.30	17.68	7.15E-09	35.58	45.84
43		GR	−2.70	0.59	−4.59	0.001	−4.01	−1.39
44								
45								
46								
47								

The table presents all the results we have already derived, plus a few more.

- The regression coefficients, standard errors and *t* ratios are given at the bottom of the table, suitably labelled. The column headed '*P value*' (this is how *Excel* refers to the *Prob-value*, discussed in Chapter 5) gives some additional information – it shows the significance level of the *t* statistic. For example, the slope coefficient is significant at the level of 0.1%,[2] i.e. there is this probability of getting such a sample estimate by chance. This is much less than our usual 5% criterion, so we conclude that the sample evidence did not arise by chance.
- The program helpfully calculates the 95% confidence interval for the coefficients also, which were derived above in equation (7.23).
- Moving up the table, there is a section headed ANOVA (Analysis of Variance). This is similar to the ANOVA covered in Chapter 6. This table provides the sums of squares values (RSS, ESS and TSS, in that order) and their associated degrees of freedom in the '*df*' column. The '*MS*' ('mean square') column calculates the sums of squares each divided by their degrees of freedom, whose ratio gives the *F* statistic in the next column. This is the value calculated in equation (7.28). The '*Significance F*' value is similar to the *P value* discussed previously: it shows the level at which the *F* statistic is significant (0.1% in this case) and saves us looking up the *F* tables.
- At the top of the table is given the R^2 value and the standard error of the error term, s_e, labelled 'Standard Error', which we have already come across. 'Multiple R' is simply the square root of R^2; 'Adjusted R^2' (sometimes called '*R*-bar squared' and written $\bar{R}^2$) adjusts the R^2 value for the degrees of freedom. This is an alternative measure of fit, which is not affected by the number of explanatory variables, unlike R^2. See Maddala (2001) Chapter 4 for a more detailed explanation.

---

[2] This is the area in *both* tails, so it is for a two-tail test.

Prediction

Earlier we showed that the regression line could be used for prediction, using the figures for Costa Rica. The point estimate of Costa Rica's birth rate is calculated simply by putting its growth rate into the regression equation and assuming a zero value for the error, i.e.

$$\hat{Y} = 40.711 - 2.7 \times 3 + 0 = 32.6$$

This is a point estimate, which is unbiased, around which we can build a confidence interval. There are, in fact, two confidence intervals we can construct, the first for the position of the *regression line* at $X = 3$, the second for an *individual observation* (on Y) at $X = 3$. Using the 95% confidence level, the first interval is given by the formula

$$\left[\hat{Y} - t_{n-2} \times s_e \sqrt{\frac{1}{n} + \frac{(X_P - \bar{X})^2}{\Sigma(X - \bar{X})^2}}, \hat{Y} + t_{n-2} \times s_e \sqrt{\frac{1}{n} + \frac{(X_P - \bar{X})^2}{\Sigma(X - \bar{X})^2}} \right] \qquad (7.29)$$

where X_P is the value of X for which the prediction is made. t_{n-2} denotes the critical value of the t distribution at the 5% significance level (for a two-tail test) with $n - 2$ degrees of freedom. This evaluates to

$$\left[32.6 - 2.228 \times 4.132 \sqrt{\frac{1}{12} + \frac{(3 - 3.35)^2}{49.37}}, \right.$$

$$\left. 32.6 + 2.228 \times 4.132 \sqrt{\frac{1}{12} + \frac{(3 - 3.35)^2}{49.37}} \right]$$

$$= [29.90, 35.30]$$

This means that we predict with 95% confidence that the *average* birth rate of all countries growing at 3% p.a. is between 29.9 and 35.3.

The second type of interval, for the value of Y itself at $X_P = 3$, is somewhat wider, because there is an additional element of uncertainty: individual countries do not lie on the regression line, but around it. This is referred to as the 95% prediction interval. The formula for this interval is

$$\left[\hat{Y} - t_{n-2} \times s_e \sqrt{1 + \frac{1}{n} + \frac{(X_P - \bar{X})^2}{\Sigma(X - \bar{X})^2}}, \right.$$

$$\left. \hat{Y} + t_{n-2} \times s_e \sqrt{1 + \frac{1}{n} + \frac{(X_P - \bar{X})^2}{\Sigma(X - \bar{X})^2}} \right] \qquad (7.30)$$

Note the extra '1' inside the square root sign. When evaluated, this gives a 95% prediction interval of [23.01, 42.19]. Thus we are 95% confident that an individual country growing at 3% p.a. will have a birth rate within this range.

The two intervals are illustrated in Figure 7.8. The smaller confidence interval is shown in a darker shade, with the wider prediction interval being about twice as big. Note from the formulae that the prediction is more precise (the interval is smaller)

- the closer the sample observations lie to the regression line (smaller s_e);
- the greater the spread of sample X values (larger $\Sigma(X - \bar{X})^2$);

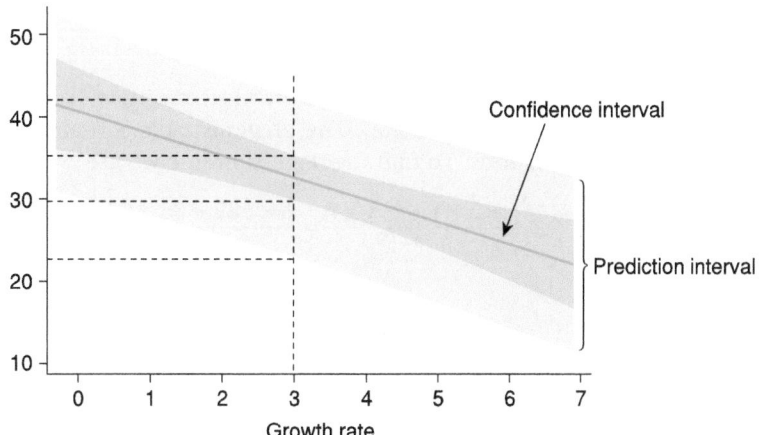

Figure 7.8
Confidence and
prediction intervals

- the larger the sample size;
- the closer to the mean of X the prediction is made (smaller $X_P - \bar{X}$).

This last characteristic is evident in the diagram, where the intervals are narrower towards the centre of the diagram.

There is an additional danger of predicting far outside the range of sample X values, if the true regression line is not linear as we have assumed. The linear sample regression line might be close to the true line within the range of sample X values but diverge substantially outside. Figure 7.9 illustrates this point.

In the birth rate sample, we have a fairly wide range of X values; few countries grow more slowly than Senegal or faster than Korea.

Exercise 7.7   Use *Excel*'s regression tool to confirm your answers to Exercises 7.4 to 7.6.

Exercise 7.8   (a) Predict (point estimate) the birth rate for a country with an income ratio of 10.

(b) Find the 95% confidence interval prediction for a typical country with IR = 10.

(c) Find the 95% confidence interval prediction for an individual country with IR = 10.

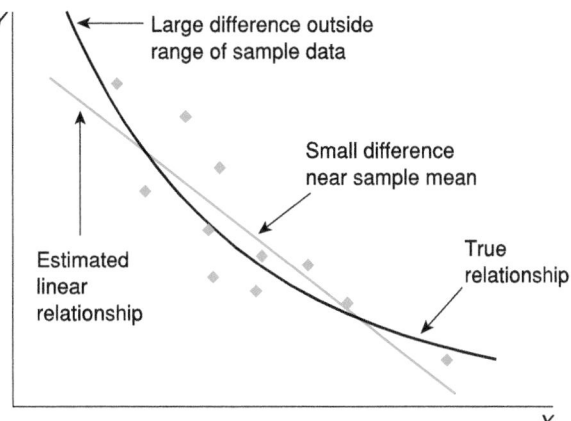

Figure 7.9
The danger of prediction
outside the range of
sample data

We continue the previous worked example, completing the calculations needed for regression. The previous table contains most of the preliminary calculations. To find the regression line we use

$$b = \frac{n \sum XY - \sum X \sum Y}{n \sum X^2 - (\sum X)^2} = \frac{6 \times 682 - 33 \times 119}{6 \times 199 - 33^2} = 1.57$$

and

$$a = 19.83 - 1.57 \times 5.5 = 11.19$$

Hence we obtain the equation

$$Y_i = 11.19 + 1.57 X_i + e_i$$

For inference, we start with the sums of squares:

$$\text{TSS} = \sum (Y_i - \bar{Y})^2 = \sum Y_i^2 - n\bar{Y}^2 = 2427 - 6 \times 19.83^2 = 66.83$$
$$\text{ESS} = \sum (Y_i - \hat{Y}_i)^2 = \sum Y_i^2 - a \sum Y_i - b \sum X_i Y_i$$
$$= 2427 - 11.19 \times 119 - 1.57 \times 682 = 23.62$$
$$\text{RSS} = \text{TSS} - \text{ESS} = 66.83 - 23.62 = 43.21$$

We then obtain $R^2 = \text{RSS}/\text{TSS} = 43.21/66.83 = 0.647$ or 64.7% of the variation in Y explained by variation in X.

To obtain the standard errors of the coefficients, we first calculate the error variance as $s_e^2 = \text{ESS}/(n - 2) = 23.62/4 = 5.905$ and the estimated variance of the slope coefficient is

$$s_b^2 = \frac{s_e^2}{\sum (X - \bar{X})^2} = \frac{5.905}{17.50} = 0.338$$

and the standard error of b is therefore $\sqrt{0.338} = 0.581$.

Similarly for a we obtain

$$s_a^2 = s_e^2 \times \left(\frac{1}{n} + \frac{\bar{X}^2}{\sum (X - \bar{X})^2} \right) = 5.905 \times \left(\frac{1}{6} + \frac{5.5^2}{17.50} \right) = 11.19$$

and the standard error of a is therefore 3.34.

Confidence intervals for a and b can be constructed using the critical value of the t distribution, 2.776 (5%, $v = 4$), yielding $1.57 \pm 2.776 \times 0.581 = [-0.04, 3.16]$ for b and [1.90, 20.47] for a. Note that zero is inside the confidence interval for b. This is also reflected in the test of H_0: $\beta = 0$ which is

$$t = \frac{1.57 - 0}{0.581} = 2.71$$

which falls short of the two-tailed critical value, 2.776. Hence H_0 cannot be rejected.

The F statistic, to test H_0: $R^2 = 0$ is

$$F = \frac{\text{RSS}/1}{\text{ESS}/(n - 2)} = \frac{43.21/1}{23.62/(6 - 2)} = 7.32$$

which compares to a critical value of $F(1,4)$ of 7.71 so, again, the null cannot be rejected (remember that this and the t test on the slope coefficient are equivalent in simple regression).

We shall predict the value of Y for a value of $X = 10$, yielding $\hat{Y} = 11.19 + 1.57 \times 10 = 26.90$. The 95% confidence interval for this prediction is calculated using equation (7.29), which gives

$$
\left[
\begin{array}{l}
26.90 - 2.776 \times 2.43\sqrt{\dfrac{1}{6} + \dfrac{(10 - 5.5)^2}{17.50}}, \\[4mm]
\quad 26.90 + 2.776 \times 2.43\sqrt{\dfrac{1}{6} + \dfrac{(10 - 5.5)^2}{17.50}}
\end{array}
\right] = [19.14,\ 34.66].
$$

The 95% prediction interval for an actual observation at $X = 10$ is given by (7.30), resulting in

$$
\left[
\begin{array}{l}
26.90 - 2.776 \times 2.43\sqrt{1 + \dfrac{1}{6} + \dfrac{(10 - 5.5)^2}{17.50}}, \\[4mm]
\quad 26.90 + 2.776 \times 2.43\sqrt{1 + \dfrac{1}{6} + \dfrac{(10 - 5.5)^2}{17.50}}
\end{array}
\right] = [16.62,\ 37.18].
$$

Units of measurement

The measurement and interpretation of the regression coefficients depends upon the units in which the variables are measured. For example, suppose we had measured the birth rate in births per *hundred* (not *thousand*) of population; what would be the implications? Obviously nothing fundamental is changed; we ought to obtain the same qualitative result, with the same interpretation. However, the regression coefficients cannot remain the same: if the slope coefficient remained $b = -2.7$, this would mean that an increase in the growth rate of one percentage point reduces the birth rate by 2.7 births *per hundred*, which is clearly wrong. The right answer should be 0.27 births per hundred (equivalent to 2.7 per thousand) so the coefficient should change to $b = -0.27$. Thus, in general, the sizes of the coefficients depend upon the units in which the variables are measured. This is why one cannot judge the importance of a regression equation from the size of the coefficients alone.

It is easiest to understand this in graphical terms. A graph of the data will look exactly the same, except that the scale on the Y-axis will change; it will be divided by 10. The intercept of the regression line will therefore change to $a = 4.0711$ and the slope to $b = -0.27$. Thus the regression equation becomes

$$Y_i = 4.0711 - 0.27X_i + e'_i$$
$$(e'_i = e_i/10)$$

Since nothing fundamental has altered, any hypothesis test must yield the same test statistic. Thus t and F statistics are unaltered by changes in the units of measurement; nor is R^2 altered. However, standard errors will be divided by 10 (they have to be to preserve the t statistics; see equation (7.25) for example). Table 7.7 sets out the effects of changes in the units of measurement upon the

Table 7.7 The effects of data transformations

Factor (k) multiplying . . .		Effect upon			
Y	X	a	s_a	b	s_b
k	1	├──────── All multiplied by k ────────┤			
1	k	Unchanged		Divided by k	
k	k	Multiplied by k		Unchanged	

coefficients and standard errors. In the table it is assumed that the variables have been multiplied by a constant k; in the above case $k = 1/10$ was used.

It is important to be aware of the units in which the variables are measured. If not, it is impossible to know how large is the effect of X upon Y. It may be statistically significant but you have no idea of how important it is. This may occur if, for instance, one of the variables is presented as an index number (see Chapter 10) rather than in the original units.

How to avoid measurement problems: calculating the elasticity

A neat way of avoiding the problems of measurement is to calculate the elasticity, i.e. the *proportionate* change in Y divided by the *proportionate* change in X. The proportionate changes are the same whatever units the variables are measured in. The proportionate change in X is given by $\Delta X/X$, where ΔX indicates the *change* in X. Thus if X changes from 100 to 110, the proportionate change is $\Delta X/X = 10/100 = 0.1$ or 10%. The elasticity, η, is therefore given by

$$\eta = \frac{\Delta Y/Y}{\Delta X/X} = \frac{\Delta Y}{\Delta X} \times \frac{X}{Y} \tag{7.31}$$

The second form of the equation is more useful, since $\Delta Y/\Delta X$ is simply the slope coefficient b. We simply need to multiply this by the ratio X/Y, therefore. But what values should be used for X and Y? The convention is to use the means, so we obtain the following formula for the elasticity, from a linear regression equation

$$\eta = b \times \frac{\bar{X}}{\bar{Y}} \tag{7.32}$$

This evaluates to $-2.7 \times 3.35/31.67 = -0.29$. This is interpreted as follows: a 1% increase in the growth rate would lead to a 0.29% decrease in the birth rate. Equivalently, and perhaps a little more usefully, a 10% rise in growth (from say 3% to 3.3% p.a.) would lead to a 2.9% decline in the birth rate (e.g. from 30 to 29.13). This result is the same whatever units the variables X and Y are measured in.

Note that this elasticity is measured at the means; it would have a different value at different points along the regression line. Later on we show an alternative method for estimating the elasticity, in this case the elasticity of demand which is familiar in economics.

Non-linear transformations

So far only *linear* regression has been dealt with, that is fitting a straight line to the data. This can sometimes be restrictive, especially when there is good reason

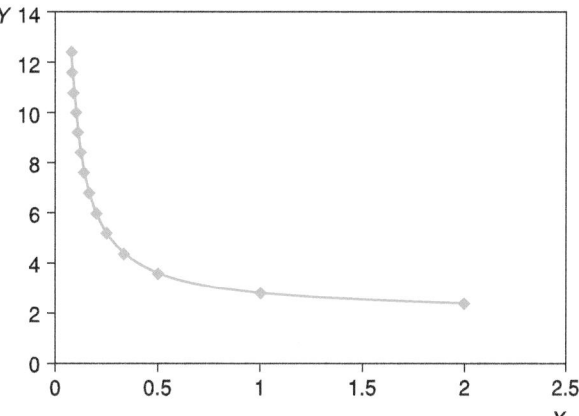

Figure 7.10
Graph of Y against X

to believe that the true relationship is non-linear (e.g. the labour supply curve). Poor results would be obtained by fitting a straight line through the data in Figure 7.10, yet the shape of the relationship seems clear at a glance.

Fortunately this problem can be solved by transforming the data, so that when graphed a linear relationship between the two variables appears. Then a straight line can be fitted to these transformed data. This is equivalent to fitting a curved line to the original data. All that is needed is to find a suitable transformation to 'straighten out' the data. Given the data represented in Figure 7.10, if Y were graphed against $1/X$ the relationship shown in Figure 7.11 would appear.

Thus, if the regression line

$$Y_i = a + b\frac{1}{X_i} + e_i \tag{7.33}$$

were fitted, this would provide a good representation of the data in Figure 7.10. The procedure is straightforward. First, calculate the reciprocal of each of the X values and then use these (together with the original data for Y), using exactly the same methods as before. This transformation appears inappropriate for the birth rate data (see Figure 7.1) but serves as an illustration. The transformed X

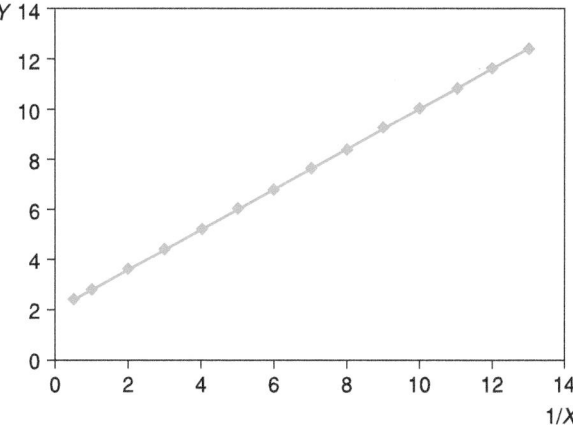

Figure 7.11
Figure 7.10 transformed: Y against 1/X

values are 0.196 (= 1/5.1) for Brazil, 0.3125 (= 1/3.2) for Colombia, etc. The resulting regression equation is

$$Y_i = 31.92 - 3.96\frac{1}{X_i} + e_i \tag{7.34}$$

s.e. (1.64)   (1.56)
$R^2 = 0.39$, $F = 6.44$, $n = 12$

This appears worse than the original specification (the R^2 is low and the slope coefficient is not significantly different from zero) so the transformation does not appear to be a good one. Note also that it is difficult to calculate the effect of X upon Y in this equation. We can see that a unit increase in $1/X$ reduces the birth rate by 3.96, but we do not have an intuitive feel for the inverse of the growth rate. This latest result also implies that a *fall* in the growth rate (hence $1/X$ rises) lowers the birth rate – the converse of our previous result. In the next chapter, we deal with a different example where a non-linear transformation does improve matters.

Table 7.8 presents a number of possible shapes for data, with suggested data transformations which will allow the relationship to be estimated using linear regression. In each case, once the data have been transformed, the methods and formulae used above can be applied.

It is sometimes difficult to know which transformation (if any) to apply. A graph of the data is unlikely to be as tidy as the diagrams in Table 7.8.

Table 7.8 Data transformations

Name	Graph of relationship	Original relationship	Transformed relationship	Regression
Double log	$b > 1$, $0 < b < 1$, $b < 0$	$Y = aX^b e$	$\ln Y = \ln a + b \ln X + \ln e$	$\ln Y$ on $\ln X$
Reciprocal	$b > 0$, $b < 0$	$Y = a + b/X + e$	$Y = a + b\frac{1}{X} + e$	Y on $\frac{1}{X}$
Semi-log		$e^Y = aX^b e$	$Y = \ln a + b \ln X + \ln e$	Y on $\ln X$
Exponential	$b > 0$, $b < 0$	$Y = e^{a+bX+e}$	$\ln Y = a + bX + e$	$\ln Y$ on X

Economic theory rarely suggests the form which a relationship should follow, and there are no simple statistical tests for choosing alternative formulations. The choice can sometimes be made after visual inspection of the data, or on the basis of convenience. The double log transformation is often used in economics as it has some very convenient properties. Unfortunately it cannot be used with the growth rate data here because Senegal's growth rate was negative. It is impossible to take the logarithm of a negative number. We therefore postpone the use of the log transformation in regression until the next chapter.

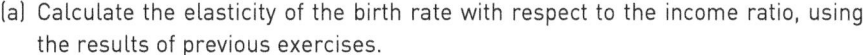

Exercise 7.9

(?)

(a) Calculate the elasticity of the birth rate with respect to the income ratio, using the results of previous exercises.

(b) Give a brief interpretation of the meaning of this figure.

Exercise 7.10

Calculate a regression relating the birth rate to the inverse of the income ratio $1/IR$.

Summary

- Correlation refers to the extent of association between two variables. The (sample) correlation coefficient is a measure of this association, extending from $r = -1$ to $r = +1$.

- Positive correlation ($r > 0$) exists when high values of X tend to be associated with high values of Y and low X values with low Y values.

- Negative correlation ($r < 0$) exists when high values of X tend to be associated with low values of Y and vice versa.

- Values of r around 0 indicate an absence of correlation.

- As the sample correlation coefficient is a random variable we can test for its significance, i.e. test whether the true value is zero or not. This test is based upon the t distribution.

- The existence of correlation (even if 'significant') does not necessarily imply causality. There can be other reasons for the observed association.

- Regression analysis extends correlation by asserting a causality from X to Y and then measuring the relationship between the variables via the regression line, the 'line of best fit'.

- The regression line $Y = a + bX$ is defined by the intercept a and slope coefficient b. Their values are found by minimising the sum of squared errors around the regression line.

- The slope coefficient b measures the responsiveness of Y to changes in X.

- A measure of how well the regression line fits the data is given by the coefficient of determination, R^2, varying between 0 (very poor fit) and 1 (perfect fit).

- The coefficients a and b are unbiased point estimates of the true values of the parameters. Confidence interval estimates can be obtained, based on the t distribution. Hypothesis tests on the parameters can also be carried out using the t distribution.

- A test of the hypothesis $R^2 = 0$ (implying the regression is no better at predicting Y than simply using the mean of Y) can be carried out using the F distribution.

- The regression line may be used to predict Y for any value of X by assuming the residual to be zero for that observation.

- The measured response of Y to X (given by b) depends upon the units of measurement of X and Y. A better measure is often the elasticity, which is the proportionate response of Y to a proportionate change in X.

- Data are often transformed prior to regression (e.g. by taking logs) for a variety of reasons (e.g. to fit a curve to the original data).

Key terms and concepts

autocorrelation	intercept
correlation coefficient	prediction
coefficient of determination (R^2)	regression line or equation
coefficient of rank correlation	regression sum of squares
dependent (endogenous) variable	slope
elasticity	standard error
error sum of squares	t ratio
error term (or residual)	total sum of squares
independent (exogenous) variable	

References

G. S. Maddala, *Introduction to Econometrics*, 2001, 3rd edn., Wiley.
M. P. Todaro, *Economic Development for a Developing World*, 1992, 3rd edn., Financial Times Prentice Hall.

Problems

Some of the more challenging problems are indicated by highlighting the problem number in colour.

7.1   The other data which Todaro might have used to analyse the birth rate were:

Country	Birth rate	GNP	Growth	Income ratio
Bangladesh	47	140	0.3	2.3
Tanzania	47	280	1.9	3.2
Sierra Leone	46	320	0.4	3.3
Sudan	47	380	−0.3	3.9
Kenya	55	420	2.9	6.8
Indonesia	35	530	4.1	3.4
Panama	30	1910	3.1	8.6
Chile	25	2560	0.7	3.8
Venezuela	35	4220	2.4	5.2
Turkey	33	1540	3.5	4.9
Malaysia	31	1840	4.3	5.0
Nepal	44	150	0.0	4.7
Malawi	56	200	2.7	2.4
Argentina	20	2560	1.9	3.6

For *one* of the three possible explanatory variables (in class, different groups could examine each of the variables):

(a) Draw an *XY* chart of the data above and comment upon the result.

(b) Would you expect a line of best fit to have a positive or negative slope? Roughly, what would you expect the slope to be?

(c) What would you expect the correlation coefficient to be?

(d) Calculate the correlation coefficient, and comment.

(e) Test to see if the correlation coefficient is different from zero. Use the 95% confidence level.

(Analysis of this problem continues in Problem 7.5.)

7.2   The data below show consumption of margarine (in ounces per person per week) and its real price, for the UK.

Year	Consumption	Price	Year	Consumption	Price
1970	2.86	125.6	1980	3.83	104.2
1971	3.15	132.9	1981	4.11	95.5
1972	3.52	126.0	1982	4.33	88.1
1973	3.03	119.6	1983	4.08	88.9
1974	2.60	138.8	1984	4.08	97.3
1975	2.60	141.0	1985	3.76	100.0
1976	3.06	122.3	1986	4.10	86.7
1977	3.48	132.7	1987	3.98	79.8
1978	3.54	126.7	1988	3.78	79.9
1979	3.63	115.7			

(a) Draw an XY plot of the data and comment.

(b) From the chart, would you expect the line of best fit to slope up or down? *In theory*, which way should it slope?

(c) What would you expect the correlation coefficient to be, approximately?

(d) Calculate the correlation coefficient between margarine consumption and its price.

(e) Is the coefficient significantly different from zero? What is the implication of the result?

(The following totals will reduce the burden of calculation: $\Sigma Y = 67.52$; $\Sigma X = 2101.70$; $\Sigma Y^2 = 245.055$; $\Sigma X^2 = 240\ 149.27$; $\Sigma XY = 7299.638$; Y is consumption, X is price. If you wish, you could calculate a logarithmic correlation. The relevant totals are: $\Sigma y = 23.88$; $\Sigma x = 89.09$; $\Sigma y^2 = 30.45$; $\Sigma x^2 = 418.40$; $\Sigma xy = 111.50$, where $y = \ln Y$ and $x = \ln X$.)

(Analysis of this problem continues in Problem 7.6.)

7.3 What would you expect to be the correlation coefficient between the following variables? Should the variables be measured contemporaneously or might there be a lag in the effect of one upon the other?

(a) Nominal consumption and nominal income.

(b) GDP and the imports/GDP ratio.

(c) Investment and the interest rate.

7.4 As Problem 7.3, for:

(a) real consumption and real income;

(b) individuals' alcohol and cigarette consumption;

(c) UK and US interest rates.

7.5 Using the data from Problem 7.1, calculate the rank correlation coefficient between the variables and test its significance. How does it compare with the ordinary correlation coefficient?

7.6 Calculate the rank correlation coefficient between price and quantity for the data in Problem 7.2. How does it compare with the ordinary correlation coefficient?

7.7 (a) For the data in Problem 7.1, find the estimated regression line and calculate the R^2 statistic. Comment upon the result. How does it compare with Todaro's findings?

(b) Calculate the standard error of the estimate and the standard errors of the coefficients. Is the slope coefficient significantly different from zero? Comment upon the result.

(c) Test the overall significance of the regression equation and comment.

(d) Taking your own results and Todaro's, how confident do you feel that you understand the determinants of the birth rate?

(e) What do you think will be the result of estimating your equation using all 26 countries' data? Try it! What do you conclude?

7.8 (a) For the data given in Problem 7.2, estimate the sample regression line and calculate the R^2 statistic. Comment upon the results.

(b) Calculate the standard error of the estimate and the standard errors of the coefficients. Is the slope coefficient significantly different from zero? Is demand inelastic?

(c) Test the overall significance of the regression and comment upon your result.

7.9   From your results for the birth rate model, predict the birth rate for a country with *either* (a) GNP equal to $3000, (b) a growth rate of 3% p.a. *or* (c) an income ratio of 7. How does your prediction compare with one using Todaro's results? Comment.

7.10   Predict margarine consumption given a price of 70. Use the 99% confidence level.

7.11   **(Project)** Update Todaro's study using more recent data.

7.12   Try to build a model of the determinants of infant mortality. You should use cross-section data for 20 countries or more and should include both developing and developed countries in the sample.

   Write up your findings in a report which includes the following sections: discussion of the problem; data gathering and transformations; estimation of the model; interpretation of results. Useful data may be found in the Human Development Report (use Google to find it online).

Answers to exercises

(a) The calculation is:

	Birth rate Y	Income ratio X	Y^2	X^2	XY
Brazil	30	9.5	900	90.25	285
Colombia	29	6.8	841	46.24	197.2
Costa Rica	30	4.6	900	21.16	138
India	35	3.1	1225	9.61	108.5
Mexico	36	5	1296	25	180
Peru	36	8.7	1296	75.69	313.2
Philippines	34	3.8	1156	14.44	129.2
Senegal	48	6.4	2304	40.96	307.2
South Korea	24	2.7	576	7.29	64.8
Sri Lanka	27	2.3	729	5.29	62.1
Taiwan	21	3.8	441	14.44	79.8
Thailand	30	3.3	900	10.89	99
Totals	380	60	12 564	361.26	1964

$$r = \frac{12 \times 1964 - 60 \times 380}{\sqrt{(12 \times 361.26 - 60^2)(12 \times 12\ 564 - 380^2)}} = 0.355$$

(c) As for (a) except $\Sigma X = 0.6$, $\Sigma Y = 38$, $\Sigma X^2 = 0.036126$, $\Sigma Y^2 = 125.64$, $\Sigma XY = 1.964$. Hence

$$r = \frac{12 \times 1.964 - 0.6 \times 38}{\sqrt{(12 \times 0.036126 - 0.6^2)(12 \times 125.64 - 38^2)}} = 0.355$$

(a) $t = \dfrac{0.355\sqrt{12 - 2}}{\sqrt{1 - (0.355)^2}} = 1.20$

(b) The Prob-value, for a two-tailed test is 0.257 or 25%, so we do not reject the null of no correlation.

(a) The calculation is:

	Birth rate Y	Income ratio X	Rank of Y	Rank of X	Y^2	X^2	XY
Brazil	30	9.5	7	1	49	1	7
Colombia	29	6.8	9	3	81	9	27
Costa Rica	30	4.6	7	6	49	36	42
India	35	3.1	4	10	−16	100	40
Mexico	36	5	2.5	5	−6.25	25	12.5
Peru	36	8.7	2.5	2	6.25	4	5
Philippines	34	3.8	5	7.5	−25	56.25	37.5
Senegal	48	6.4	1	4	−1	16	4
South Korea	24	2.7	11	11	121	121	121
Sri Lanka	27	2.3	10	12	−100	144	120
Taiwan	21	3.8	12	7.5	144	56.25	90
Thailand	30	3.3	7	9	−49	81	63
Totals			78	78	647.5	649.5	569

$$r_s = \frac{12 \times 569 - 78^2}{\sqrt{(12 \times 649.5 - 78^2)(12 \times 647.5 - 78^2)}} = 0.438$$

(b) This is less than the critical value of 0.591 so the null of no rank correlation cannot be rejected.

(c) Reversing the rankings should not alter the result of the calculation.

Exercise 7.4

(a) Using the data and calculations in the answer to Exercise 7.1 we obtain:

$$b = \frac{12 \times 1964 - 60 \times 380}{12 \times 361.26 - 60^2} = 1.045$$

$$a = \frac{380}{12} - (1.045) \times \frac{60}{12} = 26.443$$

(b) A unit increase in the measure of inequality leads to approximately one additional birth per 1000 mothers. The constant has no useful interpretation. The income ratio cannot be zero (in fact, it cannot be less than 0.5).

Exercise 7.5

(a) $\text{TSS} = \Sigma(Y_i - \bar{Y})^2 = \Sigma Y_i^2 - n\bar{Y}^2 = 12\,564 - 12 \times 31.67^2 = 530.667$

$\text{ESS} = \Sigma(Y_i - \hat{Y}_i)^2 = \Sigma Y_i^2 - a\,\Sigma Y_i - b\,\Sigma X_i Y_i$
$\quad = 12\,564 - 26.443 \times 380 - 1.045 \times 1139.70 = 463.804$

$\text{RSS} = \text{TSS} - \text{ESS} = 530.667 - 463.804 = 66.863$

$R^2 = 0.126.$

(b) This is the square of the correlation coefficient, calculated earlier as 0.355.

Exercise 7.6

(a) $s_e^2 = \dfrac{463.804}{10} = 46.3804$

and so

$s_b^2 = \dfrac{46.3804}{61.26} = 0.757$

and

$s_b = \sqrt{0.757} = 0.870$

For a the estimated variance is

$$s_a^2 = s_e^2 \times \left(\frac{1}{n} + \frac{\bar{X}^2}{\Sigma(X_i - \bar{X})^2} \right) = 46.3804 \times \left(\frac{1}{12} + \frac{5^2}{61.26} \right) = 22.793$$

and hence $s_a = 4.774$. The 95% CIs are therefore $1.045 \pm 2.228 \times 0.87 = [-0.894, 2.983]$ for b and $26.443 \pm 2.228 \times 4.774 = [15.806, 37.081]$.

(b) $t = \dfrac{1.045 - 0}{0.870} = 1.201$

Not significant.

(c) $F = \dfrac{\text{RSS}/1}{\text{ESS}/(n-2)} = \dfrac{66.863/1}{463.804/(12-2)} = 1.44$

Excel should give the same answers.

(a) $\hat{BR} = 26.44 + 1.045 \times 10 = 36.9$.

(b) $\left[36.9 - 2.228 \times 6.81\sqrt{\dfrac{1}{12} + \dfrac{(10-5)^2}{61.26}}, \; 36.9 + 2.228 \times 6.81\sqrt{\dfrac{1}{12} + \dfrac{(10-5)^2}{61.26}} \right]$

$= [26.3, \; 47.5]$

(c) $\left[36.9 - 2.228 \times 6.81\sqrt{1 + \dfrac{1}{12} + \dfrac{(10-5)^2}{61.26}}, \; 36.9 + 2.228 \times 6.81\sqrt{1 + \dfrac{1}{12} + \dfrac{(10-5)^2}{61.26}} \right]$

$= [18.4, \; 55.4]$

(a) $e = 1.045 \times \dfrac{5}{31.67} = 0.165$

(b) A 10% rise in the inequality measure (e.g. from 4 to 4.4) raises the birth rate by 1.65% (e.g. from 30 to 30.49).

$$BR = 38.82 - 29.61 \times \frac{1}{IR} + e$$

s.e.   (19.0)

$R^2 = 0.19$, $F(1,10) = 2.43$.

The regression is rather poor and the F statistic is not significant.

INDEX